JIM ☑ S0-AVS-622 ...N

Numerical Astrophysics

Proceedings of a symposium in honor of James R. Wilson
held at the University of Illinois in October, 1982

Edited by

Joan M. Centrella
University of Texas at Austin

James M. LeBlanc
Lawrence Livermore National Laboratory

Richard L. Bowers
Los Alamos National Laboratory

Foreword by

John Archibald Wheeler

with additional editorial assistance by
Mary K. LeBlanc

Jones and Bartlett Publishers, Inc.
Boston   Portola Valley

The figure on the cover shows the results of modeling the large scale distribution of galaxies using three-dimensional numerical simulations. In this model the galaxies lie in long, filamentary structures that are interconnected and surround large "holes" where no galaxies are found. These features are in agreement with the observed distribution of galaxies. (From "The Large-Scale Structure of the Universe: Three-Dimensional Numerical Models" *by Joan M. Centrella and Adrian L. Melott.*)

Editorial offices: Jones and Bartlett Publishers, Inc., 30 Granada Court, Portola Valley, CA 94025.

Sales and customer service offices: Jones and Bartlett Publishers, Inc., 20 Park Plaza, Boston, MA 02116.

Library of Congress Cataloging in Publication Data

Main entry under title:

Numerical astrophysics.

   1. Astrophysics—Data processing—Addresses,
essays, lectures. 2. Numerical analysis—Addresses,
essays, lectures. 3. Wilson, James Ricker.
  I. Centrella, Joan. II. LeBlanc, James. III. Bowers,
Richard. IV. Wilson, James Ricker.

QB461.5.N85 1984   523.01   84-15434
ISBN 0-86720-048-0

Printed in the United States of America

Printing number (last digit): 10 9 8 7 6 5 4 3 2 1

Foreword

Astrophysics lays claim to no cramped domain of space, no short run of time, and no small variety of spectacles. They range from supernovae to pulsars, from plasma waves to clouds where positive and negative electrons are being continually created and annihilated, and from jets of galactic length to black holes. We see today a richness which a few decades earlier was beyond our power to imagine, let alone observe. Indispensable in this advance have been new telescopes and new instrumentation. Equally indispensable, however, in capturing the startling richness of nature has been the computer. Who can know a bridge who only looks at the bridge? Not except by calculation can one "see" for each of its beams the stress and the margin of safety, hidden as they are beneath three layers of paint. Not except by mathematical analysis can we "see" the spiralling electrons that make the radio jet, "see" the propulsive nuclear reactions miles below the surface of the supernova and "see" the inner workings of that tangle of matter and magnetism that we call the accretion disk of a black hole. Hence numerical astrophysics!

Constant checking is needed to keep the telescopic image sharp and true; and needed, too, to keep the computer picture honest. Man first brought a bit of star down to Earth over the desert of Alamogordo, New Mexico, at 5:30 A.M. July 16, 1945, the most consequence-laden test of the soundness of numerical astrophysics in all history. Other tests of other earthbound astrophysical devices are conducted today at other places by other groups with even tighter mutual discipline of prediction and observation.

Archimedes and Galileo were not the last to derive a forward push in their science from the defense needs of the larger community. The Wilsons and Zel'doviches of our day—through their mathematical predictions and the tests which those predictions have survived—have created a standard for their scientific colleagues the world over. By no achievements do we know better what numerical astrophysics should be and do. This domain of investigation, an intellectual outgrowth of the distinguished but slower paced astrophysics, hydrodynamics and nuclear physics of earlier days, driven by the love of truth and the necessity of nations, powering advances in computer science and powered by them, is one of the glories of our times. One who reads the contributions collected here—thanks to the dedication and devotion of the editors—encounters the physics of matter at supranuclear density; ways of unsurpassed power to do hydrodynamics on a computer; the building of galaxies, clusters of galaxies, and superclusters; and recent findings in a dozen other frontier topics of hydrodynamics, gravitational wave physics and modern astrophysics generally—powerful methods and solid results, foundational to future advances in astrophysics.

Is this distinguished group of authors silent about the mystery of the quasar, powerhouse of the sky? Do not be deceived. It is the silence of the tiger before his spring!

John Archibald Wheeler

Preface

It is a privilege to write this introduction to Jim Wilson's 60th birthday festschrift. Some of the many contributions Jim has made to astrophysics are represented in this volume, in papers written by his friends and students and in two papers written by Jim for the occasion.

Jim Wilson has also added in a pivotal way to our knowledge of nuclear explosions, both through his own work and through the work of the many people whom he helped educate and inspire. His contributions span the broad range of physics which is involved in both the astrophysical and the earthly nuclear explosions.

Much of the early work of the Laboratory consisted of bringing disparate strands of physics together and making the physically appropriate approximations that would allow the computers to represent a very complex and poorly understood set of phenomena. Some of the very same people who did this work in connection with nuclear explosions also helped to usher in modern computational astrophysics: the late Lou Henyey, Stirling Colgate and Jim Wilson and their friends.

Jim made many of the early approximations which allowed for rough estimates of the behavior of the explosions. As experience was accumulated and theoretical models improved, Jim continued to focus on the most difficult problems. He helped significantly in bringing a measure of clarity into a field which is still beset by major uncertainties.

For the thirty years that Jim has been at the Lawrence Livermore National Laboratory he has been one of its moving spirits. Whether the question has to do with the functioning of nuclear explosives, computer models, or astrophysics, he goes to the heart of the matter in a physically intuitive way which allows others as well as himself to see what the basic difficulties are and what the possible solutions might be.

In addition to his qualities as a scientist, Jim is a friend and mentor to many. His generosity, his zest for life, along with his abilities have made him the best kind of leader. He leads through example and discussion, proceeding through the forest and hacking at the undergrowth himself and advising others how to do the same until there is a path through the tangle. Both an idea man and a practical man where experiments and calculations are concerned, he is unawed by the magnitude of any task.

He has also, in the words of a young colleague, never allowed his experience and success to fossilize him, perhaps the best compliment which the young can pay to the (chronologically) not so young.

This volume is a tribute we are glad to pay to a good friend and an admired leader.

Michael M. May

Lawrence Livermore National Laboratory

Contents

List of Contributors

Robert T. Barton, *Lawrence Livermore National Laboratory*

Gordon Baym, *University of Illinois at Urbana-Champaign*

R. D. Blandford, *California Institute of Technology*

S. A. Bludman, *University of Pennsylvania*

J. R. Bond, *Stanford University*

Richard L. Bowers, *Los Alamos National Laboratory*

G. E. Brown, *State University of New York, Stony Brook*

Joan M. Centrella, *University of Texas at Austin and Lawrence Livermore National Laboratory*

Stirling A. Colgate, *Los Alamos National Laboratory and New Mexico Institute of Mining and Technology*

J. Cooperstein, *State University of New York, Stony Brook*

Bryce S. DeWitt, *Relativity Center, University of Texas at Austin*

Charles R. Evans, *Relativity Center, University of Texas at Austin and Lawrence Livermore National Laboratory*

R. Fortner, *University of Illinois at Urbana-Champaign*

Katherine Freese, *University of Chicago*

G. M. Fuller, *Enrico Fermi Institute, University of Chicago and Lawrence Livermore National Laboratory*

John F. Hawley, *University of Illinois*

F. K. Lamb, *University of Illinois at Urbana-Champaign*

James M. LeBlanc, *Lawrence Livermore National Laboratory*

I. Lichtenstadt, *University of Pennsylvania and Racah Institute of Physics, Hebrew University, Jerusalem*

C. M. Lund, *Lawrence Livermore National Laboratory*

Richard Matzner, *Relativity Center, University of Texas at Austin*

Adrian L. Melott, *University of Chicago*

Michael L. Norman, *Max-Planck-Institut für Physik und Astrophysik, Munich*

C. J. Pethick, *NORDITA, Copenhagen, Denmark and University of Illinois at Urbana-Champaign*

Albert G. Petschek, *Los Alamos National Laboratory and New Mexico Institute of Mining and Technology*

William H. Press, *Harvard University*

D. G. Ravenhall, *University of Illinois at Urbana-Champaign*

Martin J. Rees, *Institute of Astronomy, Madingley Road, Cambridge, England*

Tony Rothman, *Relativity Center, University of Texas at Austin*

David N. Schramm, *University of Chicago*

Stuart L. Shapiro, *Center for Radiophysics and Space Research, Cornell University*

John H. Sloan, *University of Illinois*

Larry L. Smarr, *University of Illinois and Max-Planck-Institut für Physik und Astrophysik*

Eugene M. D. Symbalisty, *Harvard-Smithsonian Center for Astrophysics*

A. S. Szalay, *Eotvos University*

Thomas A. Weaver, *Lawrence Livermore National Laboratory*

James R. Wilson, *Lawrence Livermore National Laboratory*

Karl-Heinz A. Winkler, *Max-Planck-Institut für Physik und Astrophysik*

S. E. Woosley, *Lick Observatory, University of California at Santa Cruz and Lawrence Livermore National Laboratory*

James W. York, Jr., *University of North Carolina*

G. Zylstra, *University of Illinois at Urbana-Champaign*

Introduction

This book contains the proceedings of a symposium held, in honor of James R. Wilson on his 60th birthday, at the University of Illinois on October 21-23, 1982. Its contributed papers cover six major areas of activity in modern numerical astrophysics, including jets and radio galaxies, compact objects, numerical relativity, cosmology, supernovae, and numerical physics. The emphasis of this book is on the physics of the astrophysical systems under study. Many of the authors discuss the physical principles and theoretical models that they believe represent the various astrophysical objects. In some cases these principles and models have been incorporated into working numerical codes, and the authors are able to present details of their numerical methods and the results of computer simulations. In other cases the basic theoretical ideas have not yet been incorporated into numerical codes; articles in this category provide the basis for future numerical work.

The first section of this book deals with jet formation and radio galaxies. Blandford's paper addresses the problem of the accretion of matter onto massive black holes. Special emphasis is put on radiation tori, and the author suggests some possible numerical studies. This paper is followed by the work of Hawley and Smarr, which presents two-dimensional axisymmetric calculations of black hole accretion, and by the work of Sloan and Smarr, which discusses the basic equations for general relativistic magnetohydrodynamics in a form suitable for numerical computations. Active galactic nuclei are the topic of the paper by Rees. He discusses plasmas surrounding massive black holes, accretion onto the black hole, the generation of electron-positron photospheres, and jets. This section is concluded by the work of Norman, Smarr, and Winkler on two-dimensional gas dynamical simulations of jets.

The physics of accretion onto compact objects (white dwarfs and neutron stars) and its relation to X-ray and gamma ray bursts is presented in the second section. The paper by Fortner, Lamb, and Zylstra presents an overview of magnetofluid dynamics as it applies to matter in binary systems containing compact objects and to the accretion of interstellar matter onto neutron stars.

A thermonuclear model for high energy transients on neutron stars as a source for both X-ray and gamma ray burst events is discussed by Woosley, while the mechanism for gamma ray bursts is presented by Colgate and Petschek.

In the third section, numerical relativity, the field equations of general relativity are solved for strong gravitational fields. York's paper on spacetime engineering presents constructive algorithms for finding the free and constrained variables and for solving the equations satisfied by these variables. The remaining contributions emphasize numerical methods applicable to strong gravitational fields and present the results of numerical models generated using these methods. The model calculations of gravitational collapse, star collisions and the generation of gravitational radiation presented by Shapiro are useful tools in constructing and understanding dynamical, strong field spacetimes. Finally, Evans' paper on the numerical simulation of gravitational collapse and the generation of gravitational radiation gives actual examples of the use of spacetime engineering to construct dynamical spacetimes on a computer.

The fourth section of this volume deals with cosmology, the study of the universe as a whole. Grand unified theories and the inflationary universe model are explored by Press. Schramm and Freese then review several aspects of neutrino astrophysics, including the role of neutrinos in cosmology and cosmological constraints on their masses, lifetimes, and number of species. A computation of nucleosynthesis in a one-dimensional inhomogeneous cosmology is discussed by Matzner, Centrella, Rothman and Wilson; they discuss the numerical algorithms used for this problem and present results on the spatial variation of the light element abundances predicted by their models. The collapse of one-dimensional pancake-like perturbations driven by massive neutrinos is studied numerically by Wilson, Bond, Centrella and Szalay. They discuss the fraction of baryonic matter cool enough to permit galaxy formation in the late universe using this model. Finally, Centrella and Melott present three-dimensional numerical simulations of the formation of clusters and superclusters of galaxies in the universe.

Type II supernovae, which are believed to be associated with violent explosions at the end of a star's life, are the topic of the fifth section. Baym's introduction to supernovae reviews the basic physics governing the gravitational collapse of massive stellar cores, and the subsequent shock formation and possible prompt mass ejection mechanisms. Weaver, Woosley and

Fuller then describe the effects of new electron capture rates and a modified silicon burning model on the iron core mass of highly evolved, massive stars. Cooperstein and Brown discuss the importance of entropy as a parameter characterizing the prompt explosions of iron cores. The status of prompt explosions from the collapse of iron cores in 10 M_θ to 25 M_θ stars based on Wilson's one-dimensional core collapse code is reviewed by Bowers. Beginning with the collapse models discussed in the previous paper which do not produce prompt explosions, Wilson discusses the possibility of late time explosions. The adiabatic collapse and explosion of low mass iron stellar cores is explored in the article by Bludman and Lichtenstadt. Symbalisty then discusses stellar jet formation resulting from the collapse of a rotating magnetic star, including results obtained from a two-dimensional magnetorotational stellar collapse code. This section concludes with a review by Pethick and Ravenhall of the properties of matter at subnuclear densities which occur near core bounce; included is a discussion of the unusual shapes that nuclei may adopt at densities close to the nuclear saturation density.

The final section of the book deals with various topics in numerical physics. DeWitt reminisces about the earliest two-dimensional hydrodynamical calculations and their impact on later colliding black hole calculations. Barton then describes a modern, multimaterial, two-dimensional, arbitrary Lagrangian-Eulerian mesh computer program which has been used for modeling a number of astrophysical situations. Implicit differencing schemes for solving one-dimensional time-dependent multifrequency radiation transport problems arising in astrophysics are discussed by Lund. Finally, LeBlanc offers some comments and insight on future developments in computing and their impact on numerical astrophysics.

The papers in this volume represent some of the latest research in several areas of the rapidly developing field of numerical astrophysics. Thus, they serve as a fitting tribute to Jim Wilson, a man who has pioneered many of these areas himself and who continues to make exciting new contributions.

The task of preparation of a camera-ready manuscript is one of major proportions. We have, in editing the contributions appearing here, limited our role to scientific editing. Much of the organization of this project and its completion in satisfactory form is due to the additional and substantial contributions of Mary K. LeBlanc. Her scientific and copy editing of each manuscript is largely responsible for the overall consistency of this volume.

In performing this role, Mary has served more as a colleague than as a copy editor.

The burden of preparing a camera-ready manuscript falls not only on the editors but also on the individual authors. The editors wish to thank each of the authors for their generous help in the preparation of the manuscript.

There are many people whose efforts, patience and dedication helped make the symposium and this volume a reality. We would like to thank Lawrence Livermore National Laboratory, the National Science Foundation, the Departments of Astronomy and Physics at the University of Illinois at Urbana-Champaign, and the Department of Astronomy at the University of Texas at Austin for their support. The symposium would not have been possible without the support of C. B. Tarter, R. D. Woodruff, and J. D. Anderson at Livermore. We are especially grateful to J. Wehner, L. Smarr, and F. Lamb at the University of Illinois for their help in organizing the meeting and keeping it running smoothly. Jan Greiner deserves special mention for her secretarial support to the editors during the preparation of the manuscript.

Joan M. Centrella
James M. LeBlanc
Richard L. Bowers

August, 1984

I. Jets and Radio Galaxies

Accretion onto Massive Black Holes in Active Galactic Nuclei

R. D. Blandford
California Institute of Technology

"Large atoms formed the denser earth, and so
Depressed by its own weight, it stayed below
While on its verge the liquid element
Ran circling round, and kept the solid pent.
Thus order reigned and he whose wise control
Severed the parts and made the parts a whole,
First massed the land, some symmetry to bring,
And molded it to form a mighty ring."

Ovid: "The Metamorphoses" (Translated by
A.E. Watts, North Point Press).*

ABSTRACT

It is widely believed that the central powerhouses of active galactic nuclei are massive black holes fueled by accreting gas. Three modes of gas supply are discussed--disk accretion, and the creation of an orbiting torus supported by either radiation pressure when the accretion rate is low or gas pressure when it is high. It is suggested that Seyfert galaxies and the bright optical quasars be identified with radiation tori and radio galaxies associated with ion tori. The radio quasars may be intermediate cases in which the gas is supplied through a disk.

I. INTRODUCTION

As the above quotation attests, it has long been believed (though there are still no firm observational grounds for this belief) that active galactic nuclei are powered by massive black holes surrounded by orbiting disks of gas. In addition to being fueled by the accreted gas, these black holes may have their spins harnessed by magnetic field lines. Somehow or other, the photons that we observe at earth must be emitted in and escape from this environment. Unfortunately,

---

*Quoted by permission of the Regents of the University of California.

general-relativistic magnetohydrodynamical radiative transfer does not yet exist as a mature science and so we have to rely upon highly idealized calculations in our primitive attempts to uncover the mysteries of quasars and extragalactic radio sources. In fact the calculations that can be performed analytically are so limited that a numerical approach now seems obligatory if we are ever to form an acceptable theoretical model of these enigmatic objects. Of course, Jim Wilson realized this over ten years ago, and his early papers, in particular those in collaboration with LeBlanc and Ruffini, were very influential at the time they were written and, as I hope my talk will bring out, contain the basic ideas of more recent work. I am therefore delighted to be here at the University of Illinois to congratulate Jim on his sixtieth birthday.

Obviously, I cannot hope to review theroetical research on the subject of accretion onto black holes in the time available. I will therefore just describe some recent developments. Most theoretical effort has naturally been concentrated on the problems of spherical accretion because it is geometrically the simplest case. However, I believe that it is dangerously misleading in the context of active galactic nuclei in spite of the genuine formal challenges that it presents. The ubiquity of jets or at least linear features, together with the strong expectation that any accreted gas would have enough angular momentum to orbit the hole, both suggest that non-spherical effects are dynamically important.

Accretion with angular momentum is currently investigated in three different regimes. When the gas near the hole can cool on an inflow time a thin disk will form and this will probably be dragged into the equatorial plane of the hole, presuming that it is spinning (Bardeen and Petterson 1975), thereby defining a fixed direction in space along which may be launched a jet. This disk may also have an active corona (Galeev, Rosner and Vaiana 1979). There are two possibilities when the gas near the hole cannot cool. If the accretion rate is high enough, radiation can be trapped in the surrounding gas which forms a radiation-supported torus in orbit about the hole. Alternatively, if the accretion rate is low enough, and the viscosity large enough, a thick torus supported by ion pressure will be formed which may have similar properties to the radiation-supported torus. I believe that we have the best chance of using realistic microphysics in the study of the radiation torus and that numerical investigations are best motivated in this case. I will therefore emphasize this possibility.

II. DISK ACCRETION

The theory of disk accretion around massive black holes is even more uncertain than that for disks around stellar mass objects (e.g. Pringle 1981). The reasons are twofold. First, although we cannot calculate the viscosity from first principles, the simple prescription of assuming that the viscous stress is proportional to the gas pressure (with a coefficient of proportionality $\alpha \sim 0.1$) can be straightforwardly applied in the case of stellar disks and indeed has some observational support. However, the inner parts of hypothetical accretion disks in galactic nuclei are probably radiation-dominated, and the question arises as to whether gas or total pressure should be used. Coroniti (1981) and Sakimoto and Coroniti (1981) have argued that for the case of magnetic viscosity it is the gas pressure which is important. If true, this would have the effect of increasing the surface density in the disk over its value using the larger viscosity. The second difficulty is that the innermost parts are prone to thermal instability when they are radiation-dominated. The assumption of a stationary inflow which underlies most discussions of this problem is then quite suspect.

The broad emission lines that are characteristic of quasars and type I Seyfert galaxies may possibly originate in a disk. If so, and there is still no clear cut evidence that this is the case then this would provide a powerful diagnostic of radial variation of the disk structure (e.g. Matthews 1982). Perhaps the best way of seeing disk emission lines is by carefully monitoring their variation and correlating it with the variation of the associated continuum.

The majority of active galaxies are known to be fairly powerful X-ray sources, and a minority of these appear to be variable on time scales that can be as short as minutes. This suggests that the X-rays are probably generated within a small region around the black hole. They will illuminate the outer parts of the disk if it is concave and can Compton-heat the surface gas layers and drive a wind away from the surface at radii r satisfying

$$\frac{h\overline{\nu}}{m_p c^2} \gtrsim \frac{m}{r} \tag{1}$$

where $\overline{\nu}$ is the intensity weighted mean frequency of the X-ray irradiation and m is the gravitational radius (Begelman, McKee and Shields 1983).

There is a further dissimilarity between accretion disks within binary star systems and in galactic nuclei that is not always acknowledged. This is that in the former case, the orbital motion of the stars provides a natural sink for the angular momentum transported radially outwards by viscous torques in the accretion disk. There is no obvious counterpart in the case of a galactic nucleus where the disposal of the angular momentum does pose an interesting puzzle. One possible resolution of this difficulty is to invoke magnetic torques analogous to those which the sun and similar stars have almost certainly used to spin down over their lifetimes. David Payne and I (1982) have proposed that hydromagnetic winds are an important feature of accretion disks. Magnetic flux can be generated by dynamo action within the differentially rotating disk and, provided that a fair fraction of the disk surface area is threaded by open magnetic field lines, the torque can be large enough to be dynamically important.

It is in fact far easier to launch a wind from a Keplerian disk than from the surface of the sun. To see this, treat a poloidal field line as a wire and the plasma as a bead that slides along it. The "bead" will be flung out centrifugally as long as the wire makes an angle less than 60^{0} to the outward radius direction. In the case of the sun, the plasma must be heated until the protons move with the escape speed if it is to climb out of the solar gravitational potential well. A centrifugally driven hydromagnetic wind from the surface of an accretion disk will be collimated towards the symmetry axis by the toroidal component of magnetic field that will inevitably develop as the inertia of the plasma causes it to lag behind the disk. Hydromagnetic torques may therefore be important both in allowing accreted gas to move radially inward through the disk and in forming jets.

An alternative idea advocated by Ostriker (1983) is that a non-rotating central star cluster exerts a Poynting-Robertson-like torque on an orbiting disk. This allows a mass comparable to that of the cluster to be accreted on a dynamical relaxation time for the cluster.

III. RADIATION TORI

a) General Considerations

Another mode of gas accretion that may be relevant in galactic nuclei occurs when the accretion rate exceeds the critical value for it to liberate more than an Eddington limit of luminosity. The innermost parts of the disk will be in-flated by the radiation pressure to form a thick radiation-supported torus (Fig. 1). In recent years, the physical conditions within this type of torus have been explored by a variety of authors under a series of simplifying assump-tions (e.g. Jaroszyński, Abramowicz and Paczynski 1980, Paczynski and Wiita, 1980 and references therein). In Figure 2, we exhibit the physical conditions that will be found in the "core" of such a torus, at say six gravitational radii, as a function of the mass of the hole and the gas density. We see that for the hole masses anticipated, $10^{5}M_{\odot} \lesssim M \lesssim 10^{10}M_{\odot}$, the opacity will be predominantly Thomson, and the gas pressure will be small. Unless the viscosity is very large, and the assumption of quasi-stationary azimuthal motion consequently invalid, the

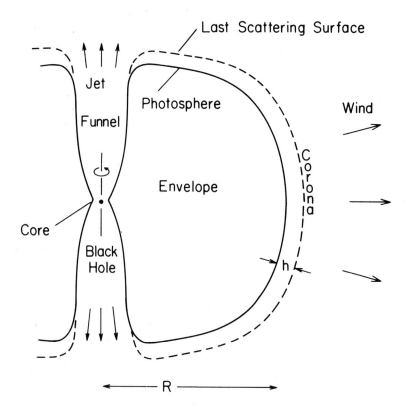

Fig. 1.–Schematic representation of a radiation torus around a massive, spinning black hole. Four regions are considered in the text: the core, the envelope, the funnel and the surface which is defined by the photosphere where the emergent photons are mostly created. R is the radius of the photosphere and h the photospheric pressure scale height.

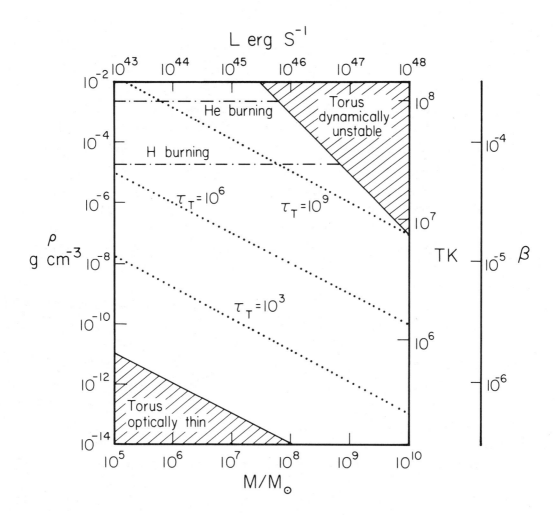

Fig. 2.-Approximate physical conditions in the "core" of a radiation torus at a distance of six gravitational radii from the massive black hole. The Thomson optical depth τ_T is shown as a function of gas density ρ and hole mass M (or equivalently the luminosity L). Also shown are the effective temperature T and β , the ratio of the gas pressure to the total pressure. If we assume that the gas accretes at roughly an Eddington rate we can compare the inflow times with the time to achieve radiative equilibrium. There will always be time for the gas to be heated or cooled to the Compton temperature of the radiation field $h\nu/4k$. If $\tau_T \gtrsim 100$, the photons can be redistributed in frequency by Compton scattering to achieve a Bose-Einstein distribution. If $\tau_T \gtrsim 1000$, then the absorption opacity is large enough for a Planckian spectrum to be established. If the gas is accreting as a consequence of viscous torques, then the ratio of the shear stress to the <u>total</u> pressure is $\alpha \sim 7/\tau_T$. If the temperature gets hot enough, then hydrogen and possibly helium can undergo nuclear burning. When the mass of the torus approaches the hole mass, then it will become dynamically unstable.

plasma will be Comptonized to the effective temperature of the radiation. Compton scattering will also ensure that the radiation and the matter can be described by a single fluid velocity. A slightly larger gas density (or smaller viscosity) is required to bring the radiation into local thermodynamic equilibrium (LTE). Fortunately, the internal dynamics of a torus is independent of the spectral character of the radiation and the gas temperature; it just depends upon the total radiation pressure and energy density. However, the surface properties do depend upon the radiation temperature, and it is probably necessary to include non-LTE effects before we can compare models of accretion tori with detailed observations of Seyferts and optical quasars.

If the viscosity is very low, then the interior temperature may become large enough for the gas within the torus to undergo hydrogen or even helium burning. Although this would probably only produce a small increment in the total energy released, it could have important local structural consequences and perhaps influence the surface composition.

Much recent research on radiation-supported tori has been directed towards accounting for radio jets which, it is suggested, may be collimated by the two "funnels" that are defined by the torus (e.g. Piran 1982). However, most of the prominent optical quasars are radio-quiet, and the majority of extragalactic radio jets are associated with galaxies whose nuclei have bolometric luminosities far below the likely Eddington limit and are therefore unlikely to be associated with radiation-supported tori. In addition, many recent discussions of the energetics have been constrained by the assumption of a constant mass accretion rate. Although we do not understand the fueling of active galactic nuclei it seems very improbable that it be steady. It seems far more likely that the gas be supplied intermittently and that the evolution of the torus should be considered between fueling episodes. Unfortunately, unlike in the stellar case, the "Kelvin" time is always comparable with the evolutionary timescale and there is no "main-sequence" phase.

The rate at which a torus radiates away the binding energy of the gas is dictated by the viscosity. This of course is the major uncertainty in all modeling of accretion disks. If the viscosity is too large then the gas will be blown away faster than it can accrete, and radiative transfer effects in the outflowing wind will establish the observed spectrum (cf. Meier 1982abc) so that the structure of the torus will be largely irrelevant. If the viscosity is too low, then the internal energy will just be radiated away and the spectrum will simply reflect the manner in which the gas was supplied. However, observations of quasars and Seyferts reveal similarities between different objects that seem to necessitate some standard structure if tori are responsible, and so we must proceed under an assumed commonality of structure from one object to the next.

In most published models of radiation tori, simple assumptions are made about the internal structure in order to avoid solving explicitly for the angular momentum transport and energy generation. In fact it is possible to avoid discussing all the internal properties of the torus simply by assuming stationarity and fixing the location of the surface through specifying one free function (e.g. Paczyński and Wiita 1980). More sophisticated models have been computed by treating the interior transport as one-dimensional rather than two-dimensional through assuming self-similarity (Begelman and Meier 1982), by assuming that the accretion only proceeds through a thin surface layer (Paczyński 1980), by assuming that the accretion is confined to the equatorial plane and that the remainder of the interior is in convective equilibrium (Paczyński and Abramowicz 1982), or by assuming a polytrope and specifying the direction of the energy and angular momentum transport (Wiita 1982). These approaches have taught us much of value although they are still quite ad hoc. If we really want to demonstrate the viability of a radiation torus, then we have to construct two-dimensional, evolutionary relativistic models that make self-consistent assumptions about the internal transport mechanisms.

b)   Evolution

The evolution of radiation tori is an ideal problem for numerical astrophysical study. The general relativistic equations of evolution (which are not that much more involved than their Newtonian counterparts) can (in principle) be solved for a given postulated initial configuration. One approach is to treat the evolutionary timescale as distinct from the orbital timescale and to solve the equations of evolution constrained by the requirement of hydrostatic equilibrium at each time step. In increasing order of speciality we can assume that: (i) the gas orbits in a Kerr spacetime can be described by Boyer-Lindquist coordinates (e.g. Misner, Thorne and Wheeler 1973) around a spinning hole with the radius r and the specific angular momentum both measured in units of the mass m (G=c=1), i.e. the self-gravity of the torus is ignorable; (ii) the torus is axisymmetric about the spin axis of the hole and the flow is steady on the dynamical timescale which is much shorter than the evolutionary timescale; (iii) the torus is radiation-dominated and the equation of state can be approximated by

$$w = \rho + 4p \qquad\qquad (2)$$

where w is the enthalpy per unit volume, ρ is the rest mass density of the matter and p is the radiation pressure; (iv) nuclear energy generation is ignorable; (v) in the absence of efficient convection radiation is transported according to the diffusion approximation

$$\vec{q} = \vec{a}/\kappa_T \qquad (3)$$

where $\vec{q}$ is the energy flux, κ_T is the Thomson opacity and $\vec{a}$ is the acceleration (the negative of the local gravity); and (vi) the microscopic viscosity is simply the radiative viscosity

$$\eta = \frac{8}{9}\frac{p}{\kappa_T\rho} \qquad (4)$$

except when the flow becomes unstable (see below); magnetic and universal turbulent viscosity is ignored. Note that assumption (vi) ensures that close to the hole, the accretion rate is at least within an order of magnitude of critical.

We use the "Eckart" representation of the velocity (e.g. Weinberg 1972). On the dynamical timescale, the velocity field is conveniently expressed in terms of four quantities expressible in terms of the co- and contra-variant components of the 4-velocity:

binding energy

$$e = -u_0 \qquad (5)$$

angular velocity

$$\Omega = u^\phi/u^0 \qquad (6)$$

angular momentum

$$1 = -u_\phi/u_0 \qquad (7)$$

redshift

$$A = u^0 \qquad (8)$$

Given the metric $g_{\alpha\beta}$, only one of these quantities is independent. The poloidal velocity responsible for the slow inflow and circulation is defined as

$$u^a = A\left[\frac{dr}{dt}, \frac{d\theta}{dt}\right]. \qquad (9)$$

We also introduce the determinant of minus the metric tensor

$$g = (r^2 + a^2\cos^2\theta)^2 \sin^2\theta . \qquad (10)$$

and the reduced determinants

$$g^* = g_{0\phi}^2 - g_{00}g_{\phi\phi} = (r^2 - 2r + a^2) \sin^2\theta \qquad (11)$$

$$\tilde{g} = g/g^* \ . \tag{12}$$

We define a reduced metric tensor g_{ab} , $a,b = r,\theta$:

$$g_{rr} = \frac{r^2 + a^2\cos^2\theta}{r^2 - 2r + a^2} \tag{13}$$

$$g_{\theta\theta} = r^2 + a^2\cos^2\theta \ . \tag{14}$$

This can be used for raising and lowering indices of two-dimensional poloidal vectors and computing scalar products in the usual manner. The gradient and divergence are defined by

$$\nabla\Omega \equiv (\Omega_{,r}\Omega_{,\theta}) , \text{ etc.}$$

$$\nabla\cdot\vec{u} \equiv g^{-1/2}(g^{1/2}u^a)_{,a} \ . \tag{15}$$

The equation of hydrostatic equilibrium is then given by

$$-\frac{\nabla p}{w} = \vec{a} = \nabla \ln e - \frac{\Omega\nabla\ell}{1 - \Omega\ell} \ . \tag{16}$$

This is a constraint which must be imposed at every timestep.

The equation of particle conservation can be written

$$\frac{\partial(\rho)}{\partial t} + \nabla\cdot(\rho\vec{u}) = 0 \ . \tag{17}$$

Likewise, the equation of energy conservation is

$$\frac{\partial wA}{\partial t} + \nabla\cdot(w\vec{u}) - A\frac{\partial p}{\partial t} - \vec{u}\cdot\nabla p = \eta g^* A^4 \nabla\Omega\cdot\nabla\Omega - \nabla\cdot\vec{q} - \vec{a}\cdot\vec{q} \ . \tag{18}$$

The first term on the right hand side corresponds to the energy released by viscous stress and the next is contributed by radiation transport. The final term is a small relativistic redshift correction which has no Newtonian counterpart. They are evaluated using flow variables that satisfy the equation of hydrostatic support. Note that the ratio of the radiative viscous dissipation rate to the divergence of the heat flux is given to order of magnitude by $\sim(\Omega r)^2$. This implies that if a radiation torus evolves solely under radiative viscosity, then the torus will deflate before much gas can accrete onto the hole. Also note that we are ignoring the kinetic energy associated with the poloidal motion, which is equivalent to assuming that the poloidal motion is quite subsonic.

Finally, the equation of angular momentum conservation is

$$wAe^2\frac{\partial\ell}{\partial t} + we^2\vec{u}\cdot\nabla\ell + \ell e\frac{\partial p}{\partial t} = \nabla\cdot(\eta g^* A^2\nabla\Omega) - \eta g^* A^2\vec{a}\cdot\nabla\Omega - e^2\vec{q}\cdot\nabla\ell \ . \tag{19}$$

The first two terms on the right hand side describe the angular momentum transported by viscous stresses. The final term on the right hand side takes into account the angular momentum carried off by the radiation field.

There are now five independent equations in five unknowns, which can be chosen to be $p, n, \Omega, \vec{v}$. These equations contain a natural homology relation as they are unchanged if the density, pressure and enthalpy are increased by a factor while at the same time the poloidal velocity is reduced by the same factor. Furthermore, they do not involve the hole mass m explicitly and so there is no independent length scale. They also reduce to the familiar nonrelativistic equations in the limit $r \gg 1$, $a = 0$.

c) Instabilities

The approach outlined above is only one of several possible ways to study the evolution of a radiation torus. It represents a formidable numerical undertaking that has apparently never been carried through nonrelativistically (e.g. for Eddington-Sweet circulation in rotating main sequence stars). In any case it is almost certainly incomplete because, even if the initial configuration is stable, the torus will probably evolve to become unstable.

Radiation-supported tori are subject to two important types of local instability. Both types have been analyzed by Seguin (1975). Dynamical instabilities can occur if two rings of fluid can be interchanged adiabatically with constant angular momentum without requiring external work to be performed. If we displace a ring by a radial distance δr , keeping it in pressure equilibrium with its surroundings, then there will be a buoyant acceleration $-(\partial(\ln w)/\partial S)_p (\delta\vec{r}\cdot\nabla S)\vec{a}$. There will also be an additional acceleration of $\vec{\gamma}(\delta\vec{r}\cdot\nabla\ell)$ as the ring has a different angular momentum from its surroundings, where

$$\vec{\gamma} = \frac{\partial\vec{a}}{\partial\ell} = e^4 g^{*-1}\nabla\ell - e^2 A^2\nabla\Omega \; , \tag{20}$$

and

$$S = p^{3/4}/\rho \tag{21}$$

is (ignoring a constant) the entropy per baryon. We therefore require that

$$\frac{1}{w^2}\left[\frac{\partial\rho}{\partial S}\right]_p (\delta\vec{r}\cdot\nabla p)(\delta\vec{r}\cdot\nabla S) + (\delta\vec{r}\cdot\vec{\gamma})(\delta\vec{r}\cdot\nabla\ell) \geq 0 \tag{22}$$

for all displacements $\delta\vec{r}$ if the fluid is to be stable. Necessary and sufficient conditions for stability to these modes turn out to be

$$(\vec{a} \times \vec{\gamma})\cdot(\nabla\ell \times \nabla(\ln S)) < 0$$

and

$$\rho(\vec{a}\cdot\nabla\ln S) + w(\vec{\gamma}\cdot\nabla\ell) > 0 \ . \tag{23}$$

This combines the well known Schwarzschild instability criterion which is applicable in the absence of rotation and the Rayleigh criterion for thin disks. If we examine these two inequalities in conjunction with the equation of hydrostatic equilibrium, then we can show that they require that the vectors $\nabla\ell$ and $\vec{\gamma}$ lie on the same side of and between the vectors ∇S and ∇p as shown in Figure 3.

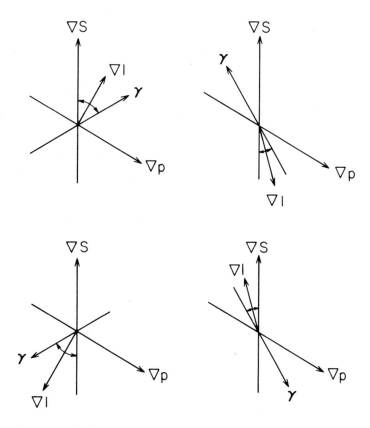

Fig. 3.–Convectively stable arrangements of the angular velocity and angular momentum gradients. The allowed orientations for the angular momentum gradient $\nabla\ell$ are shown for the few possible directions of $\vec{\gamma}$ relative to the pressure and entropy gradients. Mirror reflections and rotations of these configurations are also allowed provided that the surfaces perpendicular to the four vectors do not cross. Note that a Schwarzschild unstable entropy gradient parallel to the pressure gradient can be stabilized by a large enough angular momentum gradient. These stability criteria do not include short wavelength modes driven by viscosity which, as discussed in the text, may bring about barytropicity (i.e. $\nabla p \times \nabla S = \nabla\ell \times \vec{\gamma} = 0$). Barytropic fluids are marginally stable to convective modes.

If a region of the torus becomes convectively unstable, then we need some prescription for setting the entropy and angular momentum gradients within the unstable region. Presumably convective transport can be so efficient that the torus is maintained close to a condition of marginal stability except perhaps close to the surface. One possibility is to assume that the convective transport is only efficient at exchanging entropy and angular momentum along surfaces of cylindrical topology and so the entropy S is a unique function of the angular momentum ℓ (Bardeen 1973, Paczyński and Abramowicz 1982). In this case, the equation of hydrostatic support can be rewritten in the form

$$\nabla[\ln(we/\rho)] = \frac{\Omega}{1-\Omega\ell} + \frac{p}{w} \frac{d \ln S}{d\ell} \nabla\ell \ . \tag{24}$$

This in turn implies that the Bernoulli constant we/ρ and the quantity in braces can also be regarded as constant on surfaces of constant ℓ . This prescription allows one to solve for the entropy and angular momentum within a convective zone, given specified conditions on part of its bounding surface.

The second type of instability is driven by dissipation (i.e., thermal conduction or viscosity) and can arise when two small rings of fluid are interchanged. As the fluid is radiation-dominated, heat flows down a pressure gradient. Now a fluid element is virtually in pressure equilibrium with its surroundings during slow convective overturn and so the transport of internal energy is extremely ineffective during these interchanges. However, radiative viscosity can bring a small enough ring into co-rotation with its surroundings, thereby suppressing the possible rotational stabilization of the Schwarzschild instability. (Normally in stars, heat transport is far more important than viscosity for driving these unstable modes; Goldreich and Schumbert 1967, Fricke 1968.)

Let the specific angular momentum of the ring differ by an amount $\nabla\ell$ from its initial value and from the specific angular momentum of its surroundings by an amount $\delta\ell$. Consider a thin annular ring of thickness k^{-1}. It will experience a decelerating torque proportional to the difference $\delta\ell-\nabla\ell$. The angular momentum of the ring will evolve according to an equation of the approximate form

$$\frac{d\nabla\ell}{d\tau} = iA\omega\nabla\ell = \frac{\eta k^2(\delta\ell-\nabla\ell)}{\omega} \tag{25}$$

where the perturbation is assumed to vary with time $\propto \exp(i\omega t)$. Therefore the centrifugal acceleration term in the stability equation must be multiplied by a factor

$$\frac{\delta\ell-\nabla\ell}{\delta\ell} = (1-i\eta k^2/ w\omega A)^{-1} \ . \tag{26}$$

This is in fact the result of a full Eulerian analysis if $\vec{k}$ is interpreted as the wave vector. The continuity equation requires that $\vec{k}$ be orthogonal to $\vec{\delta r}$, and the full dispersion relation is

$$\omega(\omega - i\Omega_v) = \Omega_S^2 + \Omega_\ell^2 \, \omega(\omega - i\Omega_v)^{-1} \tag{27}$$

where

$$\Omega_v = \eta k^2 / wA \, ,$$

$$\Omega_S^2 = - \frac{\rho(\vec{k} \times \nabla\ln S) \cdot (\vec{k} \times \nabla p)}{w^2 A^2 \tilde{g} k^2} \, ,$$

$$\Omega_\ell^2 = \frac{(\vec{k} \times \vec{\gamma})(\vec{k} \times \nabla\ell)}{A^2 \tilde{g} k^2} \, . \tag{28}$$

Examining this dispersion relation, we see that it is always possible to find a growing mode (i.e. $\omega > 0$) unless Ω_S^2 is positive for all choices of $\vec{k}$. This in turn requires that ∇S be anti-parallel to ∇p. In other words we recover the Schwarzschild criterion. From the equation of hydrostatic equilibrium, we see that this then implies that the fluid is barotropic (i.e., there exists a functional relationship $p(\rho)$ or equivalently $\Omega(\ell)$ -- the relativistic von Zeipel theorem). Now if the viscous instabilities are effective at maintaining barotropicity, then there is a considerable simplification. In particular, necessary and sufficient conditions for local dynamical stability of a barotropic fluid become

$$\text{either} \quad \frac{dS}{dp} \leq 0 \quad \text{or} \quad p = \text{constant}$$

and

$$\text{either} \quad \frac{d\Omega}{d\ell} < \frac{e^2}{A^2 g_*} \quad \text{or} \quad \ell = \text{constant} \, . \tag{29}$$

It is therefore important to examine the nature of these viscous modes and to see if they can be effective at maintaining barotropicity.

Let us suppose that there is a small departure from barotropicity and there is a correspondingly small range of directions between $\nabla\ln S$ and $-\nabla p$ within which there are unstable values of $\vec{k}$. The most rapidly growing modes have $\Omega_S^2 = -\rho|\nabla\ln S||\nabla p|\epsilon^2/(4w^2 A^2 \tilde{g})$ where ϵ is the angle between ∇S and $-\nabla p$. The most important modes are those for which

$$1 \ll kr \ll \left(\frac{w\ell}{\eta}\right)^{1/2} \sim \left(\tau_T \ell\right)^{1/2} \, . \tag{30}$$

The growth rate of these modes is

$$\text{Im}(\omega) \sim \frac{-\Omega_S^2 \Omega_V}{\Omega_\ell^2}$$

where

$$\Omega_\ell^2 = \frac{|\vec{\gamma}| \, |\nabla \ell| \sin^2\theta}{\underset{\sim}{g} \, A^2} \sim \Omega^2 \sin^2\theta \qquad (31)$$

with θ being the angle between the pressure and angular momentum gradients.
Now the unstable modes comprise flattened cylindrical eddies elongated between
the isobars and isentropes (see Fig. 4). We can attempt to estimate the efficiency of the angular momentum transport in terms of a mixing length, h . After
the stabilizing angular momentum gradient has been neutralized by viscosity there
will be a residual buoyant acceleration $\sim \varepsilon(h/H_S)a$ where H_S is the entropy
scale height. We estimate the eddy velocity v by equating the acceleration to
v^2/h . Finally we estimate the rate of transport of angular momentum by

$$G \sim wvh \, \sin\theta \nabla \ell \sim \rho h^2 (\varepsilon a/H_S)^{1/2} \, \sin\theta \nabla \ell \ . \qquad (32)$$

Note that the torque requires an angular momentum gradient parallel to the isobars to operate rather than an angular velocity gradient as is usually the case.

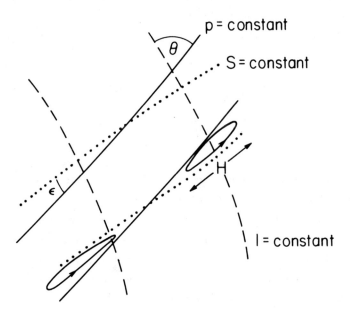

Fig. 4.-Instability of non-barotropic fluid driven by radiative viscosity.
Slender cylindrical "fingers" of fluid move slowly along isobaric surfaces
exchanging angular momentum but not entropy.

Now we should compare this torque with that necessary to maintain barotropicity. This can be shown to be $\sim \nabla \ell / \kappa$. So we can derive an equilibrium estimate of the angle ε of

$$\varepsilon \sim \left(\frac{r}{h} \right)^4 H_S \tau_T^{-2} . \tag{33}$$

If we estimate the mixing length to be a substantial fraction of the angular momentum scale height, then we see that a torus with $\tau_T \gtrsim 100$ is almost everywhere sufficiently optically thick to remain barotropic. The circulation velocity in the eddies is $\sim (r/h) \tau_T^{-1}$ which is probably larger than the infall velocity $\sim \tau_T^{-1}$.

If this analysis really does describe the non-linear development of the viscous instability and the above conditions are fulfilled, then a radiative zone will remain barotropic and we must modify our evolutionary equations. The viscous terms on the right hand side of the angular momentum equation must be replaced by a phenomenological angular momentum transport along the isobars that is just sufficient to maintain barotropicity. The energy equation will contain a term describing the energy transport associated with the angular momentum transport as well as the energy loss associated with the diffusion of photons out of the torus. It can be seen that these two terms are comparable and so there is the possibility that the viscous instability, unlike pure radiative viscosity, can drive enough gas through the torus to keep it thick in a steady state. This procedure is easier to implement numerically than express in terms of differential equations.

Global (e.g. pulsational) stability of radiation tori has apparently never been investigated. The presence of instabilities would have obvious observational implications.

d) Photosphere

As we have mentioned, the spectrum of the emergent radiation will be sensitive to the detailed photospheric conditions. We can try to estimate these in a similar fashion to the way we described the interior conditions. Electron scattering opacity dominates in the atmosphere and so the photosphere, where the photons are produced, lies well below the last scattering surface. The photosphere is located at a depth where the product of the scattering and absorptive optical depths is unity (e.g. Wiita 1982). As the gas pressure is so much smaller than the radiation pressure, the constant radiation flux through the atmosphere must be at the Eddington value $\vec{g}/\kappa$ where $\vec{g}$ is the surface gravity which is effectively constant if the pressure scale height is much smaller than the radius. Therefore the opacity must be constant if there is to be hydrostatic equilibrium. If the total opacity rises above the standard Thomson value, then a strong wind will be driven off the surface. However, if the opacity falls, then the surface layers will slowly sink down into the envelope. This suggests a possible explanation for the $\sim$30,000K black body components found in the spectra of several quasars and Seyferts (Malkan and Sargent 1982). Using the Saha equation, we see that at the densities of interest, $\rho \sim 10^{-10} \text{g cm}^{-3}$, helium recombines at just this temperature. This implies that if the surface were to become this cool then the mean molecular weight per electron would increase and the opacity would fall by 9 per cent. 30,000K is therefore a natural limiting photospheric temperature for a radiation torus and we can easily imagine that freshly accreted gas will enlarge an existing torus until the effective temperature falls to the critical value (cf. also Frank 1979). We consider the cases T=30,000K and T>30,000K in turn.

The photospheric pressure associated with a temperature $T \sim$30,000K is $\sim$3000 dyne cm^{-2}. For a photospheric density of $\rho = 10^{-10} \rho_{-10} \text{ g cm}^{-3}$ we can estimate the radius, scale height, Thomson optical depth, photospheric mass and ratio of gas pressure to radiation pressure as follows:

$$R \sim 5\times10^{15} \rho_{-10}^{-0.3} M_8^{0.5} \text{ cm}, \tag{34}$$

$$H \sim 5\times10^{11} \rho_{-10}^{-1.5} \text{ cm}, \tag{35}$$

$$\tau_T \sim 15\rho_{-10}^{-0.5}, \tag{36}$$

$$M_{ph} \sim 5\rho_{-10}^{-1} M_8 M_\odot, \tag{37}$$

$$\beta \sim 0.03\rho_{-10}. \tag{38}$$

These relations are displayed in Figure 5.

The scale height must not exceed the radius and so equations (34) and (35) imply that the photospheric radius not exceed $3\times10^{16} M_8^{0.6}$ cm. Likewise, $\beta \gtrsim 3\times10^{-5} M_8^{-0.4}$. This is of interest because by inspecting Fig. 1, one can conclude that either the torus is fairly massive, or the entropy ($\propto \beta^{-1}$) must decrease with radius; that is to say angular momentum must stabilize an unstable entropy gradient as discussed in section IIIc.

Alternatively, the history of gas accretion onto the torus may be such that the photospheric temperature exceeds 30,000K. We exhibit the photospheric conditions for this case in Figure 6, making the additional assumption that the

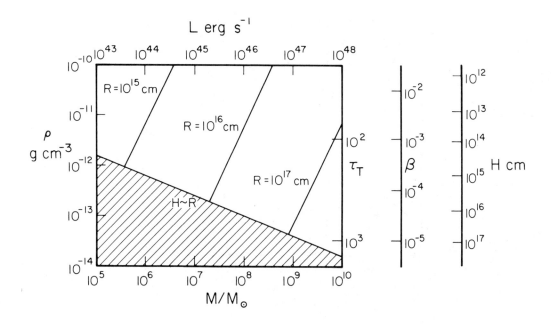

Fig. 5.–Approximate physical conditions at the photosphere of a radiation torus around a massive black hole. It is assumed that the photospheric temperature has the limiting value $\sim 3\times10^4$ K . The photospheric density ρ , radius R , scattering optical depth τ_T , gas pressure to total pressure ratio β and pressure scale height H are shown as functions of the hole mass M . β^{-1} is proportional to the entropy per baryon and so if the envelope is barotropic then the surface value of β must be similar to that in the core as shown in Fig. 2.

scale height equals the radius. From this diagram, we see that if, arbitrarily, we require the torus to have a radius in excess of ~ 30 Schwarzschild radii, then the photospheric temperature is $T < 3\times10^5$ K for $M_8 \sim 1$.

We can also estimate the Comptonization parameter $y = (4kT/m_e)\tau_T^2$ which determines whether or not photons can be efficiently Comptonized before they diffuse out of the torus. We find that $y \gtrsim 1$ (except when $T \sim 30,000$K and $M_8 \lesssim 0.1$). This causes an increase in the effective free-free opacity because low frequency photons (whose emissivity exceeds that of thermal photons by a logarithmic factor) can be heated to frequencies $\sim kT/h$. (This effect has been taken into account in drawing Figs. 5 and 6.) This also means that the emergent

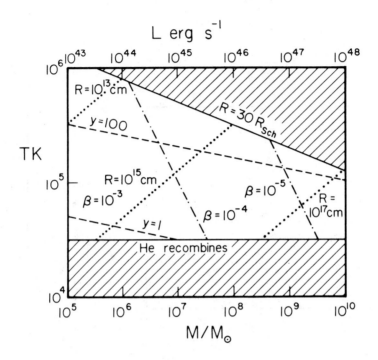

Fig. 6.-Approximate physical conditions at the photosphere of a radiation torus for different values of the photospheric temperature T>30,000K . It is assumed that the scale height is comparable with the photospheric radius R which is presumed to exceed 30 Schwarzschild radii. Also shown are the Comptonization parameter y (---) and the pressure ratio β (-·-·-).

spectrum at the last scattering surface will be closer to a black body at the effective temperature of the radiation field than to a Compton-suppressed spectrum (cf. Wiita 1982).

e) Envelope

We have described separately the approximate physical conditions to be found at both the center and the surface of a radiation torus. They are of course not independent, but are related by the structure of the intervening envelope. This may be thought to depend crucially upon the accretion history, but it is possible that it is fairly independent of all but the most recent history because of the presence of efficient meridional circulation.

There seem to be three separate mechanisms driving poloidal flow. Firstly the radial heat flow will be balanced by a compensatory infall of the gas with a speed $\sim r\tau_T(r)^{-1}$. Secondly as discussed in section IIIc there may be eddy transport of angular momentum driven by either dynamical or viscous instability. The eddy speed $\sim(\kappa\rho h)^{-1}$ will exceed the infall speed by a factor depending upon the mixing length. Thirdly there is a new effect attributable to the radiation pressure dominance of the gas. In the outer envelope, we may consider the energy equation in the Newtonian approximation. The divergence of the heat flux can then be written as

$$\nabla \cdot \vec{q} \simeq \frac{1}{\kappa\tilde{\omega}} \frac{\partial}{\partial\tilde{\omega}} (\tilde{\omega}^2\Omega^2) \tag{39}$$

where $\tilde{\omega}$ is the cylindrical radius and we ignore the self gravity of the gas. If the torus were to remain in a steady state then there would have to be a circulation speed $\vec{v}$ given by

$$\rho T(\vec{v} \cdot \nabla)S + \nabla \cdot \vec{q} = 0 \; . \tag{40}$$

In other words,

$$v \sim \tau\omega^2/ \kappa\rho \sim \ell^2/ \tau_T \; . \tag{41}$$

This velocity exceeds the infall velocity if the specific angular momentum increases outwards.

So, even if the torus is convectively stable, we expect there to be meridional circulation. However, numerical calculations seem necessary to calculate its value and the consequent effect upon the entropy and angular momentum distributions in the envelope.

f) Funnel

The above descriptions of the envelope and surface do not apply close to the spin axis. Here we expect there to be two funnels whose shapes are fixed by the surface distributions of angular momentum. The surface boundary condition of the radiative transfer within the funnel must be modified because there will be significant incident radiation (Sikora 1981). A radiation driven jet may emerge from the top of the funnel, but it is unlikely to be very well collimated nor to move ultrarelativistically (Sikora and Wilson 1981). For most viewing angles the funnel will be invisible, but an unusually bright source may be seen when the observer direction is close to the symmetry axis. This may be related to the interpretation of the optically violent variable quasars and Bl Lac objects.

g) Winds and Coronae

As hydrostatic equilibrium depends so sensitively upon the balance between radiation pressure and gravity, it is entirely reasonable that a powerful wind be driven by resonance line scattering of the continuum just as in early type stars. However, the power in this wind will be smaller than the radiative luminosity by a factor of at least $r^{1/2}$.

There may also be an active corona above the photosphere powered by circulation below the photosphere or, more promisingly, the outflow from the funnel. This corona and perhaps also the shocked wind may be the site for the non-thermal, power law infra-red to X-ray component of a typical quasar spectrum.

IV. ION TORI

When the accretion rate is low enough and yet the viscosity large enough then the infalling gas can heat up without necessarily being able to cool. In fact non-thermal emission will probably limit the electron temperature to $\sim 5 \times 10^{10}$ K and, in the absence of collective effects, Coulomb scattering is insufficient to bring about electron-ion equipartition provided that the gas spirals inwards in fewer than $\sim 30 (\dot{M}/ \dot{M}_c)^{-0.5}$ orbital periods (Rees et al. 1982). There is a possibility that collective processes bring about far faster equili- bration and thereby deflate the torus. Whether or not this actually happens is a fairly well-posed though unanswered question in relativistic plasma physics. The inner regions of ion tori are probably stationary, as the inflow times are necessarily shorter than the times over which we have been observing them. This means that numerical simulations are easier than in the case of radiation tori although the microphysics is even more uncertain.

Under these conditions, the main source of power may be the rotational energy of the hole, which will have presumably been spun up in an earlier phase of high mass accretion. Up to 29 per cent of the rest mass of the hole can be stored in this way. An attractive way to extract this energy is through the use of large scale magnetic fields supported by external currents which pass through the hori- zon of the hole. Charged particles have to be created continuously in the region outside the horizon (most plausibly as electron-positron pairs produced from gamma-ray collisions) for this mechanism to operate. Recent studies of electro- magnetic energy extraction from black holes have greatly clarified its relativistic basis (Macdonald and Thorne 1982) and shown how perfect MHD can be incorporated (Phinney 1983). It now appears that no more than 3 percent of the rest mass energy is likely to be extracted in this way. However, this still means that holes no more massive than $10^8 M_\odot$ can supply the energy requirements of the largest double radio sources. (See Rees, this volume, for further details.)

V. DISCUSSION

In this talk I have endeavored to summarize some recent theoretical ideas on a class of models of active galactic nuclei involving massive black holes and to suggest some possible numerical studies. It is of interest to ask how the three basic structures (disk, radiation torus, and ion torus) isolated theoretically can be fitted into the observational classification of active nuclei. (This presupposes that radiation tori and ion tori are both viable, something that has been demonstrated in neither case.) One interesting possibility is to presume that the hole mass and the accretion rate are the two essential parameters that control the type of object observed, just as mass and age control the appearance of stars. (This cannot be the entire story as the hole's angular momentum and the gas density in the surrounding region undoubtedly have an important influence in the same way that metallicity does in the stellar analogue.) It is then natural to associate the optical quasars and the type I Seyfert galaxies with radiation tori accreting supercritically. As the lower power Seyferts appear to be associated with spirals (and there is some evidence for this in the case of quasars; Boroson, Oke, and Green 1982), we propose that lower mass black holes be found in spirals. (Note that as discussed in section IIId there may be spectral differences between the two types of object, as Comptonization is more effective in the case of quasars than for Seyferts.) By contrast, we associate the powerful radio galaxies (which are found exclusively in ellipticals and whose nuclei are optically quiet) with massive black holes accreting subcritically and perhaps encircled by an ion torus. This requires that massive black holes be found preferentially in ellipticals. This correlation fits in with the suggestion that general elliptical galaxies, not just the cD's, are merger products (Fall 1979).

These two structures represent the extremes of what is likely to be a continuous progression as M/M is increased. The ratio of thermal to non-thermal power increases with the thickness of the radiation-supported accretion disk. Perhaps the powerful radio quasars can be associated with the intermediate case when the disk is thin enough for a non-thermal corona to extend down to the black holh.

When the power is produced non-thermally, most plausibly as an electromagnetic electron-positron outflow, it must become collimated into a pair of anti-parallel jets. This may be accomplished through magnetic hoop stress as described above or hydrodynamically through a pair of nozzles. Either way the jet should move with a relativistic speed at least close to the nucleus. In a small fraction of sources we will be observing along the direction of the beam. These will be characterized by rapid variability, high polarization and super-luminal expansion. In the case of quasars, these should be the "optically violently variable" quasars, and in the case of radio galaxies, the BL Lac objects.

Our galactic center also exhibits non-thermal activity, particularly at radio and gamma-ray energy. This too can be fitted into the above scheme if the galactic center contains a low mass black hole $\lesssim 10^6 M_\odot$ accreting subcritically. If so there is no reason to doubt that most galactic nuclei contain black holes.

This (not so grand) unified theory of nuclear activity is an attempt to account for a wealth of observational detail using a paucity of serious theoretical calculation. The gap is bridged by pure speculation. We must turn to Jim Wilson and his colleagues to either demonstrate self-inconsistency or to provide a more detailed link to the data.

ACKNOWLEDGEMENTS

I thank Joan Centrella, Fred Lamb, and Larry Smarr for their invitation to this festschrift and their hospitality. The above views have been developed during an extended collaboration with Michal Jaroszyński, Martin Rees, Mitch Begelman, and Sterl Phinney (although they do not necessarily subscribe to them all). I acknowledge financial support by the National Science Foundation under grant AST80-17752 and the Alfred P. Sloan Foundation.

REFERENCES

Boroson, T.A., Oke, J.B., and Green, R.F. 1982, Ap. J., 263, 32.

Bardeen, J.M., and Petterson, J.A. 1975, Ap. J. (Letters), 195, 65.

Bardeen, J.M. 1973, in "Black Holes," ed. C. DeWitt and B. DeWitt (New York: Gordon and Breach).

Begelman, M.C., McKee, C.F., and Shields, G.A. 1982, Ap. J., 271, 70.

Begelman, M.C., and Meier, D.L. 1982, Ap. J., 253, 873.

Blandford, R.D., and Payne, D.G. 1982, M.N.R.A.S., 199, 883.

Coroniti, F.V. 1981, Ap. J., 244, 66.

Fall, S.M. 1979, Nature, 281, 200.

Frank, J.H. 1979, M.N.R.A.S., 187, 883.

Fricke, K.J. 1968, Z. Astrophys., 68, 317.

Galeev, A., Rosner, R., and Vaiana, G.S. 1979, Ap. J., 229, 318.

Goldreich, P. and Schubert, G. 1967, Ap. J., 150, 571.

Jaroszyński, M., Abramowicz, M.A., and Paczynski, B. 1980. Acta astr., 30, 1.

Macdonald, D.M., and Thorne, K.S. 1982, M.N.R.A.S.. 198, 345.

Malkan, M., and Sargent, W.L.W. 1982, Ap. J., 254, 22.

Matthews, W. 1982, Ap. J., 258, 425.

Meier, D.L. 1982a, Ap. J., 256, 681.

————. 1982b, Ap. J., 256, 693.

————. 1982c, Ap. J., 256, 706.

Misner, C.W., Thorne, K.S., and Wheeler, J.A. 1973, "Gravitation" (San Francisco: W.H. Freeman).

Ostriker, J. 1983, Ap. J., 273, 99.

Paczynski, B. 1980, Acta Astr., 30. 347.

Paczynski, B., and Abramowicz, M.A. 1982, Ap. J., 253, 897.

Paczynski, B., and Wiita, P. 1980, Astr. Ap., 88, 23.

Piran, T. 1982, Ap. J. (Letters), 257, L23.

Phinney, E.S. 1983, "Proceedings of Turin Conference on Radio Jets," in press.

Pringle, J.E. 1981, Ann. Rev. Astr. Ap., 19, 137.

Rees, M.J., Begelman, M.C., Blandford, R.D., and Phinney, E.S. 1982, Nature, 295, 17.

Sakimoto, P.J., and Coroniti, F.V. 1981. Ap. J., 247, 19.

Seguin, F.H. 1975, Ap. J., 197, 745.

Sikora, M. 1981, M.N.R.A.S.. 196, 257.

Sikora, M., and Wilson, D.B. 1981, M.N.R.A.S., 197, 529.

Seinberg, S. 1972, "Gravitation and Cosmology" (New York: Wiley).

Wiita, P. 1982, Ap. J., 256, 666.

Numerical Models of Fat Disks: New Scenarios for Fluid Accretion into Black Holes

John F. Hawley
University of Illinois

Larry L. Smarr*
University of Illinois

ABSTRACT

High energy phenomena in astrophysics demand a compact, efficient central engine. The best candidate for this engine is a black hole accreting matter. We briefly review recent descriptions of such accretion flows with emphasis upon the role of numerical calculations in understanding these flows. Certain cases are illustrated using recent numerical computations.

High energy phenomena abound in astronomy, but with few exceptions these phenomenan are not well understood. The most outstanding examples are the quasars. These highly energetic objects have luminosity variations on the order of hours, implying a compact energy source. Another example is the double radio jet emerging from a galaxy core (see Fig. 1). Here also a compact engine is required to power the jets. Since the central regions of quasars and galaxies cannot be observed directly, gaining an understanding of these central engines has not been an easy task.

*Alfred P. Sloan Fellow

One thing astronomers do know is that the amount of energy released in the central regions of quasars can be equivalent to the rest mass energy of up to ten million solar masses. Nuclear energy, which has an efficiency of about 0.8 percent, is inadequate as the source of power. There is, however, another means of releasing energy which can be much more efficient: the release of gravitational binding energy as matter falls into an intense gravitational field. This idea predates that of nuclear power; it was the power source first suggested for a nearby object which is slightly less luminous than a quasar, the sun. A gradual decrease in the sun's radius could provide enough energy to maintain the solar luminosity---but only for about ten million years. The nuclear process proves to be more efficient for the sun but not for a 10^8 solar mass black hole. Given such a deep potential well, gravity power predominates.

Our understanding of gravity as an energy source follows the course by which astronomers came to understand the stellar nuclear burning process. Initially, there were qualitative arguments and "back-of-the-envelope" calculations which demonstrated the feasibility of fusion to power many stages of stellar evolution. Then came numerical calculations involving complex nuclear reaction networks which provided the details as well as producing a few unexpected results. Astrophysicists today have a qualitative picture of the gravity power process, but the details such as the actual net efficiency can be only roughly estimated. Analytic techniques are restricted to the most simplified systems of equations. Clearly numerical calculations are now required.

Consider a most efficient gravity engine, the black hole. The fuel is an external supply of matter, which might be provided by a companion star or surrounding interstellar gas. In the case of a supermassive black hole, entire stars, ripped apart by the intense tidal forces near the hole, could supply matter for accretion. Now, given the gravitational sink and the fuel supply, we must describe the process by which energy is extracted. In the basic analytic scenario, matter orbits the hole in a thin Keplerian disk (see e.g. Shakura and Sunyaev 1973 and Novikov and Thorne 1973). The viscous shear between differentially rotating fluid layers causes a net outward transport of angular momentum, heating the gas as it gradual-

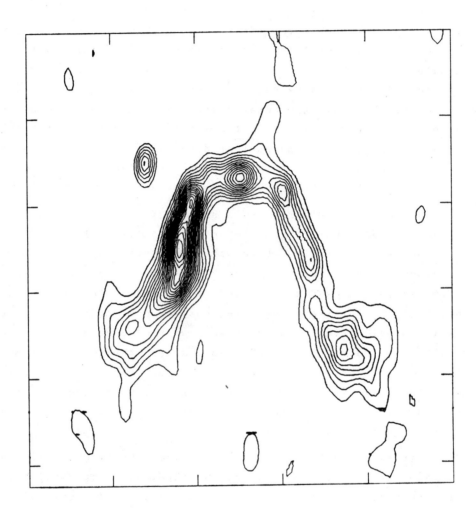

Fig. 1. A contour plot of the radio emission from the double galaxy
system Uppsala 7044-7050. The most prominent feature is the double-
lobed radio jet emerging from one of the galaxies. Such an energetic
phenomenon requires a compact central power source such as an accreting black hole. (Data obtained at the VLA observatory by R. Ekers,
L. Smarr and D. Sumi and reduced at the University of Illinois Image
Processing System by D. Sumi, Dept. of Astronomy, Univ. of Ill.)

ly spirals in towards the hole. This heat is promptly radiated away at the surface of the disk. Depending on the angular momentum of the hole itself, this process could release anywhere between 5 and 40% of the fluid rest mass energy. High luminosities are achieved by increasing the mass accretion rate. The limit is the "Eddington luminosity" at which the pressure from the radiation is sufficient to disrupt the disk. Assuming that the most energetic quasars radiate at the Eddington limit, a 10^8 solar mass black hole is required to power them.

This analytic picture is quite promising, for it implies that accretion onto black holes could indeed be just the engine needed for observed superluminous objects. The numbers are feasible, but how will accreting matter really behave as it falls in towards the black hole? To answer this we must solve the full general-relativistic equations of hydrodynamics in the gravitational field of the black hole. These equations are so complicated that analytic dynamic calculations are simply not possible. To study the equations numerically we have collaborated with Jim Wilson of Lawrence Livermore National Laboratory (LLNL) in developing a two-dimensional (2-D) general-relativistic hydrodynamic code to simulate fluid flow in the Kerr metric. We assume axisymmetry, an ideal gas equation of state, and a fixed metric to describe the gravitational field.

The first such numerical study was performed at LLNL by Jim Wilson in 1972. He had made considerable progress in generalizing the 1-D fully general-relativistic codes of Michael May and Richard White (1966), to study such phenomena as stellar collapse and supernovae. Drawing upon this experience, he designed a 2-D code to calculate axisymmetric hydrodynamic flows in the fixed Kerr metric, the gravitational field of the black hole; the fluid around the hole is assumed to have negligible mass. Several models were run in which cold material with some angular momentum was allowed to fall towards the hole. One new effect immediately discovered by this work was that shock heating could drastically alter the structure of the flow. Infalling cold fluid with nonzero angular momentum was heated by a standing accretion shock to form dynamically a pressure-supported thick or "fat" disk in which the height of the disk above the equator is comparable to the radial distance from the hole. Instead of a thin disk, the fluid had formed a non-Keplerian orbiting torus (see Fig. 2). Unfortunately, this pioneering numerical work, published in a short note to the Astrophysical Journal (Wilson 1972), went largely unnoticed.

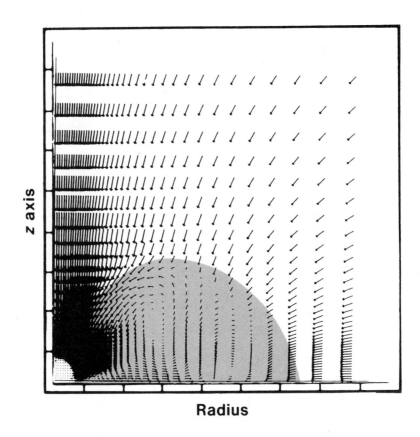

Fig. 2. Infalling cold fluid with nonzero angular momentum shocks and forms a fat disk. The Kerr black hole in this model rotates with the maximum angular momentum (Kerr parameter a = 1). (From Wilson 1972).

In the second half of the seventies the fat disk was redis-covered and considered analytically. Many new and important quali-tative features were described, one of the most important of which is a completely general-relativistic effect: in a fat disk, accretion can occur for low angular momentum fluid without viscosity. This fact was first emphasized in 1976 by B. Paczynski of the Copernicus Astronomical Center in Warsaw (unpublished).

Such accretion can occur because of a fundamental difference between the potential around a black hole and the Newtonian point mass potential. In the Newtonian case, a test particle with nonzero angular momentum will always reach a turning point in its orbit. Further, there is an angular momentum associated with a stable circular orbit for each r, regardless of how close to the origin the orbit is. This is not the case for the general relativistic description of the gravitational field of a black hole. To use the phrase coined by Misner, Thorne and Wheeler (1973), there is a "pit in the potential". Instead of increasing monotonically to infinity as r decreases (the "centrifugal barrier"), the potential turns over and goes to zero at some r outside the horizon (see Fig. 3). That is, in general relativity, the gravitational acceleration always becomes strong enough to overcome centrifugal force. Further, for sufficiently low angular momentum there comes a point where there is no turning radius and no Keplerian circular orbits.

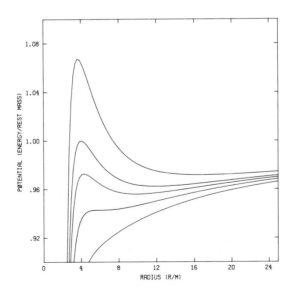

Fig. 3. The effective potential as a function of r along the equator for a Schwarzschild (nonrotating) black hole. From bottom to top the momenta are $\ell = 3.0$, $\ell = \ell_{ms} = 2\sqrt{3}$, $\ell = 3.77$, $\ell = \ell_{mb} = 4.0$ and $\ell = 4.5$. Note the important relativistic effect: the potential does not monotonically increase as r approaches the horizon. There is a "pit in the potential".

For example, the innermost circular orbit for a Schwarzschild (non-rotating) black hole is at $3r_g$, where r_g is the "Schwarzschild radius" of the event horizon. The Schwarzschild radius is given by $r_g = 2M$ where M is the mass of the hole and we have set the gravitational constant G and the speed of light c equal to one. To convert a radial distance to more familiar units, multiply by G/c^2 (= 1.5 kilometers per solar mass). Using this convention, the minimum stable Keplerian orbit for a Schwarzschild hole is at r = 6M. A particle trying to orbit at a smaller radius would spiral rapidly into the hole.

The orbits of test particles in the Kerr metric can be generalized to fluid orbits by defining an angular momentum

$$\ell \equiv -U_\phi/U_t. \qquad (1)$$

This definition is extremely well suited to the study of fluid flow with nonzero U_ϕ, since in a stationary, axisymmetric flow hU_ϕ and hU_t are separately conserved quantities (h ≡ enthalpy = $1 + \epsilon = P/\rho$, where ϵ = specific internal energy, ρ = baryon density; see Smarr, Taubes, and Wilson 1980 or Hawley, Smarr, and Wilson 1984a for a complete discussion of fluid variables and definitions.) Thus ℓ will be conserved in such flows and can be used to describe fluid orbits in a manner analogous to the test particle case (see Kozłowski et al. 1978, and Bardeen 1973).

As in the test particle case, we can define two critical angular momenta ℓ for a given hole. First, the minimum angular momentum which permits a circular orbit is referred to as ℓ_{ms} ("marginally stable"). Second, the minimum angular momentum for which there is still a turning point in the orbit of a "marginally bound" (energy/rest mass = 1) test particle falling towards the hole from rest at infinity is designated ℓ_{mb}. Any body with $\ell < \ell_{mb}$ which falls from rest at infinity must be captured by the hole. A particle can avoid capture by having less energy than the marginally bound particle, but not if $\ell < \ell_{ms}$. In general, $\ell_{ms} < \ell_{mb}$. For a Schwarzschild hole, $\ell_{ms} = 2\sqrt{3} \simeq 3.46$ (stable orbit at 6M) while ℓ_{mb} = 4.0 (turning point at 4M).

A diagram such as Figure 3 can be expanded into two spatial dimensions. Figure 4 is an example for a variety of constant angular

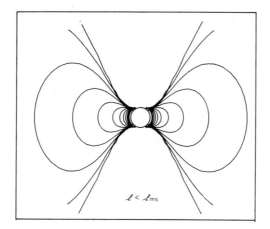

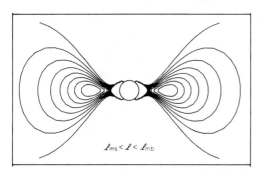 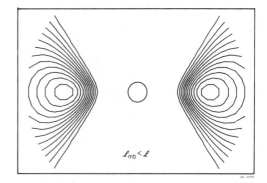

Fig. 4. These figures show surfaces of constant total potential (due to combined gravitational and centrifugal accelerations). They illustrate possible accretion scenarios: a) low angular momentum ($\ell < \ell_{ms}$) potentials are open to the hole and fluid can flow directly in; b) between marginally stable (ℓ_{ms}) and marginally bound (ℓ_{mb}) angular momenta, some potentials end on the hole and some are closed. An accreting disk structure can form; c) for angular momentum larger than ℓ_{mb}, there are stable, pressure-supported disks which remain stable in the absence of viscous dissipation.

momenta ℓ. We see that there are surfaces of equal "total potential" determined by the gravitational and centrifugal accelerations. These accelerations can be countered by a pressure force; simply fill the closed potentials with hot fluid. In equilibrium, pressure contours coincide with total potential contours. The pressure maximum will be at the "lowest point" in the potential, which in these examples is at the point of the Keplerian circular orbit for the given angular momentum (no pressure acceleration is needed to keep a particle at such a point - gravity and centrifugal force exactly cancel!). By changing the angular momentum we can change the equipotential surfaces and consequently the expected fluid behavior.

These features can be quantitatively described by assuming a purely azimuthal, time-stationary, axisymmetric fluid flow with $U^r = U^\theta = 0$ and solving the relativistic Euler equation to derive an equation of force balance (Hawley, et al. 1984a):

$$\nabla P = -\frac{1}{2} \frac{S_\alpha S_\beta}{S^t} \partial_i g^{\alpha\beta} \tag{2}$$

where momentum $S_\alpha = \rho h W U_\alpha$ and W is the relativistic gamma factor. This equation becomes more familiar if we take the weak field Newtonian limit, using

$$ds^2 = -(1 + 2\Phi)dt^2 + (1 - 2\Phi)dr^2 + r^2 d\Omega^2 \tag{3}$$

to obtain

$$\partial_i P = \rho\{\frac{1}{2} \partial_i(2\Phi) - \frac{1}{2}(U_\phi)^2 \partial_i g^{\phi\phi}\} \ . \tag{4}$$

In cylindrical coordinates this is recognized to be the usual Newtonian equations for hydrostatic equilibrium of a nonself-gravitating fluid of angular momentum U_ϕ in a gravitational potential Φ:

$$\frac{\partial P}{\partial R} = \rho\left(\frac{\partial \Phi}{\partial R} + \frac{U_\phi^2}{R^3}\right) \ ,$$

$$\frac{\partial P}{\partial z} = \rho\left(\frac{\partial \Phi}{\partial z}\right) \ . \tag{5}$$

Thus our equation (2) is the fully relativistic equation of hydrostatic equilibrium. Abramowicz et al. (1978) formulate this equation in terms of angular momentum ℓ and angular velocity $\Omega \equiv U^\phi/U^t, (U^r = U^\theta = 0)$:

$$\frac{\nabla P}{\rho h} = -\nabla_i \ln(-U_t) + \frac{\Omega \nabla_i \ell}{1-\Omega\ell} \ . \tag{6}$$

For a disk with a barytropic equation of state $\left(P = P(\rho+\rho\varepsilon)\right)$ the equipotential surfaces of constant pressure are given by:

$$\psi - \psi_{in} = \ln(-U_t) - \ln(-U_t)_{in} - \int_{\ell_{in}}^{\ell} \frac{\Omega d\ell}{1-\Omega\ell} \quad , \qquad (7)$$

where the subscript "in" refers to the inner equatorial edge of the disk. We consider disks for which ℓ = constant and the surface potential is zero ($hU_t = -1$ throughout the disk). Then equation (7) is simplified to

$$\psi = \ln(-U_t) \qquad (8)$$

and this is employed to describe the equipotential surfaces and the orbits of the fluid flow.

All these ideas lead to modified accretion scenarios. First, fluid falling towards the hole with $\ell < \ell_{mb}$ can be accreted without any additional decrease in angular momentum, since there are always some potential surfaces open to the hole. This provides a new and quite plausible description for the final dynamic infall at the inner edge of an accretion disk, as well as a description of the complete infall process for sufficiently low angular momentum matter. In general, however, fluid away from the hole will have large angular momentum and the accretion of such fluid involves the use of viscosity to decrease ℓ and heat the disk. If this heat is not immediately radiated away, the disk will become hot. This heat will provide a pressure force in the fluid, causing it to puff up away from the equator and fill the equipotential surfaces as described above. In this way a pressure supported fat disk could form from initially cold gas. Angular momentum is transported outward in the disk by the viscous stress, causing ℓ to decrease at the inner edge until it is below the marginally bound value. At this point accretion can be accomplished with no further reduction in ℓ. This tends to reduce the net efficiency of the energy release, since viscous dissipation is not required all the way down to the minimum stable orbit; the subsequent inviscid infall does not efficiently extract the binding energy from the deepest part of the gravitational potential well. On the plus side, however, the fat disk structure can support a larger luminosity: some investigators have estimated that up to 100 times the limit for a thin disk is possible. So, while the fat disk may be less efficient than a thin disk, given a large enough accretion rate it may be considerably brighter. For detailed discussions of such analytic thick disk models see Abramowicz, et al. (1980), Jaroszyński, et al. (1980), Paczyński and Wiita (1980), Sikora (1981), and Wiita (1982).

Clearly then these new scenarios can have important observational consequences. But analytic analysis of the type done to date, while revealing, cannot say exactly what flows are possible and in what manner they might proceed. How does flow vary with angular momentum? Do structures resembling those described in the equilibrium analytic theory actually develop in hydrodynamic situations? In order to approach these questions in the greater generality permitted by numerical analysis, we have expanded on the original Wilson 1972 study.

From our work, in collaboration with Jim Wilson, we present several examples of calculated inviscid fluid flow in the near hole region. We use a time-explicit, fixed grid Eulerian accretion code with a monotonic transport scheme of Van Leer (1977). To obtain various disk formation models, we introduce fluid on the outer boundary of the finite difference grid with some value of angular momentum ℓ and allow the fluid to flow into the grid. For a complete discussion of the difference techniques used in this code see Hawley, Smarr and Wilson (1984b).

The work we present here is illustrative of the types of flow expected for accreting fluid with nonzero angular momentum. This is essentially an extension of the relativistic "Bondi accretion" solution in which hot fluid with zero angular momentum undergoes steady state radial accretion through a sonic point. The analytic solution for the Bondi flow is given by Michel (1972). As angular momentum is added to the accreting fluid, centrifugal acceleration becomes important, the hydrodynamic equations become analytically untenable, and new accretion phenomena, such as fat disks, become possible.

First consider low angular momentum fluid with $\ell < \ell_{ms}$. For such a fluid there is no orbital turning point; the equipotential surfaces all end on the hole. All the fluid should fall in, and this is indeed what our computer simulation shows. If the outer boundary is continuously resupplied with fluid, a steady-state, non-radial flow is rapidly established, a flow which in many ways resembles the transonic solution for radial accretion of a hot ideal gas (the "Bondi accretion" solution); such a flow is shown in Figure 5. Now

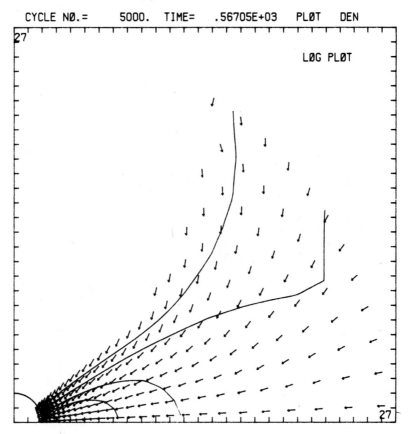

CYCLE NØ.=   5000. TIME=   .56705E+03   PLØT   DEN

LØG PLØT

Fig. 5. Density contours and flow directions for a low angular momentum (ℓ = 3.0) accretion model. The contours are logarithmic showing decades in density; the vectors indicate direction of fluid flow, not velocity magnitude. The outer boundary is at 27M in radius. A fluid with angular momentum less than the marginally stable orbit of a black hole (ℓ_{ms}) must fall into the hole on a dynamic timescale. This steady-state solution is the generalization of the Bondi accretion problem to the case of low but nonzero angular momentum.

consider the grid filled with this same low ℓ fluid and do not permit further inflow at the outer boundary. Figure 6 consists of two graphs showing density contours and flow directions at different times for this model. We find that the fluid drains into the hole on an orbital timescale. For our particular value of angular momentum

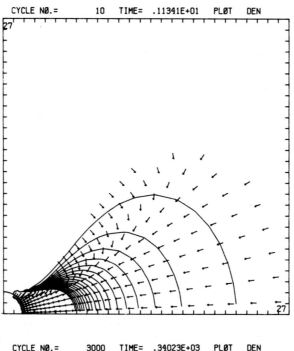

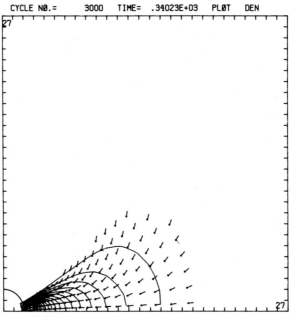

Fig. 6. We begin with ℓ = 3.0 fluid filling the potential surfaces around a Schwarzschild hole with $U_r = U^\theta = 0$. As the evolution proceeds, gravitational and centrifugal accelerations cause the fluid to spiral into the hole on an orbital timescale.

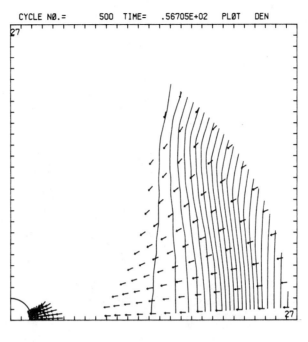

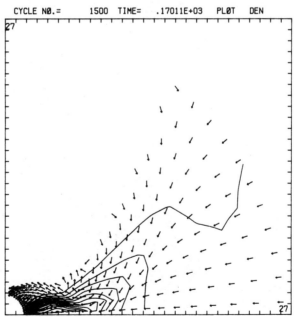

Fig. 7. Fluid with angular momentum ℓ greater than that of the marginally stable orbit flows in from the outer boundary. Much of it "bounces" at a turning radius and a fat disk is dynamically formed with a density and pressure maximum at r = 8m, appropriate for this ℓ = 3.77 disk.

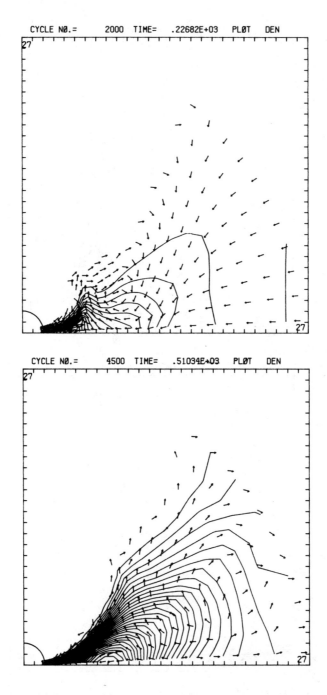

Fig. 7. continued

the orbital period at r = 8M is such that the fluid at that radius has had time to complete 2.4 orbits between the first and secod plot shown in Figure 6. Thus, our calculation verifies that for sufficiently low angular momentum, fluid spirals rapidly into the hole with no viscous shear required.

By increasing the angular momentum slightly to a value $\ell_{ms} < \ell < \ell_{mb}$, we can obtain an entirely new type of behavior in the inflow models. Figure 7 shows a series of plots for such an accretion model. This new behavior is made apparent by referring to Figures 3 and 4. For angular momentum in this range, there is a stable circular orbit and, up to a certain energy, there is also a turning radius. We choose to model a disk with ℓ = 3.77. For this value of ℓ there is an unstable circular orbit at r = 4.7M on the equator; the stable circular orbit is at r = 8M. The potential surface where U_t = -0.955 is the last closed surface; test particles with $-1 < U_t < -0.955$ can be accreted into the hole without encountering a turning point. In the course of our model's evolution we find that a portion of the inflowing fluid "bounces" as it hits an orbital turning point. A region with nonzero circulation forms behind the bounce. Infalling fluid behind begins to fill up the potentials, and gradually a disk forms with a pressure maximum at the predicted point of 8M. A compression wave moves outward and shuts off the inflow at the outer boundary, allowing the density in the disk to drop as fluid continues to drain down the hole. This drop in density permits inflow again and the process repeats itself, though much less dramatically; the disk, once formed, remains, and the maximum density in the disk fluctuates. While the accretion rate at the outer boundary continues to oscillate, the inflow into the hole remains rather steady. The outer boundary inflow rate averages out to about the same as that into the hole (see Fig. 8). Not much significance should be attached to the inflow oscillation at the outer boundary, since it reflects outer boundary conditions, rather than a likely physical phenomenon. However, the relative constancy of the flow into the hole is suggestive. It is quite likely that the potential "nozzle" into the hole can support only a certain maximum flow given an angular momentum and a fluid temperature, much like fluid flow in a nozzle. Since the accretion rate onto the hole in a realistic situation will be determined by factors at large radius away from this nozzle, it is unlike-

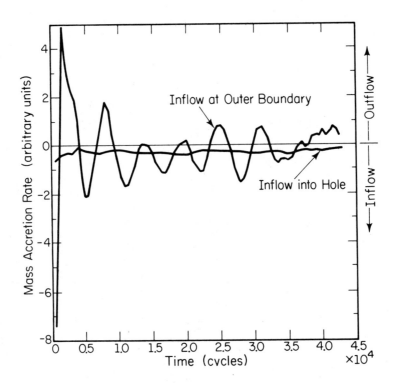

Fig. 8. Mass accretion rate vs. time for the model pictured in Fig. 7. The inflow at the outer boundary is not held fixed and it oscillates in response to dynamic changes in the disk. The inflow into the hole remains constant; the "potential spout" acts like a nozzle and allows only a certain flow rate.

ly that the inflow provided will just match the rate supported by the nozzle. A smooth, steady state flow may not be a likely scenario; a completely dynamic time-dependent flow may well be required.

To examine this nozzle scenario further we can assume a steady state flow and use Bernoulli's equation to calculate the accretion rate through the nozzle. This was first done by Kozłowski et al. (1978), who used enough assumptions to enable them to obtain a completely analytic solution for $\dot{M}$. We numerically integrate the equations in order to obtain greater generality in our results.

We begin with Bernoulli's equation

$$hU_t = \text{constant} = -1 \tag{9}$$

assuming marginally bound fluid and consequently a disk surface potential equal to zero. Next we select a sonic point inside the nozzle; such a choice, along with the assumption that the flow is purely radial, completely determines the accretion rate for a given value of ℓ. Kozłowski et al. assume that the sonic point occurs at the radius of the cusp in the potential (the unstable circular orbit see Fig. 9), here $r_c = 4.7$ M. Our numerical models for this disk indicate that a sonic point occurs at $r_s = 4.3$ M. Trying both values, we compute $U_t(\theta)$ out to the disk surface at θ_m where $U_t = -1$. Using $\ell = $ constant, $U_\theta = 0$ and velocity renormalization, we obtain

$$U_t^2 \, (g^{tt} - 2g^{t\phi}\ell + g^{\phi\phi}\ell^2) = -(1 + g^{rr}U_r^2) \; . \tag{10}$$

Then using Bernoulli's equation and assuming

$$U^r = V_{sound} = \left(\frac{\Gamma(\Gamma-1)\varepsilon}{h}\right)^{1/2} \tag{11}$$

for an ideal gas, we obtain a quadratic equation for specific internal energy ε. This yields the mass flux $\rho U^r \sqrt{-g}$ at that angle θ. This flux is numerically integrated from $\pi/2$ to θ_m to obtain the total accretion rate.

In Figure 9 the results of this calculation for an $\ell = 3.77$ fluid are displayed along with the mass flux into the hole in our numerical model. This figure shows that Bernoulli's equation yields a value comparable with the average accretion rate for the numerical model. The oscillations in the model's rate are driven by oscillations in the disk as a whole (and hence by the flow at the outer boundary), not by a change in the position of the sonic point.

These results are meant to be suggestive only. The numerical grid in this model is too coarse to allow us to draw conclusions in detail. However, the following qualitative statements can be made. 1) For fat disks with $\ell_{ms} < \ell < \ell_{mb}$, some rate of accretion over the potential cusp and into the hole can be supported. 2) In such an

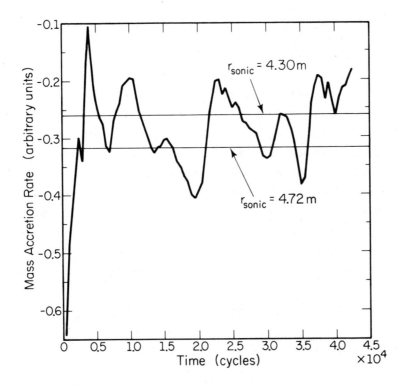

Fig. 9. Numerically calculated inflow into the hole for the ℓ = 3.77 model is displayed along with the inflow values for two sonic points r_s = 4.3 M. and r_s = 4.7 M. = r_c as calculated using the Bernoulli equation analysis. The analytic value is comparable to the average numerical accretion rate.

accretion flow, the sonic point occurs in the nozzle within the radius of the potential cusp. 3) The flow in the disk itself is subsonic, possibly supporting large-scale circulation. 4) The accretion rate into the hole can be approximated using Bernoulli's equation and treating the flow inside the nozzle as radial transonic fluid flow with constant angular momentum.

If we increase the angular momentum of the infalling fluid, we obtain the especially simple case of $\ell > \ell_{mb}$. For this angular momentum, none of the potential surfaces end on the hole; a station-ary, pressure-supported, axisymmetric fat disk can be completely

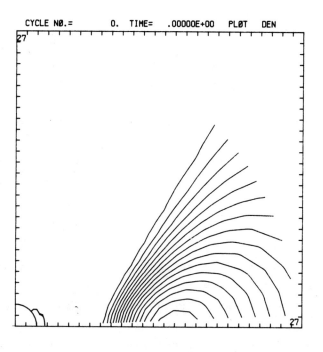

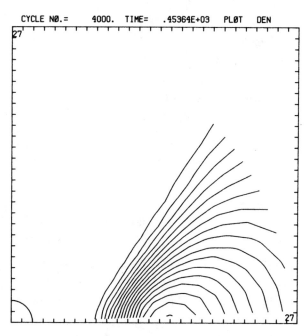

Fig. 10. For sufficiently high angular momentum, one can form a stable, pressure-supported fat disk which remains in equilibrium in the absence of dissipative forces.

specified analytically. The inner portion of such a disk is shown in Figure 10. For this disk some viscosity would be necessary to redistribute the angular momentum in order to permit accretion. In addition to being an interesting solution of the hydro equations, a model of this disk also serves the practical purpose of providing a code test. To maintain a stationary solution with a finite difference code, the various computed accelerations in both dimensions must repeatedly cancel. Such a test, combined with an ensemble of others, serves to calibrate the code and permit proper evaluation of results.

From this work we can conclude that the dynamic flow of a hot fluid with angular momentum tends naturally to form a fat disk structure and that the final accretion onto the hole is likely to proceed on dynamic freefall rather than viscous timescales once the angular momentum has dropped below ℓ_{mb}. Future work will include the magnetohydrodynamic equations to study the important effects of magnetic fields in the disk. Radiation and viscosity have obvious importance, and efforts to include those terms are also under way.

This work is but the beginning of attempts to understand the hydrodynamics of fat disks and many of our results are preliminary. The advent of supercomputers and advanced numerical hydrodynamic techniques have finally made possible the necessary studies. There is every reason to expect that our understanding of these accretion scenarios will soon increase manyfold.

Partial support for this work was provided by the National Science Foundation through grant PHY80-01496 and by the Department of Energy. The National Center for Atmospheric Research is acknowledged as the source for the graphics software. Computational work was performed on the University of Illinois Cyber 175 and the VAX and Image Processing System, operated jointly by the departments of Astronomy and Atmospheric Science and the Computer Services Office. One of us (JH) wishes to thank Martin Rees and Mitch Begelman for enlightening discussions and the Institute of Astronomy, Cambridge, UK for its hospitality. Finally we thank Joan Centrella, Mike Norman, and K.-H. Winkler for many illuminating discussions on code differencing and testing.

REFERENCES

Abramowicz, M.A., Jaroszyński, M., and Sikora, M. 1978, Astr. Ap.,
    63, 221.

Abramowicz, M., Calvani, M., and Nobili, L. 1980, Ap. J., 242, 772.

Bardeen, J.M. 1973, in "Black Holes" ed. B. DeWitt and C. DeWitt
    (New York: Gordon and Breach).

Hawley, J.F., Smarr, L.L., and Wilson, J.R. 1984a, Ap. J., 277, 296.

_____. 1984b, Ap. J. Suppl., 55, 211.

Jaroszyński, M., M., Abramowicz, M., and Paczyński, B. 1980, Acta.
    Astr., 30, 1.

Kozłowski, M., Jaroszyński, M., and Abramowicz, M.A. 1978, Astr.,
    63, 209.

May, M.M., and White, R.H. 1966, Phys. Rev., 141, 1232.

Michel, F.C. 1972, Astr. Sp. Sci., 15, 153.

Misner, C.W., Thorne, K.S., and Wheeler, J.A. 1973, "Gravitation"
    (San Francisco: W-H Freeman and Co.).

Novikov, I., and Thorne, K.S. 1973, in "Black Holes" ed. B. DeWitt
    and C. DeWitt (New York: Gordon and Breach).

Paczyński, B., and Wiita, P.J. 1980, Astr. Ap., 88, 23.

Shakura, N.I., and Sunyaev, R.A. 1973, Astr. Ap., 24, 337.

Sikora, M. 1980, M.N.R.A.S., 196, 257.

Smarr, L.L., Taubs, C., and Wilson, J.R. 1980, from "Essays in
    General Relativity", ed. F.J. Tipler (New York: Academic Press.)

Van Leer, B. 1977, J. Comp. Phys., 23, 276.

Wiita, P.J. 1982, Ap. J., 256, 666.

Wilson, J.R. 1972, Ap. J., 173, 431.

General Relativistic Magnetohydrodynamics

John H. Sloan†
University of Illinois

Larry L. Smarr*
University of Illinois

ABSTRACT

   Jim Wilson pioneered the use of supercomputers to study magnetohydrodynamic (MHD) flows near black holes. In this paper, we analyze
the differential equations of general relativistic MHD. We use the
"3 + 1" formalism to recover the physical meaning of each term in the
equations. Limits are taken to recover the special relativistic
Alfvén equation and the static balance of magnetic and pressure
forces. Particular emphasis is placed on the role of the anisotropic
magnetic inertia. A new form for the equations is found which may
simplify future numerical work.

I.   INTRODUCTION

   Jim Wilson performed a systematic numerical exploration of the
physics of accretion onto black holes during the 1970s. These pioneering efforts showed that one could use computer codes to solve the
fully nonlinear, time dependent, coupled partial differential equations of general relativistic magnetohydrodynamics. In 1972, Wilson
(1972) wrote the first code to handle two-dimensional (2-D) general
relativistic (GR) hydrodynamic accretion onto a Kerr black hole. In
a companion paper in this volume, Hawley, Smarr, and Wilson explain
how, ten years later, that code has been updated and used to investigate fat pressure supported disks around black holes.

   In a series of papers, Wilson expanded his technique to allow

---

†Address as of Fall 1983: Physics Dept., Princeton University

*Alfred P. Sloan Fellow

time-varying strong gravitational fields with and without magnetic fields (Wilson 1975, 1977, 1978). These calculations demonstrated that magnetic torques and magnetospheres (Damour et al. 1978, Ruffini and Wilson 1975) could be important around black holes.

This paper is the first in a projected series on the updated version of Wilson's magnetohydrodynamic (MHD) codes. Herein we lay out the basic physics which occurs when magnetic fields are combined with gravitation. The next phase of this refinement will be to find a set of analytic solutions to the fully general relativistic MHD equations. We can then subject the MHD code to the same rigorous updating and calibration procedure which was given the Wilson hydro-dynamics code (Hawley et al. 1984a,b).

Thorne and Macdonald (1982; hereafter TM), in an alternative treatment of electromagnetic fields near a black hole, emphasize how difficult it is for an astrophysicist to obtain an intuitive feel for the electromagnetic field variables when they are expressed in terms of the electromagnetic field tensor $\underset{\sim}{F}$ and the 4-current $\vec{J}$. There-fore, as they do, we will express the electromagnetic field in terms of the general relativistic analogs of the familiar electric field $\vec{E}$ and the magnetic field $\vec{B}$ before we look for solutions to the MHD equations. We can then generalize the vast background of work in Newtonian MHD to solve the general relativistic equations in the same way that TM have generalized the powerful integral theorems of elec-tromagnetism to find potentials which generate solutions to Maxwell's equations (Macdonald and Thorne 1982; hereafter MT).

With this as motivation, we do the following. In section II we introduce the 3+1 formalism, which allows us to express our problem in terms of the projection of the four-dimensional fields into a three-dimensional absolute space (see also TM). We then express F in the 3+1 language and derive relativistic expressions for $\vec{J}$ and $\vec{J} \cdot \underset{\sim}{\tilde{F}}$ (the Lorentz force) in terms of $\vec{E}$ and $\vec{B}$. We also find the electric field in a perfectly conducting fluid in terms of the fluid velocity $\vec{V}$ and $\vec{B}$. In section III we derive the MHD equations, by adding the expression for the Lorentz force derived in section II to the momen-tum equation, and then find solutions in the static, weak gravita-tional field limit.

Section IV contains an analysis of and solutions to the static MHD equations, a derivation of and solutions to the equations for Alfvén wave propagation in a uniform background, and a discussion of the dispersion relation for Alfvén waves in a non-uniform medium. In section V we manipulate the momentum equation into a form suitable for finite differencing using an explicit, operator-split code, and show that the displacement current term in the Lorentz force generates an anisotropic inertia in the equations of motion for the matter flow (this due to flux freezing). Finally, in section VI, we discuss some analytic code checks which can be obtained for the solutions above. We compare the "natural" potentials used by Wilson (1975) with those used by MT. Throughout this paper we assume a perfectly conducting fluid moving in a stationary metric, and that G=c=1.

II.   THE 3+1 FORMALISM

In this paper, we will use the 3+1 formalism as it is developed elsewhere (TM, York 1979, Smarr et al. 1980, Hawley et al. 1984a). (For a discussion of the history of 3+1, see TM.) This formalism chooses a set of fiducial observers and projects all four-dimensional objects onto and orthogonal to the observers' 4-velocities. Physically these are the quantities which the observers would "see" in their rest frame. We will use the global stationary time slices to define the fiducial observers.

The 4-metric, just like any other second rank tensor, can be projected in this way. This has the effect of splitting the 10 functions in the 4-metric into 1+3+6 functions. These components are called the lapse (α), shift vector ($\vec{\beta}$), and 3-metric (χ). We will use the notation of Smarr et al. (1980) unless otherwise noted. Accordingly, we denote by n^μ (greek indices= t,x,y,z; latin= x,y,z) the unit 4-velocity of the fiducial observers normal to the time slices, with a^μ as the 4-acceleration of the fiducial observers, t^μ as the vector ∂/∂_t in the time direction, and u^μ as the unit 4-velocity of the matter flow. The components of these tensors are tabulated below (Smarr et al. 1980, p. 159):

$$
g^{\mu\nu} = \begin{pmatrix} -1/\alpha^2 & \beta^i/\alpha^2 \\ \beta^j/\alpha^2 & \gamma^{ij} - \beta^i\beta^j/\alpha^2 \end{pmatrix} \quad , \quad g_{\mu\nu} = \begin{pmatrix} -\alpha^2 + \beta_k\beta^k & \beta_i \\ \beta_j & \gamma_{ij} \end{pmatrix} \quad (2.1a)
$$

$$n^\mu = (1/\alpha, \; \beta^i/\alpha), \qquad\qquad n_\mu = (-\alpha, \; \vec{0}) \qquad\qquad (2.1b)$$

$$a^\mu = (0, \; \gamma^{ik}\partial_k \ln\alpha), \qquad a_\mu = (\beta^k \partial_k \ln\alpha, \; \partial_i \ln\alpha) \quad (2.1c)$$

$$t^\mu = (1, \; \vec{0}), \qquad\qquad t_\mu = (-\alpha^2 + \beta_k \beta^k, \; \beta_i) \quad (2.1d)$$

$$u^\mu = W\alpha^{-1}(1, \; \alpha v^i - \beta^i), \qquad u_\mu = W(-\alpha + \beta_k v^k, \; V_i) \quad (2.1e)$$

$$\Gamma = -n \cdot \hat{t} = (1 - \beta_i \beta^i/\alpha^2)^{-1/2} \quad W = -n \cdot u = (1 - V_k v^k)^{-1/2}, \quad (2.1f)$$

where $\hat{t}$ is the unit vector along t.

Note that our W is Smarr et al.'s $\Gamma_2 = u^t\alpha$, while our Γ is Γ_1 of Smarr et al. Physically, α is the gravitational redshift, W is the special relativistic redshift for matter flows, $\vec{\beta}$ is the velocity at which the coordinate system flows in each time slice, and χ measures distances and angles in the 3-space.

In order to project into time slices normal to n^μ, we introduce the projection operator $h^\mu{}_\nu$ and the three dimensional antisymmetric tensor $\epsilon^{\mu\nu\gamma}$:

$$h^\mu{}_\nu = g^\mu{}_\nu + n^\mu n_\nu, \qquad\qquad (2.2)$$

$$\epsilon^{\mu\nu\gamma} = \epsilon^{\mu\nu\gamma\delta} n_\delta. \qquad\qquad (2.3)$$

A spatial 3-tensor is created by dotting all the indices on a 4-tensor with $h^\mu{}_\nu$. The upstairs time component of any spatial 3-tensor is zero, since $n_\mu h^\mu{}_\nu = 0$ and $n_i \equiv 0$ (see Eqn. 2.1b). We can also introduce differential operators D_μ and $\pounds_A$ which generalize the space and time partial derivatives of flat space. These are defined by:

$$D_\mu T^{\mu\nu}{}_\rho = h_\mu{}^\alpha h^\mu{}_\beta h^\nu{}_\delta h^\sigma{}_\rho \nabla_\alpha T^{\beta\delta}{}_\sigma, \qquad\qquad (2.4)$$

$$\pounds_A T^\mu{}_\nu = A^\delta \nabla_\delta T^\mu{}_\nu - T^\delta{}_\nu \nabla_\delta A^\mu + T^\mu{}_\delta \nabla_\nu A^\delta. \qquad (2.5)$$

D_μ is the covariant 3-gradient, and $\pounds_t = \pounds_{\alpha n+\beta}$ is the Lie derivative in the time direction. We use later that $D_\mu \epsilon^{\nu\delta\beta} = D_\mu h^{\nu\delta} = 0$.

We can now write $F^{\mu\nu}$ in terms of the electric and magnetic fields observed by n^{μ}:

$$F^{\mu\nu} = n^{\nu}E^{\mu} - n^{\mu}E^{\nu} + \varepsilon^{\mu\nu\delta}B_{\delta} \qquad (2.6)$$

Note how we covariantly divide tensors into "time" components (here E^{μ}) sitting next to n^{ν} and "space" components which vanish (here $\varepsilon^{\mu\nu\delta}$) if hit with n^{ν}. Using the Maxwell equation $\nabla_{\mu}F^{\mu\nu} = 4\pi J^{\nu}$, one can obtain the 4-current in terms of E^{μ} and B^{μ}.

$$4\pi J^{\nu} = n^{\nu}(D_{\mu}E^{\mu}) - (1/\alpha)\ [\pounds_{t} - \pounds_{\beta} + \alpha\Theta]\ E^{\nu}$$

$$+ D_{\mu}\varepsilon^{\mu\nu\delta}B_{\delta} + a_{\mu}\varepsilon^{\mu\nu\delta}B_{\delta} \qquad (2.7)$$

where $\Theta \equiv \nabla_{\mu}n^{\mu}$ is the convergence of the fiducial observers (zero in Kerr).

We now investigate the physical origin of each term in the general relativistic Maxwell equation (2.7). The term $D_{\mu}E^{\mu}$ is the spatial gradient of the electric field, which equals 4π times the electric charge density $\rho = -n_{\nu}J^{\nu}$. Thus the time component of equation (2.7) is the "Gauss's law" Maxwell equation. The spatial terms are the "Ampere's law" Maxwell equation. The term $D_{\mu}\varepsilon^{\mu\nu\delta}B_{\delta}$, or curl $\vec{B}$, is the familiar magnetic source of the spatial 3-current. The term in brackets involving Lie derivatives of the electric field is the general relativistic equivalent of the displacement current (equal to the left hand side of Eqn. (3.4c) in TM). The term $\pounds_{t}E^{\mu}$ is equivalent to $\partial_{t}E^{\mu}$; $\pounds_{\beta}E^{\mu}$ is the rate of change of E^{μ} caused by "frame dragging"; and Θ is the time rate of change of the volume element. In flat space, "observers at rest" are also "inertial (non-accelerated) observers." In curved space, however, observers "at rest" (n^{μ}) are in general noninertial (like standing on Earth). Their acceleration (a_{μ}) is necessary to balance the gravitational force trying to pull them from rest. The last term in equation (2.7) is such a noninertial term (see the discussion in section 3.2 of TM for more detail).

Equations (2.6) and (2.7) can now be used to write down the Lorentz force $J^{\nu}F_{\nu\mu}$:

$$4\pi J^\nu F_{\nu\mu} = n_\mu [-\alpha^{-1} E_\nu (\pounds_t - \pounds_\beta + \alpha\Theta) E^\nu + E_\nu (D_\delta + a_\delta)\varepsilon^{\delta\nu\beta} B_\beta]$$

$$+ (D_\delta E^\delta) E_\mu$$

$$+ B^\delta \varepsilon_{\delta\mu\nu} [\alpha^{-1}(\pounds_t - \pounds_\beta + \alpha\Theta) E^\nu \qquad (2.8)$$

$$- (D_\delta + a_\delta) \varepsilon^{\delta\nu\beta} B_\beta].$$

The spatial part is the electric field times the charge density (second line) plus the magnetic field crossed with the spatial current terms (third line) from equation (2.7). If we assume perfect conductivity (no electric field in the rest frame of the fluid), we can use $U_\mu F^{\mu\nu} = 0$ to write

$$E^\mu = (1/W)\varepsilon_{\mu\nu\delta} B_\nu U_\delta . \qquad (2.9)$$

This is equivalent to the nonrelativistic equation $\vec{E} = \vec{B} \times \vec{v}$. If we so desired, we could now substitute equation 2.9 into equation 2.8 and obtain an expression for the Lorentz force in a perfectly conducting medium dependent only upon the magnetic field (along with fluid velocity and metric terms).

III. STATIC MHD

Wilson (1976) writes down the general relativistic MHD equations for a perfect fluid with perfect conductivity. We have changed his basic variables by a factor of α as is shown below (see e.g. Hawley et al. 1984a - hereafter HSW):

$$D = W\rho, \qquad (3.1a)$$
$$E = W\varepsilon\rho, \qquad (3.1b)$$
$$S_\mu = W\rho(1 + \varepsilon + P/\rho) U_\mu \equiv W\rho h U_\mu . \qquad (3.1c)$$

where ρ is the density, ε is the specific internal energy, and P is the isotropic pressure of the fluid.

The equations of hydrodynamics are discussed in HSW using these definitions, and we shall use their equations (17), (20) and (25) as our equations of hydrodynamics. In order to obtain the MHD equations, we add the Lorentz force to the momentum equation [HSW's Eqn. (25)]. Because we have a perfectly conducting medium, the energy equation [HSW's Eqn. (20)] remains unchanged (since there is no Joule heating in a medium with zero resistivity). If the resistivity were not zero, then we would have to include a term involving $J^\mu U^\nu F_{\mu\nu}$ in the energy equation.

We now assume that we are working with a perfectly conducting medium in a Schwarzschild geometry (for details on this geometry see e.g. Misner, Thorne, and Wheeler 1973). This implies that $\theta = \vec{\beta} = 0$ and that $g_{\mu\nu}$ is diagonal. Next we combine HSW's momentum equation (25) with our equation (2.8) (while writing D_μ in terms of ∂_μ and using spatial indices when possible) to get

$$\partial_t S_j + \gamma^{-1/2}\partial_i(\gamma^{1/2}S_j v^i) + \alpha\partial_j P - (S^\mu S^\nu/2S^t)\,\partial_j g_{\mu\nu} + \alpha(D_i E^i/4\pi)E_j$$

$$- (B^i/4\pi)\varepsilon_{ijk}\partial_t E^k + \alpha(B^i/4\pi)(\partial_j B_i - \partial_i B_j)$$

$$+ \alpha(B^i/4\pi)(a_j B_i - a_i B_j) = 0 \qquad\qquad (3.2)$$

where $\gamma \equiv \det(\gamma_{ij})$ is the determinant of the Schwarzschild 3-metric.

We will now look for static solutions to the MHD equations $(\partial_t = V^i = 0,\ U^t = 1/\alpha$ and $S^\mu = (\rho h/\alpha)(1,\vec{0}))$. The condition of perfect conductivity, $\vec{E} = \vec{v} \times \vec{B}$, implies that $\vec{E} = 0$. In this limit, equation (3.2) reduces to

$$\alpha\partial_j P + \rho h a_j + \alpha(B^i/4\pi)(\partial_j B_i - \partial_i B_j) + \alpha(B^i/4\pi)(a_j B_i - a_i B_j) = 0. \qquad (3.3)$$

The terms in this equation are understandable using Newtonian physics (which should be the case, since in the static limit special relativity plays no role). The force exerted by pressure gradients is $\partial_j P$. The term $B^i(\partial_j B_i - \partial_i B_j)/4\pi \sim \vec{B}\times\vec{\nabla}\times\vec{B}$ is the static Lorentz force (since $\vec{\nabla}\times\vec{B}$ measures the current present, and $f_{Lorentz} = \vec{J} \times \vec{B}$). The term $\rho h a_j$ is the gravitational force required to keep the fluid "at rest" (since "at rest" does not mean "inertial"). If we now go to flat space $(\alpha \to 1, a^\mu \to 0)$, the gravitational acceleration goes away, just as we would expect, and equation (3.3) becomes

$$\partial_j P + (B^i/4\pi)(\partial_j B_i - \partial_i B_j) = 0. \qquad (3.4)$$

The last term is the reason that magnetic field lines are sometimes thought of as strings. Equation (3.4) can be written in the form

$$\partial_i (T^i{}_{j\,Hydro} + T^i{}_{j\,Mag}) = 0, \qquad (3.5)$$

where

$$T^i{}_{j\,Mag} = (1/4\pi)(B^2\delta^i{}_j - B^i B_j) - (B^2/8\pi)\delta^i{}_j. \qquad (3.6)$$

This is the stress tensor for a tension of $B^2/4\pi$ superposed on an isotropic pressure of $B^2/4\pi$ (see e.g. Blandford 1983).

There are two distinct symmetries for which solutions to equation (3.4) are readily found: translational and rotational. If we take all of our fields to be functions of y and z (r and z) in cartesian (cylindrical) coordinates and take the magnetic field to be pointing in the x (ϕ) direction, then $B^i\partial_i$ vanishes and equation (3.4) reduces to

$$\partial_j (P + B^2/8\pi) = 0.$$

Equation (3.7) has the obvious set of solutions $B^2 = 8\pi(P_{tot} - P)$, where P_{tot} is an arbitrary constant which is greater than or equal to the maximum value of P. This solution just balances the force due to magnetic pressure with that due to hydrodynamic pressure, which is what one would physically assume for flat space.

Next we look at MHD in a weak gravitational field with Newtonian potential Φ. The line element for such a spacetime is [Misner, Thorne and Wheeler 1973, Eqn. (16.2a)]

$$ds^2 = -(1+2\Phi)dt^2 + (1-2\Phi)dr^2 + r^2 d\Omega, \quad \Phi \ll 1. \quad (3.8)$$

This means that $\alpha \simeq 1 + \Phi$ and $a_i = \partial_i \ln\alpha \approx \partial_i \Phi$ (i.e., the gravitational acceleration is the gradient of the gravitational potential). Equation (3.3) becomes

$$\partial_j P + (B^i/4\pi)(\partial_j B_i - \partial_i B_j) + [\rho h \gamma^i_j + \{B^2\gamma^i_j - B^i B_j\}/4\pi]\partial_i\Phi = 0. \quad (3.9)$$

Notice the term in braces {}. It is from the gravitational field pulling on the energy contained in the magnetic field. Along with the term involving ρh, this term is the anisotropic moment of inertia tensor for the system (see, e.g. exercise 5.4 in Misner, et al. 1973). Even for magnetic fields with the special symmetries described above, it is not easy to get an analytic solution. Even if we assume weak magnetic fields $B^2 \ll \rho$ and nonrelativistic temperatures $h \approx 1$, the term $\rho\partial_i\Phi$ is not a perfect differential except in the trivial case of constant density everywhere. However, it would be straightforward to solve equation (3.9) numerically.

IV. ALFVÉN WAVES

We wish to obtain some dynamical solutions to the MHD equations. The simplest nontrivial solution is for Alfvén waves without dispersion. With this in mind we will derive the flat space, special relativistic, Alfvén wave equation from our general relativistic formalism. For the purposes of the calculation we will assume that the lapse function α and shift vector $\vec{B}$ vanishes.

Start with an unperturbed system at rest ($V^i \equiv 0$). Let all gradients be zero. If any of these were nonzero, they would generate dispersion (scattering) terms. Note that since we have a perfect conductor and $V^i = 0$, $E^i = 0$. Now introduce a perturbation such that $B^i \to B^i + b^i$, $V^i \to 0 + v^i$, $P \to P + p$, $\rho \to \rho + d$, and $E^i \to 0 + e^i$, and solve the equations of motion for v^i.

The momentum equation (3.2) becomes, to first order in the perturbation,

$$\rho h \partial_t v_j + \alpha\partial_j p - B^k \varepsilon_{ijk}\partial_t e^i + \alpha(B^i/4\pi)(\partial_j b_i - \partial_i b_j) = 0 \quad (4.1)$$

or

$$\partial_t v_j + (1/\rho h)(\partial P/\partial\rho)\partial_j d - B^i\varepsilon_{ijk}(\partial_t v_m)\varepsilon^{mkn}B_n/(4\pi\rho h) +$$

$$B^i(\partial_j b_i - \partial_i b_j)/(4\pi\rho h) = 0, \quad (4.2)$$

where we have substituted equation (2.9) into equation (4.1) and divided by ρh to get equation (4.2). Notice that we include relativistic temperatures $h \neq 1$, but only mildly relativistic velocities since we drop the $\sigma(v^2)$ term which makes $W \cong 1$. We also need the equation of continuity to eliminate $\partial_j d$:

$$\partial_t d + \rho \partial_i v^i = 0 \qquad (4.3a)$$

$$\partial_t \partial_j d + \rho \partial_j \partial_i v^i = 0. \qquad (4.3b)$$

Taking ∂_t of equation (4.2) yields:

$$\partial_t^2 v_j + (c^2/\rho h)\partial_t \partial_j d + B^i \varepsilon_{ijk} B_m \varepsilon^{mkn}(\partial_t^2 v_n)/(4\pi\rho h)$$

$$+ B^i(\partial_j \partial_t b_i - \partial_i \partial_t b_j)/(4\pi\rho h) = 0 \qquad (4.4)$$

where $c \equiv (\partial P/\partial \rho)^{1/2}$. We now need an expression for $\partial_t b_j$. This is obtained by using the other Maxwell equation $\nabla_\mu {}^* F^\mu{}_\nu = 0$, where

$$^* F^\mu{}_\nu = n^\mu B_\nu - n_\nu B^\mu + \varepsilon^\mu{}_{\nu\delta} E^\delta. \qquad (4.5)$$

This yields (with $\vec{\beta} = \Theta = \sigma_{\mu\nu} = \omega_{\mu\nu} = a_\mu = 0$ appropriate for flat spacetime)

$$\partial_t b_i = D_j \varepsilon_i{}^{jk} e_k. \qquad (4.6)$$

Equation 4.6 is the special relativistic form of the Maxwell equation $\partial_t \vec{b} = D \times \vec{e}$. Substituting equations (4.3b) and (4.6) into equation (4.4) and using equation (2.9) and $\varepsilon_{ijk}\varepsilon^{mkn} = \delta_i{}^n \delta_j{}^m - \delta_i{}^m \delta_j{}^n$, we get:

$$\{\delta_j^i + [(B^2\delta_j{}^i - B_j B^i)/(4\pi\rho h)]\}\partial_t^2 v_i - (c^2/h)\,\partial_j\partial_i v^i$$

$$+ (B^i \varepsilon_{ijk}\partial_m \varepsilon^{kmn}\partial^P \varepsilon_{npq} B_r \varepsilon^{qrs} v_s)/(4\pi\rho h) = 0. \qquad (4.7)$$

This is the special relativistic Alfvén wave equation for mildly relativistic velocities $W \simeq 1$. For a conventional comparison see equation (3-394) of Lang (1980). Again we see the same anisotropic inertia tensor as in equation (3.9), here multiplying $\partial_t^2 v_i$. We can now Fourier transform by letting $\vec{v} = \vec{\varepsilon}\, e^{-i(k\cdot x - \omega t)}$ and obtain

$$\omega^2 \{\hat{\varepsilon} + [V_A{}^2 \hat{\varepsilon} - (\vec{V}_A \cdot \hat{\varepsilon}) \hat{V}_A]\} - (c^2/h)(\hat{k} \cdot \hat{\varepsilon}) \vec{k}$$

$$- \vec{V}_A \times \vec{k} \times \vec{k} \times \vec{V}_A \times \vec{\varepsilon} = 0 \qquad\qquad (4.8)$$

where $\vec{V}_A \equiv \vec{B}/(\sqrt{4\pi\rho h}\ W)$ is the special relativistic Alfvén velocity (here $W = 1$).

This equation admits three different classes of solution. The first is where $\hat{k}$, $\hat{\varepsilon}$, and $\hat{V}_A$ are all parallel. Here the cross product term and the magnetic part of the inertia term vanish. This gives longitudinal waves propagating in the direction of $\hat{V}_A$ with a speed $C_{Hydro} = (c^2/h)^{1/2}$. This is the sound speed of a fluid at relativistic temperatures. The factor of h comes from the inertia of the fluid's internal energy.

A second mode is with $\hat{k}$ parallel to $\hat{\varepsilon}$ and perpendicular to $\hat{V}_A$. This corresponds to longitudinal waves propagating perpendicular (along $\hat{k}$) to the magnetic field with a speed of $C_{Magnetosonic} = ([(c^2/h)+V_A{}^2]/(1+V_A{}^2))^{1/2}$. The $V_A{}^2$ term in the numerator is due to magnetic pressure, and the factor of $1+V_A{}^2$ in the denominator is due to the inertia contained in the energy density of the magnetic field.

The final mode has $\hat{k}$ parallel to $\hat{V}_A$ and perpendicular to $\hat{\varepsilon}$ ("Alfvén waves"). This is a transverse mode propagating in the direction of $\vec{B}$ with a speed of $V_{Transverse} = (V_A{}^2/(1+V_A{}^2))^{1/2}$. This speed is a factor of $(1+V_A{}^2)^{-1/2}$ slower than the Alfvén speed obtained in most derivations. This is because most derivations throw away the term in the Lorentz force which arises from the displacement current. We only need to keep that term when V_A is large (≈ 1). It should be noted, however, that it is this term which will prevent the superluminal transfer of information as $V_A \to \infty$.

In the derivation above, we were limited to special relativity by the absence of gradients in our initial (unperturbed) system. If gradients do exist, then they will tend to scatter waves between momentum states. This makes it very difficult to find analytic solutions to even the linearized MHD equations, but we should still be able to predict the propagation of perturbations by using numerical methods. In particular, if the gradients in the background are small, one can find a Green's function for equation (4.7) and use the gradients as forcing terms.

V.   THE ANISOTROPIC INERTIA

As we saw above, the term in the momentum equation containing the displacement current will be important in regimes where the Alfvén velocity is of order one. This means that in our numerical simulations of accretion disks, there will be regions which will be field dominated in which we cannot throw out the displacement current term, as is often done in numerical treatments of (GR) MHD. This presents a problem, however, to those using a time-explicit, operator-split scheme. Since the electric field is the cross product of the velocity of the fluid and the magnetic field, the displacement current will contain a term which is dependent on the time derivative of the momentum (through the velocity term). In the old Wilson code, this term was a major problem. It was dealt with by adding the magnetic-electric density of the field components perpendicular to the acceleration to the matter density in the acceleration equation.

With this in mind, we rewrite equation (3.2) as

$$\partial_t S_j = L_j - M_j{}^i \partial_t S_i , \qquad (5.1)$$

where L_j contains all of the terms in equation (3.2) which are not proportional to $\partial_t S_i$ and $M_j{}^i$ is the matrix of coefficients of $\partial_t S_i$. In terms of our MHD field variables,

$$M_j{}^i \equiv (B^2 \delta_j{}^i - B_j B^i)/(4\pi\rho hW^2) = (V_A{}^2 \delta_j{}^i - V_{A_j} V_A{}^i) , \qquad (5.2a)$$

where again $V_A = B/(4\pi\rho hW^2)^{1/2}$ is the Alfvén velocity. We note that $\underset{\sim}{M}$ is just the anisotropic inertia tensor for the magnetic field which showed up in equations (3.9) and (4.7) renormalized by the factor $(4\pi\rho hW^2)^{-1}$. The vector $\vec{L}$ is given by

$$L_j \equiv -[\frac{1}{\sqrt{\gamma}} \partial_i (\sqrt{\gamma}\, S_j v^i) + \alpha \partial_j P + (S^\mu S^\nu / 2S^t)\, \partial_j g_{\mu\nu} + \alpha(D_i E^i/4\pi) E_j +$$

$$\alpha(B^i/4\pi)(\partial_j B_i - \partial_i B_j) + \alpha(B^i/4\pi)(a_j B_i - a_i B_j) -$$

$$(B^k/4\pi)[\partial_t(B_k/\rho hW^2)\delta_j{}^i - \partial_t(B_j/\rho hW^2)\delta_k{}^i]S_i \quad . \qquad (5.2b)$$

The formal solution to our problem (equation 5.1) is:

$$\partial_t \vec{S} = (\underset{\sim}{I} - \underset{\sim}{M})^{-1} \vec{L} \ . \tag{5.3}$$

Note that although we are still specialized to Schwarzschild, the following formal analysis should hold for any stationary spacetime. The shift vector will bury itself in the definitions of $\vec{L}$ and $\vec{V}_A$.

Looking at equation (5.2a), we see that $\underset{\sim}{M}$ is the transverse projector on $\vec{V}_A$ and has three eigenvectors. The first eigenvector is parallel to $\hat{V}_A$ and has eigenvalue zero. The other two are degenerate, perpendicular to $\hat{V}_A$, and have eigenvalue $V_A{}^2$. Physically $M_j{}^i$ is the magnetic field's renormalized anisotropic inertia tensor. The field is not affected by fluid motion parallel to it, but it is dragged along by any transverse fluid motion (because of perfect conductivity) and contributes an inertial density of $B^2/4\pi$. Using our eigenvalue analysis, we look for $(\underset{\sim}{I} - \underset{\sim}{M})^{-1}$ of the form

$$(\underset{\sim}{I} - \underset{\sim}{M})^{-1} = [(1 + V_A{}^2) \underset{\sim}{I} - \vec{V}_A \vec{V}_A]^{-1} = \kappa I + \zeta \vec{V}_A \vec{V}_A \tag{5.4}$$

where $\vec{V}_A \vec{V}_A$ is the external product. Solving for κ and ζ, we find:

$$[\underset{\sim}{I} - \underset{\sim}{M}]^{-1} = (\underset{\sim}{I} + \vec{V}_A \vec{V}_A)/(1 + V_A{}^2) \ . \tag{5.5}$$

This matrix has eigenvalues 1 for motion parallel to $\vec{V}_A$ and $1/(1 + V_A{}^2)$ for motion perpendicular to $\vec{V}_A$ and can be interpreted as the ratio of fluid inertia to total inertia. Thus we have shown that the anisotropic inertia of the magnetic field enters naturally into the momentum equation.

Using equations (5.5) and (5.2b), we obtain the new form of the momentum equation:

$$\partial_t S_j = [(\delta_j{}^i + V_{Aj} V_A{}^i)/(1 + V_A{}^2)] L_i \tag{5.6}$$

where L_i is defined in (5.2b). In order to use operator splitting on this, we would difference each term in L_i as we would treat the corresponding term in (3.2), then multiply it by $(\delta_j{}^i + V_{Aj} V_A{}^i)/(1 + V_A{}^2)$ before adding it to $\partial_t S_j$. This new method (5.6) is currently being tested numerically to see if it is accurate and stable.

VI. CODE CHECKS

The purpose of the calculations in this paper is twofold. First, we wish to manipulate the MHD equations analytically into the form most suited for finite differencing (i.e., section V). Second, we need analytic solutions to the MHD equations to use as a testbed in all of the different regimes which the code will investigate. Usually, however, the fundamental variables used in analytic and numerical techniques differ, making it messy to go from one formalism to another. The numerical variables can sometimes obscure the physics contained in the difference equations. For example, Wilson's fundamental electromagnetic variables are A_ϕ, where $\vec{A}$ is the 4-vector potential, and $H_\phi \equiv F_{RZ}$ (Wilson 1975). If we write the components of $\underset{\sim}{M}$ using these variables, things become very messy and the underlying symmetries are obscured.

On the other hand, when $\underset{\sim}{M}$ is written in terms of $\vec{B}$, the symmetries become quite clear. In the same way, Macdonald and Thorne's metric components have deep physical significance, although they may not be optimum for coding. To aid in translation between the two formalisms, Table 1 provides a list of equivalent terms in our "numerical" variables and MT's "analytic" variables. Note that Wilson's A_ϕ and H_ϕ are equivalent to Ψ and I (MT's potentials which generate static solutions to Maxwell's equations). This is an example of Wilson's deep intuition in picking the pertinent variables in a problem.

The simplest analytic tests check the ability of a code to keep a static solution static. Most of these will involve balancing magnetic pressure with hydrodynamic pressure or gravitational force according to equation (3.9). One possibility is to take a uniform gas, put a constant gravitational force on it in the z direction, then use the magnetic pressure of a field in the x direction to balance this force. A second is to put a varying pressure on a gas, then balance it with magnetic pressure in the absence of gravitational fields. The gas should not pick up a velocity in either case.

Table 1

EQUIVALENT TERMS: WILSON (1975) VS. MACDONALD-THORNE (1982)
(for Kerr spacetime)

HSW		MT
α		α
β		$-\omega\mathbf{m}$
$\mathbf{n}$		$\mathbf{u}$
$\mathbf{t}$		$\mathbf{k}$
$F^{\mu\nu}$		$-F^{\mu\nu}$
g^{tt}		$-1/\alpha^2$
$g^{t\phi}$		$-\omega/\alpha^2$
$g^{\phi\phi}$		$(1-\omega^2\ \tilde{\omega}^2/\alpha^2)/\tilde{\omega}^2$
$g_{\phi\phi}$		$\tilde{\omega}^2$
A_ϕ	*	$\Psi/2\pi$
H_ϕ	*	$\sqrt{g_{rr}g_{\theta\theta}}\ 2I/\alpha$
$(\alpha/\sqrt{-g})\ \partial_\theta A_\phi$		B^r
$(-\alpha/\sqrt{-g})\partial_r A_\phi$		B^θ
$(\alpha/\sqrt{-g})H_\phi$		B^ϕ

*Defined by MT only for time independent electromagnetic systems.

A scenario which we have not treated is the shock tube (see e.g. HSW). A shock tube with a constant magnetic field perpendicular to the shock front should have the same solution as the shock tube run without the field present. It should also be possible to derive the relativistic jump conditions for a magnetic field parallel to the shock. Another possible test is to substitute magnetic pressure for some of the hydrodynamic pressure in an analytic fat disk, and as-certain that the disk does remain stationary. In this test, however, we must watch out for Rayleigh-Taylor instabilities.

Finally, we can run tests dealing with the propagation of Alfvén waves. The easiest is to check the three modes of propagation in a uniform background. It should also be possible to check the dispersion relation obtained in equation 4.13 in simple cases. Either of the static tests outlined above should lend itself easily to such a test as the background. Green's functions, if found for equation (4.7), could be used to provide a critical test on the code's ability to propagate all three kinds of modes.

VII. CONCLUSIONS

We have used the 3+1 decomposition to analyze the MHD methods of Wilson. We find that using this notation clarifies the physical content in a way which neatly parallels that of Thorne and Macdonald (1982). Our emphasis is on the Lorentz force addition to the momentum equation. We find that the magnetic field contributes anisotropically to the inertia term in a way which is physically easy to see. Various limits of the MHD momentum equation are derived (static, Alfvén waves, etc.), and in each case we can see how relativity modifies the well-known low velocity equations. Finally, we present a new "trick" for rewriting the momentum equation in a way we hope will be useful numerically. It is clear that because of the many new degrees of freedom in MHD, the code testing will be a much more involved task than is the case for hydrodynamics alone. On the other hand, the great variety of physical effects which are present in general relativistic MHD were almost all appreciated by Wilson in his original work of almost a decade ago.

We wish to thank Roger Blandford, Joan Centrella, John Hawley, Fred Lamb, Telemachos Ch. Mouschovias, and Kip Thorne for valuable discussions. James Wilson's pioneering work and deep insight was, of course, a prerequisite of this research. Financial support was provided by the National Science Foundation under grants PHY 80-01496 and PHY 82-01948.

REFERENCES

Blandford, R. D.   1983, A. J., **88**, 245.

Damour, T., Hanni, R. S., Ruffini, R., and Wilson, J. R.   1978, Phys. Rev. **D17**, 1518.

Hawley, J. F., Smarr, L. L., and Wilson, J. R.   1984a, Ap. J., **277**, 296 (HSW).

_____. 1984b, Ap. J. Suppl., **55**, 211.

Lang, K. R.   1980, "Astrophysical Formulae" (Berlin: Springer-Verlag).

Macdonald, D., and Thorne, K. S.   1982, M.N.R.A.S., **198**, 345 (MT).

Misner, C., Thorne, K., and Wheeler, J.   1973, "Gravitation" (San Francisco: Freeman).

Ruffini, R., and Wilson, J. R.   1975, Phys. Rev., **D12**, 2959.

Smarr, L. L., Taubes, C., and Wilson, J. R.   1980, in "Essays in General Relativity" ed. F. J. Tipler (New York: Academic Press) p. 157.

Thorne, K. S., and Macdonald, D.   1982, M.N.R.A.S., **198**, 339 and Microfiche MN 198/1 (TM).

Wilson, J. R.   1972, Ap. J., **173**, 431.

_____. 1975, Ann. N. Y. Acad. Sci., **262**, 123.

_____. 1977, in "Proceedings of the Marcel Grossman Meeting", ed. R. Ruffini (Amsterdam: North Holland) p. 393.

_____. 1978, in "Proceedings of International School of Physics Fermi Course LXV" eds. R. Giacconi and R. Ruffini (Amsterdam: North Holland) p. 644.

York, J.W., Jr.   1979, in "Sources of Gravitational Radiation", ed. L. Smarr (Cambridge: Cambridge Univ. Press) p. 83.

Galactic Nuclei and Jets

Martin J. Rees
Institute of Astronomy,
Cambridge, England

ABSTRACT

The power sources in quasars and active galactic
nuclei probably involve the interaction of massive black
holes with surrounding plasma and magnetic fields. The
production of relativistic jets is a generic feature of
these systems, and the radiation may be emitted by (or
processed through) a pair-dominated plasma.

I.   INTRODUCTION

In this talk, I shall discuss — in what can only be a sketchy
fashion — several topics relevant to active galactic nuclei: the
runaway evolution to a black hole; the flows around black holes; the
exotic plasma physics involved in these flows, and in intense
radiation sources; and the properties of the relativistic beams or
jets which energize radio sources. These topics have another thing
in common: in all of them, we are still groping for even a qualitative
understanding; convincing detailed models must await the efforts of
those, such as Jim Wilson and his colleagues, who combine physical
insight with computational wizardry, and have the facilities to
exploit these skills.

II.   EVOLUTIONARY PATHWAYS IN GALACTIC NUCLEI:
SOME UNSOLVED PROBLEMS

It is easy to envisage (cf. diagram in Rees 1978a) various
evolutionary pathways whereby a galactic nucleus may run away towards

gravitational collapse. It is unclear which route is the more common one: nor do we know how (nor, indeed, whether) specific stages or routes can be associated with particular types of violent activity in galactic nuclei. Two things only seem clear:

(i) Most evolutionary pathways involve an inexorably deepening potential well, and it is hard to avoid concluding that much of the material ends up by collapsing into a black hole.

(ii) Some forms of activity are better explained by processes involving accretion onto an already-formed black hole, or energy extraction from a spinning hole, than in terms of any "precursor" stage.

The various "precursor" stages are nevertheless worth much more study; moreover, they pose many problems which require large-scale computation, and therefore merit a mention at this meeting. There are at least four such problems:

Evolution of dense star clusters. When the velocity dispersion in a cluster of ordinary stars approaches ~ 1000 km s^{-1}, stellar collisions become important. What happens next is controversial, despite the many papers on the topic, basically because the relative importance of stellar disruption and stellar coalescence is uncertain. Realistic models of stellar collisions would certainly be a great help in elucidating this, and in deciding whether a dense star cluster would give rise to ~ 100 $M_{\odot}$ coalesced stars, leading to supernovae (leaving behind a cluster of neutron stars or black holes?); or whether the stars are all destroyed, leaving an amorphous gas cloud which forms a single supermassive star.

Dynamical stability and evolution of supermassive stars. It could be interesting to compute models of supermassive stars with realistic differential rotation. If such an object goes dynamically unstable, its core collapses to a black hole, but a substantial fraction of the original mass may find itself with too much angular momentum to be swallowed. This material would form a "torus", supported by radiation pressure, which would evolve on a Kelvin or viscous timescale (whichever is shorter). (These tori are sometimes called "donuts" - the American spelling being preferred because British "doughnuts" do not have holes in the middle!) These (possibly self-gravitating) tori, which would undergo secular evolution rather than being stationary, are more complicated than those discussed by Roger Blandford in this volume. They may nevertheless be sufficiently common, long-lived and efficient to provide models for some category of radio-quiet quasars.

Stellar disruption by a massive black hole. Tidal disruption of stars is a widely discussed fuelling mechanism for black holes - a star on a highly eccentric orbit is disrupted, and the debris then evolved on a timescale controlled by viscous effects. The observational consequences depend on the answers to three interlinked questions:

(a) What fraction of the debris goes down the hole, rather than being expelled?

(b) What is the radiative efficiency for the accretion process? In other words, how many ergs of energy are radiated for each gram that is swallowed?

(c) How long does it take to "digest" one star? In particular, how does the "flare duration" and decay timescale for such a process compare with the interval between one stellar disruption and the next?

Black hole collisions. None of the formation routes for massive black holes is guaranteed to yield highly efficient gravitational wave emission. However, one can pinpoint a class of events that can generate low frequency pulses with an efficiency which would certainly be high: these involve coalescence of binary black holes. There may be black holes in most large galaxies. Moreover, "mergers" of galaxies are frequent enough that > 10% of all galaxies may have experienced such an event during the Hubble time. When two galaxies merge, they relax after a few dynamical times into an amorphous system resembling an elliptical galaxy. Any massive black holes would gravitate via dynamical friction into the central region of the merged galaxy, and then spiral together as they emit gravitational radiation (Begelman, Blandford and Rees 1980). The calculation of the gravitation wave pulse shape and efficiency for a coalescing binary has relevance to prospective searches (via interplanetary Doppler tracking, etc.) for such pulses; the possible recoil when an asymmetric binary merges is astrophysically important, especially if it could kick the resultant black hole out of the galactic nucleus.

III. BLACK HOLES: THE RELEVANT "BASICS"

The physics of dense star clusters and of supermassive objects
is complex and poorly understood. In contrast, the final state of
such a system — if indeed gravitational collapse occurs — is compara-
tively simple, at least if we accept general relativity. According
to the so-called "no-hair" theorems, the endpoint of a gravitational
collapse, however messy and asymmetric it may have been, is a
standardized black hole characterized by just two parameters — mass
and spin — and described exactly by the Kerr metric. If the collapse
occurred in a violent or sudden way, it would take several dynamic
timescales for the black hole to settle down; during that period
gravitational waves would be emitted. But the final state would be
described by the Kerr solution, provided only that the material left
behind outside the hole did not provide a strong perturbation. A Kerr
hole has two kinds of mass-energy (Christodoulou 1970): a fraction
associated with its spin, which can in principle be extracted, and an
"irreducible" mass. The fraction which can be extracted is 29% for a
maximally rotating hole. In the Kerr metric, the behavior of orbits
depends on their orientation with respect to the hole, and on whether
they are corotating or counter-rotating. For corotating equatorial
orbits, the innermost stable orbit moves inward compared to the
Schwarzschild case and becomes more tightly bound. As $J \to J_{max}$, the
maximum angular momentum for a Kerr hole, the stable orbits extend
inwards towards $r = r_g = GM/c^2$, and their binding energy approaches
$(1 - 1/\sqrt{3})c^2 \simeq 0.42c^2$. These numbers determine the maximum theoretical efficiency of accretion disks. A related inference is that
there are no stationary bound orbits whose angular momentum is less
than a definite threshold value; this important qualitative feature
of the orbits means that no axisymmetric flow pattern can extend too
close to the rotation axis.

An orbit around a spinning (Kerr) hole which does not lie in the
equatorial plane will precess with an angular velocity
$\sim 2(r/r_g)-3 \ r_g^{-1}c \ (J/J_{max})$ (Bardeen and Petterson 1975). For $J \simeq J_{max}$
this precession has a timescale $t_{BP} \simeq (r/r_g)^{3/2} t_{orb}$ when t_{orb} is the
orbital period. However, if material is spiralling slowly inwards
(at a rate controlled by viscosity) on a timescale exceeding t_{BP}, then
the precession effect can mount up. The important consequence follows

that the flow pattern near a black hole, within the radius where t_{BP} is less than the inflow time, is axisymmetric with respect to the hole irrespective of the infalling material's original angular momentum vector. The Lense-Thirring precession, an inherently relativistic effect, thus guarantees that a wide class of flow patterns near black holes will be axisymmetric — an important simplification of the problem.

It has been realized in recent years that magnetic fields around black holes may have important astrophysical effects (Blandford and Znajek 1977, MacDonald and Thorne 1982, Phinney 1983). When a black hole forms from collapsing magnetized materials, the magnetic field outside the horizon decays ("redshifts away") on the collapse timescale r_q/c. However, an external current system (associated with an accretion disk, for instance) can maintain fields which thread the hole. The event horizon (or "surface") of a black hole behaves in some respects like a spinning imperfect conductor; there are constraints on the orientations of $\underline{E}$ and $\underline{B}$ where they cross the horizon.

Just as in classical "unipolar conductor", power can be extracted by allowing a current flow between a spinning hole's equator and pole. The maximum electric potential drop is $\sim B_o r_g \, (J/J_{max})$ where B_o is the imposed field. This can be very large, as it is when a similar argument is applied to spinning magnetized neutron stars. However, just as in this latter case, a realistic external current system and plasma distribution, though very hard to calculate, is likely to "short out" the field. Nevertheless, general arguments show that, if currents are allowed to flow into the hole from larger radii where its field lines rotate with an angular velocity Ω^F of order half the hole's angular velocity Ω^H, the power dissipated (if B is measured in gauss and r_g in cm) can be of order

$$B_o{}^2 r_g{}^2 \, c \left(\frac{J}{J_{max}}\right)^2 \text{ ergs;} \qquad (1)$$

and e^+-e^- plasma produced near the hole could indeed maintain a current system flowing "into" and "out of" the hole. Power dissipated outside the hole comes, in effect, from the hole's spin energy (or "reducible mass"). Models for radio galaxies based on this mechanism are considered further in Section VI.

It may be helpful at this stage to introduce some characteristic quantities and ratios, which give a feel for the orders of magnitude involved and for what approximations are justified.

A fiducial luminosity is the "Eddington limit" at which radiation pressure on free electrons balances gravity:

$$L_E \doteq \frac{4 \pi G M m_p c}{\sigma_T} = 1.3 \times 10^{46} M_8 \text{ erg s}^{-1} , \qquad (2)$$

where M_8 is the mass in units of $10^8 M_\odot$.
Related to this is a characteristic timescale

$$t_E = \frac{\sigma_T c}{4 \pi G m_p} \simeq 4 \times 10^8 \text{ years.} \qquad (3)$$

This is the time it would take an object to radiate its entire rest mass if its luminosity were L_E. The timescale over which an accretion-driven source would double its mass is $\sim (L/L_E)^{-1}$ x (efficiency)$^{-1}$ x t_E.

The dynamical and orbital timescales near black holes are modest multiples of $(r_g/c) \simeq 500 M_8$ sec; these timescales are therefore vastly shorter than t_E. It is primarily for this reason that the mass of material in any stationary flow pattern around the hole is generally negligible compared to the mass of the hole itself - this vindicates us in assuming an undistorted Kerr metric and neglecting the self-gravity of plasma around the hole. (Radiation of the entire rest mass on a timescale r_g/c would yield a stupendous mass-independent luminosity of $c^5/G \simeq 4 \times 10^{59}$ erg s^{-1}).

A fiducial particle density in the hole's environment is

$$n_E = \frac{c^2}{\sigma_T c M} \simeq 10^{11} M_8^{-1} \text{ cm}^{-3}.$$

This is the density at $r = r_g$ if matter is falling radially inward at speed c at a rate sufficient to yield luminosity L_E if converted completely into radiation. A characteristic magnetic field strength is that for which $(B^2/8\pi) = n_E m_p c^2$:

$$B_E = \left(\frac{8 \pi c^2 m_p}{\sigma_T G M} \right)^{1/2} \simeq 2 \times 10^4 M_8^{-1/2} \text{ gauss.} \qquad (4)$$

If a field B_E were applied to a black hole with $J \simeq J_{max}$, the electromagnetic power extraction could be $\sim L_E$. In such a field, the Larmor frequency is the same as $\omega_L/2\pi = m_e c/eB_E \simeq 6 \times 10^{10} M_8^{-1/2} Hz$; the Larmor radius is therefore $<< r_g$. The maximum emf permitted by the unipolar inductor argument is then

$$\sim m_e c^2 \frac{r_g}{c/\omega_L} \left[\frac{J}{J_{max}}\right] \simeq 3 \times 10^{15} M_8^{1/2} \left[\frac{J}{J_{max}}\right] m_e c^2. \qquad (5)$$

This means that the density of charges required to "short out" the field is $\leq 10^{-12} n_E$. It is physically most unlikely that such a low density could persist: e^+-e^- pair production would maintain a much higher density throughout the hole's magnetosphere. In consequence, we expect that the plasma around a black hole is close to charge neutrality, and can be treated by the magnetohydrodynamic (MHD) approximation. (The bulk flow speeds, the Alfven speed, etc., will of course still be relativistic.)

A related inference is that the gravitational effect of charges and magnetic fields is negligible. When a gravitating system is electrically charged, the gravitational effect of the charge (and, more generally, of the electromagnetic field) modifies the Kerr metric to the more general Kerr-Newman form. The charge Q becomes significant if $Q^2 \simeq GM^2$, which requires a fractional deviation f from charge neutrality of order $N^{-1/2}$, where $N = e^2/Gm_p^2 \simeq 10^{36}$. Any gravitating plasma body (even the Sun) acquires a charge such that the electrical and gravitational binding energies of an electron are comparable. However, the value of f needed to provide a surface potential of even 10^9 volts is $\sim N^{-1}$, and for this value, f is itself only of order $N^{-1} \simeq 10^{-36}$. Even if the hole is charged to the potentials $\sim 10^{20}$ eV discussed above, the electromagnetic fractional contribution to the metric is still only of order 10^{-15}. (A related statement is that the magnetic energy density in realistic accretion flows is $< 10^{-15}$ of $(M/r_g^3)c^2$). We are thus justified, by a large margin, in treating the spacetime as given by the ordinary Kerr metric.

IV. ACCRETION WITH LOW $\dot{M}$

Roger Blandford has discussed the physics of thick accretion disks (or tori) supported by radiation pressure. I shall discuss briefly how a disk could be thickened by the gas pressure, if kT is of order $m_p c^2 (r/r_g)^{-1}$ in the inner parts.

Whereas in an optically thick radiation-supported torus the interior conditions resemble those beneath the photosphere of an O star, in a torus supported by gas pressure (requiring kinetic temperatures $\sim$ 100 MeV) things would be very different. Since the bulk velocities are comparable with c, conditions are exceptionally favourable for the acceleration of ultrarelativistic particles. Indeed, the distinction between "thermal" and "nonthermal" particles becomes rather blurred under these extreme conditions. The energy available for each "thermal" ion is $\sim$ 100 MeV, and at kinetic temperatures corresponding to this we cannot assume that the electron temperature (T_e) and the ion temperature (T_i) are equal, nor that there is any component of the plasma with a well-defined Maxwellian velocity distribution. In general, it is likely that $T_e < T_i$, the electrons being efficiently cooled and maintained at energies below a few MeV by synchrotron or Compton emissions - except for the small proportion that may have just passed through a shock, or a region of magnetic reconnection, where the coupling between electrons and ions is more efficient than that due to ordinary Coulomb encounters.

At $r < 1000\ r_g$, where the ion virial temperature exceeds the electron rest mass, cooling will always be efficient if the ions channel their energy to the electrons on a timescale shorter than the inflow time. However, this cannot occur by the usual process of Coulomb interactions for $\dot{M}/\dot{M}_E < 50(v_{infall}/v_{freefall})^2$ (Rees et al. 1982). Unless collective effects step in to couple the electrons and ions, the flow will then be unable to cool, resulting in the formation of a thick disk. The factor $(v_{infall}/v_{freefall})$ in this context is of order the viscosity parameter α. This is probably predominantly magnetic viscosity. Estimates of magnetic viscosity (e.g. Eardley and Lightman 1975) suggest α in the range of 10^{-2} - 1. However, the important point is that there is no reason why α should diminish as $\dot{M}$ falls, so that the regime of inefficient cooling would definitely be attained. The only perceptible radiation emitted from such a flow would be due to a nonthermal tail of electrons (accelerated behind shocks, or by processes related to the magnetic reconnection and viscosity).

An accretion flow where $\dot{M}$ is small, and where (furthermore) the efficiency is low, may seem a doubly unpromising model for any active galactic nucleus. However, such a torus could carry surface currents which maintain a magnetic flux through the hole, allowing energy extraction via the Blandford-Znajek (1977) mechanism. The main role of the torus in these accretion flows is thus to "anchor" the magnetic field lines that thread the hole. The torus therefore has to be a good enough conductor so that currents which produce magnetic fields can be set up and maintained in it. Even though the torus itself may not release much energy, it then acts as a catalyst for the efficient extraction of the black hole's spin energy. To give some idea of the large amount of energy available, let us consider some large but not absurd parameters for the black hole; a $10^9 M_\odot$ black hole with $J \simeq J_{max}$ has enough latent spin to power a source of luminosity 10^{45} ergs s^{-1} for several times 10^9 years. This may be a way therefore to power nonthermal nuclear sources in galaxies.

Although the ion-supported torus radiates very little, it emits some bremsstrahlung γ-rays. There is a chance that these can collide with each other in the funnel region, and this yields sufficient e^+-e^- pairs in the funnel to "complete the circuit" and allow a current system to flow through the hole.

The energy extraction only approaches maximal efficiency if the proper "impedance match" can be achieved. In the context when the power emerges as a magnetized e^+-e^- wind, one would like to know whether anything resembling this optimal situation can be set up. Phinney (1983) has considered wind solutions relevant to this model. He supposes that e^+-e^- plasma, created in some region outside (but not close to) the hole, flows inward (into the hole) and outward; he considers the critical points for each flow. If MHD can be applied, then the ratio of the effective external resistance to that of the hole is $\Omega^F/(\Omega^H - \Omega^F)$, when Ω^H is the hole's angular velocity and Ω^F the angular velocity of the field lines. Phinney finds that there are consistent wind solutions where Ω^F is as large as $0.2\Omega^H$, corresponding to an efficiency 60% of the maximum.

Rees et al. (1982) argue that electromagnetic extraction of energy from holes surrounded by low-$\dot{M}$ ion-supported tori is the dominant power source in strong double radio galaxies. These radio galaxies almost certainly do have low fuelling rates: in many cases the nuclear luminosity is only $\lesssim 10^{42}$ergs s^{-1}, i.e. $\lesssim 10^{-4}$ of the

Eddington luminosity for $10^8 M_\odot$; moreover, the relevant hole mass must be $\sim 10^8 M_\odot$ because many of these sources have giant radio lobes with energy content $\gtrsim 10^{61}$ ergs.

The consistency requirement for a thick ion-supported torus is that the ion-electron coupling timescale exceed the inflow time. This ensures that the ions do not cool down even if the electrons do, but remain at a high enough temperature ($kT_i \simeq GM/r$) to support the torus. (This is the reason for the nomenclature "ion-supported torus" rather than "plasma-supported torus".) In quantifying this (Rees et al. 1982) we have assumed that the coupling between electrons and ions is provided by Coulomb scattering alone. One question which arises is whether other more efficient collective plasma processes will couple the ions and the electrons. If there are such processes then the torus will deflate. I have consulted several plasma physicists on this question, but do not have a unique answer. There are bound to be shearing motions, due to the differential rotations in the torus, which generate local pressure anisotropies in the ion plasma and the electron plasma. There are certainly instabilities which isotropise the ion plasma and also those which iostropise the electron plasma. The key question — which still seems open — is whether these isotropisation processes which act on ions and on electrons transfer energy from ions to electrons. If they do, then the electrons would drain away the thermal energy of the ions and a thick torus supported by ion pressure would be impossible. We might still be able to have a thin magnetized disk (as Blandford and Znajek 1977 envisaged) but then may be unable to get the good initial collimation that a thick disk provides. To summarize, the ion-supported torus offers a way of producing energy in the form of ultrarelativistic electron-positron jets, without producing a lot more energy from thermal radiation.

V.   THERMAL ELECTRON-POSITRON PHOTOSPHERES

The extreme conditions around magnetized black holes (with a large $\underline{E}.\underline{B}$ can certainly create an e^+-e^- plasma. However, it is perhaps more surprising that such a plasma, generated via photon collisions with energy $> 2m_e c^2$ in the center-of-momentum frame, can be shown to exist quite generally, given simply that we observe hard radiation from a small region.

The available data on Seyfert galaxies strongly indicate relatively flat, hard X-ray spectra (energy index $\alpha \simeq 0.6$) which extend to ~ 1 MeV. A spectral turnover at about 1 MeV may be expected if the underlying radiation mechanism is a thermal plasma, for the cooling function increases dramatically if kT_e exceeds $m_e c^2$ and pair production becomes important (see e.g. Lightman 1982, Svennson 1982). Thermal equilibrium may not, however, be appropriate for rapidly varying compact sources. In that case a power-law spectrum of electrons may be generated by shock fronts, reconnection regions, localized strong electric fields, etc., and these electrons could well emit a "primary" photon spectrum extending up to >> 1 MeV.

We define a parametrized luminosity ℓ related to total luminosity L by

$$L = \ell \left(\frac{m_e c^3}{\sigma_T} \right) r.$$

(6)

Although our general results are model-independent, we note that for this definition the radiation from around a black hole has

$$\ell = \left(\frac{m_p}{m_e} \right) \left(\frac{r}{r_g} \right)^{-1} \left(\frac{L}{L_E} \right).$$

(7)

If f_γ denotes the fraction of the primary luminosity emitted as γ-rays above 1 MeV, pair-production effects will prevent these photons from escaping the entire source region if

$$f_\gamma \ell > 1.$$

(8)

The pair density (and temperature) in the source region can now estimated. Neglecting dynamics, we suppose that an equilibrium pair density (production rate = annihilation rate) is maintained in the source. Suppose also that the pairs are generated uniformly through the entire volume. The Thomson depth of the source due to pairs is then

$$\tau_{e^+-e^-} = (x f_\gamma \ell)^{1/2} \left[\frac{\sigma_T c}{\text{annihilation rate constant}} \right]^{1/2}.$$

(9)

In this expression, $x(<1)$ is the mean number of pairs produced <u>per</u> $2m_e c^2$ of energy of photons above the threshold. If $h\nu_{max}$ is only a few MeV, x is guaranteed to be not much below unity. However, if the primary spectrum is very hard, and extends to such high frequencies that most of the emission is in photons with energies $>> 1$ MeV, x may be small (but still corresponding to one pair per high energy photon) unless the kinetic energy of an ultrarelativistic pair produces further pairs via some cascade process. Whenever the source is optically thick to photon-photon collisions at ~ 1 MeV, $\tau_{e^+-e^-} > 1$ since the collision cross-section for pair production is $\sim \sigma_T$.

The net result of more detailed discussion is that, though x is uncertain, there is no reason why it should be very small (Guilbert, Fabian, and Rees 1983). Therefore all that is required in order to generate $\tau_{e^+-e^-} > 1$ is

$$f\gamma L > \left(\frac{m_e}{m_p}\right) L_E \left(\frac{r}{r_g}\right).$$

The expression in square brackets in Equation (9) is ~ 1 if the pairs are subrelativistic (see Ramaty and Meszaros 1981), and increased if the pairs are relativistic, because the annihilation rate is proportional to $\gamma^{-2}_{e^+-e^-}$ for $\gamma_{e^+-e^-} >> 1$. We can then conclude that if $(xf\gamma\ell) > 1$ we unavoidably generate and maintain $\tau_{e^+-e^-} > 1$. Moreover, it then follows that the pairs must be <u>subrelativistic</u>. This is because the nonthermal primary emission process generates predominantly soft photons, and the Comptonisation parameter $\tau^2\gamma^2_{e^+-e^-}$ (already > 1) for mildly relativistic pairs if $xf\gamma\ell > 1$ increases as $\gamma^4_{e^+-e^-}$, implying Comptonisation losses $\propto \exp[(xf\gamma\ell)\gamma^4_{e^+-e^-}]$!

The observed radiation will then have a spectrum corresponding to what is obtained by "reprocessing" the part of the primary spectrum below 1 MeV through a Comptonising medium with τ given by Equation (9), and with $kT_{e^+-e^-}$ given by the Compton equilibrium condition. The details are discussed by Guilbert <u>et al</u>. (1983), but the main result is that there is a cutoff or break in the spectrum for photon energies above $\sim m_e c^2/\tau^2_{e^+-e^-}$.

The considerations apply not just to galactic nuclei but also to smaller scale objects — gamma-ray bursts, for instance (cf. Cavallo and Rees 1978). It seems inevitable that much of the radiation observed from compact sources with hard spectra has been reprocessed by a "false photosphere" of electron-positron pairs. This may limit our ability to understand the underlying energy release mechanisms in such sources. (Large flux variations, particularly when, or if, the source temporarily switches off, may prove to be most valuable for observation.) However, there is the encouraging prospect that the emergent spectrum, and the possible e^+-e^- wind, may be amenable to detailed modeling. The observed spectrum of a galactic nucleus may, through its dependence on $\tau_{e^+-e^-}$, offer clues (independent of variability) to the dimensions of the emitting region, and to the nature of the primary radiation at high photon energies.

VI. RADIO SOURCES AND JETS

Any theory of radio sources has, in effect, three ingredients. In "beam"-type models, the basic picture involves: i) a source of relativistic plasma in the center; ii) some bifurcation and collimation mechanism, i.e., a way in which relativistic plasma can be squirted out preferentially in two opposite directions; and iii) a place far away where the beam of relativistic plasma is stopped by interaction with the intergalactic medium, in a shock front.

The speed of advance of the beam, V, is governed by ram pressure balance — the balance between the momentum density in the beam and the $\rho_{ext}V^2$ pressure force exerted by the surrounding medium. The beam energy is randomized by shocks when it impinges on the external medium; particles here are accelerated and these regions are identified with the "hot spots" observed (in the most powerful sources) at the outer edge of the components. The relativistic plasma then accumulates in a cocoon of lower energy density and lower radio emissivity.

A few comments now about the 1 - 100 kpc jets which are now mapped so beautifully with the VLA. We are probably justified in thinking of jets as basically fluid phenomena and using gas-dynamical analogies, the reason being that the gyro radius $m_e v_e \gamma_e / eB$ for the particles in the jet and the Debye length $(kT_e/n_e e^2)^{\frac{1}{2}}$ are both always <u>much</u> less than the jet dimensions. This means that charge neutrality is closely satisfied (unless the particles have energies $\gtrsim 10^{19}$ eV); also the relative velocity of the electrons and ions is small. In effect, the flow is fluid-like and the MHD approximation is valid. (As in the solar wind, even though the mean free path for two-particle collisions is very large, the presence of even small amounts of magnetic fields makes the plasma fluid-like.)

Apart from the confinement problem (discussed in detail by Begelman, Blandford and Rees 1984), there are other environmental effects which influence jet shapes, and which one infers must be present from the complicated and asymmetric structures that are revealed by the VLA. One such environmental effect is "side winds". If a jet is exposed to an external medium moving transversely to it, then a sideways pressure gradient will cause the jet to bend. This situation could obtain if (say) the parent galaxy were moving through the intergalactic medium. This is almost certainly what is happening in the radio trails of NGC 1265. One can work out the details of jet bending due to "side winds". If R is the radius of curvature of the jet's path, d is the diameter of its cross-section, and M is the mach number, then one requires that $M < (R/d)^{\frac{1}{2}}$. If this inequality is fulfilled then one has $\Delta P/P \simeq (d/R)^{\frac{1}{2}} M$, where ΔP is the extra external pressure on one side of the jet. For a side wind blowing at its internal sound speed, $\Delta P \approx P$; applied to NGC 1265 and similar sources, this model can account for the drastic bending observed (Begelman, Rees and Blandford 1979). Some people (Smith and Norman 1981 and references cited therein) have considered whether buoyancy effects could cause bending in some sources. In general this can only be a "gentle" effect, since $\Delta P/P \approx (d/\text{scale height})$, which is in general small for narrow jets.

The other type of distortion is "precession". Some sources have so-called "inversion symmetry" (or S-type symmetry). It is uncertain whether these really involve precession (since the phenomena can be interpreted otherwise); and even if precession is involved it is not clear whether this is precession of the central object (spinning black hole, Rees 1978b), or an effect on the scale of the whole galaxy.

Realistically, the contents of the jets are going to be just as complex and inhomogeneous as the interstellar medium is. In principle the beam material could consist of cool cloudlets embedded in hotter material. This colder material could be produced by entrainment of cool gas, by thermal instabilities, or by cooling behind internal shocks. This is relevant to some cases where there is evidence for emission lines with generally low velocities associated with the jet. In SS433 we certainly know that material is moving out at $\sim c/4$ but it is in the form of tiny cloudlets that radiate optical spectral lines. We should remember therefore that the beam contents can be rather complicated.

The superluminal components observed at milli-arc-second resolution by VLBI have (deprojected) lengths of $\sim 10^{20}$ cm — $\sim 10^{-4}$ of typical VLA map scales — and imply relativistic bulk motion on these scales. There are, however, persuasive reasons for attributing the primary energy production to relativistically deep potential wells on scales 10^{14} - 10^{15} cm. Moreover, the initial bifurcation and collimation must also be imposed on these small scales if the long-term stability of the jet axis in extended sources is due to the gyroscopic effect of a spinning black hole (Rees 1978b). It is important not to forget that many powers of ten difference in scale are involved: if collimation is initiated on scales of 10^{15} cm or less, the jets may face many vicissitudes before they can actually get out to the much larger distances where we observe the radio phenomena. They may be destroyed and recollimated; they could even change direction. The small scale jet may be lined up with the direction of the rotation axis of the central massive object, while the large scale one may lie along the rotation axis of the galaxy.

The stuff ejected from $< 10^{15}$ cm may be electron-positron plasma or "ordinary" electron-ion plasma. Energy can also be transported via Poynting flux — either as large-scale field carried out with the particles (a directed MHD wind) or as low-frequency wave modes (cf. Rees 1971) — and this can, in principle, swamp the flux associated with the kinetic energy of the charged particles themselves.

The structure of jets on the unobservably small scales 10^{15} - 10^{19} cm, if we could probe it in the same detail that the VLA provides for scales a million times larger, would no doubt prove just as complex - there would be entrainment of surrounding gas, bending by transverse pressure gradients, and shocks where the jet impinges on the dense gas clouds that radiate the broad emission lines. But one general statement can be made. The flow patterns would not simply be a scaled down version of those seen on larger scales, because one key number - the ratio of radiative cooling times ($\propto r^2$ for a simple diverging jet) to dynamical times ($\propto r$) - is proportional to r rather than being scale-independent. Consequently, the flows on small scales would tend to be less elastic and more dissipative; they are less likely to maintain a high internal pressure, and would dissipate more energy if bent through large angles.

Aerodynamical experiments using cylindrically symmetric supersonic flows may provide valuable insights into purely hydrodynamic aspects of jet physics. They can complement numerical simulations by providing higher resolution studies of turbulence and instabilities and (more importantly) by displaying fully three-dimensional aspects of the flow which are inaccessible to currently available computer codes. They also have limitations, including their inability to demonstrate the dynamical effects of magnetic fields and relativistic bulk velocity, and the restricted ranges of Mach number, density ratio, and adiabatic index which are practicable in the laboratory. Nevertheless, through the judicious choice of different jet gases and the use of wind tunnels and vacuum chambers, it should be possible to spot some of the trends which accompany changes in the various dimensionless quantities that characterize astrophysical jets.

The experiments might include firing a supersonic jet into undistributed gas (or head-on into a wind, so that the "working surface" is stationary in the laboratory frame); or firing jets transversely into a wind to simulate the radio trails.

A different type of experiment which could achieve higher Mach numbers than "traditional" wind tunnels would involve the propagation of intense particle beams — or, alternatively, laser beams — into an ambient gas (cf. Bekefi et al. 1980); although the internal dynamics of such beams differ crucially from those in the cosmic-scale beams, they would provide a much higher momentum density than an ordinary gas jet. The interaction with the external medium as such a beam advances may simulate the structure of "hot spots" and cocoons in very strong sources.

The greatest progress will surely come, however, from development and use of sophisticated hydrodynamical codes. Two-dimensional codes have already uncovered some gas dynamical properties of supersonic flows that were unanticipated by analytical models and may have counterparts in radio maps (Norman et al. 1983). Useful and affordable three-dimensional simulations are perhaps five years off, and we must wait for these before we can hope to simulate the nonlinear development of instabilities and the production of the symmetric bends in jets. (Some limited insight may be gleaned from the combined use of two dimensional Cartesian and cylindrical simulations.) The other important future computational development will be the use of MHD codes. Only in this way will we be able to learn if it really is practical to confine jets magnetically, whether or not the polarization patterns observed in jets can be explained in terms of the kinematics of expanding shear flows, and to study flow patterns around black holes.

VII.   CONCLUDING COMMENTS

The "central engine" plainly involves rather exotic physical processes in regions less than a light day across, with plasmas under much more extreme conditions than those which people normally study (e^+-e^- plasmas, etc.), and displays some inherently relativistic effects. We are forced to use plasma physics that we do not know too well. Moreover, we know Einstein's theory really well only in the weak field limit. It would be interesting in this context to try to get hold of a diagnostic, by using our study of active nuclei, to test strong-field general relativity — to learn whether the space-time around a rotating black hole is indeed described by the Kerr metric. This is an extra motivation for studying active galactic nuclei.

In extended sources the physics is not so exotic. However, it is here that I am more pessimistic about making progress. This is because in the compact objects, even though the physics is exotic, we have a fairly "clean" problem: axisymmetric flow in a calculable gravitational field. On the other hand, in the large scale sources environmental effects are plainly crucial; it is rather like meteorology. Weather prediction is difficult even though it does not involve exotic physics, and it may likewise be hard to interpret the detailed morphology of extended radio sources. If we want to learn something of novelty and importance for physics, it is more important to understand the compact sources (also, it is in a sense easier).

To use an unsavory but appropriate analogy, a mushroom cloud reveals rather little about the initiating thermonuclear event; likewise, the shape of big double radio sources may not tell us much about the primary object, $\sim 10^{10}$ smaller in scale, which generates the energy and produces the relativistic jets.

I am grateful to Joan Centrella, Larry Smarr and their colleagues for the invitation to participate in such a stimulating meeting, and for hospitality in Illinois. I acknowledge helpful discussions and collaboration with Mitch Begelman, Roger Blandford, Andy Fabian, Paul Guilbert and Sterl Phinney.

REFERENCES

Bardeen, J.M., and Petterson, J. 1975, Ap. J. (Lett.), 195, L65.

Begelman, M.C., Blandford, R.D., and Rees, M.J. 1980, Nature, 287, 307.

_____. 1984, Rev. Mod. Phys.,(April issue).

Begelman, M.C., Rees, M.J., and Blandford, R.D. 1979, Nature, 279, 770.

Bekefi, G., Field, B.T., Parmentola, J., and Tsipos, K. 1980, Nature, 284, 219.

Blandford, R.D., and Znajek, R.L. 1977, M.N.R.A.S., 179, 433.

Cavallo, G., and Rees, M.J. 1978, M.N.R.A.S., 183, 359.

Christodoulou, D. 1970, Phys. Rev. Lett., 25, 1596.

Eardley, D., and Lightman, A.P. 1975, Ap. J., 200, 187.

Guilbert, P.W., Fabian, A.C., and Rees, M.J. 1983, M.N.R.A.S., 205, 593.

Lightman, A.P. 1982, Ap. J., 253, 842.

MacDonald, D., and Thorne, K.S. 1982, M.N.R.A.S., 198, 345.

Norman, M.L., Smarr, L.L., Winkler, K.H., and Smith, M.D. 1983, Astr. Ap., 113, 285.

Phinney, E.S. 1983, in 'Astrophysical Jets', ed. A. Ferrari and A.G. Pacholczyk (Dordrecht: Reidel).

Ramaty, R., and Meszaros, P. 1981, Ap. J., 250, 384.

Rees, M.J. 1971, Nature, 229, 312 (errata, p. 510).

_____. 1978a, Observatory, 98, 210.

_____. 1978b, Nature, 275, 516.

Rees, M.J., Begelman, M.C., Blandford, R.D., and Phinney, E.S. 1982, Nature, 297, 17.

Smith, M.D., and Normañ, C.A. 1981, M.N.R.A.S. 194, 771.

Svennson, R. 1982, Ap. J., 258, 335.

Fluid Dynamical Mechanisms for Knots in Astrophysical Jets

Michael L. Norman, Larry Smarr,*
and Karl-Heinz A. Winkler
*Max-Planck-Institut für Physik und Astrophysik,
Munich*

ABSTRACT

Knotty jets recently discovered in a number of both young
and evolved stellar systems show remarkable similarities in
appearance to knotty extragalactic jets of vastly larger
dimensions. In every case, knot emission in stellar jets is
found to be shock-excited, which is strongly suspected to
be the case in extragalactic jets as well (e.g. M87). We
argue that fluid-dynamical instabilities (pinching and kinking) grow to nonlinear amplitude in knotty astrophysical
jets and produce large-scale shock systems of the strength
and distribution necessary to yield the observed knots. The
behavior of fluid instabilities in the nonlinear regime and
their saturation through shock formation is demonstrated by
2-dimensional gas dynamical simulations.

I. KNOTTY JETS - A UNIVERSAL PHENOMENON

An exciting development in observational astronomy over the past
five years has been the widespread discovery of jets of matter ema-
nating from astrophysical objects as diverse as galaxies and quasars
(e.g. Miley 1980; Bridle and Perley 1984), evolved binary star systems
(e.g. Margon 1982; Tapia et al. 1983), and very recently, pre-Main
Sequence stars (e.g. Mundt and Fried 1983). Although the jets in the

---

* Visitor, Max-Planck-Institut für Astrophysik; Alfred P. Sloan Fellow
   Permanent address: Departments of Astronomy and Physics, University
   of Illinois, Urbana, Illinois 60801, USA.

giant elliptical galaxy M87 (cf. Fig. 1a) and quasar 3C273 have been known for decades, these objects were, until recently, considered astronomical oddities. Now it seems that these objects are merely conspicuous examples of a universal phenomenon.

A universal phenomenon would seem to require a universal mechanism. This mechanism has three component pieces: the central energy source, the jet-forming mechanism, and the jet propagation to distances large compared to the source size. In all cases the ultimate energy source is the release of gravitational potential energy by the accretion of gas onto a compact object. This object can evidently be a young star, a white dwarf, a neutron star, or a black hole. All of these are approximately of stellar mass except the black hole, which can range from $\sim 10 M_\odot$ to $10^9 M_\odot$. Rees and his collaborators have discussed conditons under which accreting source models can be scaled from stellar to galactic power levels (Rees, Begelman, and Blandford 1981; Rees 1982).

The jet may be formed by the physical environment near the central object. Blandford reviews, in a paper in this volume, the possibilities of various kinds of accretion disks in this regard. The geometry of the disk certainly chooses two directions perpendicular to its equator. However, the physics of beam acceleration and focusing in a strong gravitational field may well involve the complex physics of viscous, radiation-coupled magnetohydrodynamics. Detailed calculations of this physics is still in its infancy (see Hawley and Smarr, these proceedings).

A different   scenario, the Twin-Exhaust Model proposed by Blandford and Rees (1974), requires the central accreting object simply to provide a point source of energy and hot matter, which blows a large bubble into the interstellar medium surrounding the central object. If the pressure falls off faster in one direction than another, this bubble will break out along the path of least resistance, forming a jet. Unfortunately, direct observation of the jet-forming regions in stars and galaxies is not yet possible, which leaves the question of jet formation unanswered. What we can see are the jets themselves.

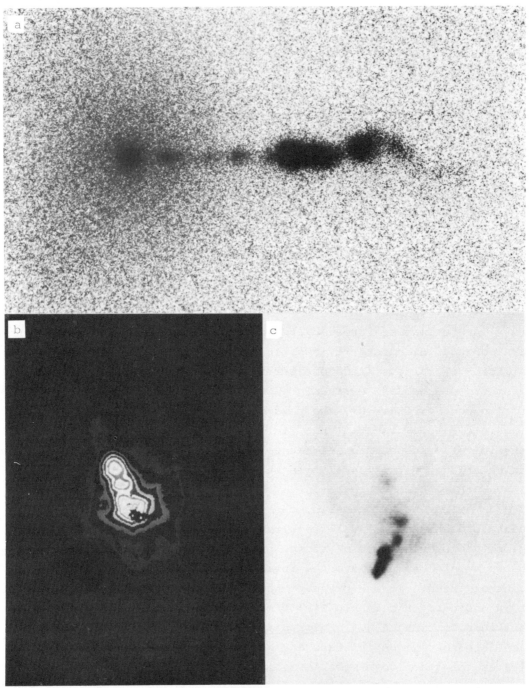

Fig. 1. - Knotty jets in a variety of astrophysical systems: a) in giant elliptical galaxy M87, U-filter, CFH prime focus (Nieto and Lelièvre, 1982): b) in symbiotic star R Aqr, Hα emission (by permission of S. Tapia); and c) in infrared source L 1551 IRS 5, r-filter (by permission of R. Mundt).

Jets are widely interpreted as continuous, highly collimated supersonic gas flows. Adopting this point of view, we therefore ask: is there observational evidence that the same underlying gas dynamics operates in jets whose lengths range from milliparsecs (stellar) to megaparsecs (extragalactic)? The existence of knots of emission with remarkably similar properties such as in the diverse objects in Figure 1 argues that the answer may be yes.

Consider the following observed properties of knots in astrophysical jets:

1. Knot emission is shock excited. In stellar jets this is readily determined due to the appearance of emission lines (Mundt and Fried 1983; Tapia et al. 1983) whose spectra are consistent with theoretical models of line formation behind radiative shockwaves (e.g. Dopita 1978). In extragalactic jets, the excitation mechanism is not unambiguously determined, although shock acceleration of the synchrotron-radiating relativistic electrons is a strong candidate (Blandford and Ostriker 1978). The recently discovered optical continuum and line emission coincident with the radio and x-ray knots in the Centaurus A jet (Brodie, Königl, and Bowyer 1983; Burns, Feigelson, and Schreier 1983) is consistent with shock excitation. But perhaps the most compelling evidence we have that shockwaves excite emission knots in extragalactic jets is the 15 GHZ VLA maps of the M87 jet by Biretta, Owen, and Hardee (1983), which show sharp intensity jumps on the upstream sides of knots A and D.

2. Knot emission in extragalactic jets is center-brightened (e.g. Fomalont 1983) indicating that the shocks responsible are large-scale (i.e. beam-filling) and not just a surface effect.

3. Knot minimum energy densities typically exceed estimates of the pressure of the confining gas (Owen, Hardee, and Bignell 1980), as one might expect downstream of a strong shock.

4. Knots often occur in fairly regularly-spaced strings, with a "wavelength" of the order of the beam diameter (Nieto and Lelièvre 1982; Biretta, Owen, and Hardee 1983), although longer spacings have also been observed.

5. Knot position and intensity frequently correlate with changes in the global structure of the jet, such as at reconfinement shoulders

(Sanders 1983; Perley, Bridle, and Willis 1984), the onset of wiggles (Nieto and Lelièvre 1982), and large-angle-deflections (e.g. wide-angle-tails, Blandford and Smarr 1983). If the beams are supersonic, such changes must have shocks associated with them.

Points 2-5 cannot be made with as much certainty for stellar jets because of the recentness of their discovery and hence the rather small sample one has to draw on. Nevertheless, this sample is growing. Mundt (private communication) has now observed a total of eight jets from young stellar objects, of which six possess knots. Although little data exists which addresses point 3, visual inspection of the CCD observations shows that the knots (which could be considered aligned Herbig-Haro objects) are consistent with the above characterization.

The above features suggest a commonality in the flow dynamics underlying the observed emission knots, namely, that knots are the observable consequences of large-scale shock systems that are excited in supersonic beams by a variety of fluid instabilities (e.g. pinching, kinking, twisting, flattening) and external influences (e.g. pressure reconfinement, bending). Because such fluid dynamical mechanisms are scale invariant, they operate in qualitatively the same way on stellar and extragalactic length scales. Dynamically important cooling, which is likely in stellar jets, will break this scale invariance by introducing a new parameter, t_{cool}/t_{flow}, which must be preserved when scaling.

The consensus among perturbation theorists who have performed linear Kelvin-Helmholtz instability analyses of supersonic beams is that their pinching modes are related to knot formation (Hardee 1979, 1982; Ferrari, Trussoni, and Zaninetti 1981a,b; Cohn 1983), although how these linear modes excite shockwaves in the nonlinear limit could not be discussed in detail. Benford (1981) has suggested that knots could be formed by the nonlinear growth of helical modes, which he argues will drive periodically-spaced shockwaves into the external medium.

The intent of this paper is to describe how the pinch and other fluid-dynamical mechanisms operate to produce shock systems of the strength and distribution necessary to yield the observed knots. The mechanisms to be described here have all been studied assuming the flow is adiabatic (i.e., $t_{cool}/t_{flow} = \infty$). We are in the process of doing a sensitivity study to see how cooling affects the flow patterns which give rise to the knots. We will emphasize the complementary role of laboratory investigations and numerical simulations in elucidating the behavior of fluid instabilities in the nonlinear regime and their saturation through shock formation.

The remainder of this paper is organized as follows. In Section II we review briefly the numerical work done together with Jim Wilson on the Blandford-Rees Twin-Exhaust Model. This mechanism, originally envisioned for radio galaxies, is attracting renewed interest among both stellar jet (Tapia et al. 1983) and quasar jet (Narlikar and Subramanian 1983) astronomers, illustrating the utility of a scale-free theory. Section III begins our discussion of knot formation via large-scale shock systems with examples from terrestrial and laboratory experience. The properties of underexpanded supersonic jets are reviewed with an emphasis on global properties that can be related to the underlying flow variables. Sections IV and V examine the shock structures that arise in pressure-matched jets through axisymmetric and nonaxisymmetric mechanisms, respectively. Here we rely on numerical simulations for investigating flows not heretofore studied in the laboratory. An astrophysical application of these mechanisms is presented in the last section, as well as a brief assessment of the current and future role of numerical simulations in understanding the physics of cosmic jets.

II. NUMERICAL INVESTIGATION OF THE TWIN-EXHAUST MODEL

In 1974 Blandford and Rees proposed a purely fluid dynamical mechanism for producing collimated twin beams of the sort that would help explain the gross structure and energetics of the classical radio doubles which appear on either side of an elliptical galaxy, such as in Cygnus A. In the Twin-Exhaust Model, a source of constant luminosity, located in the center of a flattened gas cloud (assumed to be bound in the potential well of an elliptical galaxy), inflates a cavity with buoyant material. When the size of the inflating

cavity exceeds one scale-height of the confining gas cloud, the hot
buoyant gas creates opposed de Laval nozzles through which it
escapes, accelerating to supersonic velocities beyond the throats of
the nozzles. The nozzles are assumed to form along the minor axis of
the flattened cloud. The degree of collimation of the twin jets thus
produced is determined by the run of pressure in the confining gas
cloud. Left unspecified in the model was how this flow would set
itself up, and whether it would be stable assuming it could be set
up.

Two of us (LS and MLN), working closely with Jim Wilson,
attempted a numerical investigation of the Twin-Exhaust mechanism.
We turned to Jim because addressing the model's uncertainties involved dealing with the time-dependent multidimensional gas dynamics
of a two-fluid system, which could be expected to develop nonlinear
Rayleigh-Taylor and Kelvin-Helmholtz instabilities. Jim's experience
in dealing with such complexities was, in part, embodied in a computer
code that one of us (MLN) had written under his supervision. Details
and findings of the numerical calculations are given in Norman et al.
(1981), and analyzed in Smith et al. (1981, 1983). In the following
summary, we distinguish between nozzle formation and jet collimation,
which are two separate aspects of the model.

The essential results concerning nozzle formation are given in
Figure 2. We verified that, given a flattened confining gas cloud
with a pressure distribution near the source which falls off slower
than r^{-2}, de Laval nozzles do form and can persist for a restricted
range of source luminosities. If the source luminosity is too low, a
thin nozzle is produced which is quickly broken into bubbles by the
Kelvin-Helmholtz instability (cf. Fig. 2a). Conversely, a too high
source luminosity produces such a large central cavity that a global
Rayleigh-Taylor instability removes source gas in the form of large
clouds (cf. Fig. 2c). The intermediate range of luminosity yields
quasi-steady cavity/nozzle structures that are in qualitative agreement with the Blandford-Rees picture (cf. Fig. 2b).

The flow beyond the throat of the nozzle is either highly
collimated or not, depending on the pressure-distance relation in
the confining cloud. In order to fit the confining cloud on our grid,

we assumed an exponential pressure distribution. This caused the supersonic part of the flow to be poorly collimated. A power-law dependence $p \sim r^{-\beta}$ with exponent $\beta \leq 2$ would have better collimating properties.

Besides showing that jets can be formed in at least one manner, our calculations may impact on the question of the origin of knots in jets. Before the shock mechanism described in subsequent sections was proposed (Norman et al. 1982), there were two other theories of how shocks can form in astrophysical supersonic jets. The first, described by Rees (1978), relies on variations in jet luminosity or velocity in the jet forming region. He envisioned these variations leading to a series of shocks and rarefactions in the beam. The second, given by Blandford and Königl (1979), assumes that interstellar clouds could be entrained into the beam, forming bow shocks behind the clouds.

Our calculations reveal new sources for these variations or clouds. The bubble regime is probably not important in this regard because of the low velocities and energy involved. In the jet regime, however, we observe the entrainment of blobs broken off by Kelvin-Helmholtz instabilities from the nozzle wall into the flow. The cloud regime is also promising. Rayleigh-Taylor instability of the central cavity makes the flow intermittent, and also introduces large chunks of dense cloud gas into the flow. One expects this global instability to be quasi-periodic on the dynamical timescale of the confining gas cloud. This may give both the flow modulations envisioned by Rees (1978) and the obstacles required by Blandford and Königl (1979). Shock-heating of the confining cloud by the violent cavity instability may regulate the system so as to keep it near the jet regime, thus allowing quasi-continuous flow to take place.

The Twin-Exhaust Model may be the primary collimation mechanism for jets in some radio galaxies and quasars (Smith et al. 1983). Also, since nozzles may form on any scale, they may recollimate a flow that was collimated by some other mechanism on smaller length scales, but subsequently decollimated by its passage through the intervening medium. Königl (1982) has applied the Twin-Exhaust Model to bipolar flows, where the energy source is a young star with a

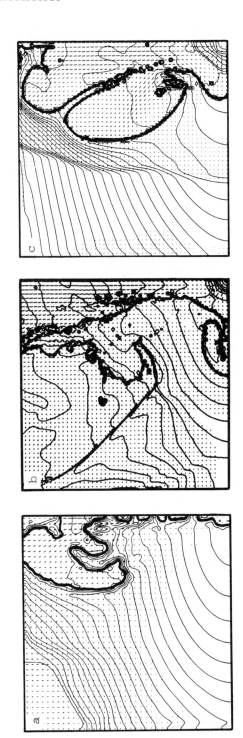

Fig. 2. - The three regimes of bipolar flow in the context of the
Twin-Exhaust Model, as determined by hydrodynamical simulations.
Density contours and velocity vectors are shown for one quadrant of
the system. Axis of symmetry is vertical, equator is horizontal.
Vectors are drawn at every 2nd zone.

strong stellar wind, and the confining agent is a dense molecular cloud. Tapia et al. (1983) suggest that the nozzle mechanism may be responsible for the opposed jets in R Aqr. Narlikar and Subramanian (1983) have proposed a "Single Exhaust Model", which they adapted from the Blandford and Rees model, to explain quasars with one-sided jets. Begelman and Rees (1983) have extended the basic model to a generic situation of an energy source swamped by outside gas, which feeds the central source by accretion. Their so-called Cauldron Model may be applicable to any compact object, regardless of scale, which produces jets fueled by a super-Eddington level of accretion. These examples illustrate the utility of purely fluid dynamical mechanisms for constructing models of related phenomena in a variety of astrophysical settings and on vastly different scales.

III. KNOTS IN TERRESTRIAL JETS

Nearly a century ago, Mach (Ernst) and Salcher (1889) noticed that the supersonic air jet they were using in their investigations of flow past projectiles exhibited a "customary appearance so remarkable that a detailed study of the jet itself seemed worthwhile". To this end, Ernst Mach's son Ludwig began a series of careful experiments that resulted in photographs such as the one reproduced in Figure 3a (Mach 1897). He observed that pressurized air escaping into the atmosphere through an orifice produces a jet which, when properly illuminated, exhibits "uniformly distributed, nearly equidistant luminous knots, whose spacing decreases with the further decrease of the reservoir pressure." When the jet was observed with Schlieren techniques, wherein density gradients in the flow modulate the intensity of the illuminating light, the knots were seen to be embedded in a network of crisscrossing lines (cf. Fig. 3b), which Mach determined were stationary compressive waves (shockwaves).

This pattern of shockwaves is characteristic of supersonic jets emerging from nozzles out of pressure equilibrium with the ambient gas (e.g. Adamson and Nicholls 1959), and is the object of study among experimental aerodynamicists and rocket designers. The shockwaves are responsible for the "beaded" appearance of the plumes of

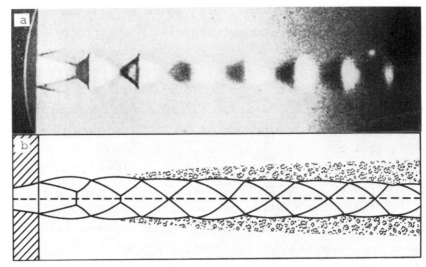

Fig. 3. - Characteristic oscillation of a supersonic airjet exiting a nozzle with greater-than-ambient pressure. a) Schlieren photograph by L. Mach (1897) showing periodic density enhancements (knots). b) Flow schematic showing system of crisscrossing shockwaves and turbulent boundary layer.

Fig. 4. - Optical knots in the supersonic exhaust plume of the rocket plane Bell X-1 (Anderson 1981).

rocket engines, such as shown in Figure 4. Indeed, Wormhoudt and
Yousefian (1982) have shown that patches of luminous emission in the
exhaust plumes of the Space Shuttle main engine are excited by
passage of the chemicallly reactive fuel through these embedded
shockwaves.

One can qualitatively understand the global shock pattern and
the resulting knots as a nonlinear oscillation of a supersonic jet
out of pressure equilibrium with its surroundings. A complete mathematical understanding of the phenomenon is currently lacking, because
of the nonlinearities of the flow, and because of the little attention this problem has received. Modern experimental work since 1941
has been primarily engineering in nature, and has considered only the
structure of the flow adjacent to the nozzle up to and including the
first shock reflection (e.g. Ladenburg et al. 1949; Chang and Chow
1974). In addition, even the most comprehensive studies (e.g. Love et
al. 1959) are limited to dense jets with Mach numbers in the range of
1 to 3. Here we summarize what is known about the local and global
structure of the underexpanded supersonic jet. Potential applications
to astrophysical jets are discussed in Section VI.

Figure 5 shows the flow structure in a supersonic jet exiting a
nozzle with greater-than-ambient pressure. As the high pressure gas

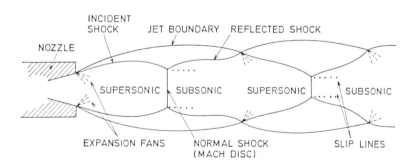

Fig. 5. - Structural details of a highly underexpanded supersonic
jet, adapted from Adamson and Nicholls (1959).

leaves the confining walls of the nozzle, it undergoes a Prandtl-Meyer expansion (cf. Sec. 109, Courant and Friedrichs 1948) to decrease its pressure and match onto the atmospheric pressure. This causes the jet boundary to expand radially and the interior of the jet to rarify to lower-than-ambient pressures. This overexpansion reverses first at the jet boundary; its reconvergence drives the so-called incident shock towards the jet axis, which communicates the external conditons to the interior of the jet. Depending upon the angle of incidence, which in turn depends on the pressure ratio at the nozzle, this shock either reflects at a point on the axis (regular reflection), forming with the reflected shock a biconical structure, or, as depicted in Figure 5, reflects by forming a Mach disk. A Mach disk is a strong shock that forms normal to the flow direction and meets the incident and reflected shocks at a shock triple point. Triple shock intersections generate vorticity in the form of slip lines or surfaces. The reflected shock propagates outward, reversing the motion of radially convergent jet gas. When the reflected shock hits the jet boundary, the cycle is complete, for the gas immediately downstream of the reflected shock and Mach disk (if there is one) is again at higher-than-ambient pressures. The flow is subsonic just behind the Mach disk but accelerates to supersonic velocities in a second Prandtl-Meyer expansion zone. As is evident in Figures 3 and 4, this nonlinear oscillation can repeat itself many times downstream of the nozzle before damping.

The global structure of the jet can be quantified by the oscillation wavelength in units of the mean jet diameter and the number of oscillations before damping or disruption sets in. The first systematic investigation of the global flow pattern was made by Emden (1899), who determined that a simple relation exists between reservoir pressure P, orifice diameter D, and oscillation wavelength W, namely $W/D = 0.89 \sqrt{P-1.9}$, where P is measured in atmospheres. The range of reservoir pressures Emden used in his experiments was $2 < P < 8$ atm. These experiments promted Prandtl (1904) to analyze an ideal axisymmetric supersonic beam for an oscillating mode of linear amplitude, which he found to obey the relation $W/D = 1.307 \sqrt{M^2-1}$, where M is the Mach number of the beam. This relation Prandtl showed

to be consistent with Emden's empirical law for low reservoir pressures and therefore low Mach numbers (i.e., small pressure mismatches
at the nozzle and weak shocks).

However, for higher reservoir pressures and Mach numbers, both
Emden's relation and Prandtl's analysis break down. For example,
Emden's relation predicts a W/D of 3.2 for the P=15 atm. jet in
Figure 3a (Mach 1897), whereas W/D can be measured on the photograph
to be ~1.7. Hartmann and Lazarus (1941) discuss this breakdown,
showing that W/D saturates at roughly 2 due to the formation of
strong shockwaves of the Mach-disk type for reservoir pressures P
$\gtrsim$ 4.5 atm. (M $\gtrsim$ 1.6). Figure 5 shows a supersonic jet in this regime.

No detailed theory yet exists which can predict the spatial
extent of the oscillations, because the damping and disrupting
mechanisms are not well understood. The oscillation is damped by two
dissipative processes related to the network of internal shockwaves.
First, entropy is produced at shocks at the expense of directed
motion. Second, because the shocks are generally nonuniform, vorticity is produced which leads to microturbulence. These two effects
combine and become dominant in highly underexpanded jets (P $\gtrsim$ 20 atm.)
which completely disrupt downstream of the first Mach disk (e.g.
Figure 10 of Ladenburg et al. 1949). For smaller pressure ratios, the
spatial extent of the oscillations is usually limited by the inward
propagation of the turbulent boundary layer at the jet edge, or by
the onset of large-scale nonaxisymmetric motions.

A detailed and comprehensive theory of the underexpanded supersonic jet will be difficult to achieve, for not only are the individual processes just mentioned incompletely understood, but they are
also intimately coupled. Thus, the boundary layer provides an ever-
broadening and time-dependent surface off of which the internal
shocks reflect, whereas the rate of growth of the boundary layer is
effected by the impinging shockwaves. Nevertheless, certain gross
properties of the flow, such as the saturation of the oscillation
wavelength at roughly two jet diameters, are fairly well determined.
We discuss the astrophysical implications of this signature in
Section VI. But first we turn to a summary of our recent numerical
work on pressure-matched jets, where quasi-periodic internal shockwaves show up in different but related guises.

IV. KNOTS IN PRESSURE-MATCHED SUPERSONIC JETS

Many of the jets seen in radio galaxies appear to be pressure confined by the surrounding gas, and a number of these have well developed knots (e.g. Centaurus A, Burns, Feigelson, and Schreier 1983). In the last section we described how systems of shockwaves and knots are excited by the reconfinement of an underexpanded jet. Here we pose the following questions: what is the behavior of a supersonic beam of gas that exits the nozzle with the same pressure as the ambient gas? (This is termed "pressure-matched".) In particular, do internal shocks and knots arise in the absence of gross pressure mismatches between jet and ambient medium? In contrast to the usual laboratory situation, we observe astrophysical jets in the process of boring through the gaseous confining medium. Therefore, in addition to the jet's time-average properties, we are also interested in the transient behavior of the jet as it propagates outwards, and this for a wide variety of beam densities and Mach numbers.These questions have received very little attention experimentally because of the difficulty of producing pressure-mathced jets, particularly those of low enough density and high enough Mach numbers to be relevant to astrophysical jets. Finally, the "far from the nozzle" behavior of supersonic jets has not been addressed in enough detail experimentally; therefore, we summarize here what we have learned on the basis of our ongoing program of numerical simulations. A comprehensive overview of our program and results can be found in Smarr, Norman, and Winkler (1983).

Our physical model, numerical methodology, and some early results were reported in Norman et al. (1982, hereafter Paper I). Since then, we have extended our study to include a wider variety of jets (density ratios and Mach numbers), and these for longer evolutionary times and hence lengths. The propagation and morphology of the new parameter set are described in Norman, Winkler, and Smarr (1983, hereafter Paper II). Distinguishing characteristics of the numerical simulations are their high resolution ($\sim$ 50,000 zones) and the use of a 2-fluid Eulerian hydrodynamics code that allows us to study the detailed behavior of fluid instabilities of the boundary between jet and ambient gas (Norman 1980; Norman and Winkler 1984). This has been decisive for elucidating fluid dynamical mechanisms for the production of knots in pressure-matched supersonic jets.

We find that two qualitatively different mechanisms operate to produce knots in pressure-matched axisymmetric supersonic jets. Both mechanisms create local knots of high pressure by exciting large-scale systems of shockwaves in the supersonic beam. These two mechanisms may operate together, individually, or not at all, depending on the parameters of the jet and its evolutionary age or length. The two parameters are η, the density ratio of the undisturbed beam gas to the undisturbed ambient gas, and M, the Mach number of the beam defined as the ratio of the beam's inflow velocity with respect to the undisturbed gas to its internal sound speed. All calculations were made assuming an ideal gas equation of state for both jet and ambient gas, with the ratio of specific heats in each gas equal to 5/3.

The existence of two distinct mechanisms is the result of a simple morphological trend described in Paper II, which is that the heads of diffuse beams ($\eta < 1$) are embedded in a thick cocoon of backflowing gas which "splashes back" from the advancing head of the jet, whereas all dense beams ($\eta > 1$) are essentially "naked". The dividing line between the two regimes is not sharp, and is indicated only approximately in Figure 6. The boundary's dependence on Mach number reflects a second morphological trend, namely that a high Mach number diffuse beam supports an extensive (in length) cocoon, whereas a low Mach number diffuse beam supports only a lobe in the vicinity of the working surface.

Knots in the cocoon-dominated regime (cf. Fig. 6) are produced behind oblique shockwaves which are excited in the beam by perturbations arising in the cocoon. Perturbations are caused either by Kelvin-Helmholtz instability of the cocoon/ambient gas boundary (see Paper I, Fig. 13a), or by flow dynamics within the cocoon itself (cf. Fig. 7). The dynamics of the working surface of a diffuse jet (i.e., unsteadiness due to the Rayleigh-Taylor instability and vorticity generation at shock triple points) ensures that the cocoon will always dynamically perturb the central supersonic beam. This is illustrated for the case shown in Figure 8.

Figure 8a shows the shock/rarefaction structure of the jet with a flow visualization technique analogous to that described for the kinematic structure plots in Paper II. Large positive and negative

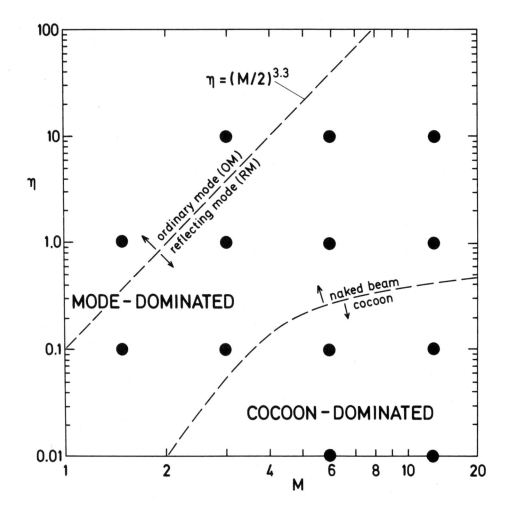

Fig. 6. - Regions in the (η,M) plane showing the dominant causes producing internal shockwaves in pressure-matched supersonic jets, as
determined numerically. Black dots indicate 13 cases computed. Shocks
in diffuse beams (η < 1) are excited by motions in the surrounding
cocoon (cocoon-dominated, cf. Fig. 8). Jets without cocoons (naked
beams) lie above the lower dashed line (approximate), and develop
internal shocks through the nonlinear growth of pinching modes of the
Kelvin-Helmholtz instability (mode-dominated, cf. Fig. 9). Perturbation theory distinguishes between the ordinary mode (OM), and reflecting modes (RM) (Ferrari, Trussoni, and Zaninetti 1981a; Cohn
1983). Cohn's boundary is given by the upper dashed line.

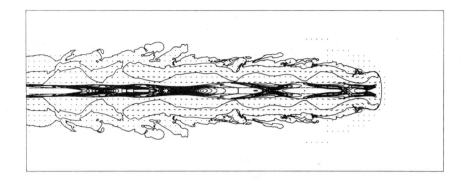

Fig.7. - Contour plot of kinetic luminosity ($\rho v_\parallel^3$) and velocity
vectors in a cocoon-dominated jet (η = 0.01, M = 12), showing how
internal shocks are excited in the beam by flow dynamics in the
cocoon. Vectors are drawn at every 8th zone.

flow divergences $\nabla \cdot v$ identify strong rarefaction and shock waves,
respectively, and are indicated by the light and dark grey regions
within the jet boundary shown in black. Downstream of each shockwave
are produced the high-pressure knots and hotspots shown in Figure 8b.
Pressure values are represented by fifteen shades of grey ranging
between the minimum (black) and maximum (white) pressure in the flow.
In general, the maximum pressure exceeds the ambient pressure by a
factor of M^2.

The dynamic nature of the knots thus produced is shown in Figure
8c. Here, pressure on the axis of the jet is plotted as a function of
space (horizontal axis) and time (vertical axis) for the duration of
the jet's computed evolution. For orientation, the space-time trajec-

Fig. 8. - Shock structure, strength and history of a cocoon-dominated
jet (η=0.01, M=6). a) Composite jet structure showing: shockwaves
(dark grey), rarefaction zones (light grey), jet gas (white),
external gas (dark grey), and contact discontinuity (black). b) Grey
plot of gas pressure where white is maximum and black is minimum.
Note the formation of high-pressure knots behind intersecting shockwaves in beam. c) Grey plot of pressure on the axis of the jet as a
function of space (horizontal axis) and time (vertical axis) records
strength and motion of working surface shock(s) and beam shocks.
P_{max}=92, P_{min}=1.4x10^{-2} (P_{amb}=1).

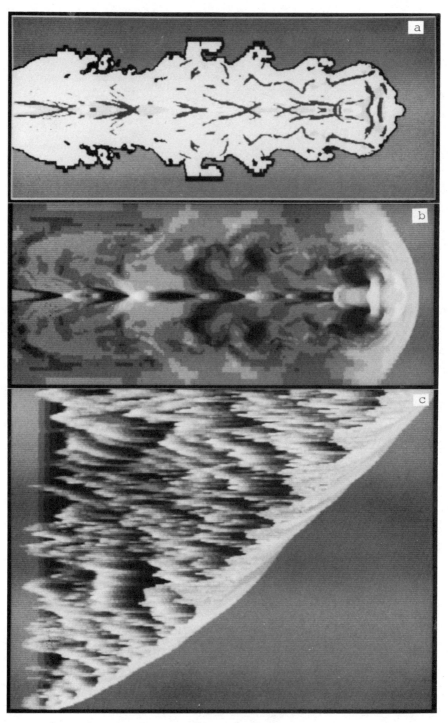

Fig. 8

tory of the head of the jet is from lower left to upper right, and
can be seen to be a decelerating one. Variations in the pressure at
the working surface derive from the previously mentioned unsteadiness
of the contact discontinuity, and produce the negative velocity high-
pressure features (knots) seen moving to the left. Knot velocity is
limited to the cocoon backflow velocity; knot pressure can thereby
exceed the naively drived ram-pressure value $\rho_{beam}v^2_{beam}$ due to the
higher relative velocity between beam gas and shock. The existence
of strong rarefaction waves immediately preceeding the strong shocks
leads to pressure jumps of 3-4 orders of magnitude within the beam.

Knots in cocoon-dominated jets have a rather disordered strength
and distribution history due to the rather chaotic nature of the
driving mechanisms. On the other hand, we find that jets without
cocoons (naked beams) develop knots via the nonlinear growth of
specific modes of the Kelvin-Helmholtz instability of the beam/
ambient gas boundary. These unstable modes then saturate through
shock formation, leading to knots which are ordered in their spacing
and strength. Figure 9 shows an example of a mode-dominated knotty
jet.

We can see from Figures 9a and 9b that this η = 0.1, M = 3 beam
has developed a regularly spaced pattern of alternating shock and
rarefaction waves. The shocks have the characteristic X shape (biconical considering the assumed axisymmetry) encountered in the
oscillation of an underexpanded supersonic jet (cf. Fig. 3b). The
mode's wavelength is approximately twice the mean jet diameter, again
reminiscent of the behavior of laboratory supersonic jets in the
saturation limit (cf. Section III). Notice, however, that in contrast
to the laboratory situation, the shocks are not being excited by a
large pressure imbalance at the inlet, but rather grow in strength as
the flow proceeds downstream. This observation argues that the shocks
are the result of a physical instability which saturates at finite
amplitude. The high-pressure knots behind each shock intersection
bear a remarkable similarity to those in Figure 3 as well, except for
one thing: as Figure 9c shows, this is a propagating mode, whereas
the pattern of shocks and knots in Figure 3 is stationary. As can be
seen in Figure 9c, the pattern velocity is comparable to the velocity
of the head of the jet, which is also comparable to the sound speed

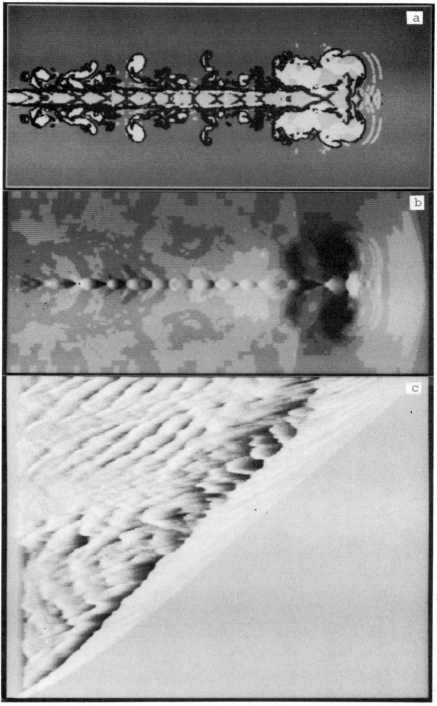

Fig. 9. - Shock structure, strength and history of a mode-dominated jet (η=0.1, M=3). a) Jet structure showing multiple internal shock-waves. b) Grey pressure plot showing periodic high-pressure knots. c) Space-time plot of gas pressure on the axis showing development of ordered mode. P_{max}=7.5, P_{min}=1.5x10^{-2}.

in the external medium. Thus, the amplitude and pattern velocity of the instability seem to be limited by the formation of external shockwaves. What is this propagating mode, and what is its relation to the mode excited in laboratory jets?

To answer this, we studied several "clean cases" - initially homogeneous cylindrical beams with vortex-sheet outer boundaries (i.e., sharp discontinuity). The perturbation theory of Kelvin-Helmholtz instabilities in such beams has recently been developed (Hardee 1979; 1982; 1983; Ferrari, Trussoni, and Zanietti 1978; 1981a; Ray 1981; Cohn 1983), and we hoped to make an identification on this basis. An important discovery by Ferrari et al. (1981a) was that pinching modes come in two varieties: the well-known ordinary mode (OM), which is important at low Mach numbers ($M \lesssim 2$), and an infinite spectrum of so-called reflecting modes (RM), at least one of which is important at any given Mach number $M \gtrsim 2$. Reflecting modes derive their name from the special property of a supersonic shear surface investigated by Miles (1957), which is that for certain angles of incidence, a plane linear wave (sound wave) will be reflected from the surface with a greater amplitude than it had upon incidence. A reflecting mode instability relies on the existence of two supersonic shear surfaces in close proximity, such as in a supersonic beam, between which waves can repeatedly reflect. One can imagine that after enough amplifying reflections, an initial wave of linear amplitude could grow to nonlinear amplitude and disrupt the flow in the beam. Ferrari et al.'s linear analysis showed that the reflecting modes' dominant wavelength is of the order of the beam circumference, independent of Mach number. Cohn (1983), in a similar analysis, emphasized the importance of the RM's for jets of astrophysical interest especially regarding knot formation, and divided the (η,M) plane into OM and RM dominated regimes. Cohn's boundary is redrawn on our parameter space of models in Figure 6.

We computed two clean cases on either side of the boundary with parameters (η = 1, M = 1.5 and 3). Small perturbations were applied at the beam inlet. Results are shown in Figure 10. We see in Figure 10a that perturbations of the Mach 1.5 beam grow to become large-amplitude oscillations of the beam boundary which neck down the flow.

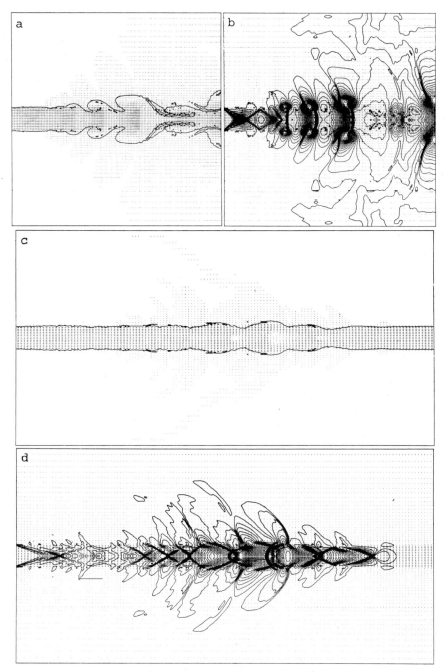

Fig. 10. - Structure of pinch instabilities in the nonlinear regime and their dependence on Mach number. a,b) η=1, M=1.5; c,d) η=1, M=3; a,c) Beam boundary and velocity vectors (drawn at every 3rd zone); b,d) Pressure contours, showing planar shocks in OM regime and bi-conical shocks in RM regime.

Planar shockwaves form just upstream of the pinched regions (Figure 10b). Figure 10c shows that the undulations of the Mach 3 jet's boundary are less severe, and are coupled to the network of criss-crossing (biconical) shockwaves in the beam seen in Figure 10d. The former mode is seen to be more disruptive than the latter for two reasons. First, the large amount of entrainment in the M = 1.5 case decelerates the bulk flow through momentum sharing with the entrained gas. Second, the planar shockwaves standing upstream of the constrictions make the flow locally subsonic, whereas in the M = 3 case the flow remains wholly supersonic. This is because in an oblique shockwave, only the component of velocity normal to the front is rendered subsonic.

Thus, we observe a change in the character of the nonlinear flow which coincides with the change in modal structure as predicted by the linear theory. On this basis, we tentatively identify Figures 10a,b with the nonlinear development of the OM, and Figures 10c,d with the nonlinear development of the first RM. There are also some suggestive similarities between the transverse structures of the modes in both the linear and nonlinear solutions which point to this conclusion. Nevertheless, we feel that additional detailed studies are required in order to substantiate this identification. Therefore, in order to avoid confusion with the linear modes, we shall refer to the nonlinear modes displayed in Figure 10 by the shock structures they produce, i.e., planar (Fig. 10b) and biconical (Fig. 10d).

Returning to Figure 9, we identify the series of biconical shockwaves as qualitatively the same nonlinear mode which manifests itself in Figures 10c and 10d. This is made plausible by noting how near the two cases are in parameter space (cf. Fig. 6), and that the cocoon of the jet in Figure 9a has quite mixed with the ambient gas, leaving the beam naked. At advanced times, the two calculations are therefore quite similar, although the initial conditions were quite different.

We find regularly spaced biconical shocks and high pressure knots in all the cases we computed which lie between Cohn's reflecting mode boundary and our cocoon boundary in Figure 6. We observe that the growth-length scales roughly with the Mach number, yet the

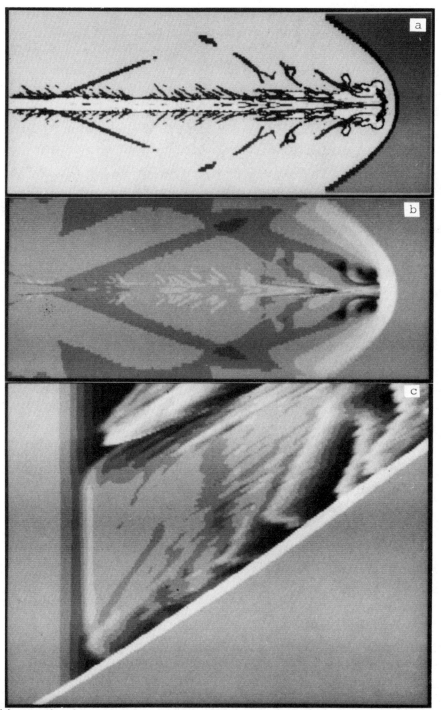

Fig. 11. - Shock structure, strength and history of a quasi-ballistic jet ($\eta=10$, $M=12$). a,b) Note relative absence of internal shocks despite impingement of spurious waves which reflect from boundaries. c) Space-time pressure plot showing that the working surface hotspot is the dominant feature.

wavelength of the mode when fully saturated is rather insensitive to the Mach number (2.3 < W/D < 2.6). This behavior is consistent with the properties of the linear reflecting pinching modes (Ferrari et al. 1981a; Cohn 1983), and further suggests that an intimate relationship exists between the RM and the biconical mode. Again, careful quantitative studies must be undertaken to establish this connection convincingly.

The scaling of growth length with Mach number means that a jet which is shorter than one growth length of the dominant mode will have no large-scale internal shocks and hence no knots (assuming nonaxisymmetric modes do not excite them). An example of this is shown in Figure 11. An examination of the three modes of display reveals very little shock dissipation in the beam until it encounters the working surface shock at the end of the jet. At M = 12, the growth length is at least 24 beam diameters (one round trip of the sound wave across the beam), which is only slightly less than the length of the jet in Figure 11 (35 beam diameters). However, if we continue the evolution to greater lengths (cf. Fig. 12), we indeed find that the biconical mode grows to large amplitude.

The two cases we computed which lie in the ordinary mode regime (cf. Fig. 6) were found to develop the pinching mode displayed in detail in Figures 10a and 10b. The jets were rapidly disrupted

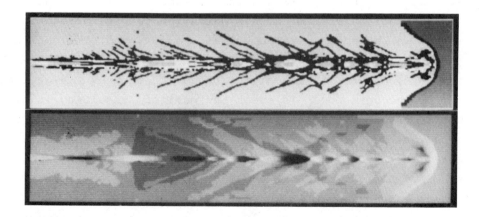

Fig. 12. - a) Development of internal shocks, and b) high-pressure knots due to biconical mode in a high Mach number jet ($\eta = 10$, M=12).

through the entrainment of external gas and the formation of planar
shockwaves, as described above. Therefore, one of the major results
of our numerical investigations is that jets unstable to the planar
shockwave mode cannot propagate supersonically to large distances,
unless they are exceedingly dense and hence essentially ballistic.
On the other hand, jets on the right side of the OM/RM boundary may
have strong internal shocks with very little effect on the jet
transport.

V. KNOTS IN NONAXISYMMETRIC JETS

It has become customary to consider knots and wiggles to be two
independent classes of small-amplitude structures in the general
morphology of astrophysical jets (e.g. Trussoni, Ferrari, and
Zaninetti 1983). This division derives partly from perturbation
theorists' attempts to explain knots and wiggles on the basis of two
independent modes of instability for supersonic beams - the pinching
and helical modes, respectively (e.g. Hardee 1983; Ferrari et al.
1983). The helical mode is but one special case in a general class
of modes involving bends. Likely sources of perturbations which may
excite nonaxisymmetric modes are precession and/or orbital motion of
the jet-producing source, and gradients, inhomogeneities, and cross-
winds in the ambient medium through which the jet is propagating. We
shall show, on the basis of a numerical example, that the nonlinear
development of a bend in a supersonic flow also produces shock-
excited knots, due to kinking at the bends. At a kink, a significant
fraction of the beam power is shock-thermalized, resulting in high-
pressure knots of geometrical character and distribution different
from those produced by the nonlinear biconical pinch instability of
the last section.

We model helical modes in a 3-d cylindrical beam by studying
kinking modes in a 2-d infinite slab. Ferrari et al. (1982) found
that the two systems have entirely analogous instability properties
in the linear regime; a nonlinear comparison will have to await 3-d
numerical simulations. We proceed as with the cylindrical jets,
continuously introducing slab gas at the left in Figure 13a. Again,

pressure balance between the incoming jet and undisturbed medium is assumed. To simulate a helical perturbation, we wiggle the slab at the inlet through ±0.05 radians with a frequency corresponding to half the fundamental wavelength $\lambda_f \equiv 2W\sqrt{M^2-1}$; W is the slab width. Physically, λ_f is the distance downstream from a disturbance which is required for a signal, propagating at the Mach angle $\theta_M = \sin^{-1}(1/M)$ with respect to the slab boundary, to cross the slab, reflect, and return.

The smooth bend becomes a kink in one wavelength (cf. Fig. 13b), exciting shockwaves both inside and outside the slab. The internal shocks are those required to deflect the supersonic flow through a finite angle at the kinks; the external shocks are driven by the supersonic advance of the kinks through the external medium. The latter were first discovered in the numerical calculations of Tajima and Leboeuf (1980) and investigated more recently by Nepveu (1982) and Woodward (1982, 1984). The shocks yield the characteristic alternating pattern in the pressure field shown in Figures 13c,d.

Such behavior in astrophysical jets may have interesting observational consequences. First, the existence of shockwaves in both media may give rise to different sorts of emission (here we should point out that nonlinear pinch instabilities also drive shocks into the external medium, cf. Fig. 10). The knotty nonthermal emission in galactic jets would presumably be excited by the internal shockwaves, while the observed line emission (e.g. Miley 1983) could be excited by the external shockwaves. In stellar jets, shock-excited gas both inside and outside the jet could be contributing to the characteristic emission line spectra observed.

This picture contrasts with Benford's (1981) for the bright knots in the M87 jet, in which he did not consider the internal shocks, but rather suggested that the external "bow shocks" were responsible for in situ particle acceleration and thereby knotty synchrotron emission. Conceivably, both shocks may help in the acceleration process, especially for the highest energy particles, since the shocks are physically so close. However, the relative amounts of synchrotron emission coming from inside and outside the beam depend on the local magnetic field strengths, which may be vastly different and favor the jet interior.

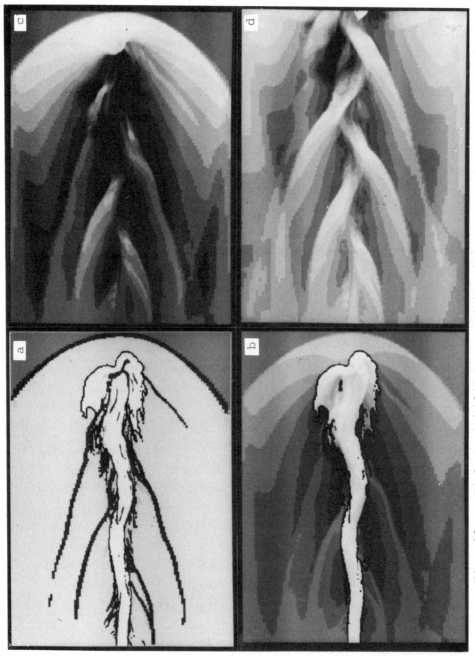

Fig. 13. - Kink instability in a slab-symmetric supersonic jet
($\eta=10$, M=12), excited with a 5% perturbation applied at the inlet:
a) shock structure; b) grey plot of density; c,d) grey plots of
pressure at two evolutionary times, showing the development of
high-pressure features at kinks with characteristic side-to-side
distribution.

As a second observational consequence, kink-related knots may be far apart yet regularly spaced, unlike the pinch-related knots discussed in Section IV. Woodward (1984), in a series of high-resolution numerical simulations of kink instabilities in slabs, has determined that the fundamental odd mode with wavelength $\lambda \approx \lambda_f$ is the fastest-growing odd mode. High Mach number jets would accordingly be expected to produce kinks with a wavelength $\lambda \approx 2MD$.

Finally, in the region where a sinusoidal mode attains nonlinear amplitude, one should see increasingly brighter knots with a more pronounced side-to-side distribution. The fine structure of the knots should be elongated in the direction of the bend, and become increasingly oblique to the jet axis as the kinks reach large amplitude. Thus, knot spacing, lateral distribution, brightness, and fine structure may all be physically related to the underlying flow variables via a simple fluid dynamical model of kinking supersonic beams.

VI. APPLICATIONS AND OUTLOOK

In Section III-V we have described a number of fluid-dynamical mechanisms which induce large-scale systems of shockwaves in supersonic jets. The effect of these embedded shockwaves is to create local regions of high energy density in the flow which would be observed as knots of enhanced emission if these mechanisms were operative in astrophysical jets.

The idea of using shockwaves to excite emission knots is not new; both Rees (1978) and Blandford and Königl (1979) proposed shock models for the knots in the M87 jet (cf. Fig. 1a). However, there is an important qualitative difference between the present mechanisms and these previous theories; namely, that the system of shockwaves and knots produced by mechanisms described herein reflect local properties of the jet flow, and not properties of the jet source as in the time-variability theory of Rees (1978), nor do they reflect the earlier and perhaps far-upstream history of the jet as in the cloud-entrainment model of Blandford and Königl (1979). As such, there is the hope and the possibility that the observed properties of emission knots, such as their spacing, lateral distribution, motion, brightness, and fine structure, may allow us to infer the physical parameters of the underlying flow. This is particularly important in the case of extragalactic jets, where these quantities are especially hard to determine.

The basic approach of attempting to infer flow parameters of radio jets on the basis of observed small-scale morphologies (i.e., knots and wiggles) was perhaps first clearly expressed by Hardee (1979), who interpreted these morphologies with the aid of linear Kelvin-Helmholtz instability analyses of supersonic beams. Recent attempts of this nature are given in Ferrari et al. (1983) and Hardee (1983). The numerical gas-dynamical simulations described herein and in Woodward (1982, 1984) extend this approach and complement the linear analyses by addressing and answering questions that are out-side the realm of perturbation theory, such as determining the dominant mode of instability in a given situation, and characterizing its structural, propagation, saturation, entrainment, and disruption properties in the nonlinear regime. Before considering an astro-physical application of the knot-producing mechanisms described in the previous sections, we summarize the results of our numerical investigations on Kelvin-Helmholtz instabilities in supersonic beams and slabs.

1) Pinching modes in the OM regime (cf. Fig. 6) disrupt the beam when they become nonlinear through extensive entrainment of external gas and the formation of planar shockwaves within the beam normal to its flow direction (cf. Fig. 10a,b).

2) Pinching modes in the RM regime (cf. Fig. 6) saturate by forming large-scale biconical shock systems (cf. Fig. 10d) which have peak strength in the center of the jet. Assuming knot emissivity scales with some positive power of the energy density, center-brightened knots are produced.

3) Biconical shockwaves can be excited at high Mach numbers (cf. Fig. 12), with a spatial growth-length which increases roughly linearly with the Mach number.

4) In a constant or near-constant pressure background, the biconical shockwaves produce quasi-periodic knots with a spacing of 2-3 beam diameters. The knots move with a pattern velocity in excess of the external sound speed, but limited by the advance velocity of the

head of the jet.

5) Knot-interknot and knot-ambient pressure ratios increase with the
   Mach number.

6) Biconical pinching modes are less disruptive than the ordinary
   mode (cf. Fig. 10c), allowing the jet to propagate to large distances assuming it is of high Mach number (cf. Fig. 12).

7) Wiggles growing from linear perturbations in a high Mach number
   jet will be of long wavelength ($\lambda \approx 2MD$, Woodward 1984) and
   spatial growth-length.

8) Wiggles in the nonlinear regime become kinks and excite internal
   and external shockwaves, which could excite knots and diffuse
   emission (cf. Section V).

We reiterate that the relationship between linear reflecting
modes and nonlinear biconical shock systems is not completely understood. Therefore some of our conclusions are partly conjectural, and
provide a framework for further study.

As an application of the knot-producing mechanisms discussed
above, we present an interpretation of the detailed structure of the
radio jet in NGC6251 as mapped with the VLA by Bridle and Perley
(1983), and exhaustively discussed by Perley, Bridle, and Willis
(1984, hereafter PBW). The total intensity contours in Figure 14,
taken from their work, show this object to be prototypical of a
morphological class first addressed by Hardee (1979), and to which
the jets in M87, 3C111, 3C465, 4C32.69 and others seem to belong -
namely, a long straight jet exhibiting well-developed knots close to
the compact source, yet deviating significantly from straightness
only much farther out.

This segregation of the jet into axisymmetric and nonaxisymmetric segments (PBW) is difficult to explain with a simple application
of the perturbation theory of fluid instabilities if one assumes: a)
the ordinary pinching mode is responsible for knots, b) the helical
mode is responsible for wiggles, c) the beam is of constant Mach
number, and d) all modes grow from linear amplitude. The difficulty
is that under these circumstances, the helical mode will always
dominate the pinching mode (ordinary) except for Mach numbers of
about unity (Hardee 1979). Accordingly, a long straight jet without
inner knots would result at high Mach numbers, or a short straight

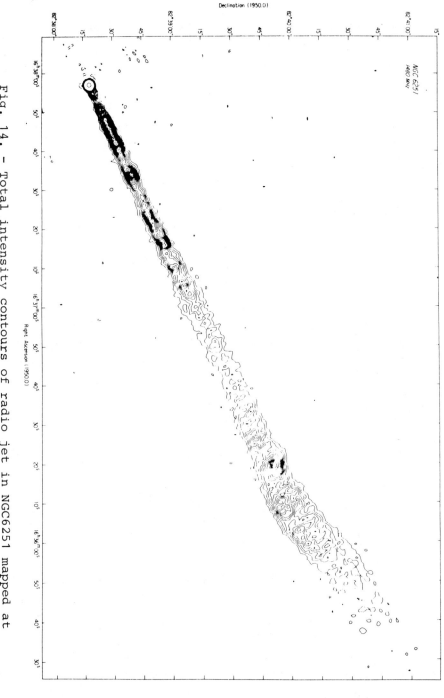

Fig. 14. - Total intensity contours of radio jet in NGC6251 mapped at 1.48 GHz with the VLA (Bridle and Perley 1983), showing a long straight jet with well-developed inner knots and outer wiggles.

jet with inner knots would result at low Mach numbers. Hardee's remedy was to invoke low Mach numbers near the source to allow the pinching mode to dominate, followed by a rapid acceleration to high Mach numbers which would convect the helical perturbation far down the jet before it could grow.

PBW derive a Mach number of order 14 for the innermost 8 kpc (20") of the jet, ruling out such an interpretation. We can also rule out Hardee's interpretation on the grounds that, as we have shown, the OM pinching mode is a disruptive instability. Clearly, what is needed is a pinching mode which is competitive with kinking or helical modes at high Mach numbers, yet one which does not disrupt the flow, and a mechanism for preferentially exciting this mode.

With these considerations in mind, we suggest the following interpretation for the structure of the NGC6251 jet. Pinching modes which saturate as strong biconical shocks are responsible for the inner knots. These pinching modes are excited with nonlinear amplitude via the jet reconfinement mechanism of Sanders (1983). Jet widening and/or mode damping is responsible for the middle fading region (PBW). A kink mode, which grows from a small initial amplitude, is responsible for the outer wiggle ($\theta > 240"$, PBW) and associated emission knots as it grows to finite amplitude. The jet is of constant or slowly increasing Mach number which is large enough ($M > 10$) to allow only a few growth-lengths of the kink mode to fit between the reconfinement shoulder and the outher wiggle. Implicit in our interpretation is that the emission features reflect the underlying flow structure. This is a natural consequence of the shock model, although many details have yet to be worked out.

Jet reconfinement is a natural mechanism for exciting the axisymmetric mode with nonlinear amplitude, which we require to produce the observed segregation of axisymmetric and nonaxisymmetric parts of the jet. As discussed by Sanders (1983), a supersonic jet propagating down a pressure gradient steeper than r^{-2} will come out of pressure equilibrium with its surroundings and eventually become free. Should the free jet encounter a plateau in the ambient pressure which is decreasing less rapidly than r^{-2}, it will be reconfined and generate a convergent shock in an entirely analogous manner to underexpanded laboratory jets. Sanders was able to fit the shape of the reconfinement shoulder in NGC315 with this model, and made the important observation that the position of an emission knot produced by the reconfinement shock would be related to the gross structure of the flow. Significantly, PBW report the existence of a strong emission knot in the NGC6251 jet whose location correlates with the observed position of the reconfinement shoulder as would be expected from the Sanders model.

How can numerical simulations help verify the model proposed above, and what is their role in understanding the physics of astro-physical jets? Numerical simulations can play a role in modeling realistic global flow patterns that cannot be investigated experimen-tally because of unique physical effects and regimes that exist in these jets (e.g. relativistic speeds, pressure and temperature stratifications in the confining gas, extreme Mach numbers and density ratios). Although 3-d simulations with meaningful numerical resolutions are not feasible on current machines, much can be learned through parallel 2-d simulations in axial and slab symmetry. An important test of this approach would be to model the general mor-phology of the NGC6251 jet to see whether a segregation of even and odd modes in a high Mach number slab symmetric "jet" is possible. In axisymmetry, one could try to reproduce its average intensity dis-tribution by building in simple but representative emission models based on shock particle-acceleration theory. If a satisfactory fit could be demonstrated, then it would provide support for both our interpretation of the NGC6251 jet and the utility of this "hybrid" approach.

Aside from detailed modeling, numerical simulation is useful for investigating physical mechanisms. The work described in this paper is an example of this approach. We have attempted to show how numerical simulation can be used to test the range and validity of a proposed mechanism, to elucidate the behavior and effects of a mechanism in the nonlinear and time-dependent regime, to search for systematic behavior in solution space, to act as a bridge between experiment and analytic theory, and to serve as a laboratory for discovering new mechanisms. However, if numerical simulations are really to do these things and address topics of current interest with regard to astrophysical jets such as large-scale bends, vortex dynamics and turbulence, nonaxisymmetric instabilities, and magnetic effects, then 3-dimensional models are needed. This has not been possible up to now because of insufficient computer storage and speed. Next generation supercomputers will begin to allow such an undertaking, and those that are planned for the second half of the 1980's should make high-resolution 3-d modeling a reality.

We would like to thank Reinhard Mundt, Jean-Luc Nieto, Richard Perley, and Santiago Tapia for allowing us to reproduce some of their latest jet observations. We gratefully acknowledge fruitful discussions with Peter Biermann, Reinhard Mundt, Colin Norman, and Norman Zabusky. LS thanks the Alfred P. Sloan Foundation and the National Science Foundation under grants PHY 80-01496 and PHY 83-08826 for partial financial support. LS also wishes to thank the Max-Planck-Institut für Astrophysik for their generous support and hospitality during which part of this work was done.

REFERENCES

Adamson, T.C., and Nicholls, J.A. 1959, J. Aerospace Sci., 26, 16.
Anderson, F.W. 1981, "Orders of Magnitude", NASA SP-4403.
Begelman, M.C., and Rees, M.J. 1983, in "Astrophysical Jets", ed.
     A. Ferrari and A.G. Pacholczyk (Dordrecht:Reidel).
Benford, G. 1981, Ap. J., 247, 792.
Biretta, J.A., Owen, F.N., and Hardee, P.E. 1983, Ap. J. (Letters),
     274, L27.
Blandford, R.D., and Königl, A. 1979, Ap. Letters, 20, 15.
Blandford, R.D., and Ostriker, J.P. 1978, Ap. J. (Letters), 221, L29.
Blandford, R.D., and Rees, M. 1974, M.N.R.A.S., 169, 395.
Bridle, A.H., and Perley, R.A. 1983, in "Astrophysical Jets", ed.
     A. Ferrari and A.G. Pacholczyk (Dordrecht:Reidel).
_____. 1984, Ann. Rev. Astr. Ap. 21, in press.
Brodie, J., Königl, A., and Bowyer, S. 1983, Ap. J., 273, 154.
Burns, J.O., Feigelson, E.D., and Schreier, E.T. 1983, Ap. J., 273,
     128.
Chang, I.-S., and Chow, W.L. 1974, AIAA J., 12, 1079.
Cohn, H. 1983, Ap. J., 266, 73.
Courant, R., and Friedrichs, K.O. 1948, "Supersonic Flow and Shock
     Waves", (New York:Springer).
Dopita, M.A. 1978, Ap. J. Supp., 37, 117.

Emden, R. 1899, Ann. d. Phys. und Chemie, 69, 264.
Ferrari, A., Trussoni, E., and Zaninetti, L. 1978, Astr. Ap., 64, 43.
_____. 1981a, M.N.R.A.S., 196, 1054.
_____. 1981b, in "Optical Jets in Galaxies", ESA SP-162.
_____. 1982, M.N.R.A.S., 198, 1065.
_____. 1983, Astr. Ap., 125, 179.
Fomalont, E.B. 1983, in "Astrophysical Jets", ed. A. Ferrari and
     A.G. Pacholczyk (Dordrecht:Reidel).
Hardee, P.E. 1979, Ap. J., 234, 47.
_____. 1982, Ap. J., 257, 509.
_____. 1983, Ap. J., 269, 94.
Hartmann, J., and Lazarus, F. 1941, Phil. Mag., 31, 35.
Königl, A. 1982, Ap. J., 261, 115.
Ladenburg, R., Van Voorhis, C.C., and Winckler, J. 1949, Phys. Rev.,
     76, 662.
Love, E.S., Grigsby, C.E., Lee, L.P., Woodling, M.J. 1959, NASA
     Technical Report TR-R-6.
Mach E., and Salcher, P. 1889, Wien. Ber., 98, 1303.
Mach, L. 1897, Wien, Ber., 106-II, 1025.
Margon, B. 1982, Science, 215, 247.
Miles, J.W. 1957, J. Acous. Soc. Amer., 29, 226.
Miley, G. 1980, Ann. Rev. Astr. Ap. 18, 165.
Miley, G. 1983, in "Astrophysical Jets", ed. A. Ferrari and A.G.
     Pacholczyk (Dordrecht:Reidel).
Mundt, R. and Fried, J.W. 1983, Ap. J. (Letters), 274, L83.
Narlikar, J.V., and Subramanian, K. 1983, Ap. J., 273, 44.
Nepveu, M. 1982, Astr. Ap. 105, 15.
Nieto, J.-L., and Lelièvre, G. 1982, Astr. Ap., 109 95.
Norman, M.L. 1980, Ph.D. dissertation, University of California at
     Davis; Lawrence Livermore Laboratory Report UCRL-52946.
Norman, M.L., Smarr, L., Wilson, J.R., and Smith, M.D. 1981, Ap. J.,
     247, 52.
Norman, M.L., Smarr, L., Winkler, K.-H.A., and Smith, M.D. 1982,
     Astr. Ap., 113, 285, (Paper I).
Norman, M.L., Winkler, K.-H.A., and Smarr, L. 1983, in "Astrophysical
     Jets" ed. A. Ferrari and A.G. Pacholczyk (Dordrecht:Reidel),
     (Paper II).
Norman, M.L., and Winkler, K.-H.A. 1984, in preparation.
Owen, F.N., Hardee, P.E., and Bignell, R.C. 1980, Ap. J. (Letters),
     239, L11.
Perley, R.A., Bridle, A.H., and Willis, A.G. 1984, Ap, J. Suppl.,
     54, 800, (PBW).
Prandtl, L. 1904, Phys. Zs., 5, 599.
Ray, T.P. 1981, M.N.R.A.S., 196, 195.
_____. 1982, M.N.R.A.S., 198, 617.
Rees. M.J. 1978, M.N.R.A.S., 184, 618.
_____. 1982, in "Extragalactic Radio Sources", Proc. I.A.U.
     Symposium 97, ed. D.S. Heeschen and C.M. Wade (Dordrecht:
     Reidel).
Rees., M.J., Begelman, M.C., and Blandford, R.D. 1981, in "Tenth
     Texas Symposium on Relativistic Astrophysics", ed. R. Ramaty
     and F.C. Jones, Ann. New York Acad. Sci., 375, 254.
Sanders, R.H. 1983, Ap. J., 266, 73.
Smarr, L., Norman, M.L., and Winkler, K.-H.A. 1983, in "Fronts,
     Interfaces, and Patterns", ed. L. Campbell, Physica, in press.

Smith, M.D., Smarr, L., Norman, M.L., and Wilson, J.R. 1981, Nature, 293, 277.
_____, 1983, Ap. J., 264, 432.
Tajima, T., and Leboeuf, J.N. 1980, Phys. Fluids, 23, 884.
Tapia, S., Jacoby, G., Butcher, H.R., Craine, E.R., Stockman, H.S. 1983, Ap. J., submitted.
Trussoni, E., Ferrari, A. and Zaninetti, L. 1983, in "Astrophysical Jets", ed. A. Ferrari and A.G. Pacholczyk (Dordrecht:Reidel).
Woodward, P.R. 1982, Bull. Amer. Astron. Soc., 14, 4, 810.
_____, 1984, in "Astrophysical Radiation Hydrodynamics", ed. K.-H.A. Winkler and M.L. Norman, (Dordrecht:Reidel).
Wormhoudt, J. and Yousefian, V. 1982, Journal of Spacecraft and Rockets, 19, 4, 382.

II. Compact Objects

Magnetofluid Dynamics of Accretion by Neutron Stars

B. Fortner, F. K. Lamb,[1] **and G. Zylstra**
University of Illinois at Urbana-Champaign

ABSTRACT

Most of the bright, pulsing X-ray sources in the Galaxy are strongly magnetic, rotating neutron stars, accreting matter from a binary companion. Some X-ray and gamma-ray burst sources may also be strongly magnetic neutron stars accreting matter from a binary companion or the interstellar medium. This review provides an introduction to the magnetofluid dynamics of accretion by such stars for workers interested in numerical methods. We first describe the basic features that are characteristic of all flows onto strongly magnetic neutron stars and then discuss accretion from a thin disk and spherically symmetric radial accretion in more detail. Finally, we indicate some of the features that make numerical simulations of these flows a challenging problem.

I. INTRODUCTION

The study of accretion by magnetic neutron stars began with the discovery, in the early 1970s, of bright pulsing X-ray sources in the Galaxy (Schreier et al. 1972; Tananbaum et al. 1972) and the interpretation of these as rotating neutron stars (Pringle and Rees 1972; Davidson and Ostriker 1973; Lamb et al. 1973). (Pulsing X-ray sources should not be confused with pulsars, in which the primary energy

---

[1] Also, Department of Astronomy, University of Illinois at Urbana-Champaign.

source, the physical conditions, and the important radiation processes are completely different. A recent report on pulsars may be found in Sieber and Wielebinski 1981.) Research has been further stimulated by the discovery of bursting X-ray sources (Grindlay et al. 1976) and the evidence that at least one of them, the so-called Rapid Burster, is a strongly magnetic neutron star (see Lewin and Joss 1981). Finally, there is mounting evidence that the gamma-ray burst sources are also strongly magnetic neutron stars (see Lamb 1982 and Woosley 1982).

Most of the energy emitted by these stars is in the form of X-rays with energies in the range 0.1–30 keV and is supplied by accretion of matter to the surface of the neutron star. The X-radiation is pulsed if the accretion flow is channeled by a stellar magnetic field that is not axisymmetric about the rotation axis. The brightest X-ray stars have luminosities $\sim 10^{36}$–10^{38} ergs s^{-1}, implying mass accretion rates $\sim 10^{-10}$–10^{-8} $M_\odot$ yr^{-1}. Such large rates require the presence of a companion star to supply matter. Direct evidence for the binary nature of many of these stars comes from observations of periodic eclipses of the X-ray star by its companion, from measurements of the Doppler shift of the spectral lines of the companion star and the pulsation period of the X-ray star, and in some cases from the heating of one face of the companion star by the X-rays. Typical binary periods are $\sim$days.

This review emphasizes the physical conditions characteristic of the pulsing binary X-ray sources, because much less is known about other X-ray stars. The evidence that these are strongly magnetic, accreting neutron stars is compelling. For example, the observed spin-up rates agree quantitatively with models of accretion by such stars, but are several orders of magnitude larger than expected for degenerate dwarfs, while the observed spectra agree qualitatively with models of X-ray production by accreting neutron stars and indicate surface magnetic field strengths as high as 10^{12}–10^{13} gauss. By now there is a substantial body of observational data on pulsing X-ray sources and the magnetic neutron star model has had considerable success in interpreting it (for reviews, see Lamb 1977; Joss and Rappaport 1982).

The strong magnetic field of the neutron star profoundly affects the accretion flow near the star. The large-scale structure of the resulting magnetosphere is important astronomically, because many of the directly observable properties of the pulsing sources, such as their spectra, spin-up rates, and intensity fluctuations, depend on it. It is also a fascinating physical problem that provides a check on our understanding of plasma and magnetospheric physics, since it involves changes of scale by many orders of magnitude from planetary magnetospheres.

The purpose of this review is to provide an introduction to the magnetofluid dynamics of accreting neutron stars for workers interested in numerical methods. None of the flows that we shall describe have yet been simulated, and we suspect that it may not have been possible to do so with the current generation of computers, for reasons that we shall describe. However, it appears likely that one will be able to attempt simulations of these flows with the very much larger computers that will become available during the next few years.

We first discuss the basic features that are characteristic of all flows onto strongly magnetic neutron stars. We then focus on two idealized flows that are, as a result, somewhat more tractable than the general case: accretion from a thin disk, and spherically symmetric radial accretion. Although the latter type of flow surely never occurs in nature, it is close enough to flows that do occur to be interesting, yet simple enough that one can hope to make progress in understanding it. After reviewing the largely analytical work that has been done in trying to gain a basic understanding of these flows, we shall return to why simulations of them are so chal- lenging. In passing, we shall touch on another problem that is important observationally, namely the problem of how the X-rays are actually produced, which depends on the flow near the surface of the neutron star. Our perspective is a personal one, emphasizing the work that has been done at Illinois. More complete reviews of the literature are given by Lamb (1979; 1984) and Vasyliunas (1979).

II. OVERVIEW

Matter can be transferred to the neutron star from its binary companion in at least two ways: by a stellar wind, or by atmospheric overflow (see Fig. 1). In the case of accretion from a wind, some of

the plasma lost by the companion star is drawn toward the neutron
star by the latter's gravity, cools, and is captured. The wind
capture radius is generally smaller than the separation between the
two stars, but larger than the radius of the neutron star's magnetosphere. Plasma captured from a wind has some angular momentum with
respect to the neutron star, but may not have enough to form an
accretion disk. The same is true of plasma that an isolated neutron
star accretes from the interstellar medium.

     In the case of atmospheric overflow, relatively cold plasma
flows slowly over the gravitational saddle point between the two
stars and is immediately captured by the neutron star. Plasma
captured in this way has a large amount of angular momentum with
respect to the neutron star and will form a Keplerian accretion
disk. In such a disk the gravitational attraction of the neutron
star is balanced by centrifugal force, and the plasma spirals slowly
inward as its angular momentum is transported outward by shear
stresses.

     Let us turn first to a discussion of the qualitative features
shared by both types of flows. Both are inflows driven by gravity,
which causes the streamlines to converge on the neutron star.

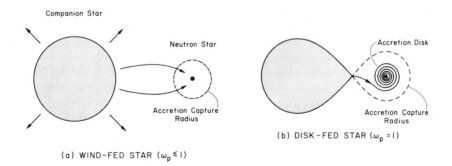

(a) WIND-FED STAR ($\omega_p \lesssim 1$)

(b) DISK-FED STAR ($\omega_p = 1$)

Fig. 1. - Schematic diagram illustrating mass accretion from a
stellar wind and from a Keplerian accretion disk. The dimensionless
number $\omega_p \equiv \Omega(r_m)/\Omega_K(r_m)$ is a useful measure of the dynamical
importance of plasma circulation. Here $\Omega(r_m)$ is the angular velocity
of the plasma at the magnetospheric boundary and $\Omega_K(r_m)$ is the
Keplerian angular velocity there. Rotation is dynamically unimportant for approximately radial accretion flows (those with $\omega_p \ll 1$) but
important for orbital flows (those with $\omega_p \sim 1$). For Keplerian
accretion disks, $\omega_p = 1$.

Because of this convergence, the plasma flow traps the stellar magnetic field and sweeps it inward toward the star. As a result, in the case of Keplerian disk accretion as well as in the case of radial accretion (where it is perhaps more obvious), a magnetic cavity forms around the star (Lamb et al. 1973).

In general, most of the stellar magnetic field lines do not extend outward into the accretion flow, but are confined to the cavity. As a result, the inflowing plasma does not have ready access to the interior of the cavity. This presents a problem from the point of view of understanding how the plasma eventually makes its way to the surface of the neutron star, since in order to get to the surface it must somehow penetrate the cavity (Lamb et al. 1973).

A second feature shared by both types of flows is that the ordinary collisional resistivity is so low that there is negligible cross-field diffusion (Lamb et al. 1973; Elsner and Lamb 1984). The very large rates of mass transport into the magnetosphere that are inferred from observation must therefore be the result of large-scale magnetohydrodynamic processes, and not the result of microscopic processes. One consequence of this is that numerical simulations of these flows appear to be a realistic possibility.

One of the complications that occur in both types of flows is that they are trans-Alfvénic: at large distances from the star the flow is super-Alfvénic in the stellar magnetic field, and yet very close to the star it is extremely sub-Alfvénic (Lamb et al. 1973). The resulting transition in the flow is generally very difficult to handle.

Both types of flows are also potentially affected by rotation. Here there are two angular velocities to consider (Elsner and Lamb 1977). One is the angular velocity of the accreting plasma. In most systems, the angular velocity of the plasma at the magnetospheric boundary appears to be comparable to the Keplerian velocity there (Ghosh and Lamb 1979b). Thus, one usually has to worry about the dynamical effects of plasma circulation. The radial accretion problem, on the other hand, is essentially defined by the assumption that the circulation of the accreting plasma can be neglected.

A second angular velocity is that of the neutron star. In the systems that we know about, the neutron stars appear to run the gamut from those rotating so slowly that the dynamical consequences are quite unimportant to those rotating so fast that the dynamical effects are crucial (Ghosh and Lamb 1979b). In most of the work on radial accretion, the star is assumed to be rotating sufficiently slowly that the dynamical consequences of stellar rotation can be ignored (but see Burnard et al. 1983).

Table 1 lists some of the length scales that are important in X-ray binaries containing a magnetic neutron star while Figure 2 shows some of the basic features of accretion onto such a star. The effect of the stellar magnetic field on the flow becomes important when the kinetic energy density in the poloidal flow (ρv_p^2, where v_p is the poloidal velocity of the flow) becomes less than the magnetic energy density in the poloidal field ($B_p^2/8\pi$). In field-aligned flows, this is the Alfvénic point, inside which the magnetic field can stably control the flow. For the X-ray stars that we are considering, with luminosities $\sim 10^{37}$ ergs s^{-1}, this radius is about 300 times the radius of the neutron star and may be taken as a measure of the extent of the magnetosphere.

TABLE 1.

MACROSCOPIC LENGTHS

Length	Symbol	Typical Value (cm)
Binary separation	a	$\sim 10^{11}\text{-}10^{12}$
Accretion capture radius	r_a	$\sim 10^{10}\text{-}10^{11}$
Magnetospheric (Alfvén) radius*	r_A	$\sim 10^8\text{-}10^9$
Stellar radius	R	$\sim 10^6$

*Assuming an accretion rate of 10^{-9} M$_\odot$ y^{-1} $\sim 10^{17}$ g s^{-1} onto a 1.4 M$_\odot$ neutron star with a dipole moment of 10^{30} gauss cm^{-3}.

Another key aspect of the neutron star accretion problem is the flow of plasma from the magnetospheric boundary to the stellar surface and the resulting production of X-rays. At the surface, the kinetic energy acquired by the accreting plasma in falling into the gravitational potential of the neutron star is converted into heat, and then into radiation (very little is conducted into the star, even when it is cold). The total accretion luminosity is

$$L \approx \dot{M}(GM/R) , \qquad (1)$$

where $\dot{M}$ is the mass accretion rate and M and R are the mass and radius of the star. For a neutron star with an extensive magnetosphere (Alfvén radius $r_A \gg R$), the energy released near the stellar surface completely dominates that released near the magnetospheric boundary.

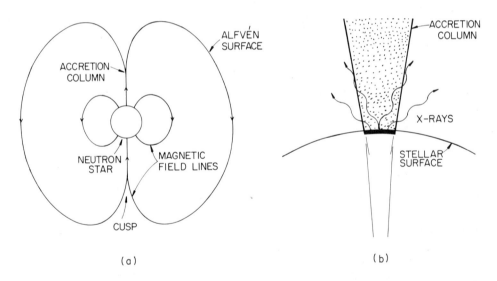

(a)   (b)

Fig. 2.-Idealized picture of some of the basic features of radial accretion by a magnetic neutron star. (a) Overall view of the magnetosphere showing the location of the Alfvén surface, the cusplike configuration of the magnetic field above the magnetic poles, and the two accretion columns. (b) Close-up view of an idealized accretion column near the stellar surface, showing how matter collides with the surface of the neutron star, is shock-heated, and emits X-rays. A more realistic picture would show more complex flows within the magnetosphere, perhaps with many accretion columns. Moreover, the structure of the magnetosphere is much more complex for nonradial accretion flows (see, for example, Fig. 5). (After Lamb et al. 1973.)

Here it is appropriate to mention that Jim Wilson, in collaboration with Marv Alme, just one year after the discovery of pulsing X-ray sources and their interpretation as accreting neutron stars, published a paper that has become a standard one on the emission of radiation from the surface of a neutron star. Building on the work of Zel'dovich and Shakura (1969), Alme and Wilson (1973) calculated the spectrum of X-rays emerging from the surface of a neutron star that is undergoing spherical accretion, when the accreting particles are stopped by collisions with the plasma at the stellar surface.

When the neutron star has a significant magnetic field, one does not expect the flow within the magnetosphere to be spherical, but rather to be channeled onto some small fraction of the stellar surface (Lamb et al. 1973). The canonical picture has been one in which the plasma is focused toward the magnetic poles, in an accretion bundle or bundles, so that the effective radiating area is a small fraction of the surface. The velocities in this flow are very high, so that after the infall is halted the ion temperature is $\sim 10^{12}$ K. In contrast, the radiation temperature is typically much lower, $\sim 10^8$ K. How the very high temperature of the ions gets converted into the much lower temperature of the X-rays that eventually emerge is a very complex problem. We shall return to this question near the end of this review, to discuss some of the difficulties of simulating this conversion.

Many workers have tried to apply models of the geomagnetosphere directly to accreting neutron stars. This approach has its uses but can also be extremely misleading, because there are fundamental differences between the magnetospheres of accreting neutron stars and planetary magnetospheres. These differences have too often been ignored. We shall therefore mention the most important ones here (see also Lamb 1979, 1984).

First, all of the planetary magnetospheres are immersed in a similar environment, namely the solar wind. In contrast, accreting neutron stars are immersed in a wide variety of flows, ranging from nearly radial to Keplerian disk flows, all of which differ dramatically from the solar wind.

A second key difference is that in the planetary magnetospheres gravity plays little or no role, whereas in the neutron star magnetospheres gravity is the dominant force. This is a profound difference, and it has important effects on the gross structure of the magnetosphere.

A third important difference is that the stresses associated with mass transport into the geomagnetosphere are quite small compared to the stresses that determine its size and shape, whereas the dynamical stresses associated with mass transport into neutron star magnetospheres are usually dominant. Very little of the plasma impinging on the geomagnetosphere actually gets inside, so one can estimate the size and shape of its nose, for example, using simple (static) pressure balance. Here, in contrast, all of the impinging plasma penetrates the magnetosphere. Thus, one expects the size and shape of accreting neutron star magnetospheres to be determined by considerations quite different from those that determine the size and shape of the geomagnetosphere.

Finally, we mention two other important differences. As noted earlier, rotation is important in most accreting neutron stars; only in Jupiter is it really important among the planetary magnetospheres. Also, radiation pressure and cooling by radiative processes are very important in accreting neutron stars, but play little or no role in planetary magnetospheres.

III. DISK ACCRETION

Let us turn now to a more detailed discussion of disk accretion. To illustrate the highly dynamical character of the disk-magnetosphere interface, consider the relative sizes of the various stresses, first in the disk and then just inside the magnetosphere (see Table 2). In the disk, the radial ram pressure is quite small, typically $\sim 10^{-4}$ times the thermal pressure. However, the off-diagonal part of the matter stress in the disk is typically comparable to the thermal pressure, while the kinetic energy density in the azimuthal motion is large compared to the thermal pressure. Just inside the magnetosphere, all the dynamical stresses are much larger than the thermal pressure. The size and structure of the magnetosphere is clearly a dynamical problem, not a static one.

In approaching this dynamical problem, one could address the X-ray pulsing behavior by trying to model an oblique rotator, and there have been some attempts to do this. However, two fundamental features make the oblique rotator much more difficult to handle than the aligned rotator. First, the rotation of the star imposes an explicit time dependence on the flow. Second, the oblique rotator has no symmetry, so one is forced to attempt three-dimensional modeling. These difficulties have so far prevented detailed, quantitative calculations of accretion by oblique rotators. In contrast, the aligned rotator allows the possibility of a stationary flow solution and, because the flow is axisymmetric, two-dimensional modeling. For these reasons, we shall restrict ourselves in the following discussion to the aligned case.

In thinking about disk accretion in a general way, there are two kinds of problems that one can formulate. First, one can pose initial value problems, to look at the development of the system from some initial state. Second, one can ask what steady flow solutions might look like under various conditions.

Consider first, as a kind of gedanken experiment, an initial value problem. Let us assume that there is in place around the neutron star a Keplerian disk that excludes the magnetic field of the

TABLE 2.

MATERIAL STRESSES NEAR THE DISK-MAGNETOSPHERE BOUNDARY[*]

Location	Material Stress	Typical Value
Disk	ρv_r^2	$\sim 10^{-4}$ P
"	$\rho v_r v_\phi$	$\sim$ P
"	ρv_ϕ^2	$\sim 10^4$ P
Magnetosphere	ρv_p^2	$\sim 10^3$ P
"	$\rho v_p v_\phi$	$\sim 10^3$ P
"	ρv_ϕ^2	$\sim 10^4$ P

[*] X-ray source parameters are the same as in Table 1. P is the thermal pressure.

star (see Fig. 3). We can then ask: is this a stable configuration
that can persist for a reasonable length of time? One important
measure of time is the interval it takes for plasma to flow onto the
neutron star, which is comparable to the radial drift time in the
disk. There are several reasons why this configuration is unlikely
to persist for such a time (Ghosh and Lamb 1979a).

First, at its inner edge, the disk is Kelvin-Helmholtz unstable.
The modes that are potentially capable of disrupting the disk and
hence having a big effect on the flow are those that have a wavelength comparable to or greater than the thickness of the disk. One
can estimate the growth time of these modes analytically, using the
MHD dispersion relation for this type of system. What one finds is
that the Kelvin-Helmholtz growth times are about 10^{-5} times the
inflow time, so it looks like there is plenty of time for these modes
to grow and disrupt the initially smooth, orderly flow near the inner
edge of the disk before the plasma there can drift inward.

Another effect is turbulent diffusion within the disk (see Fig.
4). This is important where the kinetic energy density of the convective or turbulent motions in the disk exceeds the energy density
of the magnetospheric field just outside the disk. In this region
one expects the external, magnetospheric field to be entrained in the
convective motions and carried into the disk. Once inside the disk
the field can reconnect to itself, and various other complex
processes can occur. If one takes a mixing length approach to this
turbulent diffusion problem and assumes a diffusion coefficient of,
say, a seventh of the turbulent velocity times the size of the

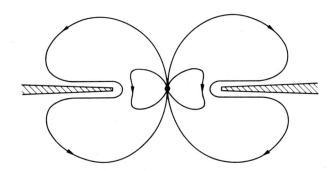

Fig. 3.-Side view of a perfectly diamagnetic accretion disk
surrounding an aligned rotator. Configurations similar to this are
assumed by Aly (1980) and Riffert (1980).

largest eddies, as a rough estimate, then one finds that the turbulent diffusion time is again a very small fraction of the inflow
time. It looks like the magnetic field cannot be excluded from the
disk on the radial drift time scale. One has to confront the fact
that the stellar magnetic field will probably thread the disk plasma.

One consequence of this threading is that the magnetic field of
the star is itself likely to be distorted sufficiently to reconnect.
As a result, magnetic islands will be produced in the disk flow, even
if they weren't there initially. These islands will of course be
modified and distorted by convection and turbulence within the disk,
and by the resulting diffusion.

If there are magnetic fields within the disk, either because
magnetic fields were present in the accreting plasma that formed the
disk or because the magnetospheric field earlier diffused into the
disk, it is energetically favorable for the magnetospheric field to
reconnect to these fields. In the usual reconnection picture, almost

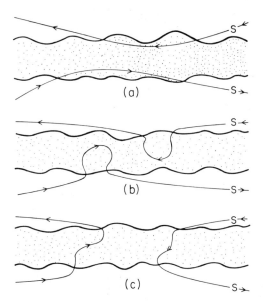

Fig. 4.-Side view of an accretion disk (shaded) being threaded by the
stellar magnetic field (above and below disk) via turbulent diffusion
and reconnection. Field lines that connect to the neutron star are
denoted by the letter S. The stellar magnetic field first diffuses
into the disk (a-b) and then reconnects (c), creating a magnetic
island (left field line) within the disk. Such an island will subsequently be distorted and dissipated by turbulence and convection
within the disk. Later, its orientation could favor further
reconnection to penetrating stellar magnetic field lines.

all of the magnetic flux is conserved, but the topology is radically
changed. As a result, field lines that initially only connected
fluid elements in the disk to one another now connect to the star.
As a further result, the rotation of the star can exert a torque on
the disk plasma. The time scales that we have discussed and their
typical values are listed in Table 3.

In summary, it appears that a disk that excludes the magnetic
field of the central object, even if it could somehow be created
initially, cannot persist for a radial drift time. Given the very
short diffusion and reconnection time scales, it's hard to see how
such a configuration could have arisen in the first place.

Ghosh and Lamb (1978, 1979a,b) went on to ask what type of
steady flow one might expect as a result of these processes. The
basic picture that emerged from their work is shown in Figure 5 and
may be described as follows. The region where the stellar magnetic
field threads the disk constitutes a transition zone between the
unperturbed accretion disk and the magnetosphere. The radial motion
of the disk plasma in this zone generates currents, which confine the
stellar magnetic field inside a screening radius, r_s. The screening

TABLE 3.

IMPORTANT TIME SCALES FOR DISK ACCRETION[*]

Time Scale	Symbol	Typical Value (s)
Radial drift	τ_r	$\sim 10^3$
Keplerian orbit	τ_K	$\sim 10^{-1}$
Kelvin-Helmholtz growth	τ_{KH}	$\sim 10^{-2}$
Turbulent Diffusion	τ_D	~ 1
Magnetic flux reconnection	τ_R	$\sim 10^{-1}$

[*]Just outside the disk-magnetosphere boundary. X-ray source
parameters are the same as in Table 1. For more complete
discussions, see Ghosh and Lamb (1978, 1979a).

radius is generally much larger than the radius, r_{co}, inside which the plasma is forced to corotate with the star. The transition zone divides naturally into two parts, an outer part, where the angular velocity is Keplerian, and an inner part, where it departs significantly from the Keplerian value. The boundary between these two parts defines the radius r_0.

The <u>inner transition zone</u> between r_{co} and r_0 behaves like a boundary layer, in that the flow velocity and magnetic field change there on the length scale $\delta_0 \ll r_0$. In this zone the angular velocity of the plasma is reduced from the Keplerian value to the corotational value by the magnetic stress, and circulating currents screen the magnetospheric field, typically by a factor ~5. The inner transition zone or boundary layer is also the region where the magnetic stress disrupts the disk and the plasma begins to fall toward the star along field lines.

The broad <u>outer transition zone</u> between r_0 and r_s has a structure very similar to that of an unperturbed disk except that the

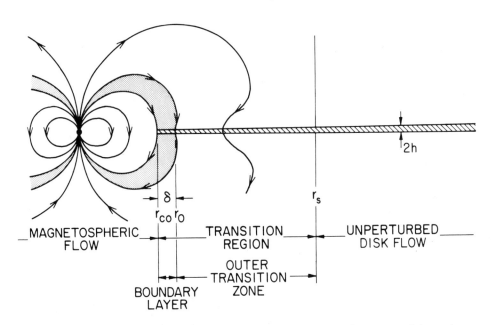

Fig. 5.-Side view of an accretion disk surrounding an aligned rotator, illustrating the character of the flow solutions obtained by Ghosh and Lamb (1978, 1979a,b).

magnetic stress associated with the twisted stellar field lines
transports angular momentum between the disk and the star, while the
viscous dissipation of energy associated with the velocity shear is
augmented by the resistive dissipation of energy associated with the
cross-field motion of the plasma.

IV. RADIAL ACCRETION

Consider now the second type of idealized flow that we introduced above, namely spherically symmetric radial accretion. Since
the radius of the magnetosphere is typically much smaller than the
accretion capture radius but much larger than the stellar radius,
processes that occur near the magnetospheric boundary can usually be
treated separately from the capture process and processes at the
stellar surface. An exception is cooling. If there is little or no
accretion to the stellar surface, plasma near but outside the
magnetosphere cools predominantly by electron-ion bremsstrahlung. If
instead there is a substantial flow of plasma to the stellar surface,
the resulting X-rays rapidly cool the electrons in this plasma by the
inverse Compton process. The electrons then cool the ions by
collisional energy exchange. Whereas the bremsstrahlung cooling time
is longer than the free-fall time to the stellar surface, the cooling
time for electrons and ions exposed to X-rays is typically shorter
than the free-fall time, and hence plasma accreting to the stellar
surface cools as it falls. For electrons moving in the magnetospheric field, the cyclotron cooling time is shorter still, while ion
cyclotron cooling becomes important near the stellar surface. As a
result of cooling, neither the electrons nor the ions mirror in the
magnetosphere. The most important time scales and their typical
values are listed in Table 4.

Here again one can ask what one can learn from initial value
problems, on the one hand, and from trying to model steady flows, on
the other. When plasma first approaches the star, it cannot penetrate the magnetospheric cavity, and hence does not reach the stellar
surface to produce large amounts of radiation (Elsner and Lamb 1976,
1977). Consequently, Compton cooling is initially unimportant, and
the cooling time scale at the magnetospheric boundary is therefore
much longer than the dynamical time scale there. There is plenty of

time for the magnetosphere to settle down and achieve dynamical equilibrium before the plasma cools (Elsner and Lamb 1977).

This is clearly illustrated by preliminary results from a one-dimensional Lagrangian code that has been used at Illinois to simulate this type of flow. Figure 6a shows the behavior of the radii of various shells of accreting plasma as a function of time. The region below the curve labeled "1" represents the volume occupied by the magnetosphere. Initially the infalling plasma compresses the magnetosphere, since at first it is not very rigid. However, as the compression proceeds the magnetosphere becomes increasingly rigid, until finally it bounces. At this point the magnetic pressure has become large enough to turn the flow around, and a shock wave forms and moves off. In some of the simulations, the magnetosphere oscillates several times before settling down.

Figure 6b shows the temperature of the accreting plasma as a function of radius, at different times. As noted above, once the magnetosphere starts to rebound, a shock develops in the plasma just outside the magnetopause. The infalling plasma is highly supersonic,

TABLE 4.

IMPORTANT TIME SCALES FOR RADIAL ACCRETION[*]

Time Scale	Symbol	Typical Value (s)
Bremsstrahlung cooling (X-rays off)	τ_{br}	~ 1
Compton cooling (X-rays on)	τ_c	$\sim 10^{-3} - 10^{-1}$
Electron-ion energy exchange	τ_{e-i}	$\sim 10^{-1}$
Free-fall (dynamical)	τ_{ff}	$\sim 10^{-1}$

[*]At the magnetospheric boundary. X-ray source parameters are the same as in Table 1. For more complete discussions, see Arons and Lea (1976a, Elsner 1976), and Elsner and Lamb (1977, 1984).

so the shock is very strong, and the shocked plasma is very hot
($\sim 10^9$ K). Because the cooling time is longer than the dynamical
time, hot plasma piles up between the shock front and the
magnetosphere. This continues until something else happens.

During this equilibrium phase one can solve for the equilibrium
shape (see Arons and Lea 1976a; Elsner and Lamb 1977; Michel
1977a,b). At this time the accreted plasma is separated from the
interior of the magnetosphere by a thin current layer, which may be
treated as a tangential discontinuity. Here we shall refer to this
layer as the magnetopause, following the terminology used for the
thin current layer at the nose of the geomagnetosphere. (For non-
radial accretion flows, and even for radial flows in which plasma is
actually flowing into the magnetosphere, the existence of a thin
current layer analogous to the magnetopause of the geomagnetosphere
is doubtful; see, for example, Fig. 5.) In static equilibrium, the
shape of the magnetopause is given by pressure balance across it,

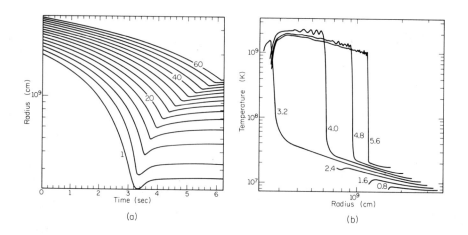

(a)   (b)

Fig. 6(a).-Simulation of spherically symmetric radial accretion by a
magnetic neutron star. The curves show the trajectories of
representative mass shells. X-ray source parameters are the same as
in Table 1. The magnetosphere rebounds at $\sim$ 3.2 s, causing a shock
wave to form and propagate outward through the infalling plasma.
(b) Temperature profiles at a succession of times, for the same flow
as in (a). Each profile is labeled by the time (in seconds) from the
start of the inflow. Note the accumulation of hot plasma between the
shock front and the magnetosphere.

i.e.,

$$(B^2/8\pi)_{in} = P_{out} \approx (\rho k_B T/m_i)_{out} \quad . \qquad (2)$$

Here B is the magnetospheric field, P_{out} is the plasma thermal pressure outside the magnetosphere, ρ and T are the density and temperature of the accreted plasma, and m_i is the ion mass.

Eventually the accreted plasma cools. One possibility is that the magnetopause becomes Rayleigh-Taylor unstable. The condition for marginal stability is (Elsner and Lamb 1977)

$$g_{eff} \equiv g_\perp - \kappa B_{in}^2/4\pi\rho_{out} = 0 \quad . \qquad (3)$$

Here $g_\perp$ is the acceleration of gravity normal to the magnetopause, κ is the curvature of the magnetic field lines at the magnetopause, B_{in} is the magnetic field just inside the magnetopause, and ρ_{out} is the density just outside the magnetopause. Using the equilibrium condition (2), the marginal stability condition (3) may be rewritten as

$$k_B T_{out} = k_B T_{crit} \equiv m_i g_\perp/2\kappa \quad . \qquad (4)$$

Initially, T_{out} exceeds T_{crit} and the magnetopause is stable. As the accreted plasma cools, T_{out} falls whereas $g_\perp$ and κ are little changed. When T_{out} reaches T_{crit}, the magnetopause becomes unstable and the accreted plasma falls toward the stellar surface on the dynamical time scale. Once appreciable plasma reaches the surface, X-rays are produced and cooling becomes much more rapid.

Although there is general agreement on the conditions under which the magnetopause is unstable, there is less agreement on the scale of the modes that are most important for transporting plasma into the magnetosphere. Lamb (1975) and Elsner (1976) have emphasized the importance of relatively long-wavelength modes (see Fig. 7) whereas Arons and Lea (1976b, 1980) have argued that only short-wavelength modes can exist (see Fig. 8). The longest possible wavelengths are favored both because their growth tends to saturate less quickly than that of shorter wavelengths, and because there are numerous effects, including rotation, viscosity, and magnetic shear, that preferentially stabilize the shorter-wavelength modes. If the most important modes do have relatively long wavelengths, tangential pressure gradients and inertial stresses may distort the shape of the outer magnetosphere, and the transition zone (here defined as the region that contains screening currents and in which the magnetic field transfers momentum to the inflowing plasma through $\underset{\sim}{j} \times \underset{\sim}{B}$ forces) could broaden to become an appreciable fraction of the magnetopause radius, r_m. Large sheets or filaments of plasma may fall in, distributing plasma over a larger fraction of the stellar surface.

Michel (1977c) has drawn attention to the possible importance of stagnant plasma above the polar cusps when there is an extensive plasma atmosphere outside the magnetosphere. He has emphasized that the bremsstrahlung cooling time for plasma above the cusps is shorter than that for plasma above the equator of the magnetosphere, which he argues will cause a steep pressure gradient in the plasma above the cusps accompanied by a much flatter pressure gradient in the plasma above the magnetic equator. If the pressure variation above the cusps were to become steeper than r^{-6} and to remain sufficiently localized in magnetic latitude, the magnetopause in the cusps would

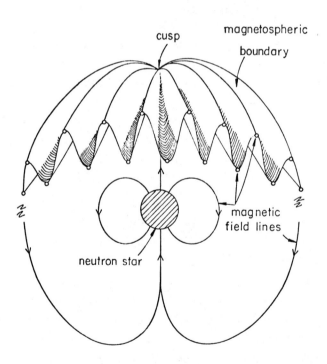

Fig. 7.–Illustration of the growth of relatively long-wavelength Rayleigh-Taylor unstable modes (from Lamb 1975 and Elsner 1976).

remain stable while descending to the stellar surface, carrying the stagnant plasma with it. The latter would be possible because the magnetopause is more stable above the cusp axis than at any other

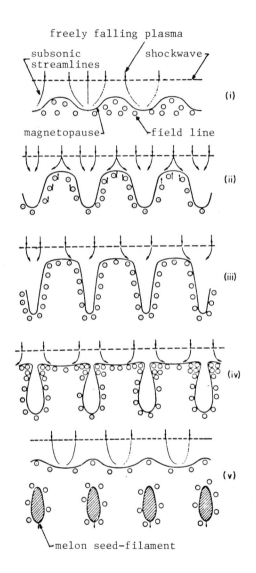

freely falling plasma

subsonic
streamlines   shockwave

(i)

magnetopause   field line

(ii)

(iii)

(iv)

(v)

melon seed-filament

Fig. 8.-Illustration of the growth of relatively short-wavelength Rayleigh-Taylor unstable modes. From Arons and Lea (1976a).

point. Michel suggests that, rather than causing a steady flow, this process would cause plasma to "drip" down the polar axes.

Elsner and Lamb (1984) have recently shown that descent of the cusps cannot be the dominant entry process if the star has a persistent luminosity greater than L_{crit} $\sim 10^{36}$ ergs s^{-1} and, as in the presently known pulsing sources, a substantial fraction of the magnetopause is illuminated. The basic reason is that for $L \gg L_{crit}$, plasma at the magnetopause is cooled by Compton cooling to a temperature below the critical temperature for Rayleigh-Taylor instability in a time much shorter than the free-fall time there. As a result, the equatorial magnetopause becomes unstable before the cusps can descend and before plasma has time to flow from the magnetic equatorial region to the cusps. Descent of the cusps may be a significant entry process for lower luminosities or strongly anisotropic illumination.

Consider now what happens if Rayleigh-Taylor unstable inflow continues. Is a quasi-steady flow possible? Such a flow obviously cannot be truly stationary, because the only way the plasma can get into the magnetosphere is by continuing instability of the boundary, which will result in large-scale fluctuations in its position. Approximate analytical treatments assuming a stationary flow between the shock wave and the magnetopause have been developed by Arons and Lea (1976a) and Elsner (1976).

When there is plasma flow into the magnetosphere, the structure of the magnetosphere is necessarily more complex than that of the static equilibrium models used in the stability analyses discussed above. Although the flow boundary conditions at the transition zone used by Arons and Lea and Elsner are plausible, a completely satisfactory treatment has not yet been given. Some of the difficulties may be seen by considering the relation that replaces equation (2), which is no longer valid. Even assuming that the transition zone remains thin compared to r_m, and that the magnetic field in the accreting plasma can be neglected, momentum balance across the transition zone implies (Elsner and Lamb 1977)

$$(B^2/8\pi)_{in} + P_{in} + (\rho v_n^2)_{in} = P_{out} + (\rho v_n^2)_{out} , \qquad (5)$$

where ρv_n^2 is the dynamic pressure of the plasma in terms of its velocity component v_n normal to the transition zone. The flow boundary conditions used by Elsner and by Arons and Lea are based on the dispersion relation for a static atmosphere outside the magnetosphere. A necessary condition for the curvature of the field lines at the transition zone to remain unchanged is that P_{in}, $(\rho v_n^2)_{in}$, and $(\rho v_n^2)_{out}$ all be negligible compared to P_{out}. Since the cooling length is relatively large, $P_{in} \ll P_{out}$ requires $\rho_{in} \ll \rho_{out}$ and hence $v_{in} \gg v_{out}$. But the assumed boundary conditions give $(\rho v_n^2)_{out}$ only a little smaller than P_{out}, while the ratio of $(\rho v_n^2)_{in}$ to $(\rho v_n^2)_{out}$ is v_{in}/v_{out}. Thus, it is not clear that this necessary condition can be satisfied. The flow boundary conditions assumed by these authors also neglect the deformation of the magnetospheric boundary by the development of the instability itself.

V. COMPUTATIONAL CHALLENGES

Let us briefly describe why these problems are challenging from the point of view of numerical simulation. Although there are many

similarities between the two types of flows we have discussed, there
are also some fundamental differences. In the case of accretion from
a thin disk, for example, one must model the flow in two dimensions
for it to bear any resemblance to the true flow, and it may turn out
that one actually has to go to three dimensions to obtain a realistic
model. One of the real bug-a-bears is that the radial drift time is
$\sim 10^4$ times the dynamical or orbital time, so one has a very wide,
two-time-scale problem. It's also important to model the Kelvin-
Helmholtz instability at the disk-magnetospheric boundary. Other
complications include the fact that the flow is both trans-sonic and
trans-Alfvénic in the region of interest. Also, the boundary layer
at the inner edge of the disk appears to be very narrow, which forces
one to consider two very different radial length scales. Finally, it
looks like some treatment of reconnection is crucial.

In the case of radial accretion, one-dimensional simulations can
address some questions. However, one needs at least two dimensions
in order to describe the shape of the magnetosphere. This is also a
two-time-scale problem, because the cooling time is initially much
longer than the dynamical time at the magnetospheric boundary.
However, once the magnetosphere goes unstable this difficulty
temporarily goes away, since the inflow then proceeds on the
dynamical time scale. The two-time-scale nature of the problem reap-
pears when significant quantities of matter reach the stellar surface
and liberate cooling X-rays, resulting in a cooling time much shorter
than the dynamical time at the magnetospheric boundary. One also has
to model the development of the Rayleigh-Taylor instability, because
it determines the sizes of the sheets or filaments that fall into the
magnetosphere and the time-development and distribution of the mass
inflow. This flow is also both trans-sonic and trans-Alfvénic.
Because the Compton cooling time is much shorter than the free-fall
time at the magnetospheric boundary, the layer of plasma between the
boundary and the shock front is quite narrow. This layer has to be
modeled carefully in terms of the coupling between the electrons,
ions, and radiation.

Finally, let us return briefly to the accretion flow near the
stellar surface (for a recent review, see Meszaros 1982). It also is
a very challenging, multi-dimensional simulation problem. The
fundamental physics of this problem is complicated by the fact that

the magnetic field is strong enough to require a quantum electro-
dynamical treatment of the electron motion, while in some cases the
energies of both ions and electrons are such that their relativistic
gamma factors are of order unity. In this regime, neither nonrelativistic nor ultrarelativistic approximations can normally be
used. There are also very large radiation stresses that have to be
taken into account. Furthermore, the opacities are highly energy-
and angle-dependent, which makes the radiation transport problem
extremely complicated.

Numerical as well as analytical work on all three problems is
currently underway at Illinois.

VI. CONCLUDING REMARKS

Much could be learned from detailed simulations of the flows we
have been considering that would help to develop better analytical
approximations and a better understanding of what is going on. None
have so far been carried out, owing to their complexity. However,
with the more powerful computers that are now becoming available
realistic simulations of these flows should be possible, and we
therefore look forward with excitement to the developments of the
next few years.

This research was supported in part by NSF Grant PHY80-25605 and
NASA Grant NSG 7653.

REFERENCES

Alme, M. L., and Wilson, J. R. 1973, Ap. J., **186**, 1015.

Aly, J. J. 1980, Astr. Ap., **86**, 192.

Arons, J., and Lea, S. M. 1976a, Ap. J., **207**, 914.

_____. 1976b, Ap. J., **210**, 792.

_____. 1980, Ap. J., **235**, 1016.

Burnard, D. J., Lea, S. M., and Arons, J. 1983, Ap. J., **266**, 175.

Davidson, K., and Ostriker, J. P. 1973, Ap. J., **179**, 585.

Elsner, R. F. 1976, Ph.D. thesis, University of Illinois at Urbana-
     Champaign.

Elsner, R. F., and Lamb, F. K. 1976, Nature, **262**, 356.

_____. 1977, Ap. J., **215**, 897.

_____. 1984, Ap. J., in press.

Ghosh, P., and Lamb, F. K. 1978, Ap. J. (Letters), **223**, L83.

_____. 1979a, Ap. J., **232**, 259.

_____. 1979b, Ap. J., **234**, 296.

Grindlay, J., Gursky, H., Schnopper, H., Parsignault, D. R., Heise, J., Brinkman, A. C., and Schrijver, J. 1976, Ap. J. (Letters), **205**, L127.

Joss, P. C., and Rappaport, S. A. 1982, preprint, scheduled to appear in Ann. Rev. Astr. Ap., **22** (1984).

Lamb, D. Q. 1982, in Gamma Ray Transients and Related Astrophysical Phenomena, Proc. AIP Conference No. 77, ed. R. E. Lingenfelter, H. S. Hudson, and D. M. Worrall (New York: AIP), p. 249.

Lamb, F. K., Pethick, C. J., and Pines, D. 1973, Ap. J., **184**, 271.

Lamb, F. K. 1975, in Proc. 7th Texas Symposium on Relativistic Astrophysics (Ann. N.Y. Acad. Sci., **262**, 312).

_____. 1977, in Proc. 8th Texas Symposium on Relativistic Astrophysics (Ann. N.Y. Acad. Sci., **302**, 482).

_____. 1979, in Magnetosphere Boundary Layers, Proc. Sydney Chapman Conference in Alpbach, Austria, June 11-15, 1979, ed. B. Battrick (ESA, SP-148 Addendum), p. 1.

_____. 1984, in High Energy Transients in Astrophysics, ed. S. E. Woosley (AIP Conf. Proc. No. 115), p. 179.

Lewin, W. H. G., and Joss, P. C. 1981, Space Sci. Rev., **28**, 3.

Meszaros, P. in Accreting Neutron Stars, Proc. Workshop held in Munich, July 19-23, 1982, ed. W. Brinkmann and J. Trumper (Max-Planck Institut, Garching bei München), p. 253.

Michel, F. C. 1977a, Ap. J., **213**, 836.

_____. 1977b, Ap. J., **214**, 261.

_____. 1977c, Ap. J., **216**, 838.

Pringle, J. E., and Rees, M. J. 1972, Astr. Ap., **21**, 1.

Riffert, H. 1980, Ap. Space Sci., **71**, 195.

Schreier, E., Levinson, R., Gursky, H., Kellogg, E., Tananbaum, H., and Giacconi, R. 1972, Ap. J. (Letters), **172**, L79.

Sieber, W., and Wielebinski, R. 1981, ed., Pulsars, Proc. IAU Symp. No. 95 (Dordrecht:Reidel).

Tananbaum, H., Gursky, H., Kellogg, E. M., Levinson, R., Schreier, E., and Giacconi, R. 1972, Ap. J. (Letters), **174**, L143.

Vasyliunas, V. M. 1979, Space Sci. Rev., **24**, 609.

Woosley, S. E. 1982, in Gamma Ray Transients and Related
    Astrophysical Phenomena, Proc. AIP Conference No. 77, ed. R.
    E. Lingenfelter, H. S. Hudson, and D. M. Worrall (New
    York:AIP), p. 273.

Zel'dovich, Ya. B., and Shakura, N. I. 1969, Astron. Zh., **46**, 225
    (Transl. Soviet Astr. - AJ, **13**, 175, 1969).

The Thermonuclear Model for High Energy Transients

S. E. Woosley

University of California, Santa Cruz

Lawrence Livermore National Laboratory

ABSTRACT

For a broad range of accretion rates the matter that accumulates on the surface of a neutron star will ignite thermonuclear burning in an unstable manner leading to a brief episode of hard radiation. Without a strong magnetic field the observed event is an X-ray burst or transient; with a strong field (B $\sim 10^{12}$ gauss) a γ-ray burst results.

I. INTRODUCTION

The thermonuclear model for X- and γ-ray transient events has been recently reviewed in a number of publications (cf. Woosley 1982 a,b; Woosley and Wallace 1982, and references therein) as well as in the extensive literature dealing with Type I X-ray bursts (cf. Ayasli and Joss 1982; Taam 1982; Fujimoto, Hanawa, and Miyaji 1981; Hanawa and Sugimoto 1982; and Joss and Rappaport 1984). Here I will present only a brief overview of certain well studied aspects of this model and will concentrate instead on a few outstanding problems currently under study, especially with regard to the production of γ-ray bursts.

Thermonuclear flashes are expected to occur in the atmospheres of neutron stars that are accreting matter at rates in the range 10^{-14} $M_\odot$ yr^{-1} to 10^{-8} $M_\odot$ yr^{-1}. The upper end of this range is relevant to a neutron star that is in a close binary system while the lower values might be achieved in a detached binary or even by a solitary neutron star in a dense phase of the interstellar medium (Hameury et al. 1982). The upper bound is set by that accretion rate for which the steady accretion luminosity exceeds the peak luminosity produced in a nuclear flash. Since higher accretion rates imply higher burning temperatures, decreased degeneracy, and smaller critical masses, the bolometric energy of a flash decreases at higher accretion rates (adding to its invisibility) as does the interval between flashes. Eventually steady continuous burning occurs. As has been emphasized by Joss (eg. 1978, although see also Woosley and Taam 1976 and Taam and Picklum 1978), this explains why X- and γ-ray bursts are not seen from strong "classical" X-ray sources or high luminosity X-ray pulsars (but see also Section III of this paper). The lower bound on accretion rate that gives nuclear instability is more difficult to estimate, but corresponds to that value for which both hydrogen and helium (and perhaps carbon as well) burn stably to heavy elements by reactions that are insensitive to temperature (so called "pycnonuclear" reactions; Lamb and Lamb 1978, Ruderman 1982, and Hameury et al. 1982).

It is especially important to note that these accretion rates correspond to the simple case where matter (and temperature) are distributed uniformly over the spherical surface of the neutron star. In the case of magnetically focused accretion, appropriate, for example, to X-ray pulsars, the relevant accretion rate scales inversely as the fraction of surface area experiencing the mass flow, i.e., accretion at 10^{-12} $M_\odot$ yr^{-1} on 0.1% of the surface resembles locally accretion at 10^{-9} $M_\odot$ yr^{-1} over the entire surface. The correspondence is not identical, however, because the temperature distribution of the atmosphere does not scale as a simple geometry factor. If burning transpires only on 0.1% of the surface, energy can flow laterally from the accreting/burning region and be radiated from the rest of the surface, a process for which there is no one-dimensional analogue. This implies an uncertainty in the boundary temperature one adopts in a γ-ray burst model (Woosley 1982b) that can only be addressed with

multi-dimensional calculations. Difficult too is the question of how
far the material accumulated from accretion will spread before igniting a nuclear runaway. Woosley and Wallace (1982) present arguments
that this spreading distance is short, on the order of a kilometer or
so, but their estimate depends critically upon a very uncertain shear
modulus for the neutron star atmosphere.

     Within this range of unstable accretion rates, a variety of nuc-
lear processes may participate in the runaway. On the high end
(roughly 3×10^{-10} to 10^{-8} $M_\odot$ yr^{-1}, with exact values sensitive to
mass, radius, metallicity and thermal history of the neutron star),
hydrogen burns stably by the β-limited CNO-cycle at a rate strictly
proportional to the abundance of CNO-nuclei and independent of the
temperature (Wallace and Woosley 1981). As the base of the hydrogen
burning shell is pushed ever deeper, a density is reached where helium
burning by the 3α-reaction is ignited (Taam and Picklum 1979). This
not only raises the temperature but also makes more CNO-catalyst for
hydrogen burning and the runaway accelerates. Eventually most of the
hydrogen and helium fuel in the atmosphere is burned to ^{56}Ni by the rp-
process (Wallace and Woosley 1981) with the liberation of 5×10^{18}
erg g^{-1}. This energy factor and the critical mass involved, $\sim 10^{21}$ g,
imply transient outburst near the Eddington limit having duration $\lesssim$
1 min.

     For somewhat lower accretion rates ($\sim 5 \times 10^{-11}$ to 3×10^{-10} $M_\odot$
yr^{-1}), hydrogen burning is still β-limited (i.e., $T > 7 \times 10^7$ K) but
hydrogen is depleted at the base of the burning shell before the critical density required for helium burning is reached. Thus a separate
helium shell exists and, when helium finally does ignite, it does so
in the absence of hydrogen (Taam 1981; Fugimoto, Hanawa, and Miraji
1981). Because the lower accretion rates correspond to lower steady
state burning temperatures, quite a substantial layer of helium may
accumulate. This gives more energy and, since the luminosity in the
absence of strong magnetic fields or large scale mass motion is
Eddington limited, a transient event of longer duration. Calculations
(Joss 1977; Lamb and Lamb 1978; Taam 1982; Wallace, Woosley, and
Weaver 1982) show that transient events ranging from a few minutes to
a few hours should be a common result.

     For still lower accretion rates hydrogen burning is not β-limited
and may itself become unstable. Few reliable calculations exist in

this range (Fugimoto, Hanawa, and Miyaji 1981) because the results
are quite sensitive to an uncertain temperature boundary condition
that depends upon the thermal history of the neutron star and the
occurrence of previous flashes. For quite low temperatures, $T \lesssim 5$
x 10^6 K, which in the simplest steady state case corresponds to the
lowest accretion rates, hydrogen reaches the critical density for
electron capture (1.45 x 10^7 g cm^{-3}) before igniting. Then the burning of hydrogen by the reaction sequence $p(e^-,\nu)n(p,\gamma)^2H(p,\gamma)^3He(^3He,$
$2p)^4He$ raises the temperature sufficiently that the CNO-cycle is ignited, eventually becoming β-limited. Finally continued burning
ignites helium burning and a violent runaway ensues ($T_{peak} \sim 4$ x 10^9 K).
This type of transient has been discussed by Hameury et al. (1982)
and recently calculated for neutron stars of varying radius by Woosley
and Weaver (1982; see also Woosley 1982b). First all of the helium
burns out of the atmosphere. This takes less than 0.1 s. The combustion to ^{56}Ni in the roughly 10^{23} g atmosphere yields $\sim 10^{41}$ erg and
generates a convective zone reaching to the surface of the star. As
helium burning dies out the convective zone recedes and the temperature at the base of the hydrogen layer (now hydrogen and ^{56}Ni with no
helium or CNO-catalyst) begins to rise slowly as hydrogen burns by the
weak interaction. The product of this burning is also ^{56}Ni but yields
about 5 times the specific energy. An X-ray transient having duration
of several hours ensues. The slow rise to maximum (Eddington or near
Eddington) luminosity, the long thermal tail as the explosively heated
atmosphere cools, and the possibility of a hard precursor as the helium
convective zone breaks through the surface (still to be demonstrated
in the calculations) are all characteristics of the class of "rapid X-
ray transients" (cf. Hoffman et al. 1978).

II. CURRENT PROBLEMS IN THE MODELING OF TYPE I X-RAY BURSTS

The success of the thermonuclear model in explaining many of the
observed properties of Type I X-ray bursts has been reviewed extensively in the literature (cf. Lewin and Joss 1982). The existence of
sources, such as the rapid burster, for which both the energy liberated from accretion and the energy in thermonuclear flashes can be
measured and the inferred proportionality factor, ~ 100 as expected
from the relative efficiency of the two processes, offers compelling

evidence that thermonuclear flashes do in fact occur. Moreover, the similarities among Type I bursts from many sources, especially their long thermal "tails" which presumably come from explosively heated plasma cooling on the surface of the neutron star, suggest that thermonuclear flashes are a common phenomenon.

A number of outstanding difficulties still confront the thermonuclear model for X-ray bursts, however. These have been recently summarized by Lewin (1982) and Woosley (1982b). Two deserve special mention: (1) the observation of a number of X-ray bursts in which the peak luminosity substantially exceeds the Eddington limit (by a factor perhaps as great as 10 depending upon very uncertain distance estimates) for a stellar mass of ~ 1 $M_\odot$ (Grindlay et al. 1980; Inoue et al. 1980, Grindlay and Hertz 1981, Hoshi 1981) and (2) observations of several X-ray flashes, seemingly Type I, with an interval between two bursts far too brief to have accommodated the accretion of a critical mass (Murakami et al. 1980, Oda and Tanaka 1981, Oda 1982). In the latter case the ratio of accretion luminosity to burst luminosity averaged over a pair of bursts may be smaller than unity as opposed to a value more typically 100 for thermonuclear flashes.

Joss and Li (1980) have pointed out that super-Eddington luminosities can occur in the presence of a strong magnetic field owing to the reduction in electron scattering opacity (Tsuruta et al. 1972). If so, one might expect the field ($\sim 10^{12}$ gauss is required for a substantial modification) to have other important effects on both the accretion to critical mass and the spectrum (see Section IV), not the least of which would be a cyclotron opacity some 10^4 times the ordinary electron scattering opacity used in all calculations to date (Lamb 1982)! I prefer to relate the super-Eddington luminosities (if, in fact, the distances are well enough known that there are super-Eddington luminosities) to the radiatively driven mass loss that would occur in such situations (Woosley 1982b; Wallace, Woosley, and Weaver 1982). With a photospheric density $\sim 10^{-6}$ g cm^{-3}, as is typical when there is mass loss, $\rho v_{esc}^2 \sim 10^{14}$ erg cm^{-3}. This momentum flux could be balanced by a magnetic "pressure", $B^2/8\pi$, with B of only $\sim 10^8$ gauss. Thus even a relatively weak field, far weaker, for example, than that required to alter the opacity significantly, could impede the flow of plasma somewhere interior to the photospheric radius that

one calculates in the absence of a field and give rise to super-
Eddington luminosities. Alternatively, the mass loss may not be radially symmetric but may be characterized by large scale mass overturn,
in which case the advective luminosity (actually the "convective"
luminosity) could be considerably super-Eddington. The cyclotron
opacity (cf. Lamb 1982) may play an extremely important role here by
giving an opacity that increases radially outwards (due to Doppler
broadening in the radiatively accelerated plasma). Dramatic effects
may occur in the velocity gradient of the ejecta even for fields commonly regarded as quite weak ($\gtrsim 10^{10}$ gauss (see Lamb 1982, Kylafis
et al. 1980). Multi-dimensional calculations of radiation transport
in the presence of mass loss and magnetic fields are clearly indicated

Recurrence intervals as short as 8 min have been reported for
two bursts from Terzan 5 (Oda 1982) and several other sources. Ostensibly both bursts are Type I bursts having remarkably similar mutual
properties. If the second of these bursts is not thermonuclear then
one must worry about the first as well and, indeed, ascribing any X-
ray flash to a thermonuclear runaway. If we are to have faith in the
thermonuclear model then we must understand the nature of these rapid
recurrences.[1] The most likely explanation is that the first of the
two flashes does not consume all of the fuel so that a reservoir remains to power the second flash. Because hydrogen burns by a weak
interaction, it is not difficult to arrange the burst model so that
substantial unburned hydrogen remains at the end of the explosion (cf.
Ayasli and Joss 1982). The amount of residual hydrogen is enhanced
by high accretion rates (hence smaller critical masses and less violent explosions) and by lower metallicity (so that a smaller proportion of hydrogen burns hydrostatically before the runaway commences).
Unfortunately hydrogen, by itself, is not particularly explosive.
The same inefficient weak interaction that preserves the hydrogen also
makes it refractory. Helium is the explosive fuel, but helium is depleted at the base of the accreted shell during the (first) explosion.

---

[1] In principle, it is possible to understand all X-ray bursts as
a consequence of accretion instabilities. The "thermal tails" characterizing Type I events could just be the manifestation of a trail-
ing off of the accretion following a rapid dumping. But then one
would lose the nice explanation for the ratio of accretion to burst
luminosities inferred from a number of sources.

New helium can be generated by burning residual hydrogen, but the
time scale for doing so is quite long since the CNO-catalyst necessary for the transformation is also consumed during the explosion.
Some CNO may be created by helium burning during the cool down phase,
~ 1% by mass at most, but this gives a characteristic time scale for
hydrogen burning by the β-limited cycle of at least 10^4 - 10^5 s
(Wallace and Woosley 1981), far too long to explain an 8 min recurrence.

Two other possibilities, both under current investigation, may
offer a way out of this dilemma. Both require that helium fuel be
preserved from the first event and both take advantage of the explosion geometry to do so. In the first case we realize that sub-
stabtial helium may remain, especially for models with high accretion
rates, in the layers above the base of the exploding shell. Following the explosion there exists a gradient of helium abundance approaching the original initial value near the surface. If this layer
could be suddenly mixed, explosive burning might be rekindled. This
may actually occur because, following the first explosion, there exists an inverted profile of mean atomic mass number, i.e., there is a
greater abundance of hydrogen at the base of the burned-out region
than there is further out in the envelope. This inverted profile is
a consequence of burning by the rp-process which is less efficient at
consuming hydrogen at higher temperatures (at the highest temperature
the rp-process burns only helium; Wallace and Woosley 1981). This
configuration may, and in preliminary calculations I have done does,
become Rayleigh-Taylor unstable with the consequent overturn bringing
new fuel to the base of the shell. Whether this overturn occurs on
the right time scale and, especially, whether or not it provides sufficient energy to explain the observational results remain to be determined. Alternatively one may seek to accelerate the burning of
residual hydrogen by pushing the shell all the way down to the density
required for electron capture. But then one wonders why one of the
bursts is not a very long one.

If all else fails, one may have to consider the multi-dimensional
nature of the burning front (Fryxell and Woosley 1982), in particular
the possibility that expansion of the ashes of a localized thermonuclear runaway may cool and quench the outburst before lateral propagation has ignited all the fuel (Shara 1982). A slight magnetic
field at the base of the burning region could inhibit electron conduction, making Shara's "volcanoes" a more likely occurrence.

III.   X-PERSEUS: A γ-RAY BURST IN THE MAKING?

There exists a class of low luminosity X-ray pulsars, of which X-Per is an extreme but certainly not unique example (White 1982, Rappaport 1982), that exhibit pulsed emission and a steady luminosity many orders of magnitude smaller than that of strong X-ray pulsars such as Cen X-3. The observed steady X-ray flux from X-Per, $\sim 4 \times 10^{33}$ erg s^{-1}, implies an accretion rate of only $\sim 5 \times 10^{-13}$ M$_\odot$ yr^{-1}. Because the emission is pulsed the accretion must be focused upon a fraction of the surface area, presumably by a strong magnetic field $\sim 10^{12}$ gauss being a typical value inferred from cyclotron resonance measurements in other X-ray pulsars. However, the pulsed emission in X-Per is noticeably less structured and energy dependent than in the higher L_x systems, which is indicative of material not being as well collimated onto the magnetic pole (White 1982). This is theoretically understood as a consequence of the low accretion rate (Arons and Lea 1976, 1980). Generally one takes a fractional area 0.1% for the "hot spot" in bright X-ray pulsars (eg. Ghosh and Lamb 1979), but apparently for X-Per a larger fraction, say 1% to 10%, is more appropriate. If so, the accretion rate per unit area in X-Per is the same as for a neutron star undergoing spherical accretion at a rate $\sim 5 \times 10^{-12}$ to 5×10^{-11} M$_\odot$ yr^{-1}. The important point is that this range of accretion rates (per unit area) is known to give nuclear instability (see Section I). Past investigators have been correct in stating that luminous X-ray pulsars are not likely to burst, an accretion rate of $> 10^{-11}$ M$_\odot$ yr^{-1} focused on only 0.1% of the area guaranteeing such high burning temperatures that nuclear instability is suppressed, but that simply is not the case for X-Per (and 4U1145-62 and presumably many other sources in our Galaxy). It is inevitable that this object is going to produce a high energy transient of some sort someday. The questions, of course, are "When?" and "What kind?"

Estimating the recurrence time is difficult, especially without better knowledge of the accretion area and the thermal state of X-Per (although, in principle, both could be measured and calculated). Limits can be set, however. Because the accretion rate is quite low and because of the possibility of cooling by conduction to the larger area of the neutron star that is not experiencing accretion, it seems most reasonable to assume that the transient will be initiated by the ignition of hydrogen at the electron capture threshold. Other assumptions would give shorter recurrence intervals and less energetic outbursts. For reasonable neutron star parameters (1.41 $M_\odot$, 8.32 km radius), this implies a critical mass of $\sim 10^{21}$ (F/.01) g where "F" is the fraction of the surface area experiencing a-cretion (and neglecting spreading). For the inferred accretion rate this critical mass would accumulate roughly every year (times F/.01). When it occurs the explosion will liberate $\sim 5 \times 10^{18}$ erg g^{-1} (for complete combustion of a Population I set of abundances to ^{56}Ni), implying a transient event with bolometric energy 5×10^{39} erg (times F/0.01).

What will this event look like? If the common paradigm is correct, it will not be a Type I X-ray burst. Such events are believed to involve weak magnetic fields and an explosion that occurs all over the surface of the neutron star with no magnetic confinement. I claim that this event will be a γ-ray burst (Woosley and Wallace 1982; Woosley 1982a,b). Whatever it is, it will certainly involve the interaction of explosively heated plasma with a strong magnetic field, and that interaction is likely to be very complex.

IV.   THE γ-RAY BURST SPECTRUM

As discussed elsewhere (Woosley and Wallace 1982; Woosley 1982a, b), the spectrum of a γ-ray burst should involve both thermal and non-thermal components. For any reasonable distribution of matter on the surface of the neutron star, the explosion will always begin at a magnetic pole where the layer is thicker and the temperature higher. The principal result of <u>any</u> explosion then, at least during its initial stages, will be to push explosively heated plasma (T ~ 1 to 4×10^9 K) above the surface of the neutron star in a locality where the field lines are oriented perpendicular to the surface. What follows depends critically upon the nature of magnetic instabilities. If the field is strong enough to confine the plasma, then a column of hot material stands above the surface in near hydrostatic equilibrium radiating copiously from its sides, much as in the case of supercritical accretion of an X-ray pulsar. Unlike a pulsar, however, energy is being deposited from beneath, not from above, and a greatly super-Eddington radiation flux (per unit area) is driving mass up open field lines and away from the neutron star. The loss of radiation from the sides of the plasma column leads to a steep temperature gradient between plasma just above and just below the surface, so steep in fact that the subsurface layer is likely to become convective. If so (and while this effect remains to be demonstrated in the models, it seems inevitable), then the bulk of the explosion energy can be transported to the surface and emitted in a very short time. The time scale is set by the efficiency of cooling from the sides of the plasma column, since convection may, in principle, transport energy on a time scale approaching the sonic time ($\sim 10^{-4}$s).

Cooling from the sides of the column will be much more efficient than the Eddington limit for gravitationally confined plasma ($T_{eff} \sim$ 2 keV). The sides are supported against gravity by radiation pressure. If they are not efficiently heated by energy transported from the interior of the column, then they will fall to the surface revealing hotter layers beneath (Woosley and Wallace 1982). Unpublished 2-dimensional calculations by J. R. Wilson, Bob Barton and myself at Livermore suggest an effective emission temperature $\sim$ 10 keV (with substantial variation about that value as one moves up and down the column) and a luminosity $\sim 10^{31}$ erg s^{-1} (cm of column circumference)$^{-1}$ or, for a radius of 1 km, about 10^{37} erg s^{-1}. These numbers are in fact lower bounds to the actual values, since no energy transport from beneath the surface was allowed and magnetic instabilities were neglected. The calculations should also be redone including the effect of cyclotron opacity.

Perhaps more interesting (and more realistic) is the case where the magnetic field is not adequate to confine the plasma efficiently above the surface and keep it from continually spreading over a considerably larger fraction ($\sim$ km) of the neutron star. Some such spreading will certainly occur by the interchange instability and will lead to expansion and cooling. Consequently, plasma below the surface experiences not only a diminished surface boundary temperature (promoting convection) but also a decreased surface boundary pressure. As a result, more plasma rises up above the surface, expands and cools, decreases in pressure, allowing still more plasma to rise up, and so forth.   In this manner, most of the explosion energy can be extracted in a time limited only by the rate at which magnetic instabilities allow the plasma to expand.   The time scale for these instabilities is difficult even to guess.   A frequently quoted lower bound is 10 to 100 times the Alfvén crossing time (Petschek 1964, Petschek and Thorne 1967), or for dimensions ~ 1 km and field strengths $\sim 10^{12}$ gauss, ~ 0.01 s; but unlike the solar case to which Petschek's mechanism is immediately applicable, the field lines on a neutron star remain rigidly anchored within the surface.   Thus the interchange instability may be inhibited and our estimate of time scale an extreme lower bound.   As plasma pushes through the magnetic field, the energy stored in the form of magnetic stress will be converted into heat. Alfvén waves, or nonthermal particle acceleration or perhaps all three. A definitive calculation may be long in the making, but we note in passing that the energy in Alfven waves alone may be adequate to power a γ-ray burst.[2]   The critical question is where the waves damp.

Consider now the effect the decreased surface pressure has on the base of the burning region.   Owing to its high temperature and large pressure scale height this material wishes to rise up to the surface.   At the same time adjacent unburned material experiences the same pressure as before (or slightly greater as the ashes of the burning region spill over on top).   Thus unburned fuel from adjacent regions (or iron if the extremity of the accreted fuel has been reached) will tend to flow beneath the burning region, buoying it up and leading to even further expansion above the surface.   The new fuel will burn eventually, but its ignition may be delayed as one awaits the propagation of a diffusion or deflagration wave (Fryxell and Woosley 1982) through a region where electron conductivity is impeded by a strong magnetic field.   A similar phenomenon has been qualitatively explored for white dwarfs by Shara (1982) with the conclusion that the nuclear runaway may actually go out, at least temporarily.   Shara calls these occurrences "volcanoes" and it is tempting to make an

---

[2] The energy flux is $j \sim (\delta B^2/8\pi) \, V_A$ or, for $\delta B \sim 1\% \, B$ and $V_A \sim 10^9$ cm s^{-1}, $j \sim 10^{38}$ erg s^{-1} km^{-2}.

association with this irregularity in the nuclear burning and the
irregular temporal structure seen in many γ-ray bursts (eg., March 9,
1979) which seemingly "turn off" for periods ranging from several
seconds to a fraction of a minute. This delay may be related to the
time scale for conduction to the base of the accreted layer which,
for a layer 30 m thick having density at the base several times 10^6 g
cm^{-3}, is roughly one minute. Still shorter temporal structure may
result from bulk oscillations of the magnetically confined plasma itself. With an Alfven velocity $\sim 10^9$ cm s^{-1} and typical dimensions
~ 1 km such oscillations can give coherent temporal structure down to
the level 0.1 ms.

So far we have not discussed the production of radiation harder
than that from a keV black body of perhaps 10 keV or so. This, by
itself, is obviously inadequate to explain the full spectrum of most
γ-ray bursts. There are two principal modes by which the thermonuclear model may produce hard radiation (although see also Colgate
and Petschek, this volume). The first employs the efficient acceleration of electrons to relativistic velocity by the magnetic instabilities inherent in the laterally expanding plasma column described above.
The hard component would then be the result of synchrotron radiation
(cf. Liang 1981). Most of the column is itself quite optically thick
and the acceleration and emission would have to occur in a low density
region outside the photosphere. Magnetic recombination seems the most
likely mechanism, although realistic calculations relating the model
to the nonthermal acceleration are totally lacking.

A second site for the production of hard radiation is in the
plasma driven up the open field lines by the super-Eddington luminosity at the base of the column (see also Woosley 1982a) and heated by
Alfvén waves. Numerical calculations (Wallace, Woosley, and Weaver
1982) show that a substantial fraction of the total explosion energy,
perhaps more than half, goes into driving this mass loss, and we estimated earlier a large energy flux in Alfvén waves. In an explosion
having radial symmetry, the mass current driven by a radiation flux
twice the Eddington value, i.e., $L \sim 3 \times 10^{38}$ $M_\odot$ erg s^{-1}, will be comparable to the accretion flux for an Eddington-limited accretor. For
a 1.4 $M_\odot$ neutron star having radius 10 km this mass flux is $\sim 10^{18}$ g
s^{-1}, or in more appropriate units, $\sim 10^5$ g cm^{-2} s^{-1} averaged over the

surface. For explosions exceeding the Eddington value be a substantial margin, this mass flux may be approximately scaled by the
super-Eddington factor. In general, at least in the one-dimensional
models calculated so far, the flux at the base of the atmosphere ad-
justs (on a dynamical timescale) so as to be nearly Eddington.

If one adds a strong magnetic field, the nature of this radiatively accelerated plasma becomes quite unusual. The energy of
electrons perpendicular to magnetic lines of force B $\sim 10^{12}$ gauss) is
very small owing to extremely efficient cyclotron energy losses
($\sim 10^{-14}$ s being a typical cooling time; Lamb 1982). Most electrons,
in fact, are in their quantum mechanical ground state, $1/2 h\omega$, or about
6 keV at 10^{12} gauss. Thus, perpendicular to field lines, the
"temperature" is very cold. On the other hand, plasma is streaming
along field lines with very high velocity. Taking a super-Eddington
factor of 2 as representative, the outward acceleration due to radiation pressure is approximately equal to the local acceleration due to
gravity, or $\sim 2 \times 10^{14}$ cm s^{-2}. Thus escape velocity, $\sim 10^{10}$ cm s^{-1}, is
achieved in $\sim 5 \times 10^{-5}$ s. This acceleration transpires over a distance,
$1/2$ at^2, or ~ 3 km. At that radius the mass current, $\rho v \sim 10^5$ $(10^6$ cm/
r)^3 g cm^{-2} s^{-1}, is still roughly equal to its surface value; thus
$\rho \sim 10^{-5}$ g cm^{-3}. This implies a mean free path to electron scattering
(Thomson) of several kilometers, comparable to the radius of the
plasma column itself. Thus escape velocity is achieved just as the
plasma column is becoming optically thin. A larger super-Eddington
factor would result in escape velocity being achieved while the plasma
is still optically thick. A large cyclotron opacity has a similar
effect, although it can only be experienced by hard photons on macroscopic dimensions (see below). A very large cyclotron opacity spread
out in frequency by Doppler broadening might even block the flow of
radiation to the extent that convection occurs in the vicinity of the
"photosphere".

Consider now the environment experienced by a photon during the
last dozen or so optical depths that it remains trapped within the
column. The large streaming velocity of the plasma is accompanied
by a comparable velocity dispersion owing to the inefficient communication of momentum across field lines by any means other than
radiation and a spatially incoherent input of energy at the base by
convection and Alfvén waves. This dispersion may be even greater if

Rayleigh-Taylor instability develops owing to a radially increasing (Doppler broadened) cyclotron opacity. Then there would be
plasma falling back along field lines adjacent to plasma streaming
out from the surface. Either way, radiation that is initially trapped within one magnetic flux tube experiences a large velocity shear
as it diffuses to an adjacent flux tube. This is more easily visual-
ized by considering a frame moving outwards with the mean radial
velocity of the radiation. In this frame a light ray is batted about,
both up and down, as it diffuses through regions of variable velocity.
Several hundred such scatterings will pump a low energy (cyclotron?)
photon of some 10 keV up to an energy of several hundred keV. Pump-
ing ~ keV photons from the expansion-degraded radiation field would
take only a little longer. A large cyclotron opacity (cf. Lamb 1982)
aids in this process. Within each coherently moving flux tube the
cyclotron width is very narrow (although very intense), but as the
photon diffuses a substantial distance (say ~ 10 m) varying velocities
are encountered that amount to a Doppler broadening of the cyclotron
resonance. Each photon seeks an electron with its (Doppler-shifted)
cyclotron line tuned to the photon energy and, because the cyclotron
opacity, even Doppler broadened by 10%, exceeds ordinary electron
scattering opacity by ~ 10^4, it readily finds one. The overall process is much akin to the Fermi mechanism for cosmic ray acceleration.
The effective "temperature" of the Comptonized distribution, if equipartition is achieved, should be comparable to the escape velocity of
the neutron star, i.e., ~100 - 200 keV

    At still higher photon energies electron-positron pairs will be
produced, first by the γ-γ interaction (for E_γ > 511 keV) and ultimately by the interaction of photons with the magnetic field and ions
(for E_γ > 1 MeV). The effective Eddington luminosity for pairs is
smaller by a factor 1836 (positron/proton mass ratio) than the
Eddington luminosity for ordinary matter. Since the local opacity
is, almost by definition, equal to some substantial fraction of this
latter value, any pairs are quickly accelerated to relativistic velocity along the field lines. Eventual annihilation in the beam (blue-
shifted) contributes to the very hard emission, E_γ >> 1 MeV, seen in
some γ-ray bursts (Rees 1982).

Thus the complete γ-ray burst spectrum is composed of contributions from (1) thermal and nonthermal emission from near the base of the confined plasma column and from its sides (∼ 10-100 keV); (2) inverse Compton scattering in the radiatively accelerated "wind" (∼ 100-500 keV); and (3) pair annihilation within a relativistic beam (> 1 MeV). Additional components may also come from (4) cyclotron absorption, (5) magnetic instabilities at the base of the plasma column, and (6) electrons accelerated by Alfvén and magnetosonic waves.

Many calculations and much model building need to be done to verify some of the more ambitious of these claims (eg., acceleration by inverse Compton scattering resulting from velocity shear) and to delineate the relative importance of the several possible mechanisms for producing hard radiation. Also required is a much better understanding of the effects of the strong magnetic field upon the propagation of the burning region beneath the surface and of the cyclotron opacity in the radiatively accelerated wind. The complexity of such studies is, at times, overwhelming, and the solution perhaps even (dare we admit it?) impossible. With Jim Wilson as an example this presumably means that it may take at most a year or two!

This work has been supported by the National Science Foundation (AST-81-09509) and the Department of Energy (W-7405-ENG-48) at the Lawrence Livermore National Laboratory.

REFERENCES

Arons, J., and Lea, S. M. 1976, Ap. J., 207, 914.

_____. 1980, Ap. J., 235, 1016.

Ayasli, S., and Joss, P. C. 1982, Ap. J., 256, 637.

Fujimoto, M. Y., Hanawa, T., and Miyaji, S. 1981, Ap. J., 247, 267.

Fryxell, B. A., and Woosley, S. E. 1982, Ap. J., 258, 733.

Ghosh, P., and Lamb, F. K. 1979, Ap. J., 232, 259.

Grindlay, J. E., Marshall, H., Hertz, P., Soltan, A., Weisskopf, R. F.,
    et al. 1980, Ap. J. (Lett.), 240, L121.

Grindlay, J. E., and Hertz, P. 1981, Ap. J. (Lett.), 247, L17.

Hameury, J. M., Bonazzola, S., Heyvaerts, J., and Ventura, J. 1982,
    Astr. Ap., in press.

Hanawa, T., and Sugimoto, D. 1982, Publ. Astr. Soc. Japan, 34, 1.

Hoffman, J. A., Lewin, W. H. G., Doty, J., Jernigan, J. G., Haney, M.,
    Richardson, J. A. 1978, Ap. J. (Lett.), 221, L57.

Hoshi, R. 1981, Ap. J., 247, 628.

Inoue, H., Koyama, K., Makishima, K., Matsuoka, M., Murakami, T.,
    et al. 1980, Nature, 283, 358.

Joss, P. C., and Li, F. K., 1977, Nature, 270, 310.

_____. 1978, Ap. J. (Lett.), 225, L123.

Joss, P. C., and Li, F. K. 1980, Ap. J., 238, 287.

Joss, P. C., and Rappaport, S. A. 1984, Ann. Rev. Astr. Ap., 22, 000,
    preprint.

Kylafis, N. D., Lamb, D. Q., Masters, A. R., and Weast, G. J. 1980,
    Ann. NY Acad. Sci., 336, 520.

Lamb, D. Q. 1982, in "Gamma Ray Transients and Related Astrophysical
    Phenomena", ed. R. Lingenfelter, H. Hudson, and D. Worrall (Am.
    Inst. Phys., Conf. Proc. #77), p. 249.

Lamb, D. Q., and Lamb, F. K. 1978, Ap. J., 220, 291.

Lewin, W. H. G. 1982, in "Accreting Neutron Stars", ed. W. Brinkmann
    and J. Trumper (MPE Report 177, Proc. Workshop at MPI, Garching,
    July, 1982), p. 76.

Lewin, W. H. G., and Joss, P. C. 1982, in "Accretion Driven Stellar
    X-Ray Sources", ed. W. H. G. Lewin and E. P. J. van den Heuvel
    (Cambridge: University Press), in press.

Liang, E. P. T. 1981, Nature, 292, 319.

Murakami, T., Inoue, H., Koyama, K., Makishima, K., Matsuoka, M.,
    et al. 1980, Ap. J. (Lett.), 240, L143.

Oda, M. 1982, in "Gamma-Ray Transients and Related Astrophysical
    Phenomena", ed. R. Lingenfelter, H. Hudson, and D. Worrall (Am.
    Inst. Phys., Conf. Proc. #77), p. 319.

Oda, M., and Tanaka, Y. 1981, Research Note No. 150, Institute of
    Space and Astronautical Science, Komaba, Meguro, Tokyo 153,
    Japan.

Petschek, H. E. 1964, AAS-NASA Symposium on the Physics of Solar
    Flares (NASA SP-50), p. 425.

Petschek, H. E., and Thorne, R. M. 1967, Ap. J., 147, 1157.

Rappaport, S. 1982, in "Be Stars", ed. M. Jaschek and H. -G. Groth
    (Dordrecht: D. Reidel), p. 327.

Rees, M. J. 1982, in "Accreting Neutron Stars", ed. W. Brinkmann and
    J. Trumper (MPE Report 177, Proceedings of Workshop held at MPI,
    Garching, July 1982), p. 179.

Ruderman, M. 1982, Prog. Part. Nucl. Physics, 6, 215.

Shara, M. M. 1982, Ap. J., 261, 649.

Taam, R. E. 1981, Ap. J., 247, 257.

_____. 1982, Ap. J., 258, 761.

Taam, R. E., and Picklum, R. E. 1978, Ap. J., 224, 210.

_____. 1979, Ap. J., 233, 327.

Tsuruta, S., Canuto, V., Lodenquai, J., and Ruderman, M. 1972, Ap. J.,
    176, 739.

Wallace, R. K., and Woosley, S. E. 1981, Ap. J. Suppl., 45, 389.

Wallace, R. K., Woosley, S. E., and Weaver, T. A. 1982, Ap. J., 258,
    696.

White, N. E. 1982, in "Accreting Neutron Stars", ed. W. Brinkmann and
    J. Trumper (MPE Report 177, Proc. of Workshop held at MPI,
    Garching, July 1982), p. 29.

Woosley, S. E. 1982a, in "Gamma-Ray Transients and Related Astro-
    physical Phenomena", ed. R. Lingenfelter, H. Hudson, and D.
    Worrall (Am. Inst. Phys., Conf. Proc. #77), p. 273.

_____. 1982b, in "Accreting Neutron Stars", ed. W. Brinkmann and
    J. Trumper (MPE Report 177, Proc. of Workshop held at MPI,
    Garching, July 1982), p. 189.

Woosley, S. E., and Taam, R. E. 1976, Nature, 263, 101.

Woosley, S. E., and Wallace, R. K. 1982, Ap. J., 258, 716.

Woosley, S. E., and Weaver, T. A. 1982, Bull. AAS, 14, 892.

Gamma Bursts

Stirling A. Colgate and Albert G. Petschek
Los Alamos National Laboratory

New Mexico Institute of Mining and Technology

ABSTRACT

Gamma bursts are believed to have a local origin in the Galaxy and to be associated with neutron stars. The primary conceptual difficulty in modeling gamma bursts is to explain the emission of hard photons while restricting the emission of soft photons. The limited size of a neutron star enhances the required surface intensity and also creates strong gravitational and possibly magnetic fields. These conditions strongly favor black body emission especially with strong magnetic fields, in which case the hard photon flux is precluded. As an alternative mechanism we suggest that rapid periodic and sequential accretion onto a neutron star surface of a finite thickness layer of matter will naturally lead to the observed spectrum. A charge separation electric field in the accreting matter ensures that electrons follow the ions. Soft photons ($h\nu \cong$ several keV) originally present are compressed and adiabatically heated in the short time of free fall accretion by a layer only a few Compton mean free paths thick. Some of these heated photons, constant in number, escape and become the cushion for the next layer. A sequence of compressions with diffusive escape gives rise to a smaller and smaller fraction of higher and higher energy photons. Each photon energy group contains roughly the gravitational potential energy of one layer. All photons then escape by diffusion before bremsstrahlung or the surface flux significantly adds to the photon number. The resulting spectrum roughly corresponds to equal energy per logarithmic interval as observed.

I. INTRODUCTION

Gamma bursts are now universally accepted as having an origin associated with neutron stars. The maximum absolute luminosity inferred for an origin local to our region of the Milky Way is then close to the Eddington limit for a solar mass. This is consistent with the distribution in luminosity, the log N log S curve, considered by Jennings (1981) and Jennings and White (1980). This then allows for the large observed departure from slope 3/2 due to the disc structure of the galaxy as well as a large intrinsic variation in gamma burst size. The possible identification of one event with an earlier outburst in the visible by Schaefer (1981) further suggests a local origin and hence a neutron star source. The difficulty with any simple mechanism for the production of gamma bursts in the vicinity of a neutron star is the extremely nonthermal character of the observed spectrum (Bussard and Lamb 1981, Fenimore et al. 1981) and the large optical thickness associated with accreted matter when gravitational energy release occurs on the neutron star. The gravitational binding energy of matter reaching a neutron star surface is of the order of 1/10 to 2/10 of its rest energy. This is a likely maximum specific energy for a gamma burst. Since the required material would have an optical thickness of about 10^5 Compton mean free paths, if it were all heated simultaneously on the neutron star surface, the mechanism for producing thin spectrum, high temperature radiation is still obscure. Somehow or other the radiation must find its way around the matter that is releasing the energy. This difficulty is exaggerated 100-fold if the energy source is thermonuclear, because the energy released is 100 times smaller per gram of matter and thus 100 times the mass is required. Explanations of gamma burst spectra that are made independent of the thickness of the radiating matter suffer because of this one major difficulty.

The March 5 event was singular in many aspects; in particular the spectrum was softer than that of most events by a factor of 3. The spectrum was soft enough that it is reasonable to model the radiation emitted as being a superposition of black body regions of different temperatures, with a maximum black body temperature that could be associated with either accretion or thermonuclear burning. The fact that the black body radiation flux even for this softer spectrum would vastly exceed the Eddington limit can be circumvented by the constraining the matter in a strong magnetic field (Colgate and Petschek 1981). The same strong field, however, absolutely insures a black body spectrum of emitted photons.

II. RADIATION THERMALIZATION IN MAGNETIC FIELDS

A high-temperature plasma in a strong magnetic field emits harmonics of the cyclotron frequency (Trubnikov 1961). The field strength necessary to confine the high temperature plasma is $\gtrsim 10^{10}$ gauss when the plasma is radiating at the black body limit associated with a characteristic temperature of the March 5 event, $kT \cong 20$ keV. Then the effective photon absorption mean free path is a small fraction $\cong 2 \times 10^{-3}$ of a Compton scattering mean free path. Therefore the emission and absorption rapidly thermalize the radiation field so that Compton scattering cannot be invoked to produce a large nonthermal component. As a consequence, we see no consistent way to use a magnetic field to confine a high temperature plasma and at the same time emit the highly nonthermal spectrum characteristic of gamma bursts. This problem has been well recognized in the attempts to model spectra by thin magnetic synchrotron emission (Liang 1982, Lamb 1980).

III.   SPECTRAL MECHANISMS

Other models of the high temperature nonthermal gamma burst spectrum employ bremsstrahlung (Bussard and Lamb 1981) and, more recently, comptonized black-body radiation (Fenimore et al. 1981). A problem with both these mechanisms is that the emission region must be thin, and as a consequence it has a low heat capacity and the energy of the emission region must continually be replaced. If bremsstrahlung is the source of the photons, the plasma must be less than a Compton mean free path thick. Otherwise comptonization of the low energy bremsstrahlung photons overwhelms the energetics of the emitted radiation. The comptonization of an already formed, low temperature black body photon distribution ($kT = 400$ to 1000 eV) as suggested by Fenimore et al. (1981) allows for a significantly greater thickness of hot matter, of the order of 1 to 2 Compton mean free paths. Even this larger thickness poses an extraordinary constraint on electron heating. If the electrons heat the soft photons and if the matter is distributed in a thickness comparable to the radius of the neutron star, the electron energy must be replaced recurrently in less than a microsecond. This short time precludes Coulomb collisions with nuclei by many orders of magnitude (10^5, for $Z = 1$ and almost independent of Z), and so any classically proposed electron heating mechanism becomes unlikely.

IV.   CHARGE SEPARATION AND PHOTON HEATING

If matter is being accreted onto a neutron star at close to the Eddington limit, the ions are gravitationally attracted to the star while the electrons are repelled from it by the radiation stress exerted on them by scattering. The electrons are however coupled to the ions by the electric field due to the charge separation. The electrons are dragged through the photon gas by this field whose value must be $m_p M_\odot G/R^2 e$, or 100 V/cm. Compton scattering ensures a rapid thermodynamic equilibrium between electrons and the photon gas (without change of photon number) and the motion of the ions, relative to the photon gas, allows PdV work to be done on the photon gas. The photons have an energy density many times that of the particle thermal energy so that it is the work done on the photon gas that absorbs the gravitational energy of the ions. To the extent that no new photons are produced within the time of compression of the photon gas, the mean energy of the photons will increase. This increase in energy of the photons or PdV heating of the photon gas we envisage to be cyclic. Each time the photon gas is heated by one layer of in-falling matter, a fraction of the heated photons escapes and serves as the photon gas at a higher temperature and lower density for the succeeding collapsing layer. This process of cyclic PdV compression of a number-limited photon gas and subsequent diffusion and further heating by another layer is what we propose as the origin of the hard spectrum of gamma bursts. Modeling of this phenomenon is currently being considered. The compression of a photon number-limited gas depends upon the speed of compression. Only for accretion onto a neutron star where the free fall velocity is $\cong c/3$ can this happen.

Finally, we suggest how the mass that drives the photon heating mechanism, consisting of 5 to 10 layers each several Compton mean free paths thick ($\cong 10$ g cm^{-2}) can be replenished 10^4 times during a γ-burst. Among several possibilities, the most likely is accretion disc instability.

This work was supported by the Department of Energy and the Astronomy Section of NSF. We are indebted to Robert Sarracino for discussions.

REFERENCES

1.   R. W. Bussard and R. K. Lamb, "The Low Energy Spectra of Gamma-Ray Bursts," preprint University of Illinois at Urbana-Champaign (1981).

2.   S. A. Colgate, and A. G. Petschek, Ap. J. 248, 782 (1981).

3.   E. E. Fenimore, W. D. Evans, R. W. Klebesadel, J. G. Laros, and J. Terrell, Nature, 289, 42 (1981).

4.   M. C. Jennings, "Gamma Ray Transients," ed. R. Lingenfelter, M. Hudson, and D. Worrall, Am. Inst. Phys., Conf. Proc. No. 77, p. 107 (1981).

5.   M. C. Jennings and R. S. White, Ap. J. 238, 110 (1980).

6.   D. Q. Lamb, "Gamma Ray Transients," ed. R. Lingenfelter, et al., Am. Inst. Phys., Conf. Proc. No. 77, p. 249 (1981).

7.   E. P. T. Liang, Nature 299, 321 (1982).

8.   B. E. Schaefer, Nature 294, 722 (1981).

9.   B. A. Trubnikov, Phys. Fluids 4, 195 (1961).

III. Numerical Relativity

Spacetime Engineering

James W. York, Jr.
University of North Carolina, Chapel Hill

ABSTRACT

Spacetime engineering refers to the construction of gravitational fields that satisfy the Einstein equations with or without matter. The intention is to produce solutions that are sufficiently realistic to be of interest in either cosmological or astrophysical settings. The nonlinearity, coupling, and coordinate freedom of the gravitational equations force two things: (1) sorting out the pieces of the gravity and matter variables that are relatively simple and can be put back together in a natural way, and (2) using numerical methods for reassembly and propagation of the pieces. In this article, which is dedicated to Jim Wilson, one of the great spacetime eningeers, I outline a handbook for process (1) and some recent results that I hope soon will become part of the lore of the subject.

I.   INTRODUCTION

Important qualitative information about the free motion of a classical rigid body can be obtained from its invariant coordinate-free formulation. For instance, from Poinsot's construction one can show that "the polhode rolls without slipping on the herpolhode lying in the invariable plane" (Goldstein 1959). Yet who would deny that a specific practical enumeration of the rigid body degrees of freedom, such as provided by the Eulerian angles, is essential in practice?

The same thing can be said of general relativity. From more or less invariant formulations, powerful qualitative conclusions can be obtained, such as the singularity theorems and an upper bound on the gravitational radiation produced in black hole collisions (Hawking and Ellis 1973). Yet to obtain the details needed for the progress of gravitational physics, one needs coordinates. The notion of coordinates enters at two levels here. First, one needs a chart or charts of coordinates $x^a = (t, x^1, x^2, x^3)$ in which to display the metric. At a deeper level one needs an analog of the Euler angles, that is, a sorting of the pieces of the metric in which some characterize the dynamical degrees of freedom ("Euler angles"), others are constrained ("rigid body conditions"), and yet others are essentially kinematical ("motion of the space frame").

In relativity, all metric components g_{ab}, Christoffel symbols Γ^a_{bc}, and curvature components R^a_{bcd} are equal, but some are more equal, a situation that results solely from the notion of causality embodied in the signature (-+++), in which the minus sign is associated with timelike directions. This causes us to regard the spatial metric γ_{ij} (+++) induced on a slice t = time = constant as the metric, while we write in the familiar way α = lapse = $\sqrt{(-g^{tt})}$, β_i = shift = g_{ti}. (Systematic reviews of the present material and of much what is given in this article are found in York 1979 and York 1983.) Hence we have

$$g_{ab} \to \{\gamma_{ij}; \frac{\partial}{\partial t} = \alpha \frac{\partial}{\partial n} + \beta^i \frac{\partial}{\partial x^i}\} \qquad (1.1)$$

in which $\partial/\partial n = n^a$ is the timelike unit normal of the slice.

Similarly, the distinguished Christoffel symbols are called the second fundamental form or extrinsic curvature tensor of the slice:

$$K_{ij} = - \alpha \Gamma^t_{ij}. \qquad (1.2)$$

The meaning of this is that K is equal to (-1/2) (proper-time velocity of γ in the direction normal to the time slice).

Furthermore, we break R_{abcd} into pieces using the operator $P^a_b = \delta^a_b + n^a n_b$ that projects onto the spacelike slice ("Pythagorean theorem when the squared length of n^a is minus one"). Thus, by repeated projections,

$$P^{abcd}_{ijkl} R_{abcd} = R_{ijkl}(\gamma) + (K_{ik} K_{jl} - K_{il} K_{jk}), \qquad (1.3)$$

$$P^{abc}_{ijk}R_{abcd}n^d = \nabla_j K_{ik} - \nabla_i K_{jk}, \tag{1.4}$$

$$P^{ab}_{ij}R_{abcd}n^c n^d = \alpha^{-1}(\partial_t - \pounds_\beta)K_{ij} + K_{i\ell}K^\ell{}_j + \alpha^{-1}\nabla_i\nabla_j\alpha, \tag{1.5}$$

where ∇_i is the covariant derivative associated with γ_{ij} and $\pounds$ denotes the Lie derivative. Here, i, j, k, ... are spatial indices and $R_{ijk\ell}$ is the spatial Riemann tensor. The first two equations are the Gauss-Codazzi equations, which are necessary and sufficient for the embedding of a slice characterized by (γ_{ij}, K_{ij}) into an ambient spacetime of curvature R_{abcd}. The last equation tells what happens to these quantities when you go to a nearby slice ("time evolution").

The Einstein equations contain second time derivatives of γ_{ij} ($\partial_t\partial_t\gamma_{ij} \sim \partial_t K_{ij}$) but not of α and β_i. So it seems that our "Euler angles" are the γ_{ij}'s (modulo the arbitrary choice of spatial coordinates). But unfortunately we haven't reached this goal, because four of the ten Einstein equations, obtained by contractions of equations (1.3) and (1.4), do nothing but constrain the initial choice of γ_{ij} and K_{ij} ("position and velocity"). In many ways sorting out of the meaning of these constraints is the key to spacetime engineering in its theoretical aspect. What next? I have never been able to find any general method that is not based in essence on the following further breakup:

$$\gamma_{ij} \rightarrow \{(\det \gamma)^{1/3}; \; \tilde{\gamma}_{ij} = (\det \gamma)^{-1/3}\gamma_{ij}\}, \tag{1.6}$$

or

$$\gamma_{ij} \rightarrow \{\psi^4; \; \hat{\gamma}_{ij} = \psi^{-4}\gamma_{ij}\}, \tag{1.7}$$

where $\psi > 0$ can be regarded as a scalar. The first to employ this step was Lichnerowicz (1944). However, this is not enough. We must also make a split if K_{ij} into its trace and trace-free parts:

$$K_{ij} \rightarrow A_{ij} = K_{ij} - \frac{1}{3}\gamma_{ij}\text{trK}; \quad \text{trK} = \gamma^{ij}K_{ij} \tag{1.8}$$

It turns out that $\hat{\gamma}_{ij}$, which is to say the <u>conformal equivalence class</u> of γ_{ij}, represents in a suitable way the dynamical degrees of freedom of the gravitational field with respect to a given slicing (modulo choice of spatial coordinates). That is, we have found our "Euler angles."

II. SCALAR AND VECTOR POTENTIALS

The ten Einstein equations divide neatly into four constraints and six evolution equations. Here I shall focus attention on the constraints. Many of the lssons learned here are also useful in the evolution problem.

The constraints are ($G = c = 1$)

$$\nabla_j (K^{ij} - \gamma^{ij} trK) = 8\pi j^i \qquad (2.1)$$

and

$$R(\gamma) + (trK)^2 - K_{ij}K^{ij} = 16\pi\rho, \qquad (2.2)$$

where ρ is the energy density of matter and j^i its momentum density. Given $\hat{\gamma}_{ij}$, equation (2.2) will provide a scalar elliptic equation for the potential function ψ and the desired three-metric will be $\gamma_{ij} = \psi^4 \hat{\gamma}_{ij}$. But how do we handle equation (2.1)? An answer is to find a suitable vector potential. I shall now outline the needed mathematics quite apart from appliction to equations (2.1) and (2.2). In the next section I outline the application to the constraints. I shall defer a mention of boundary conditions until later.

Let T^{ij} be any symmetric tensor and γ_{ij} be any three-dimensional Riemannian metric. (As long as the dimension is three or greater, everything that follows goes through with minor changes. Dimension two is exceptional because every Riemannian two-metric is locally conformally flat.) Write (York 1973, 1974)

$$T^{ij} = T^{ij}_* + (LX)^{ij} + \frac{1}{3}\gamma^{ij} trT, \qquad (2.3)$$

$$(LX)^{ij} \equiv \nabla^i X^j + \nabla^j X^i - \frac{2}{3}\gamma^{ij}\nabla_\ell X^\ell. \tag{2.4}$$

Solve

$$(\Delta_L X)^i = \nabla_j (T^{ij} - \frac{1}{3}\gamma^{ij} trT), \tag{2.5}$$

$$(\Delta_L X)^i = \nabla_j (LX)^{ij} = (\Delta X)^i + \frac{1}{3}\nabla^i(\nabla_\ell X^\ell) + R^i{}_\ell X^\ell. \tag{2.6}$$

This "vector Laplacian" is linear, elliptic, and formally self-adjoint. Its kernel (with standard boundary conditions), consisting of the analogs of the solutions of Laplace's equation $\Delta F = (\gamma^{ij}\nabla_i\nabla_j)F = 0$ for which $F \neq 0$ and $\nabla_i F = 0$ (constants), is composed of the conformal Killing vectors C^i of γ_{ij} (if there are any - this is a special symmetry). These vectors satisfy the conformal Killing equations $(LC)^{ij} = 0$.

The tensor is found by substituting X^i into equation (2.3). The asterisk means it is trace-free and has vanishing covariant divergence. The following behavior of the above objects with respect to conformal re-scalings $\psi(x)$ of the metric are of essential importance. One has

$$\gamma_{ij} = \psi^4 \hat{\gamma}_{ij}, \tag{2.7}$$

$$\Gamma^i{}_{jk}(\gamma) = \hat{\Gamma}^i{}_{jk}(\hat{\gamma}) + 2\psi^{-1}(\delta^i_j \hat{\nabla}_k\psi + \delta^i_k \hat{\nabla}_j\psi - \hat{\gamma}^{im}\hat{\gamma}_{jk}\hat{\nabla}_m\psi), \tag{2.8}$$

$$(LX)^{ij} = \psi^{-4}(\hat{L}X)^{ij} \quad (X^i = \hat{X}^i; \ X_i = \psi^4 \hat{X}_i). \tag{2.9}$$

and if S^{ij} denotes the trace-free part of T^{ij}, then

$$\nabla_j S^{ij} = \psi^{-10}\hat{\nabla}_j \hat{S}^{ij}, \quad S^{ij} = \psi^{-10}\hat{S}^{ij}. \tag{2.10}$$

The caret denotes quantities formed using $\hat{\gamma}_{ij}$. In particular, one sees that the "*" property of a tensor depends only on its conformal equivalence class according to equation (2.10). (Incidentally, such conformal splittings can be defined for symmetric tensors of any valence; hence, we are ready for boson fields of spin $\geqslant$ 3 if such ever become useful in physics or geometry.)

Other "vector Laplacians" exist and I have recently discussed them (York 1983). However, the present methods also yield an interesting second order tensor operator that is finding use in numerical relativity [Evans and Smarr 1983; Evans 1984 and this volume]. This operator (York 1973) is found from the observation that the operators "div" and "L" are in adjoint relation. Hence one defines an operator taking tensors to tensors by reversing the order in which they were used above (on vectors) to obtain

$$(0_L S)^{ij} = [L(\delta S)]^{ij} \tag{2.11}$$

where $(\delta S)^i = \nabla_j S^{ij}$. The remarkable property of 0_L is that its kernel consists of all tensors that are divergence-free and trace-free ("*"). This kernel is infinite-dimensional and characterizes all "vectors" in the infinite dimensional space of conformal equivalence classes of Riemannian metrics.

As a final remark in preparation for the next section, we note the conformal transformation of scalar curvature, the "Lichnerowicz formula" for three dimensions:

$$R(\gamma) = \hat{R}(\hat{\gamma})\psi^{-4} - 8\psi^{-5}\hat{\Delta}\psi. \tag{2.12}$$

The reader will observe in the next section that the method of solution of the constraints has been arranged so that <u>no derivatives of the unknown potentials ψ and W^i ever appear except in linear elliptic self-adjoint operators in "divergence form"</u> (the simplest type),

$$\hat{\Delta}\psi = \hat{\nabla}_i(\hat{\nabla}^i\psi), \tag{2.13}$$

$$(\hat{\Delta}_L W)^i = \hat{\nabla}_j(\hat{L}W)^{ij}. \tag{2.14}$$

III.   SOLVING THE CONSTRAINTS: A SPACETIME ENGINEER'S HANDBOOK

Instead of starting from the constraints (2.1) and (2.2), applying the machinery, and ending up with four elliptic equations for four unknowns, I shall present the final equations and indicate how to obtain from the solutions the data (γ_{ij}, K_{ij}, ρ, j^i) that satisfy equations (2.1) and (2.2). It is important that the process goes both ways, provided only that the $\psi(x)$ one has obtained is everywhere strictly positive. Discussions of the existing theorems for this are found in Choquet-Bruhat and York (1980), Cantor (1979), Cantor and Brill (1981), and York (1983). Whenever a $\psi(x) > 0$ does not exist, say for example it has a zero ("node") somewhere, it means you are trying to do something that is physically impossible according to Einstein's theory (if we accept that physical space-times must be everywhere regular mathematically--but see Cantor and Piran 1982).

Step One: Give freely $\hat{\gamma}_{ij}$, trK, and $\hat{A}_*^{ij}$, the latter constructed as in the previous section. These are the free gravitational data.

Step Two: Give $\hat{\rho}$ and $\hat{j}^i$, the free matter data. If you put $\hat{\rho} \geqslant + (\hat{\gamma}_{ij} \hat{j}^i \hat{j}^j)^{1/2}$, your physical data ρ, j^i will turn out automatically to satisfy the "weak" and "dominant energy" conditions (Hawking and Ellis 1973).

Step Three: Define $\hat{A}^{ij} = \hat{A}_*^{ij} + (\hat{L}W)^{ij}$.

Step Four: Solve the semi-linear elliptic system

$$8\hat{\Delta}\psi - \hat{R}\psi + (\hat{A}_{ij}\hat{A}^{ij})\psi^{-7} - \frac{2}{3}(trK)^2\psi^5 + 16\pi\hat{\rho}\psi^{-3} = 0, \quad (3.1)$$

$$(\hat{\Delta}_L W)^i - \frac{2}{3}\psi^6\hat{\Delta}^i trK - 8\pi\hat{j}^i = 0. \quad (3.2)$$

Note the following remarkable fact (York 1972): If trK = constant (the initial slice has "constant mean (extrinsic) curvature"), then ψ drops out of equation (3.2) and W^i can be found independently of ψ. This "uncoupling" of the constraints greatly eases the burdens of the spacetime engineer's life! Then plug W^i into equation (3.1) and find ψ.

Step Five: The physical data satisfying the constraints are given by

$$\gamma_{ij} = \psi^4 \, \hat{\gamma}_{ij}, \qquad (3.3)$$

and

$$K_{ij} = \psi^{-2}[\hat{A}^{*}_{ij} + (\hat{L}W)_{ij}] + \frac{1}{3}\psi^{6}\hat{\gamma}_{ij}\,trK, \qquad (3.4)$$

$$\rho = \hat{\rho}\,\psi^{-8}, \quad j^{i} = \hat{j}^{i}\psi^{-10}. \qquad (3.5)$$

That's it.

IV.   BOUNDARY CONDITIONS

In asymptotically flat spacetimes, we require that as $r \to \infty$, $\psi \to 1 + O(r^{-1})$ and $W^i \to O(r^{-1})$. The $O(r^{-1})$ part of ψ contains the total energy E and, if $\hat{A}^{ij}_{*} = O(r^{-3})$, the $O(r^{-1})$ part of W^i encodes the total linear momentum P^i, i.e., E and P^i are, respectively, the monopoles of the potentials ψ and W^i. The problem is that in numerical calculations one uses finite grids. This causes a problem if we put, say, $\psi = 1$ on the edge of the grid. This causes ψ to decrease too fast at large r and overestimates that most important of quantitites, the energy. (We know ψ decreases to one as $r \to \infty$ because of the positive energy theorems that now exist.)

A way around this problem that I recommend to spacetime engineers is to impose a Robin boundary condition at the edge of the grid. This boundary condition can be stated accurately in a form independent of E. This has been formulated and used in numerical work (York and Piran 1982). Such conditions for scalar elliptic problems have long been in existence (Duff 1959). I have developed a similar condition for the vector elliptic problem; it eliminates the monopole P^i (York and Piran 1982, equation [59]). The latter has been successfully employed in numerical work on rotating collapse by Nakamura (1983).

V. DATA FOR N BLACK HOLES

An overall goal that guided me through the work described above
was to understand general relativity well enough (as a necessary,
but not sufficient condition) to be able to construct a theory of
quantum gravity. For this it seemed important to understand the
constraints, in part because that would tell me about the reduced
Hamiltonian (symplectic) structure of the theory--although, of
course, this "royal road" won't tell you everything. Along the way
I acquired the compelling desire to see a genuine solution of the
two-body problem, which, in its purest form, means the collision of
two black holes. We all know that, based on Misner's (1960, 1963)
initial data for non-rotating black holes initially at rest, Smarr
and Eppley (Smarr 1979) succeeded in a difficult and very important
calculation of a head-on collision. However, a more general set of
data, describing spinning and/or spiraling holes, has not been
available. This, together with the enormous computing capacity
required for such a problem, has meant that a sufficiently general
several-parameter two-body problem has never been done. It seems
now, however, that both of these obstacles no longer exist. Here I
will sketch the general ideas about the initial data.

The method is to generalize Misner's (1963) "method of images
in geometrostatics". His procedure results in two asymptotically
flat universes ("sheets") connected by two (or N) throats or
Einstein-Rosen bridges. The great virtue of this work is that the
two sheets are isometric (physically identical), with each throat
being a minimal two-surface fixed under the isometry from top to
bottom. Because the apparent horizons of the holes lie "outside"
the minimal surfaces, one can evolve one sheet only, with the
coordinate location of each throat fixed. The isometry insures that
no spurious "signal" can "propagate", as it were, from the ignored
bottom sheet. (Remember that one must solve elliptic problems, for
which the "signal" velocity is infinite.) To get the holes to spin
and/or spiral, one must give up Misner's restriction $K_{ij} = 0$.
However, one wants to preserve the topology and isometry of his
model.

One again (with Misner) uses the method of inversion through spheres. Because, on flat space, inversions produce a kind of conformal change of the metric, it seems natural to base the generalization on the conformal techniques outlined in this article. The problem was partly solved by Bowen and York (1980), who managed the construction for one moving and/or spinning hole. In so doing, they learned to invert an extrinsic curvature tensor through one center. They also showed how to solve the resulting version of equation (3.1) as a boundary value problem for ψ on <u>one</u> sheet, and that the problem has a unique solution and moreover guarantees the desired isometry between the two sheets. The results depend crucially on the particular $\hat{K}_{ij}$'s one builds and on the behavior of the flat space Laplacian under inversions. (In this work, the <u>initial</u> physical three-metric will be of conformally flat.)

The generalization of the above to N holes has recently been accomplished by Kulkarni, Shepley, and York (1983). One begins with flat three-space minus N non-intersecting spheres of radius $a_\alpha(\alpha=1,\ldots,N)$. A general point is denoted by $x(=\vec{x})$ and for each hole one has the inversion map

$$x \rightarrow J_\alpha(x) = J_\alpha x = \frac{a_\alpha^2}{r_\alpha} n_\alpha + C_\alpha \qquad (5.1)$$

where x, n_α, and C_α (= origin) are vectors and $r_\alpha = |x - c_\alpha|$, $n_\alpha = (x - C_\alpha)r_\alpha^{-1}$. Dropping the label α for notational ease, we see that the Jacobian of J_α is

$$J^i_{\ j} = (\frac{a}{r})^2 (\delta_j^{\ i} - 2n^i n_j) \equiv (\frac{a}{r})^2 R_j^{\ i}. \qquad (5.2)$$

Now define for each α an operator B on symmetric tensors T_{ij} by

$$(BT)_{ij}(x) = \pm (\frac{a}{r})^6 R_i^m R_j^n T_{mn}(Jx). \qquad (5.3)$$

It can be shown that if T_{ij} is symmetric, trace-free, and divergence-free (in the <u>flat</u> metric $\hat{\gamma}_{ij}$), then so also is $(BT)_{ij}$, and similarly when one operates with any string of B_α's on T_{ij}.

This means that if we start with a $T_{ij} = \hat{K}_{ij}$ satisfying the momentum constraints $\hat{\nabla}_j \hat{K}^{ij} = 0$ ($trK = j^i = 0$), it will still be a solution after any number of operations "B".

Next define

$$\underline{B} + I + \sum_{[\alpha_i]} \left(\prod_{i=1}^{m} B_{\alpha_i} \right) \tag{5.4}$$

where each α_i takes any of the values 1, ..., N and the sum extends over all finite sequences α_1, ..., α_m of length m = 1,2,3,... subject to $\alpha_{i+1} \neq \alpha_i$. One sees that $B_\alpha \underline{B} = \underline{B}$ for all α Hence $\hat{K} = \underline{B}\hat{K}$ will solve the momentum constraints if K does. Moreover, provided that the conformal fctor ψ satisfies

$$\psi(x) = \left(\frac{a}{r}\right)\psi(Jx) \tag{5.5}$$

for each α, and that $\hat{\underline{K}}$ is transformed conformally to the physical $\underline{K}$ as described in Section III, then we will have

$$\underline{K}(x) = \pm(\text{pull-back of } \underline{K} \text{ at } J_\alpha x) \tag{5.6}$$

for all x and α = 1, ..., N. This is the required isometry condition. (Either sign can be allowed because K enters quadratically in the constraint equation for ψ.)

To find ψ, one solves the boundary value problem

$$\nabla^2 \psi = -\frac{1}{8}(\hat{\underline{K}})^2 \psi^{-7} \tag{5.7}$$

$$- 2a_\alpha \left(\frac{\partial(\ln\psi)}{\partial r_\alpha}\right)_{r_\alpha = a_\alpha} = 1 \tag{5.8}$$

for all α, with $\psi \to 1$ at infinity. Condition (5.8) forces equation (5.5) to hold for any smooth solution to this elliptic problem.

For N holes, one begins with K corresponding at each site C_α to spin S_α (constant skew tensor with dual equal to spin vector) and constant linear momentum vector P_α. Suppressing the α's, this means take

$$\hat{K}_{ij} = \sum_{\alpha=1}^{N} \frac{3}{16\pi r^2} [P_i n_j + P_j n_i + (n_i n_j - \hat{\gamma}_{ij}) P_\ell n^\ell]$$

$$+ \sum_{\alpha=1}^{N} \frac{3}{8\pi r^3} [n^\ell S_{\ell i} n_j + n_i n^\ell S_{\ell j}] \tag{5.9}$$

(cf. York [1979]); then $\underline{\hat{K}} = B\hat{K}$. In practice, one will have to truncate these expressions, so a detailed study of their convergence properties is important. See Kulkarni (1983). If N=1, this reduces to the results of Bowen (1979) and Bowen and York (1980).

The elaboration of these results is in progress (Bowen, Rauber, and York [1984]; Kulkarni [1984]) and should result in sufficiently general two (or more) - body data for an energetic spacetime engineer (computer division!) to evolve. Probably the best starting case will be two holes of equal mass, initially at rest, with their spins equal and parallel or anti-parallel. Thus it seems at long last that we will be able to solve the two-body problem of Einstein's theory.

VI.   EPILOGUE

"In the theory of gravitation, as in all other branches of theoretical physics, a mathematically correct statement of a problem must be determinate to the extent allowed by the nature of the problem; if possible, it must ensure the uniqueness of its solution" (Fock 1959).

To this statement (which I have borrowed from page 484 of Misner, Thorne, and Wheeler [1973]), I can only add an opinion as to how you find a "mathematically correct" formulation of a theory: you take the theory apart and put it back together in such a way as to orchestrate calculations.

REFERENCES

Bowen, J. 1979, "Initial value problems on non-Euclidean topologies", Ph.D. thesis, University of North Carolina.

Bowen, J., Rauber, J., and York, J. W. 1984, Class. and Quant. Grav., to appear.

Bowen, J., and York, J. W. 1980, Phys. Rev. D 21, 2047.

Cantor, M. 1979, J. Math. Phys., 20, 1741.

Cantor, M., and Brill, D. 1981, Compositio Math., 43, 317.

Cantor, M., and Piran, T. 1982, Gen. Rel. and Grav., to appear.

Choquet-Bruhat, Y. and York, J. W. 1980, in "General Relativity and Gravitation", ed. A. Held (New York: Plenum), p. 99.

Duff, G.F.D. 1959, "Partial Differential Equations" (Toronto: University of Toronto Press).

Evans, C. 1984 "A Method for Numerical Relativity: Simulation of Axisymmetric Gravitational Collapse and Gravitational Radiation Generation", Ph.D. Thesis, University of Texas at Austin.

Evans, C. and Smarr, L. 1983, personal communication.

Fock, V. A. 1959, "The Theory of Space, Time, and Gravitation" (New York: Pergamon).

Goldstein, H. 1959, "Classical Mechanics" (Reading: Addison-Wesley).

Hawking, S. W. and Ellis, G.R.R. 1973, "The Large Scale Structure of SpaceTime" (Cambridge: Cambridge University Press).

Kulkarni, A. 1983, J. Math. Phys., to appear.

Kulkarni, A. 1984, Gen. Rel. and Grav., to appear.

Kulkarni, A., Shepley, L., and York, J. W. 1983, Phys. Lett., 96A, 228.

Lichnerowicz, A. 1944, J. Math. Pures et Appl., 23, 37.

Misner, C. W. 1960, Phys. Rev., 118, 1110.

Misner, C. W. 1963, Ann. Phys. (N.Y.), 24, 102.
Misner, C. W., Thorne, K. S., and Wheeler, J. A. 1973, "Gravitation" (San Francisco: Freeman).

Nakamura, T. 1983, in "Gravitational Radiation", ed. N. Deruelle and T. Piran (Amsterdam: North Holland), p. 443.

Smarr, L. 1979, in "Sources of Gravitational Radiation", ed. L. Smarr (Cambridge: Cambridge University Press), p. 245.

York, J. W. 1972, Phys. Rev. Letters, 28, 1082.

York, J. W. 1973, J. Math. Phys., 14, 456.

York, J. W. 1974, Ann. Inst. Henri Poincaré, 21, 319.

York, J. W. 1979, in "Sources of Gravitational Radiation", ed. L. Smarr (Cambridge: Cambridge University Press), p. 83.

York, J. W. 1983, in "Gravitational Radiation", ed. N. Deruelle and T. Piran (Amsterdam: North Holland), p. 175.

York, J. W. and Piran, T. 1982, in "Spacetime and Geometry", ed. R. Matzner and L. Shepley (Austin: University of Texas Press), p. 147.

Gravitational Collapse, Star Collisions and the Generation of Gravitational Radiation

Stuart L. Shapiro
Cornell University, Ithaca, New York

ABSTRACT

Gravitational radiation from several promising astro-physical sources is calculated. Both strong and weak field scenarios are considered. The calculations provide useful estimates for the construction of gravitational wave detectors. They also provide insight into the dynamical nature of a nonlinear field theory.

I. INTRODUCTION

It is an enormous pleasure for me to participate in this gathering to honor Jim Wilson on the occasion of his 60 birthday. Through the pioneering efforts of Jim and others closely identified with him, numerical astrophysics has developed into a sophisticated and vital branch of theoretical astrophysics. This conference provides a wonderful opportunity to acknowledge this development and to recognize Jim Wilson's role in helping to bring it about. We take this occasion to celebrate Jim's unique and innovative approach to computational physics. We also celebrate his courage to tackle and ability to solve horrendously complicated, nonlinear problems. We applaud not only his important contributions to the literature in the field but also the valuable guidance he has freely offered over the years to many others working on similar numerical problems.

The model calculations which I have been asked to describe have all been influenced by and/or geared toward related numerical work

by Jim and his collaborators. The motivation for performing these
calculations has always been twofold. From an astrophysical point
of view, recent advances in gravitational wave detector technology
inspire the need for reliable estimates of gravitational wave emission from promising astrophysical sources. The importance of this
endeavor has been emphasized by Kip Thorne (1980).

From a numerical point of view, the computations discussed
below provide "simple" (i.e., "analytic" or one-dimensional) model
calculations of complicated geometrodynamical phenomena to serve as
guides for the construction and verification of more detailed (e.g.
two-dimensional) numerical codes. [Note that here and below I shall
adopt Jim Wilson's style of using the word "analytic" when referring
to anything which is not a partial differential equation (PDE).
Accordingly, integrating an ordinary differential equation (ODE)
(however complicated), searching for roots of transcendental equations, etc., are all "analytic" operations.] In addition, these
model calculations allow us to explore on the computer the dynamical
nature of a nonlinear field theory: here the field is gravity
coupled to hydrodynamic matter flow. Field theory on the computer
has become a booming enterprise in several different branches of
theoretical physics. (Curiously, the leading pioneers in this area
are preferentially named "Wilson"! See, e.g., K. Wilson (1975,
1980) and J. Wilson (1979)). This activity has had the magnificent
side effect of bringing numerical astrophysicists and relativists in
closer contact with their colleagues in fluid dynamics, plasma
physics, solid state and particle physics even though they are all
tackling ostensibly different theoretical physics problems.

In the next few sections I will quickly review highlights of
several gravitational collapse and collision calculations recently
performed at Cornell. The calculations are characterized by varying
degrees of rigor and detail. Taken together, they establish general
criteria for and assess the likelihood of high efficiency generation
of gravitational radiation from favorable astrophysical events. For
a quick summary and comparison of the various calculations, see
Table 1.

TABLE 1

SUMMARY AND COMPARISON OF CORNELL MODEL CALCULATIONS

Scenario	SMS collapse to a black hole	Stellar Core collapse	Head-on Collision of Identical Neutron Stars	Head-on Collision of a Star (m) with a Black Hole (M)	Shell (m) Accretion Onto a Hole (M)
Gravity	strong	weak	weak	strong	strong
Field Theory	general relativity	Newtonian	Newtonian	general relativity	general relativity
Equation of State	radiation + gas pressure	adiabatic "hot" nuclear matter (Lamb et. al. 1978)	polytropic fit to nuclear matter	dust	dust
Key Approximation	none	homogeneous ellipsoids	motion confined along collision axis	$m \ll M$	$m \ll M$
Symmetry	spherical	triaxial	planar	axisymmetric	axisymmetric
Dimensions	1+1	3+1	1+1	2+1	2+1
Equations	PDE's	ODE's	PDE's	ODE's	ODE's
Maximum Gravitational Radiation Efficiency ($\Delta E/M$)	0	10^{-4}	10^{-2}	$\leq 10^{-2} \, m/M$	$\leq 10^{-2} \, m/M$
References	Shapiro & Teukolsky (1979, 1980)	Shapiro (1979); Saenz & Shapiro (1981)	Shapiro (1980)	Haugan, Shapiro and Wasserman (1982)	Shapiro and Wasserman (1982)

II.   SPHERICAL COLLAPSE OF A SUPERMASSIVE STAR TO A BLACK HOLE

The most detailed and accurate collapse calculation that I will describe involves the spherical collapse of a supermassive star (SMS) to a supermassive, Schwarzschild black hole. Since the collapse is spherical, no gravitational radiation is generated (Birkhoff's theorem). Nevertheless, the calculation is quite interesting for several distinct reasons. Astrophysically, SMS's $(M/M_\odot > 10^5)$ were proposed by Hoyle and Fowler (1963a,b) as the sources of energy in quasars and active galactic nuclei. Following Salpeter (1964) and Zel'dovich (1964) it has become more fashionable today to suppose that these energy sources are supermassive black holes (see Blandford and Thorne 1979 for discussion and references). However, here again, the collapse of a SMS is the likely progenitor of the final black hole. It has further been proposed by Thorne and Braginsky (1976) that the nonspherical collapse of SMS's and collisions of supermassive black holes in quasars and active galactic nuclei may give rise to bursts of long wavelength gravitational radiation $[\lambda > 10^6 \ (M/M_\odot) \ km]$.

The collapse of a SMS has much in common with supernova core collapse, since both are governed in the initial stages by equations of state which share the same adiabatic index $\Gamma \approx 4/3$. This fact, which we shall exploit in §III, further motivates their study.

Numerically, SMS collapse provides a unique laboratory for testing a new numerical code which Saul Teukolsky and I constructed for spherical, adiabatic collapse in general relativity. Details of the code, together with applications to stellar core and SMS collapse, have been discussed elsewhere (see, e.g., Shapiro and Teukolsky 1979, 1980). Suffice it to say that the field equations we solve are the familiar 3+1 or ADM equations for the metric coefficients (Arnowitt, Deser and Misner 1962), for which we developed our own numerical algorithms. To solve the matter equations we adopted a modified version of the battle-tested hydrodynamic code developed over the years by Jim Wilson and his collaborators and by Larry Smarr. Coordinate gauge freedoms were exploited by choosing maximal time slicing and minimal shear (isotropic) coordinates. The choice of maximal time slicing was motivated by the desire to "hold back" the collapse at the center (i.e., to hold back the advance of proper time at the center) and thereby postpone the formation of singularities there (see Smarr and York 1978, Smarr, Taubes and Wilson 1980, Eardley and Smarr 1979, and references therein).

The result of our efforts is that collapse to a black hole can now be followed accurately without encountering physical or numerical singularities, even long after (i.e. $\Delta t \gg M$) the formation of an event horizon.

Consider the fate of a 10^6 $M_\odot$ SMS which sits at rest on the unstable branch of the hydrostatic equilibrium curve (model A in Fig. 1). Taking such a star as the initial data for our computer calculations we find, sure enough, that the unstable star immediately undergoes gravitational collapse: all of the matter implodes toward the center. Collapse and accretion proceed smoothly and without singularities. No shocks form, no mass is ejected, and there are no numerical singularities.

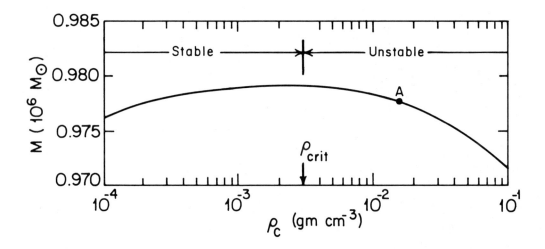

Fig. 1 - Equilibrium mass versus central density for supermassive stars of constant specific entropy.

Geometrically, the most interesting phase of the collapse is shown in the spacetime diagram in Figure 2. The dotted lines are matter world lines labelled by the interior baryon fraction. The

arrows show the slope of ingoing and outgoing light rays at asymptotically large radii. Solid lines denote outgoing radial light
rays emitted near the center at various times. That these rays are
not parallel to the outgoing asymptotic ray is a manifestation of
the strong gravitational fields which are developing near the center
as a black hole forms. By finding pairs of rays emitted from the
same radius, one of which escapes and one of which does not, we can
trace the growth of the event horizon as more and more matter flows
into the black hole. The shaded portion of the diagram represents
the region of trapped surfaces, where even an outgoing spherical
flash of light immediately becomes a sphere of smaller area. It is
satisfying that (1) the event horizon first appears at the center
and grows monotonically outward to an areal (Schwarzschild-like)
radius $r_s \approx 2M$, and (2) the apparent horizon (outermost trapped
surface) always lies inside the event horizon and asymptotically
approaches it at late times. These numerical results are in ac-
cordance with theorems on black holes (Hawking and Ellis 1973).

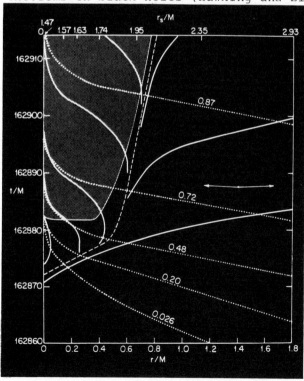

Fig. 2 - Spacetime diagram of the collapse of a $10^6 M_\odot$ supermassive
         star to a black hole. The initial configuration is the
         unstable equilibrium configuration A shown in Fig. 1.

We terminate our integration when most of the matter is inside the black hole and the central redshift (1/"lapse") rises to 10^{11}. By this time most of the radial grid has been "sucked down" the black hole along its "throat" (see Shapiro and Teukolsky 1980 for a full discussion).

Hydrodynamically, the most significant feature of the collapse is that prior to the appearance of an event horizon, the collapse proceeds quite homologously (cf. Appenzeller and Fricke 1972 and Wilson 1979). This result is not surprising in light of the demonstration by Goldreich and Weber (1980) that the Newtonian adiabatic collapse of a sphere with $\Gamma = 4/3$ admits a similarity solution. Astrophysically, the homologous, coherent nature of the implosion suggests that, when nonspherical distortions are present, an appreciable burst of gravitational radiation may be emitted during the short time interval during which the bulk of the matter streams across the event horizon. Such coherent behavior is necessary (but not sufficient) for the efficient generation of gravitational radiation (see Rees 1977 and §V below).

III. NONSPHERICAL STELLAR CORE COLLAPSE MODELED BY HOMOGENEOUS ELLIPSOIDS

Richard Saenz and I have performed a series of calculations employing homogeneous Newtonian ellipsoids to determine the gravitational radiation emitted during the nonspherical collapse of a rotating, stellar core (see Shapiro 1979 for a general review of ellipsoidal collapse calculations and Saenz and Shapiro 1981 for a recent analysis). The collapsing core models the 1.4 $M_\odot$ degenerate core of a massive, evolved star ($M > 8\ M_\odot$) which undergoes catastrophic collapse. Presumably, the collapse is followed by a supernova explosion which leaves behind a neutron star remnant. The justification for employing homogeneous ellipsoids to model such an event is that the pressure during the implosion is dominated by degenerate, relativistic electrons. This means that the adiabatic index Γ of the gas remains close to 4/3 until nuclear densities are reached (Lamb et al. 1978, Bethe et al. 1979). Accordingly, the collapse of the inner region of the core (~0.8 $M_\odot$) proceeds homologously (recall §II). Since homologous motion is the distinguishing characteristic

of ellipsoidal motion, where velocities are always linear functions
of the coordinates, ellipsoids can model many aspects of core collapse quite well.

In general, Newtonian ellipsoids provide convenient "beginner"
models for exploring 2+1 and 3+1-dimensional fluid flow. They can
be embellished with sufficient micro- and macrophysical properties
(e.g. internal gravity, a realistic equation of state, "shock" and
acoustic dissipation, etc.) to reproduce reliably many of the key
results found by more detailed, hydrodynamical calculations of collapse, where they exist. Moreover, the Newtonian 3+1 <u>PDE's</u> for the
hydrodynamic flow of a homogeneous ellipsoid separate to coupled
<u>ODE's</u>, which are much easier to integrate. It is this feature which
makes ellipsoids so attractive for modeling nonspherical fluid
motion: the resulting solutions are (numerically speaking) "exact".

In the most recent model calculations by Saenz and Shapiro, the
adiabatic, "hot" equation of state for dense matter due to Lamb
et al. (1978) was employed, together with a realistic shock dissipation algorithm. We found that, following collapse and rebound, all
<u>large</u> amplitude density oscillations were effectively damped after
the first few core bounces. However, <u>small</u> amplitude ($\delta\rho/\rho \ll 1$),
highly eccentric oscillations about the high temperature, equi-
librium state persist and can give rise to appreciable amounts of
gravitational radiation.

The radiation efficiency $\Delta E/M$ as a function of the core angular
momentum J is plotted in Figure 3. The initial eccentricity e_i and
rotation period P_i are also shown. The results for the first bounce
(dashed line) exhibit the familiar form

$$\Delta E/M \;\propto\; e_i^4 \;\propto\; J^4 \qquad \text{(low J)} \tag{1}$$

for low J (i.e., low e_i), with a maximum at large J (large e_i) and
decreasing for higher J. The efficiency is low for low J since the
collapsing configuration is nearly spherical and the quadrupole moment remains small. The efficiency is low for very high J since
centrifugal forces prevent the collapse from reaching high densities
and short collapse timescales ($t_{coll} \sim 1/\sqrt{G\rho}$); accordingly, the time
rate of change of the quadrupole moment is small.

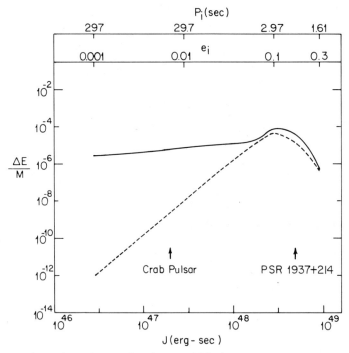

Fig. 3 – Gravitational radiation efficiency versus angular momentum
        for nonspherical stellar core collapse.

     The solid curve shows the total gravitational radiation effi-
ciency after all oscillations have decayed and the core has settled
into a final (hot) equilibrium state. For the high $J > 10^{48}$ erg-
sec cores, the energy loss occurs mainly during the initial collapse
and rebound. For the low-J cores with $10^{46} < J < 10^{48}$ erg-sec, the
radiation loss is considerably enhanced after the first few bounces.
The enhancement results from the numerous small amplitude oscillations about the hot equilibrium state which drive the eccentricities
to large values. However, the efficiency only attains a maximum
value of 10^{-4}, even for the high-J cores. Interestingly, the collapse associated with the formation of the recently discovered
millisecond pulsar, PSR 1937+214 (period = 1.55 ms; Backer et al.
1982) manages to achieve this value. Here we assume that the angular momentum characterizing this pulsar was already present in the
collapsing core and not "accreted" later on (Brecher and Chanmugan

1983; but see Backer et al. 1982, Gold 1983; and Arons 1983 for
alternative scenarios).

Wave amplitudes were also calculated for the collapse sequence
shown in Figure 3. For cores collapsing with the estimated angular
momentum of the Crab pulsar (the second shortest period pulsar), the
amplitude has a peak value of

$$h \sim 0.01 \frac{GM}{rc^2} , \qquad\qquad (2)$$

where r is the distance to the source. This amplitude corresponds
to $h \sim 10^{-22}$ for a source in the Virgo cluster, where the collapse
rate should be ~ 1 per month. This amplitude is close to the minimum value that should be detectable sometime in the future by
ground-based laser interferometers now being constructed (Thorne
1980 and private communication, this meeting). Although larger
amplitudes are expected from the collapse of faster (e.g. millisecond) or nearby cores, such events are less likely. Moreover, if
anything, our ellipsoidal models may overestimate the post-shock
oscillations and corresponding wave emission. In a recent axisymmetric, Newtonian, hydrodynamical calculation of a collapsing core
with rotation, Müller (1982) found maximum efficiencies an order of
magnitude below those given by ellipsoidal models. These calculations, however, adopted a somewhat different equation of state and
terminated immediately after the first bounce, so a direct comparison is not yet available.

IV. HEAD-ON COLLISION OF IDENTICAL NEUTRON STARS:
HYDRODYNAMIC CALCULATIONS IN ONE DIMENSION

A more efficient, if less frequent, source of gravitational
radiation is a direct collision of two compact objects. Possible
sites for collisions between supermassive black holes, supermassive
stars and neutron stars are the dense nuclei of active galaxies and
quasars (Thorne and Braginsky 1976, Rees 1977, and Blandford and
Thorne 1979), and such collisions provide plausible models for the
violent activity observed in these regions (Zel'dovich and Novikov
1971, Ostriker 1979). Collisions between neutron stars could also

occur in close binary systems, following the decay of the binary orbits via gravitational radiation (Clark and Eardley 1977). With the exception of head-on collisions between two black holes (Smarr 1979) few reliable calculations exist for the collision of two compact stars and the collision-induced generation of gravitational radiation. This situation is again due to numerical complexities which arise when treating a hydrodynamical process which is inherently 2+1 -dimensional and relativistic (see, e.g., Wilson 1979).

Undaunted by these difficulties, I recently performed an amusing, if imperfect, hydrodynamical model calculation of the collision of two identical neutron stars which collide head-on at free-fall velocity (Shapiro 1980). The hydrodynamical treatment was Newtonian and adiabatic, with gravitational radiation calculated as a perturbation in the slow-motion, weak-field limit. My key simplification consisted in restricting all motion to be parallel to the collision axis. This one-dimensional approximation, though naive, should yield reasonable estimates provided, as I suspect, the dominant contribution to the radiation results from the initial compression, deceleration and reexpansion of the gas along the collision axis.

Partial justification for this one-dimensional approach is provided by the two-dimensional hydrodynamic calculations of Seidl and Cameron (1979) for head-on collisions of solar-type stars. They found that for low impact velocities (< free-fall), little sideward expansion of the gas occurred and most of the ejected material was driven back by two recoil shocks along the collision axis. Similar conclusions were indicated by the preliminary numerical results of Smarr and Wilson (1978), who, in collaboration with Evans (this volume), are developing a fully relativistic, two-dimensional hydrodynamical code to treat collisions between compact stars.

Consider the head-on collision illustrated schematically in Figure 4 of two "planar polytropes" moving towards each other along the z-axis. The calculation focuses on two, oppositely moving, cubical regions of mass M in the colliding polytropes (see the upper right-hand insert). Hatched regions indicate the density profile ρ inside the two stars. Prior to collision each star is supported in hydrostatic equilibrium by cold, polytropic gas pressure. The stars are assumed to collide at free-fall velocity at t = 0 = z (Phase I).

Following the collision, all gravitational forces are included but energy dissipation is ignored. Recoil shocks decelerate the coalescing material, heating the gas to finite temperature $T > 0$ (Phase II). After some initial oscillations, the gas settles down to a finite temperature, quasi-static state. Eventually, energy dissipation causes the gas to cool and contract to a final, zero-temperature equilibrium state (Phase III). Most of the radiation is generated during Phase II.

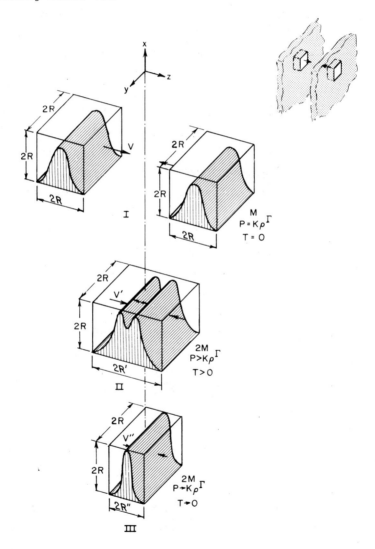

Fig. 4 – Schematic illustration of the head-on collision of two
     neutron stars modeled as "planar polytropes."

For the scenario depicted in Figure 4, I found that the amount of radiation generated <u>after</u> the collision can significantly exceed the (free-fall) radiation generated before the collision, due to gravitational acceleration of infalling gas following impact. The gravitational radiation efficiency, $\Delta E/M$, is larger than 1% for a typical neutron star collision if each star has a mass M satisfying $M > 0.5\ M_\odot$. This promising result seems to be rather insensitive to the adopted nuclear equation of state.

The high wave efficiency calculated for colliding neutron stars is appreciably larger than the efficiency found for stellar core collapse. The reason is that the colliding matter distribution is inherently aspherical, the propagation of recoil shocks back through the matter produces rather rapid time variations in the quadrupole moment, and the initial compression attains higher densities and shorter dynamical timescales than are attained in core collapse. It is interesting that a head-on collision of two neutron stars may also generate more radiation than the head-on collision of two black holes of comparable mass (for colliding black holes, $\Delta E/M \sim 10^{-3}$; Smarr 1979. Although the gravitational fields in a black hole collision are inherently stronger, they serve to redshift and recapture the radiation more than anything else. The importance of matter pressure, strong shocks and angular momentum for efficient radiation generation is highlighted in §V, where we consider strong-field scenarios involving matter.

Event rates for the destruction of compact binary systems have been estimated by Clark, van den Heuvel, and Sutanyo (1979) and by Clark (1979). They find an upper limit of $\sim$ 1 event per year within $\sim$ 40 Mpc of the Earth, requiring detector sensitivities of $h \sim 10^{-22}$ to be observable. Wave amplitudes exceeding this magnitude are indeed achieved in the collisions considered here and may be detectable in the future by ground-base laser interferometers.

V. NONSPHERICAL, STRONG-FIELD CALCULATIONS

Gravitational radiation should be produced most efficiently during asymmetric, dynamical phenomena occurring in <u>strong</u> gravitational fields. However, numerical relativity is as yet in its infancy, so few calculations of the generation of gravity waves in

strong fields currently exist. Most of the analyses have been based
on the perturbation methods of Regge and Wheeler (1957) and Zerilli
(1970). Davis, Ruffini, Press and Price (1971; hereinafter DRPP)
calculated the total energy released in gravitational radiation when
a point mass, m, falls from rest at infinity into a more massive
black hole, $M \gg m$. They obtained

$$\Delta E^{(one)} \simeq 0.0104 \; \mu^2/M \; , \tag{3}$$

where $\mu = mM/(m+M)$ is the reduced mass and the superscript "(one)"
refers to the single point particle falling into the hole.
Detweiler and Szedenits (1979) allowed the point mass some angular
momentum and found that the energy radiated could be much greater
than $\Delta E^{(one)}$ for particular trajectories. Cunningham, Price and
Moncrief (1978, 1979) computed the gravitational radiation arising
from the collapse of a dust cloud, deformed slightly by differential
rotation, to a black hole.

    Fully relativistic, nonperturbative calculations involving the
head-on collision of equal mass black holes have been performed by
Smarr and Eppley (Smarr 1979). Interestingly, the calculated energy
outflow in gravitational radiation is surprisingly close to $\Delta E^{(one)}$
given by equation (3) with $m=M$. Fully relativistic, nonlinear calculations of the gravity wave emission from the one-dimensional collapse of an infinite cylinder have been performed by Piran (1979).
In a somewhat different vein, the one-dimensional propagation of
nonlinear gravity waves in an expanding universe has been analyzed
by Centrella (1980).

    To explore further the generation of gravitational radiation in
strong fields, Mark Haugan, Ira Wasserman and I analyzed the emission from extended axisymmetric distributions of dust particles
(total mass m) falling radially onto a Schwarzschild black hole of
mass $M \gg m$.

    We performed these calculations for two distinct reasons.
First, our results can be used as guides for the construction of
two-dimensional, time-dependent numerical codes in general relativity which can handle strong fields and matter. Such codes are
designed to follow the evolution of an axisymmetric matter

distribution in a strong gravitational field and to compute the resulting gravitational radiation. Numerical codes of this type are
now being developed by, for example, Evans, Smarr and Wilson (see
Wilson 1979, Dykema 1980 and Evans (this volume) for status reports). We derived "analytic" scaling laws, including numerical
coefficients, which can be used to test the accuracy of such codes.
The formulation of reliable numerical procedures for calculating the
gravitational wave emission from raw field data on a spacetime lattice is somewhat subtle in these nonspherical codes. Our "exact"
results should thus prove useful in checking and/or comparing the
numerical algorithms designed to calculate such a quantity. In
particular, the scenarios we calculated can be set up as (nonsingular) initial data and integrated via the ADM equations in a relativistic, 2+1-dimensional numerical program. Second, our calculations, in addition to their usefulness for the numerical relativist,
may give some insight into the generation of gravitational radiation
in a number of realistic and potentially promising strong field
astrophysical events. We shall discuss two applications below.

a) Formulation

Our approach is based on the perturbation equations of Regge
and Wheeler (1957) and Zerilli (1970). For an azimuthally symmetric, radially infalling dust cloud, the Fourier transform of the
2^L-pole component of the metric perturbation is related to a radial
wave function $R_L^{(e)}(r,\omega)$, the solution to the Zerilli wave equation

$$\frac{d^2 R_L^{(e)}(r,\omega)}{dr*^2} + \left[\omega^2 - V_L(r)\right] R_L^{(e)}(r,\omega) = S_L(r,\omega) . \tag{4}$$

In equation (4), $r* = r + 2M \ln (r/2M - 1)$, $V_L(r)$ is an "effective
potential", and the source term, $S_L(r,\omega)$, depends linearly on $T^{\mu\nu}$,
the stress-energy tensor of the matter field. Now $T^{\mu\nu}$ for a dust
particle swarm is obtained from $[T^{\mu\nu}]^{(one)}$ for a single particle by
a simple superposition:

$$T^{\mu\nu} = \sum_i [T^{\mu\nu}]^{(one)}_{(i)} \; .$$

(5)

Accordingly, the linear nature of the source term in equation (4) implies that the solution to the radial wave equation for the swarm may be obtained by a superposition of one-particle solutions. We find

$$R_L^{(e)}(r,\omega) = [R_L^{(e)}(r,\omega)]^{(one)} \, f_L(\omega) \; ,$$

(6)

where the "suppression form factor" $f_L(\omega)$ is given by

$$f_L = \frac{1}{N} \int d^3r \; \sqrt{-g} \; u^o n(\underset{\sim}{r},T_o) \; P_L(\cos\,\theta) \; \exp[i\omega(T_o - T(r))] \; ,$$

(7)

and N, the total particle number in the swarm, is given by

$$N = \int d^3r \; \sqrt{-g} \; u^o \; n(\underset{\sim}{r},\,T_o) \; .$$

(8)

In equations (7) and (8), $n(\underset{\sim}{r},\,T_o)$ is the proper number density, u^μ is the 4-velocity of dust particles at $\underset{\sim}{r} = (r,\Omega)$ at some fiducial time T_o, and $P_L(z)$ is the Legendre polynomial of order L. The resulting wave energy spectrum then becomes

$$\left[\frac{dE(\omega)}{d\omega}\right]_{2^L\text{-pole}} = \left[\frac{dE(\omega)}{d\omega}\right]^{(one)}_{2^L\text{-pole}} \; \left|f_L(\omega)\right|^2 \; ,$$

(9)

where the first factor on the right hand side has been determined by DRPP. By inspection of equations (7) and (8), we have the crucial result

$$\left|f_L(\omega)\right|^2 < 1 \; .$$

(10)

b)   Radiation Efficiency: Upper Limit

Equation (10) implies that the total radiated energy is restricted via

$$\Delta E = \int d\omega \; \frac{dE}{d\omega} = \sum_{L} \int d\omega \; \left[\frac{dE}{d\omega}\right]^{(one)} \left| f_L(\omega) \right|^2 < \Delta E^{(one)}. \tag{11}$$

In other words, <u>the total energy radiated by a freely-falling dust swarm is always less than the energy radiated by a point-particle of the same mass.</u>

The physical reason for this severe suppression arises from <u>phase incoherence</u>: independent, freely-falling mass points in an extended distribution emit outgoing gravity waves that are out of phase with one another. Superposing the far-field metric perturbations from each of the radiating fragments leads to a reduced energy outflux. (This point has already been noted in the context of aspherical collapse in strong gravitational fields by Nakamura and Sasaki 1981.) In the limit where the particles approaching the horizon are widely separated (i.e., separations $\gg$ M) the radiation from the individual masses is completely incoherent. In this limit we simply add the energies radiated by each particle, given by equation (1), to determine the total energy radiated. For a body of mass m disrupted into N "point" masses of equal mass m/N, the total energy generated is

$$\Delta E^{(N)} = \frac{1}{N} \Delta E^{(one)} \qquad \text{(incoherence limit)} , \tag{12}$$

where $\Delta E^{(one)}$ is the energy for a single particle of mass m. Notice that as the number of particles increases without limit, the energy radiated decreases to zero. The radiative behavior of finite-size, continuous bodies falling into black holes is intermediate between that of coherent radiation from a single point mass and that of incoherent radiation from widely separated, distinct point masses. For many cases heretofore regarded as promising astrophysical scenarios for the generation of copious gravitational radiation, phase incoherence significantly reduces the total emitted energy and corresponding wave amplitudes.

(c)   Application 1:   Head-On Collision of a Star with a More
Massive Black Hole

Figure 5 is a schematic illustration of a head-on collision of
a star with a more massive black hole. Far from the hole the star
remains in rough spherical equilibrium, as its internal stresses
greatly exceed the tidal forces of the hole. At $r \approx \bar{r}_o$ the tidal
forces become comparable to the internal forces and the star is disrupted. As it falls still closer to the hole, the star behaves
roughly as a ball of dust since the hole's tidal field dominates the
internal forces of the star. We expect that the calculations of the
previous section will apply to this late phase $\bar{r}_o \gg r$. We shall
assume that

$$\bar{r}_o \gg M \text{ and } \bar{r}_o \gg a ,$$

where a is the radius of the star.

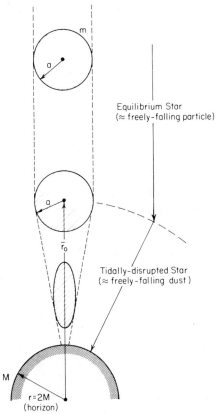

Fig. 5 - Schematic illustration of a head-on collision of a star
with a more massive, Schwarzschild black hole.

The radius $\bar{r}_o$ may be equated to the Jeans tidal limit,

$$\bar{r}_o \approx 2a \, (M/m)^{1/3} \tag{13}$$

(Chandrasekhar 1969, §56). We note that inside $\bar{r}_o$, the stellar radius will be tidally stretched in the radial direction to a value

$$\delta r \approx a \, (\bar{r}_o/r)^{1/2} \, , \qquad (\bar{r} < r_o) \, . \tag{14}$$

Hense as $r \rightarrow 2M$, the radius will increase to

$$(\delta r)_{2M} \approx a(\bar{r}_o/2M)^{1/2} \, , \quad (r \rightarrow 2M) \, . \tag{15}$$

Equation (15) establishes a critical scale for the suppression of radiation by phase incoherence. Low frequencies satisfying $\omega(\delta r)_{2M} \ll 1$ suffer little suppression, while high frequencies satisfying $\omega(\delta r)_{2M} \gg 1$ are heavily suppressed. This behavior is reflected in the functional form of $f_L(\omega)$.

Define a critical frequency according to

$$\omega_{crit} = (\delta r_{2M})^{-1} \, . \tag{16}$$

Now the energy spectrum $[dE(\omega)/d\omega]^{(one)}$ for the one-particle case (DRPP 1971, Wagoner 1979, Shapiro and Teukolsky 1983) peaks sharply at $\omega \approx 0.32 \, M^{-1}$. Recalling equations (9) and (11), we then conclude that significant suppression of the gravitational radiation from a freely-falling dust cloud will occur whenever $\omega_{crit} \ll 0.32 \, M^{-1}$ or whenever

$$\frac{(\delta r_{2M})}{M} = \frac{a}{M} \, (\frac{\bar{r}_o}{2M})^{1/2} \gg 1 \quad (\text{suppression}) \, . \tag{17}$$

As a consequence of equation (17), we conclude that radiation suppression will always be appreciable whenever "big" stars of large radius fall into "small" black holes. Specifically, our calculations show that the single point particle result should remain approximately valid for the gravitational radiation emitted by neutron stars falling into black holes more massive than ~ 3 $M_{\odot}$. However, significant suppression of the total energy emitted is found for main sequence stars and white dwarfs falling into holes less massive than ~ 7×10^5 $M_{\odot}$ and ~ 6×10^3 $M_{\odot}$, respectively. Results are summarized in Haugan, Shapiro and Wasserman (1982), Table 2.

d)   Application 2: Nonspherical Dust Shell Accretion
onto a Black Hole

Figure 6 illustrates the case of a spheroidal dust shell of mass m and arbitrary eccentricity e falling radially into a Schwarzschild black hole of mass M $\gg$ m. The matter distribution is shown at some fiducial time t = T_O when the particles are uniformly distributed with density n_O. The shell lies within the boundaries r_{min} = r_O g(μ) and r_{max} = K r_{min}, where the distortion function g(μ) is given by

$$g(\mu) = 1 + e^2(1 - \mu^2) \qquad [\text{oblate shell}]$$
$$= 1 + e^2 \mu^2 \qquad [\text{prolate shell}] \qquad (18)$$

and where K and r_O are constants (we assume for simplicity that r_O $\gg$ M, K $\gg$ 1).

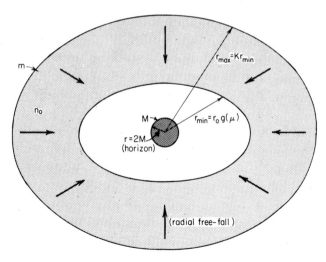

Fig. 6 - Radial infall of a spheroidal dust shell into a
         Schwarzschild black hole.

Adopting the perturbation formalism described above to analyze the emitted radiation, Shapiro and Wasserman (1982) obtained the results plotted in Figure 7 for the radiation efficiency as a function of eccentricity e^2. Only the L=2 (quadrupole) contribution is shown (the odd parity waves with L = 3,5,...etc. vanish identically). Circles denote our numerical results for Kr_o = 10, triangles for Kr_o = 30 and squares for Kr_o = 100. Open symbols were computed for oblate shells, for which a smooth solid line has been drawn through the data. Filled symbols were computed for prolate shells; dashed lines have been drawn through these data. The solid lines proportional to e^4, $e^{-2/3}$ and e^{-7} show the expected scaling behavior in the appropriate e^2 regimes. Analytic coefficients for these scaling laws were computed in these limiting regions. The DRPP limit $\Delta E^{(one)}$ = 0.0092 m/M is shown at the upper right in the figure.

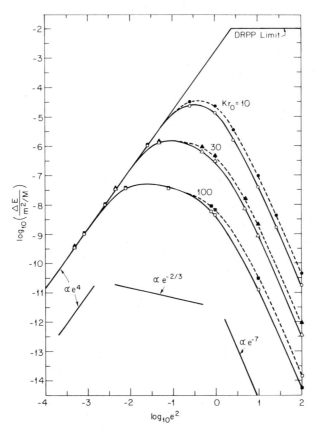

Fig. 7 - Gravitational radiation efficiency versus eccentricity for the scenario depicted in Fig. 6.

It should be observed that at fixed Kr_o, the shape of the efficiency curve is very comparable to the shape found for spheroidal core collapse depicted in Figure 3. At low e we again find $\Delta E \propto e^4$ [cf. Eqn. (1)]. This is evident from the quadrupole emission formula, $\Delta E \propto Q^2/\tau^5$, where Q is the quadrupole moment and τ is the collapse timescale. For low e, $Q \propto e^2$ while τ = independent of e. For very high e, however, the increase in τ with e dominates the behavior and the emission falls with increasing e. The low eccentricity regime resides in the domain $e \ll e_{crit}$, where

$$e_{crit} \approx (Kr_o)^{-3/4} .$$
\hfill (19)

The nonspherical dust calculations described here have obvious applications to nonspherical collapse to a black hole and to nonspherical accretion onto a black hole. The details of the radiation efficiency curve are not as important as the fact that they now exist, to high accuracy, for an interesting (albeit idealized) nonspherical, strong-field scenario.

e)   Summary and Conclusions

The principal conclusions to be drawn from these strong-field computations are:

(1) $\Delta E \le \Delta E^{(one)}$, so that even in a strong gravitational field, the radial infall of nonspherical dust provides only a weak source of gravitational radiation. Of course, we have only shown that $\Delta E \le 0.01 \ \mu^2/M$ when $m \ll M$. However, we suspect that this result probably holds even when $m \approx M$, as was found for the vacuum case of a head-on, black hole collision.

(2)   Efficient wave generation from infall requires (a) pressure (to induce bounces, shocks, etc.) and/or (b) angular momentum (cf. Detweiler and Szedenits 1979). In the latter case, test mass calculations probably yield upper limits to the radiation efficiency, due to phase incoherence in extended sources.

(3)   The axisymmetric, strong-field dust calculations described here may prove useful for testing general relativistic, 2+1-dimensional hydrodynamical codes which treat both matter and fields. In

particular, such codes can set up as initial data and subsequently solve the axisymmetric matter distribution we consider (note that the central black hole can be replaced by a nonsingular, collapsing spherical dustball of the same mass whose surface lies inside the exterior matter field). The "analytic" results summarized above should be especially useful in checking the dynamical component of the far-field metric (i.e., the radiation). Since the numerical determination of the gravitational radiation from raw data on a finite spacetime lattice is somewhat subtle, the availability of "analytic" results and scaling laws may now provide code builders with some welcome means of verification.

In this spirit we offer Figures 6 and 7 and the associated "analytic" results to Jim Wilson as our "gift" to him on his 60th birthday. I predict that in the not too distant future he and his colleagues will provide in return a rugged numerical code which can reliably reproduce our "analytic" results as trivial special cases!

This work was supported in part by National Science Foundation Grant AST 81-16370 and by an Alfred P. Sloan Foundation Grant.

REFERENCES

Appenzeller, I., and Fricke, K.J. 1972, Astr. Ap., **18**, 10.

Arnowitt, R., Deser, S., and Misner, C.W. 1962, in "Gravitation", ed. L. Witten (New York: Wiley) (ADM).

Arons, J. 1983, Nature, **302**, 301.

Backer, D.C., Kulkarni, S.R., Heiles, C., Davis, M.M., and Goss, M.W. 1982, Nature, **300**, 615.

Bethe, H.A., Brown, G.E., Applegate, J., and Lattimer, J.M. 1979, Nucl. Phys., **A324**, 487.

Blandford, R., and Thorne, K.S. 1979, in "General Relativity. An Einstein Centenary Survey", ed. S.W. Hawking and W. Israel (Cambridge: Cambridge University Press).

Brecher, K., and Chanmugan, G. 1983, Nature, **302**, 124.

Centrella, J. 1980, Ap. J., **241**, 875.

Chandrasekhar, S. 1969, "Ellipsoidal Figures of Equilibrium" (New Haven: Yale University Press).

Clark, J.P.A. 1979, in "Sources of Gravitational Radiation", ed. L.L. Smarr (Cambridge: Cambridge University Press).

Clark, J.P.A., and Eardley, D.M. 1977, Ap. J., **215**, 311.

Clark, J.P.A., van den Heuvel, E.P.J., and Sutanyo, W. 1979, Astr. Ap., **72**, 120.

Cunningham, C.J., Price, R.H., and Moncrief, V. 1978, Ap. J., **224**, 683.

Cunningham, C.J., Price, R.H., and Moncrief, V. 1979, Ap. J., **230**, 870.

Davis, M.R., Ruffini, R., Press, W.H., and Price, R.H. 1971, Phys. Rev. Lett., **27**, 1466 (DRPP).

Detweiler, S.L., and Szedenits, E., Jr. 1979, Ap. J., **231**, 211.

Dykema, P.G., 1980, Ph.D. Thesis (University of Texas at Austin).

Eardley, D.M., and Smarr, L. 1979, Phys. Rev. D, **19**, 2239.

Gold, T. 1983, private communication.

Goldreich, P., and Weber, S.V. 1980, Ap. J., **238**, 991.

Haugan, M. Shapiro, S.L., and Wasserman, I. 1982, Ap. J., **257**, 283.

Hawking, S.W., and Ellis, G.F.R. 1973, "Large Scale Structure of Spacetime" (Cambridge: Cambridge University Press).

Hoyle, F., and Fowler, W.A. 1963a, M.N.R.A.S., 125, 169.

Hoyle, F., and Fowler, W.A. 1963b, Nature, 197, 533.

Lamb, D.Q., Lattimer, J.M., Pethick, C.J., and Ravenhall, D.G. 1978, Phys. Rev. Lett., 41, 1623.

Müller, E. 1982, Astr. Ap., 114, 53.

Nakamura, T., and Sasaki, M. 1981, Phys. Letters, 106 B, 69.

Ostriker, J.P. 1979, in "Sources of Gravitational Radiation", ed. L.L. Smarr (Cambridge: Cambridge University Press).

Piran, T. 1979, in "Sources of Gravitational Radiation", ed. L.L. Smarr (Cambridge: Cambridge University Press), p. 409.

Rees, M.J. 1977, "Proc. Internat. Symp. Experimental Gravitation" (Rome: Academia Nazionale dei Lincei), p. 423.

Regge, T., and Wheeler, J.A. 1957, Phys. Rev., 108, 1063.

Saenz, R.A., and Shapiro, S.L. 1981, Ap. J., 244, 1033.

Salpeter, E.E. 1964, Ap. J., 140, 796.

Seidl, F.G.P., and Cameron, A.G.W. 1972, Ap. Space Sci., 15, 44.

Shapiro, S.L. 1979, in "Sources of Gravitational Radiation", ed. L.L. Smarr (Cambridge: Cambridge University Press), p. 335.

Shapiro, S.L. 1980, Ap. J., 240, 246.

Shapiro, S.L., and Teukolsky, S.A. 1979, Ap. J. Lett., 234, L177.

Shapiro, S.L., and Teukolsky, S.A. 1980, Ap. J., 235, 199.

Shapiro, S.L., and Teukolsky, S.A. 1983, "Black Holes, White Dwarfs and Neutron Stars: The Physics of Compact Objects" (New York: Wiley).

Shapiro, S.L., and Wasserman, I. 1982, Ap. J., 260, 838.

Smarr, L. 1979, in "Sources of Gravitational Radiation", ed. L.L. Smarr (Cambridge: Cambridge University Press). p. 245.

Smarr, L. Taubes, J.R., and Wilson, J.R. 1980, in "Essays in General Relativity", ed. E. Tipler (New York: Academic Press).

Smarr, L., and Wilson, J.R. 1978, talk given at the Battelle workshop "Sources of Gravitational Radiation".

Smarr, L. and York, J.W. 1978, Phys. Rev. D, **17**, 2529.

Thorne, K.S. and Braginsky, V.B. 1976, Ap. J. Lett., **204**, L1.

Thorne, K.S. 1980, Rev. Mod. Phys., **52**, 285.

Wagoner, R.V. 1979, Phys. Rev. D, **19**, 2897.

Wilson, J.R. 1979, in "Sources of Gravitational Radiation", ed.
    L.L. Smarr (Cambridge: Cambridge University Press).

Wilson, K.G. 1975, Rev. Mod. Phys., **47**, 773.

Wilson, K.G. 1980, in "Recent Developments in Gauge Theories", eds.
    G. 'tHooft et. al. (New York: Plenum).

Zel'dovich, Ya.B. 1964, Soviet Phys. Doklady, **9**, 195.

Zel'dovich, Ya.B., and Novikov, I.D. 1971, "Relativistic
    Astrophysics" (Chicago: University of Chicago Press).

Zerilli, F.J. 1970, Phys. Rev. D., **2**, 2141.

A Method for Numerical Simulation of Gravitational Collapse and Gravitational Radiation Generation

Charles R. Evans[1,2,3]

The University of Texas at Austin

Lawrence Livermore National Laboratory

ABSTRACT

A mathematical method is given for obtaining fully constrained numerical solutions to the Einstein equations for asymptotically flat matter-filled or vacuum spacetimes. Suitable boundary conditions for the solution of the elliptic constraint equations in a finite region are formulated. An application of this approach is discussed for axisymmetric and nonrotating models of gravitational collapse. The equations so derived have been incorporated successfully in a computer code. In addition, this method uses a simplifying 3-gauge which allows a natural "dynamical" component of the metric to be identified. This variable is related to the weak-field transverse-traceless gravitational radiation variable $h_+^{TT}(t-r)$. Mass and radiation flux (edit) formulae are discussed with reference to numerical results from several core collapse and bounce calculations.

---

[1] Associated Western Universities Laboratory Graduate Fellow

[2] Present address: Astronomy Department, University of Illinois, Urbana, IL 61801

[3] In partial fulfillment of the degree of Ph.D. in Physics at the University of Texas at Austin

I. INTRODUCTION

This paper is meant to serve as a report on the progress, since Jim Wilson's (1979) discussion, in our effort to simulate axisymmetric gravitational collapse numerically. The emphasis here is on the mathematical technique we are now using to produce stable and regular numerical solutions. Elsewhere (Evans, Smarr, and Wilson, 1984a) we discuss a number of the numerical techniques that are used in our computer code.

Jim Wilson has brought to numerical relativity a number of sophisticated numerical techniques and experience from other areas of numerical astrophysics. Our present method owes much to several innovative approaches Jim introduced and which I highlight here. It has been my great pleasure and benefit to have been able to collaborate with and study under Jim on his project. I greatly value the experience. Our other collaborators on this effort are Larry Smarr and Pieter Dykema.

One objective in numerical relativity is to calculate the dynamics and emitted gravitational radiation from violent, strong-field, asymmetric, and high (internal) velocity gravitational collapse (for applications to cosmology see Centrella and Wilson 1983, 1984). The calculation of such energetic sources is currently out of reach of analytic techniques. Yet it is precisely these violent events which are likely to be the most efficient sources of gravitational radiation and therefore (provided they occur frequently enough) may be the first sources detected experimentally. Recent, and expected, improvements in detector sensitivities (Epstein 1979, Weiss 1979, Thorne 1980a, and Fairbank 1984) are making detailed predictions of source characteristics all the more necessary.

A number of authors have taken varied approaches to modeling gravitational radiation generation from core collapse. Turner and Wagoner (1979) have studied slowly rotating, axisymmetric perturbations about detailed spherical Newtonian gravitational collapse (supernova) models. Their limiting assumption is that the rotation be dynamically insignificant, and under this restriction their observed efficiencies are very small ($\Delta E/M < 10^{-12}$). In an article in this volume, Shapiro describes a numerical program (see also Shapiro 1979, Saenz and Shapiro 1981) to calculate gravitational radiation emission based on simplified Newtonian ellipsoidal uniform density, uniformly rotating models of collapse. Varying degrees of complexity for the equation of state (EOS) for supernova core collapse are assumed and an attempt is made to model "shock dissipation", though true hydrodynamic freedom is not allowed by their assumptions. Müller (1982) has computed quadrupole and octupole emission resulting from slowly and rapidly rotating stellar core collapse from calculations (Müller and Hillebrandt 1981) produced by a full two-dimensional, Newtonian hydrodynamic code with a realistic nuclear EOS.

We have taken a different approach and have sought first to obtain fully self-consistent solutions of the Einstein equations and relativistic hydrodynamics. This approach has been motivated in part by the recognition that strong fields and high velocities are important effects in gravitational radiation emission from supernova core collapse (Evans, Smarr, and Wilson 1984a,b) and by a more general desire to probe the structure of general relativity. Our method at present allows the simulation of axisymmetric and nonrotating gravitational collapse, i.e., the collapse to a black hole or deep hydrodynamic bounce of oblate or prolate compact objects. In addition, vacuum spacetimes (Brill waves) and the head-on collision of two neutron stars (Wilson 1979) can be studied. Less emphasis has been placed so far on detailed microphysics and core asymmetry generation mechanisms (rotation or magnetic fields). Our EOS is typically taken to be $p = (\Gamma-1)\rho\varepsilon$ with adiabatic index Γ, rest energy density ρ and specific internal energy density ε. We usually model the entire core with a constant Γ ($\Gamma = 2$ to model a stiff EOS, for example). Future work will include the addition of axial rotation, magnetic fields and a realistic nuclear EOS. Altering the initial model and the EOS should allow supermassive stars ($M \sim 10^6 M_\odot$) to be studied as well.

In the next section the mathematical method to compute a fully constrained evolution of the Einstein equations is described. The York method for obtaining initial data, used in our code, is briefly discussed (see York, this volume, for a more complete discussion). In addition a new technique is described for obtaining the constrained parts of the gravitational field at subsequent times (off the initial time slice) during the evolution. Some general aspects of how boundary conditions can be posed at large but finite radius for these (elliptic) constraint equations are treated, including the formulation of several new boundary conditions.

Section III displays the particular differential equations and boundary conditions that result from application of the method to axisymmetric, nonrotating collapse. Using the constrained approach and the simplifying gauge, the evolution problem for the gravitational field reduces to evolving a single pair of fields representing precisely the single dynamical degree of freedom (only one independent polarization state exists with the assumed symmetries). The chosen "dynamical" component can be related in the weak-field wave zone to the usual transverse-traceless gravitational radiation amplitude $h_+^{TT}(t-r,\theta,\phi)$. This is shown in section IV to provide an added means (cf. Smarr 1979) of analyzing the emitted radiation, and the amplitude h_+^{TT} is the quantity of most direct interest to gravitational wave experimenters (Hamilton 1983).

In section IV, I discuss how the mass-energy of the isolated system is measured and how the energy flux and angular structure of the gravitational radiation can be calculated. The system mass and radiation flux edits are demonstrated with results from several core collapse and bounce calculations.

II. ASPECTS OF THE (3 + 1) DYNAMICAL FORMALISM
a) Gravitational Field

In order to carry out numerically the kinds of calculations we have mentioned it is necessary to pose general relativity as a dynamical (Cauchy) problem (see Eardley and Smarr 1979, Choquet-Bruhat and York 1980 for mathematical definition). In this approach one first solves an initial value problem. This amounts to finding a gravitational field and matter fields on an initial spacelike slice, Σ_0, consistent with the four constraint equations of general relativity. Then gauge conditions are given which determine, as the calculation unfolds, a set of nonintersecting spacelike surfaces in the future of Σ_0, each characterized by a constant coordinate time t, and a set of curves crossing these slices which carry along the spatial coordinates $\{x^i\}$. The remaining Einstein equations plus hydrodynamic equations are dynamical and give the evolution along these coordinate trajectories of the gravitational field and matter off of Σ_0.

We follow the (3 + 1) formalism of Arnowitt, Deser, and Misner (ADM; 1962). This involves using the unit timelike normal vector field n^μ to the spacelike surfaces $\Sigma(t)$, along with its associated projection operator $P^\mu{}_\nu = \delta^\mu{}_\nu + n^\mu n_\nu$, to decompose all 4-dimensional tensors into tensors that are tangent to the 3-surfaces. The projected tensors thus are 3-dimensional objects. The line element is given in the form

$$ds^2 = (-\alpha^2 + \beta_i \beta^i)dt^2 + 2\beta_i dx^i dt + \gamma_{ij} dx^i dx^j \quad , \qquad (2.1)$$

where indices run from 1 to 3. The 3-surfaces are characterized by t = constant and γ_{ij} is the (projected) intrinsic metric for the slice. The shift vector β_i is a spatial vector with $\beta^i = \gamma^{ij}\beta_j$, where $\gamma^{ij}\gamma_{jk} = \delta^i{}_k$, and α is the lapse function. The geometrical interpretation of the lapse and shift is as follows. If dt is the coordinate time separation between adjacent slices, αdt is the local orthogonal proper time interval. The vector αn^μ is then a natural vector field which connects the slices $\Sigma(t)$ and represents the tangents of curves parametrized by t which orthogonally intersect $\Sigma(t)$. The shift vector β^μ whose space components appear in the metric is spatial, i.e., $\beta^\mu n_\mu = 0$, and can be used to form the vector $t^\mu = \alpha n^\mu + \beta^\mu$, also parametrized by t, along which time derivatives are calculated. Comprehensive reviews of this material are given in York (1979) and York (1983). The freedom embodied in α and β^i represents the general covariance of relativity. When we wish to construct a numerical solution, however, specific kinematical conditions must be made which determine the lapse and shift.

Also associated with the slices is the second fundamental form or extrinsic curvature tensor,

$$K_{ij} = \frac{1}{2\alpha}(-\partial_t \gamma_{ij} + D_i\beta_j + D_j\beta_i) \quad , \qquad (2.2)$$

$$\partial_t \gamma_{ij} = -2\alpha K_{ij} + D_i \beta_j + D_j \beta_i \quad , \tag{2.6}$$

along with the hydrodynamic equations (given below), guarantee that equations (2.3) and (2.4) continue to be satisfied at subsequent times. While this is true analytically, it is important to note that this will not exactly hold during a numerical evolution. It thus becomes an issue whether the evolution is carried out by solving only the evolution equations or whether a reduced dynamical problem is solved, with the constraints being explicitly enforced (inverted) on each successive time slice to reconstruct the rest of the gravitational field. This latter approach, originally taken by Wilson (1979), is the one we have used in constructing our code, and our implementation of this procedure will form a central part of this discussion. An added bonus of using this approach in a numerical simulation is the resultant reduction in high frequency noise when fewer evolution equations are involved. These equations and the hydrodynamic equations which follow must be reduced further so that they can be used in a numerical calculation. The reduction involves turning covariant derivatives into partial derivatives as well as invoking any assumed symmetries. An example treating axisymmetric gravitational collapse will be discussed in section III.

b) Hydrodynamics

The hydrodynamic equations are derived by decomposing the equations of motion

$$\nabla_\mu T^{\mu\nu} = 0 \tag{2.7}$$

and any additional "conservation" laws for the fluid. Our derivation follows Wilson (1979) and Smarr, Taubes, and Wilson (1980), and differs slightly from the direct (3 + 1) method. Wilson writes the equations in a form that mimics as closely as possible Newtonian hy-

where D_i is the covariant derivative compatible with γ_{ij}, i.e., $D_k\gamma_{ij}$ = 0, and the time derivative ∂_t along t^μ has been used. The extrinsic curvature thus represents a time derivative of the metric.

The (3 + 1) method then uses α, β^i, γ_{ij}, K_{ij} and their derivatives (using ∂_t and D_i) to represent the gravitational field in the decomposition. In addition the 3-dimensional projections of the stress-energy tensor $T_{\mu\nu}$, namely the energy density $\rho_H = T_{\mu\nu}n^\mu n^\nu$, the momentum density $S_i = -T_{\mu\nu}n^\nu p^\mu{}_i$, and spatial stresses $S_{ij} = T_{\mu\nu}p^\mu{}_i p^\nu{}_j$ must be used to give the Einstein equations. These are the fluid properties as measured in the frame at rest within the slice rather than in the fluid rest frame. The Einstein equations, $G_{\mu\nu} = T_{\mu\nu}$ (with units $c = 1$, $G = (8\pi)^{-1}$), are rewritten by projecting the Riemann tensor and contracting to form $G_{\mu\nu}$. This leads to three sets of equations (York 1979):

$$\text{Hamiltonian constraint:}\quad R + K^2 - K^{ij}K_{ij} = 2\rho_H \quad , \qquad (2.3)$$

$$\text{Momentum constraint:}\quad D_j(K^j{}_i - \delta^j{}_i K) = S_i \quad , \qquad (2.4)$$

and

$$\partial_t K_{ij} = -D_i D_j \alpha + \alpha[R_{ij} - 2K_{i\ell}K^\ell{}_j + KK_{ij}$$

$$-S_{ij} + \frac{1}{2}\gamma_{ij}(S - \rho_H)] + \beta^\ell D_\ell K_{ij}$$

$$+ K_{i\ell}D_j\beta^\ell + K_{\ell j}D_i\beta^\ell \quad , \qquad (2.5)$$

where R_{ij} and R are respectively the Ricci tensor calculated from γ_{ij} and its trace, and K and S are respectively the traces of K_{ij} and S_{ij}.

Equations (2.3) and (2.4) contain only first time derivatives of the metric and thus are the four constraint equations representing the initial value problem. They must be satisfied by the data (K^{ij}, γ_{ij}, ρ_H, S_i) on the initial slice in order that there exist a proper embedding of the slice in the full spacetime. Given such data initially, the remaining evolution equations (2.5) and equations (2.2) rewritten as evolution equations for the 3-metric,

drodynamics. In this way standard, stable numerical transport techniques can be brought to bear on general relativistic hydrodynamics.

The source is taken to be a perfect fluid (except in the presence of shocks, where an artificial viscosity is introduced) with
stress-energy tensor

$$T^{\mu\nu} = \rho h U^{\mu} U^{\nu} + p g^{\mu\nu} \quad . \qquad (2.8)$$

Here $h = 1 + \varepsilon + p/\rho$ is the relativistic specific enthalpy, ρ the
rest energy density, ε the specific internal energy density, p the
isotropic pressure, and U^{μ} the fluid 4-velocity with $U^{\mu} U_{\mu} = -1$. The
energy densities and pressure are those present in the local fluid
rest frame. Conservation of rest mass is also used:

$$\nabla_{\mu}(\rho U^{\mu}) = \frac{1}{\sqrt{-g}} \, \partial_{\mu}[\sqrt{-g} \, \rho U^{\mu}] = 0 \quad , \qquad (2.9)$$

with g the determinant of $g_{\mu\nu}$. Equation (2.7) contains both the
dynamical behavior of the momentum density and the total energy density. An equation for the internal energy density is obtained in
place of the total energy density by combining equations (2.7) and
(2.9).

The following quantities are introduced:

$$U = \alpha U^{t} = -n^{\mu} U_{\mu} \quad , \qquad V^{i} = \frac{U^{i}}{U^{t}} \quad ,$$

$$D = \rho U \qquad , \qquad E = \rho \varepsilon U \quad ,$$

$$S_{i} = \rho h U U_{i} = (D + E + pU) U_{i} \quad , \qquad (2.10)$$

where S_{i} is the (3 + 1) definition of momentum density used in equation (2.4) and D and E are effective rest energy and internal energy
densities, respectively. Making connection with (3 + 1) quantities

we then have $\rho_H = \rho h U^2 - p$ and $S = \rho h(U^2 - 1) + 3p$ as required in equations (2.3) and (2.5).

The equations of motion become (Dykema 1980)

$$\partial_t(\gamma^{1/2} D) + \partial_i(\gamma^{1/2} DV^i) = 0 \quad , \qquad (2.11)$$

$$\partial_t(\gamma^{1/2} E) + \partial_i(\gamma^{1/2} EV^i) = -p[\partial_t(\gamma^{1/2} U) + \partial_i(\gamma^{1/2} UV^i)] \quad , \quad (2.12)$$

and

$$\partial_t(\gamma^{1/2} S_j) + \partial_i(\gamma^{1/2} S_j V^i) = -\alpha\gamma^{1/2}[\partial_j p + \frac{1}{2}\rho h U_\mu U_\nu \partial_j(g^{\mu\nu})] \quad , \quad (2.13)$$

with $\gamma = \det(\gamma_{ij})$. Part of the analogy with Newtonian hydrodynamics comes from the divergence form of the transport terms. Equation (2.12) represents our general relativistic version of the first law of thermodynamics, with the right hand side containing the pdV work term. The source for the momentum density (2.13) contains the pressure gradient term and the term $U_\mu U_\nu \partial_j(g^{\mu\nu})$, which remains to be simplified, supplying the gravitational and kinematical accelerations. The ρh in this term plays the role of effective inertial energy density (Smarr et al. 1980). We note that the factor U appearing in the definition (2.10) of D, E, and S_i reduces in flat space to the usual special relativistic Lorentz factor. Additional general relativistic effects in equations (2.11)-(2.13) are due to the appearance of $\gamma^{1/2}$.

Finally, equations (2.11)-(2.13) must be supplemented by an equation of state. As we have stated, a polytropic gas EOS, $p = (\Gamma-1)\rho\epsilon$, has been used. However, for the most part capability has been kept to handle a more general EOS.

c) Kinematical Conditions

So far we have said nothing about kinematical choices, conditions on α and β^i that determine the coordinates in the future of Σ_0. From the discussion in section II(a) the choice of α first determines the new time slice, with β^i giving the flow of the spatial coordinates onto that slice. The condition on the lapse is of fundamental importance when a black hole forms, since many choices for α cause the time slices to intersect the singularity (Eardley and Smarr 1979, Smarr and York 1978). We use the maximal slicing condition, first given by Lichnerowicz (1944), which follows from demanding $K = \partial_t K = 0$. Equation (2.5) is then used to obtain an elliptic equation for α:

$$\Delta\alpha = \alpha[K^{ij}K_{ij} + \frac{1}{2}(\rho_H + S)] \quad , \qquad (2.14)$$

where $\Delta = \gamma^{ij}D_i D_j$. The boundary condition $\alpha \rightarrow 1$ as $r \rightarrow \infty$ is applied (see section III(b) for modification).

There is no guarantee that maximal slicing will always avoid singularities. However, it has been successful in a number of applications to date. In calculations made with our code, the lapse decreases exponentially with time in the central regions when a black hole forms (Fig. 1). This halts the advance of proper time in the

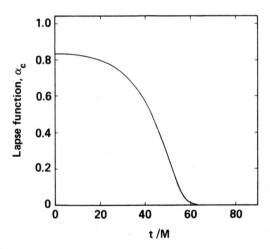

Fig. 1a.-The central (minimum) value of the lapse function, α, is shown plotted versus time in units of the core mass as a black hole forms. An apparent horizon formed at roughly t = 53M.

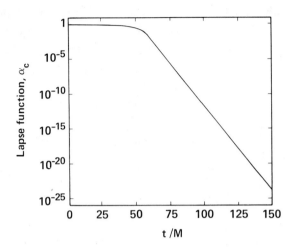

Fig. 1b.—Logarithm of the central value of the lapse function, α, is plotted for the same calculation. As the lapse collapses to exceedingly small values, the advance of proper time in the interior is halted and the interior "freezes". The calculation continues for > 100M past horizon formation.

interior of the black hole at a finite proper time away from the singularity. The proper energy densities and pressure in the collapsing star never become too extreme (the interior motion freezes), and the results confirm a simplified analytic calculation done for spherical collapse (Smarr and York 1978).

The conditions placed on the shift β^i are of less fundamental importance since they represent only a relabeling of the events on the time slices. However, there are important practical considerations relating to the choice of shift that arise in formulating a specific mathematical algorithm to be used in a numerical calculation. For instance, the choice $\beta^i = 0$ (used in the two-black-hole collision of Smarr 1979) leads to a simplification in the evolution equations (2.5) and (2.6). Smarr and York (1978) have proposed another gauge (minimal distortion) which minimizes the coordinate shear in the presence of gravitational waves. Both of these gauges have the advantage of being 3-covariant; freedom still exists to pick coordinates on the initial slice. We have followed a different course (Wilson 1979, Dykema 1980, Centrella and Wilson 1983,1984), which seeks to use the shift vector to impose conditions which simplify the form of the 3-metric (see also Smarr 1979). This may involve demanding either that a given component of γ_{ij} vanish at all times (i.e., $\gamma_{pq} = \partial_t \gamma_{pq} = 0$ for some particular p,q) or that two or more components be functionally related by a time independent expression (see Bardeen and Piran 1983 for discussion related to axisymmetry). These gauges have the great practical advantage of vastly simplifying expressions that involve the covariant derivatives, D_i. The conditions on β^i are themselves not 3-covariant. The implementation of a particular gauge of this type is displayed in section III.

d) Solution of Constraint Equations

Methods for solving the constraint equations (2.3) and (2.4) have received extensive attention in the last decade (Choquet-Bruhat and York 1980, Ō Murchadha and York 1973 and 1974, York 1973; see York 1979 for an excellent review, and York this volume) following the pioneering work of Lichnerowicz (1944) on the conformal approach. Since these techniques form a major part of York's discussion in this volume, our comments here will be brief, dwelling only on points essential to our asymptotically flat application. We note at the outset that for our purposes it is important to consider how the constraints are solved on subsequent time slices as well as on the initial slice.

The problem is to find a way to (nearly) decouple, in a physically interesting way, equations (2.3) and (2.4). A conformal transformation is introduced between the physical metric γ_{ij} and a metric $\hat{\gamma}_{ij}$,

$$\gamma_{ij} = \phi^4 \, \hat{\gamma}_{ij} \quad , \tag{2.15}$$

with ϕ as the conformal factor. This rule determines the conformal transformation of connection and curvature components as well; in particular, the scalar curvature transforms by

$$R = \phi^{-4} \hat{R} - 8\phi^{-5} \hat{\Delta}\phi \quad , \tag{2.16}$$

where $\hat{R}$ is calculated from $\hat{\gamma}_{ij}$ and $\hat{\Delta} = \hat{\gamma}^{ij}\hat{D}_i\hat{D}_j$. However, equation (2.15) does not tell us how $K^i{}_j$, S_i, ρ_H, etc., are to be treated. This is where the method gains its utility, since we can make up their conformal transformation rules so that the constraints are nearly decoupled.

i) The momentum constraints.

The trace-free part of K^{ij}, $A^{ij} = K^{ij} - \frac{1}{3}\gamma^{ij}K$, is split off. This is the spin-2 part of the extrinsic curvature. If we choose that $A^{ij} = \phi^{-10}\hat{A}^{ij}$, $K = \hat{K}$, and $S^i = \phi^{-10}\hat{S}^i$, then the momentum constraints (2.4) become

$$\hat{D}_j\hat{A}^{ij} = \hat{S}^i + \frac{2}{3}\phi^6\hat{D}^i\hat{K} \quad , \tag{2.17}$$

and if $\hat{D}^i\hat{K} = 0$ the momentum constraints are <u>independent of ϕ</u> and contain only conformally related quantities. There are, however, a great many $\hat{A}^{ij}$ which will satisfy equation (2.17) for a given $\hat{S}^i$, so York (1973, 1979) identifies a useful, freely specifiable part by a covariant orthogonal splitting of $\hat{A}^{ij}$ into transverse and longitudinal parts. The decomposition is

$$\hat{A}^{ij} = \hat{K}_T^{ij} + \hat{K}_L^{ij} \quad , \tag{2.18}$$

with

$$\hat{K}_L{}^{ij} \equiv (\hat{L}W)^{ij} \equiv \hat{D}^iW^j + \hat{D}^jW^i - \frac{2}{3}\hat{\gamma}^{ij}\hat{D}_kW^k \quad . \tag{2.19}$$

The transverse part satisfies $\hat{D}_i\hat{K}_T^{ij} = 0$, and W^i is a vector potential for the longitudinal part. Substitution of equation (2.18) in equation (2.17) gives

$$(\hat{\Delta}_L W)_i \equiv \hat{D}_j(\hat{L}W)^j_i \equiv \hat{\Delta}W_i + \frac{1}{3}\hat{D}_i(\hat{D}_j W^j) + \hat{R}_{ij}W^j = \hat{S}_i + \frac{2}{3}\phi^6\hat{D}_i\hat{K} \quad ,$$

$$(2.20)$$

with $\hat{\Delta}_L$ a vector "Laplacian" which is a strongly elliptic and self-adjoint operator. Since $\hat{K}_T^{ij}$ has not appeared, it becomes freely specifiable (subject to $\hat{D}_j\hat{K}_T^{ij} = 0$); and with boundary conditions which make the solution of equation (2.20) unique, the vector potential gives $\hat{K}_L^{ij} = (\hat{L}W)^{ij}$. This completes a solution of equation (2.17).

To obtain boundary conditions for the vector potential W^i at large but finite radius, a vacuum multipole expansion of equation (2.20) can be derived (Evans 1984). The conformally flat operator $\Delta_L^{(flat)}$ admits a basis of Green's vectors

$$G^i_{(k)}(x-x') = -\frac{7}{32\pi|x-x'|}\left[\delta^i_k + \frac{1}{7}\frac{(x_k-x'_k)(x^i-x^{i\,'})}{(x-x')^2}\right]$$

satisfying $(\hat{\Delta}_L^{(f)}G_{(k)})^i = \delta^i_k\delta^3(x-x')$. Assuming conformal flatness (and $\hat{D}_i\hat{K} = 0$) these can be used to invert equation (2.20): $W_k(x) = \int dv' G^i_{(k)}(x-x') S_i(x')$. The form of the multipoles should be the same even if $\hat{\gamma}_{ij} \neq f_{ij}$ (flat metric); the expansion through $\mathcal{O}(r^{-2})$ in asymptotic cartesian coordinates with $n^i = x^i/r$ is

$$W^k(x) = -\frac{7}{32\pi r}(\delta^{ki} + \frac{1}{7}n^k n^i)P_i + \frac{1}{16\pi r^2}(\delta^{ki}n^j - \delta^{kj}n^i)J_{ij}$$

$$+ \frac{1}{64\pi r^2}[3(n^j\delta^{ki} + n^i\delta^{kj}) - n^k(\delta^{ij} - 3n^i n^j)]D_{ij} \quad . \quad (2.21)$$

Here P_i, J_{ij}, and D_{ij} are moments representing respectively the isolated system's linear momentum, angular momentum tensor, and a symmetric tensor related (in the special relativistic limit) to $\partial_t I_{ij}$ where I_{ij} is the second moment of the mass distribution.

For systems with nonvanishing linear momentum P_i, York and Piran (1982) have given a Robin boundary condition

$$(\hat{L}W)^{kj} n_j (\delta^i{}_k - \frac{1}{2} n^i n_k) + \frac{6}{7 r_m} W^k (\delta^i{}_k - \frac{1}{8} n^i n_k) = \mathcal{O}(r_m^{-3}) \ , \qquad (2.22)$$

suitable for obtaining unique solutions for large radius r_m. Most numerical calculations will generally be done in the center of momentum frame (however, see York and Piran (1982) for calculation of moving black hole data) where equation (2.22) cannot provide an accurate boundary condition. If $J_{ij} \neq 0$ and in addition $|J_{ij}| \gg |D_{ij}|$ (i.e., a slowly collapsing rotating object), then a new Robin condition (Evans 1984)

$$(\hat{L}W)^{kj} n_j + \frac{3}{r_m} W^j (\delta^k{}_j + n^k n_j) = \mathcal{O}(r_m^{-4}) \qquad (2.23)$$

can be used to obtain unique solutions.

However, a number of nontrivial problems can be posed for which both $P_i = 0$ and $J_{ij} = 0$. In these cases the lowest order non-vanishing moments will be D_{ij} from equation (2.21). These moments are nonstationary, unlike P_i and J_{ij}, and one cannot find a corresponding Robin-type boundary condition. Instead an approximate Dirichlet condition can be imposed by directly obtaining the moments (in cartesian coordinates; on maximal slices)

$$D_{ij} = -2 \int dv \ \hat{S}_{(i} x_{j)} \ , \qquad (2.24)$$

as if the conformal manifold were flat. To serve as a good approximation, it must be true that $|\hat{\gamma}_{ij} - f_{ij}| \ll |f_{ij}|$ globally. Use of this boundary condition is demonstrated in section III.

ii) The Hamiltonian constraint.

In contrast to the momentum constraints, the Hamiltonian constraint is nonlinear in the three-metric. The conformal approach turns the Hamiltonian constraint (2.3) into a quasilinear elliptic equation for the conformal factor ϕ by combining equations (2.3) and (2.16)

$$\hat{\Delta}\phi = \frac{1}{8} \phi \left[\hat{R} - 2\hat{\rho}_H \phi^{-2} - \hat{A}_{ij}\hat{A}^{ij}\phi^{-8} + \frac{2}{3} K^2 \phi^4 \right] \quad , \tag{2.25}$$

where the conformal scaling of $K^i_{\ j}$ has been included. The scaling of ρ_H is somewhat arbitrary. We choose here as an example $\rho_H = \phi^{-6}\hat{\rho}_H$. Other scaling rules for ρ_H are possible (York 1979), and indeed in our code we use a non-power-law function of ϕ which scales our rest energy density D and internal energy density E separately. The specifics of this transformation and the numerical motivation will be discussed below. Solutions to equation (2.25) have been shown to exist (on maximal hypersurfaces) for a broad range of conditions on $\hat{R}$, $\hat{\rho}_H$, $\hat{K}^{ij}\hat{K}_{ij}$ (Cantor 1977, 1979; for non-maximal slices see York 1983). The conformal factor is used to transform $(\hat{\gamma}_{ij}, \hat{K}^{ij}, \hat{\rho}_H, \hat{S}_i)$ back to physical data $(\gamma_{ij}, K^{ij}, \rho_H, S_i)$ which now automatically satisfy the constraints.

In practice, for the initial value problem (solution of the constraints on the first surface Σ_0) one often assumes $\hat{\gamma}_{ij} = f_{ij}$ and $\hat{K}_T^{ij} = 0$ (no wavelike momentum in the initial conformal gravitational field) which simplifies the task of solving equations (2.20) and (2.25) considerably. However, equations (2.20) and (2.25) are in a form that can be used to invert the constraints on subsequent time slices when in general $\hat{\gamma}_{ij} \neq f_{ij}$ and $\hat{K}_{Tj}^i \neq 0$.

On these later time slices, the quantities $\hat{\gamma}_{ij}$, $\hat{K}_T^{ij}$, $\hat{\rho}_H$, and $\hat{S}_i$ are no longer freely specifiable, but rather follow from the evolution. Determining $\hat{\gamma}_{ij}$, $\hat{\rho}_H$, and $\hat{S}_i$ on a new time slice presents no problem, since evolution equations for these are obtained from equations (2.6), (2.11), (2.12) and (2.13). However, no evolution equations, as such, exist for the transverse momentum $\hat{K}_T^{ij}$. Evolution equations do exist for $\hat{K}^{ij}$ (and thus $\hat{A}^{ij}$) and are found by combining equations (2.5) and (2.6), so these can be used with (2.18) to read off $\hat{K}_T^{ij} = \hat{A}^{ij} - (\hat{L}W)^{ij}$. However, this violates the aim of solving the constraints on successive time slices which is to avoid having to evolve the full extrinsic curvature. What we are after is a reduced evolution involving, in general, two components of the metric and two components of the extrinsic curvature which represent the two dynamical degrees of freedom of the gravitational field. The constraints (plus gauge conditions) then determine the rest.

To find $\hat{K}_T^{ij}$, note that $\hat{A}^{ij}$ has five independent components. Three are fixed by the constraint (2.17), leaving two dynamical components of the extrinsic curvature. After the momentum constraints (2.17) are decomposed, solving equation (2.20) for the vector potential determines only the longitudinal parts of $\hat{A}^{ij}$, including the longitudinal parts of the two chosen "dynamical" components. Evolving just these dynamical components and solving equation (2.20), we can then use equation (2.18) to find the transverse parts of these two components. Then the other half of the decomposed momentum constraint,

$$\hat{D}_i \; \hat{K}_T^{ij} = 0 \quad , \qquad\qquad (2.26)$$

can be used to determine the transverse parts of the remaining three constrained components of $\hat{A}^{ij}$.

In practice, solving the first order partial differential equations of (2.26) proves conceptually and numerically difficult. The questions of how to pose proper boundary conditions and find convergent iterative finite difference algorithms are most naturally discussed in terms of second order (elliptic) differential equations. Fortunately, there exists a means of finding a second order elliptic equation for $\hat{K}_T^{ij}$. York (1973) has shown that the operators $\hat{L}$ (see Eqn.[2.19]) and $\hat{D}$ that form the elliptic self-adjoint vector "Laplacian" $\hat{\Delta}_L \equiv \hat{D}\hat{L}$, are adjoint operators. This implies that the operator formed by $\hat{\Delta}_T \equiv \hat{L}\hat{D}$, which takes tensors to tensors, is also elliptic and self-adjoint. The remarkable property of this operator is that with proper boundary conditions, the solutions of

$$(\hat{\Delta}_T \, \hat{K}_T)^{ij} \equiv [\hat{L}(\hat{D} \cdot \hat{K}_T)]^{ij} \equiv \hat{D}^i \hat{D}_\ell \hat{K}_T^{\ell j} + \hat{D}^j \hat{D}_\ell \hat{K}_T^{\ell i} - \frac{2}{3} \hat{\gamma}^{ij} \, \hat{D}_m \hat{D}_\ell \hat{K}_T^{\ell m} = 0$$

$$(2.27)$$

are identically the solutions of equation (2.26).

III. AXISYMMETRIC MODEL
a) Gauge, Metric, and Shift

The general techniques of the preceding sections are now shown applied to a particular physical model. The differential equations are derived in a form (nearly) suitable for finite differencing (see Evans, Smarr, and Wilson 1984a, and Dykema 1980 for numerical details). The systems we consider are those exhibiting axisymmetry, with no axial rotation, and equatorial plane symmetry. The choice of axisymmetry and no rotation eliminates one of the two dynamical degrees of freedom in the gravitational field (one independent polarization state). The fully constrained method then involves evolution of only one pair of components from γ_{ij} and K^{ij}.

We have chosen to use spherical coordinates[*] with the symmetry axis along $\theta = 0$. The first task in deriving the equations is to specify the 3-gauge and coordinates. With axisymmetry and no rotation, we have $\gamma_{r\phi} = \gamma_{\theta\phi} = \beta^\phi = 0$. The additional freedom in β^r and β^θ is used to set conditions on the "velocity" of components of γ_{ij}, and we require

$$\partial_t \gamma_{r\theta} = 0 \quad , \qquad \partial_t(\gamma_{\theta\theta} - r^2 \, \gamma_{rr}) = 0 \quad . \qquad (3.1)$$

In addition we choose the coordinates on the initial slice by demanding

---

[*] In earlier work on this problem Smarr and Wilson (Wilson 1979) used cylindrical coordinates.

$$\gamma_{r\theta} = 0 \quad , \qquad \gamma_{\theta\theta} - r^2\gamma_{rr} = 0 \qquad\qquad (3.2)$$

as initial values which together with conditions (3.1) maintain a diagonal 3-metric in quasi-isotropic form. With the definitions $\gamma_{rr} = A^2$ and $\gamma_{\phi\phi} = B^2 r^2 \sin^2\theta$ the line element (2.1) becomes

$$ds^2 = -\alpha^2 dt^2 + A^2(dr + \beta^r dt)^2 + A^2 r^2(d\theta + \beta^\theta dt)^2 + B^2 r^2 \sin^2\theta d\phi^2 \quad ,$$

$$(3.3)$$

with the 3-metric in the form

$$\gamma_{ij} = \text{diag}(A^2, \ A^2 r^2, \ B^2 r^2 \sin^2\theta) \quad . \qquad\qquad (3.4)$$

This gauge is called quasi-isotropic (also "isothermal") because in static spherical symmetry it reduces to the isotropic coordinates for Schwarzschild geometry (see discussion in Smarr 1979, Dykema 1980, Evans 1984). Another simplifying choice, the "radial" gauge, which reduces to Schwarzschild coordinates, has been recommended by Bardeen and Piran (1983; see also Bardeen 1983 and Piran 1983).

The two gauge conditions (3.1) and (3.2) fix two relations between the shift components β^r and β^θ found from equation (2.6):

$$r \ \partial_r\left(\frac{\beta^r}{r}\right) - \partial_\theta\beta^\theta = \alpha(2K^r{}_r + K^\phi{}_\phi) \quad , \qquad\qquad (3.5)$$

and

$$r \ \partial_r\beta^\theta + \partial_\theta\left(\frac{\beta^r}{r}\right) = 2\alpha \ \frac{K^r{}_\theta}{r} \quad . \qquad\qquad (3.6)$$

This system is elliptic (Evans 1984). Finding a numerical scheme to solve these first order equations proves difficult. It is necessary to find potentials which allow equations (3.5) and (3.6) to be rewritten as a second order system. Discussion of these points will be left until later.

The metric (3.4) can be written in the alternative form

$$\gamma_{ij} = \phi^4 \, \text{diag}(T^{2/3}, \, T^{2/3}r^2, \, T^{-4/3}r^2\sin^2\theta) = \phi^4\hat{\gamma}_{ij} \quad , \qquad (3.7)$$

where $[\det(\hat{\gamma}_{ij})]^{1/2} = r^2\sin\theta$ and

$$\phi^6 = A^2B \qquad \text{and} \qquad T = \frac{A}{B} \quad . \qquad (3.8)$$

These definitions identify our choice of the conformal factor (Evans 1984), and $\hat{\gamma}_{ij}$ is similar to the "conformal 3-metric" of York (1973) and Ō Murchadha and York (1974). The variable T, taken to be unity on the axis, reduces to unity everywhere in spherical symmetry. Thus the quantity ℓnT is used as a measure of the anisotropy of space, and, as we will see, it has nice properties as a radiation variable.

b) Field Evolution and Lapse

In our scheme, the Hamiltonian constraint is used to obtain ϕ on each time slice and ℓnT becomes the "dynamical" component of the metric. In practice we have use for evolution equations for both. From equation (2.6),

$$\partial_t \ell nT = \beta^r\partial_r \ell nT + \beta^\theta\partial_\theta \ell nT + \partial_\theta\beta^\theta - \beta^\theta\cot\theta + \alpha(K^r_{\ r} + 2K^\phi_{\ \phi}) \quad , \qquad (3.9)$$

and

$$\partial_t(\phi^6) = \frac{1}{r^2} \, \partial_r[r^2\phi^6\beta^r] + \frac{1}{\sin\theta} \, \partial_\theta[\sin\theta \, \phi^6\beta^\theta] \quad . \qquad (3.10)$$

Equation (3.10) was derived by taking the trace of equation (2.6) to obtain $\partial_t \ell n(\gamma^{1/2}) = D_i\beta^i$ (given maximal slicing; note that for normal coordinates, $\beta^i = 0$, the conformal factor is constant).

The symmetries admit only the following nonvanishing components of the extrinsic curvature: $K^r{}_r$, $K^\theta{}_\theta$, $K^\phi{}_\phi$, $K^r{}_\theta$. However, maximal slicing, $K = 0$, eliminates $K^\theta{}_\theta = -K^r{}_r - K^\phi{}_\phi$ leaving only $K^r{}_r$, $K^\phi{}_\phi$, $K^r{}_\theta$ independent. We replace $K^r{}_r$ with the linear combination $\lambda = K^r{}_r + 2K^\phi{}_\phi$, where $\lambda = 0$ on axis always, and vanishes identically in spherical symmetry. The new variable λ shares this property with $\ln T$ and, indeed, from inspection of equation (3.9), λ is the sole component of the extrinsic curvature contributing to the source of $\ln T$. In this sense λ and $\ln T$ are a canonical pair of dynamical variables and their evolution represents our reduced dynamical system.

As was shown in section II(d), the momentum constraint and the source in the Hamiltonian constraint use the conformally related extrinsic curvature, $\hat{k}^i{}_j = \phi^6 K^i{}_j$. Thus equation (3.10) is combined with equation (2.5) to obtain

$$\partial_t \hat{\lambda} = \frac{1}{r^2} \partial_r(r^2 \beta^r \hat{\lambda}) + \frac{1}{\sin\theta} \partial_\theta(\sin\theta \ \beta^\theta \hat{\lambda}) + \frac{\hat{K}^r{}_\theta}{r} \left(r\partial_r\beta^\theta - \partial_\theta\left(\frac{\beta^r}{r}\right)\right)$$

$$+ \frac{\alpha B \ S_\theta{}^2}{r^2(D + E + pU)U} + \frac{1}{r^2} \partial_r[r^2 \alpha B \ \partial_r \ln T]$$

$$+ \frac{AB^2\sin\theta}{r^2} \partial_\theta \left[\frac{1}{AB\sin\theta} \partial_\theta\alpha\right] + \frac{\alpha B^2\sin\theta}{r^2} \partial_\theta \left[\frac{1}{AB\sin\theta} \partial_\theta A\right] \ , \qquad (3.11)$$

where the hydrodynamic quantities from equation (2.10) have been employed. Evolution equations exist for the other components of $\hat{k}^i{}_j$, but these quantities are obtained instead by solving the momentum constraints. At the outer radius, outgoing wave boundary conditions (Evans, Smarr, and Wilson 1984a) are applied for $\hat{\lambda}$ and $\ln T$.

Finally, the lapse equation (2.14) for α (when $\partial_t K = 0$) becomes, in our gauge,

$$\frac{1}{r^2} \partial_r [r^2 B \, \partial_r \alpha] + \frac{1}{r^2 \sin\theta} \, \partial_\theta [\sin\theta \, B \, \partial_\theta \alpha]$$

$$= \alpha\phi^6 \left\{ 2\lambda^2 - 6\lambda K^\phi_\phi + 6K^\phi_\phi{}^2 + 2\left(\frac{K^r_\theta}{r}\right)^2 \right.$$

$$\left. + (D + E)\left(U - \frac{1}{2U}\right) + pU\left(U + \frac{1}{2U}\right) \right\} \ . \qquad (3.12)$$

A modified version of this equation is used numerically (Evans 1984). The boundary condition used is $\alpha = B^{-1}[1 - r^{-2}(\frac{1}{4} M^2 + \eta_2)]$ where M is the configuration mass and η_2 is a time dependent gauge correction (see Evans 1984).

c) Hydrodynamics

The hydrodynamic equations of motion (2.11) – (2.13) can now be specified. Using $\gamma^{1/2} = \phi^6 r^2 \sin\theta$, these become

$$\partial_t(\phi^6 D) + \frac{1}{r^2} \, \partial_r(r^2\phi^6 DV^r) + \frac{1}{\sin\theta} \, \partial_\theta(\sin\theta \ \phi^6 DV^\theta) = 0 \ , \qquad (3.13)$$

$$\partial_t(\phi^6 E) + \frac{1}{r^2} \, \partial_r(r^2\phi^6 EV^r) + \frac{1}{\sin\theta} \, \partial_\theta(\sin\theta \ \phi^6 EV^\theta)$$

$$= -p\left[\partial_t(\phi^6 U) + \frac{1}{r^2} \, \partial_r(r^2\phi^6 UV^r) + \frac{1}{\sin\theta} \, \partial_\theta(\sin\theta \ \phi^6 UV^\theta)\right] \ , \qquad (3.14)$$

$$\partial_t(\phi^6 S_r) + \frac{1}{r^2} \, \partial_r(r^2\phi^6 S_r V^r) + \frac{1}{\sin\theta} \, \partial_\theta(\sin\theta \ \phi^6 S_r V^\theta)$$

$$= -\alpha\phi^6 \left[\partial_r p + (D + E + pU)\left(U\partial_r \ln\alpha + \left(\frac{1}{U} - U\right)\partial_r \ln A\right)\right.$$

$$\left. - \frac{S_\theta{}^2}{(D+E+pU)Ur^3 A^2} \right] + \phi^6(S_r \partial_r \beta^r + S_\theta \partial_r \beta^\theta) \ , \qquad (3.15)$$

and

$$\partial_t(\phi^6 S_\theta) + \frac{1}{r^2}\partial_r(r^2\phi^6 S_\theta V^r) + \frac{1}{\sin\theta}\partial_\theta(\sin\theta\;\phi^6 S_\theta V^\theta)$$

$$= -\alpha\phi^6[\partial_\theta p + (D + E + pU)(U\partial_\theta\ln\alpha + (\frac{1}{U} - U)\partial_\theta\ln A)]$$

$$+ \phi^6(S_r\partial_\theta\beta^r + S_\theta\partial_\theta\beta^\theta)\quad,\tag{3.16}$$

with $A^2(D + E + pU)^2(U^2 - 1) = S_r^2 + r^{-2}\,S_\theta^2$ to be solved for U.

The transport terms in equations (3.13), (3.15), and (3.16) are in the form of the divergence of a flux, which allows these terms to be conservatively differenced. This implies, in the case of equation (3.13), that the total particle number

$$\int dr d\theta\; r^2\sin\theta\;\phi^6 D = constant\tag{3.17}$$

can be globally conserved throughout the numerical evolution. When we update ϕ (i.e., when the Hamiltonian constraint is solved on a new time slice), the density D is partially updated so as to preserve $\phi^6 D$ = constant, locally. This identifies the natural conformal scaling for the rest energy density,

$$\hat{D} = \phi^6 D\quad,\tag{3.18}$$

in our application. Equations (3.15) and (3.16) similarly lead to

$$\hat{S}_i = \phi^6 S_i\quad,\tag{3.19}$$

though this rule would be used in any case in order to (nearly) decouple the momentum constraints (see Eqn.[2.17]).

The internal energy equation (3.15) is handled differently. Since E appears implicitly through the pressure p, we cannot preserve E as was done with D in equation (3.17). However, we note that with the adiabatic EOS, $pU = (\Gamma-1)E$, equation (3.14) can be rewritten in the conservative form

$$\partial_t(\phi^6 E^{1/\Gamma} U^{1-1/\Gamma}) + \frac{1}{r^2} \partial_r(r^2\phi^6 E^{1/\Gamma} U^{1-1/\Gamma} v^r)$$

$$+ \frac{1}{\sin\theta} \partial_\theta(\sin\theta \, \phi^6 E^{1/\Gamma} U^{1-1/\Gamma} v^\theta) = 0 \qquad (3.20)$$

in the absence of shocks. Where shocks are present, an artificial viscosity (Crowley 1975) is added in the numerical algorithm; this means that a global conservation of entropy similar to the result (3.17) for particle number is not possible in general. Without shocks, combining equations (3.20) and (3.13) leads to $EU^{\Gamma-1}D^{-\Gamma}$ being conserved along fluid flow lines: $U^\mu \nabla_\mu (EU^{\Gamma-1}D^{-\Gamma}) = 0$. This implies the usual locally adiabatic result $\epsilon = \kappa\rho^{\Gamma-1}$ with κ a constant along flow lines. Based on equation (3.20) a partial update of E due to changes in ϕ or U is accomplished by holding $\phi^6 E^{1/\Gamma} U^{1-1/\Gamma}$ constant. The transport terms (spatial gradients) are kept in the form (3.14). We therefore better maintain motion along the adiabat in regions free of shocks. Several hydrodynamic and field quantities are shown plotted in Figure 2 for an oblate core bounce calculation.

Equation (3.20) also indicates the natural conformal transformation of E, namely

$$\hat{E} = \phi^{6\Gamma} E \quad . \qquad (3.21)$$

This means we do not have a homogeneous scaling for ρ_H in the source of the Hamiltonian constraint (see Eqn.[2.25]).

d) Constraints

The Hamiltonian constraint is solved in a form that is slightly different from that given in equation (2.25). We solve for the metric variable $B^{1/2} \equiv \psi$ instead of ϕ, these quantities being related

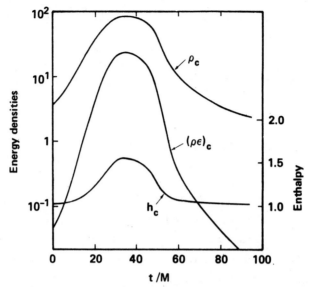

Fig. 2a.-Central values of rest energy density, ρ, and internal energy density, $\rho\epsilon$, in geometrized units versus time. These are converted to CGS mass densities by multiplying by $(c^2/8\pi G)^3(1/M^2)$ where M is the core mass. For a $1.4\ M_\odot$ core, the peak rest density corresponds to $\rho_c \approx 1.67 \times 10^{15}\text{gcm}^{-3}$. The relativistic enthalpy is also shown, indicating directly the size of relativistic effects.

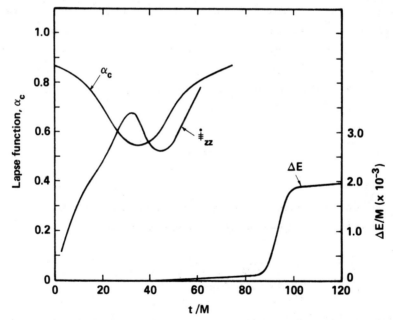

Fig. 2b.-Central value of the lapse is shown during core bounce. A minimum value of 0.54 is reached. Relative changes in the time rate of change of the quadrupole moment are indicated during the bounce. The later arrival and integrated energy loss (efficiency) of the gravitational wave is displayed.

by $\phi^6 = T^2\psi^6$. The reason for this change is that the differential operators involving ψ and T have a simpler form.

We must write the source in terms of quantities which have already been updated (using partial updating or operator splitting; see Wilson 1979 and Centrella and Wilson 1984 for operator splitting) on the new slice. These are the conformally related quantities $\hat{K}^i{}_j$, $\hat{D}$, $\hat{E}$ and the metric component T. Note that we do not yet know the new physical values of $K^i{}_j$, D, or E until the Hamiltonian constraint is solved. Equation (2.25) is then written as

$$\frac{1}{r^2}\partial_r(r^2\partial_r\psi) + \frac{1}{r^2\sin\theta}\partial_\theta(\sin\theta\,\partial_\theta\psi) = -\frac{\psi}{4}\left[\frac{1}{r}\partial_r(r\partial_r\ell nT) + \frac{1}{r^2}\partial_\theta\partial_\theta\ell nT\right.$$

$$+ T^{-2}\psi^{-8}\left(\hat{\lambda}^2 - 3\hat{\lambda}\hat{K}^\phi{}_\phi + 3\hat{K}^\phi{}_\phi{}^2 + \left(\frac{\hat{K}^r{}_\theta}{r}\right)^2\right)$$

$$\left. + \psi^{-2}\hat{D}U + \left(\Gamma U + \frac{1-\Gamma}{U}\right)\psi^{4-6\Gamma}\hat{E}T^{2(1-\Gamma)}\right]\ . \qquad (3.22)$$

The boundary condition is the same as discussed in section II(d). Once ψ has been obtained, the new conformal factor is known and the physical values of the extrinsic curvature and matter fields can be formed using equations (3.18), (3.19), (3.21), and $K^i{}_j = \phi^{-6}\hat{K}^i{}_j$.

The momentum constraints are now used to obtain the extrinsic curvature components $K^\phi{}_\phi$ and $K^r{}_\theta$ (which were not evolved). We first solve the equation (2.20) for the vector potential components W^r and W^θ ($W^\phi = 0$, $S_\phi = 0$ in our symmetry) to give the longitudinal part. The tensor "Laplacian" (2.27) then gives the transverse part. These equations have been written in terms of conformally related quantities. This is advantageous since they only involve the metric component T and not ϕ, and thus can be solved independently of the Hamiltonian constraint.

The system for the vector potential W^i then becomes

$$\frac{4}{3} \frac{1}{r^2} \partial_r[r^4 \partial_r(\frac{W^r}{r})] + \frac{1}{\sin\theta} \partial_\theta[\sin\theta \partial_\theta(\frac{W^r}{r})] + F_1(\frac{W^r}{r})$$

$$+ \frac{2}{3} r^4 T \partial_r[\frac{1}{r^3 T} \partial_\theta W^\theta] - \frac{1}{3} T^2 r\sin\theta \partial_\theta[\frac{1}{T^2\sin\theta} \partial_r W^\theta] + F_2 W^\theta = r\hat{S}_r$$

$$(3.23)$$

and

$$\frac{1}{r^2} \partial_r[r^4 \partial_r W^\theta] + \frac{4}{3} \frac{1}{\sin\theta} \partial_\theta[\sin\theta \partial_\theta W^\theta] + F_3 W^\theta$$

$$+ \frac{2}{3} rT \partial_\theta[\frac{1}{T} \partial_r(\frac{W^r}{r})] - \frac{1}{3} r^{10} T^2 \partial_r[\frac{1}{T^2 r^9} \partial_\theta(\frac{W^r}{r})] + F_4(\frac{W^r}{r}) = \hat{S}_\theta \quad ,$$

$$(3.24)$$

where

$$F_1 = \frac{2}{3} \frac{T^2}{r^2} \partial_r[\frac{r^4}{T^2} \partial_r \ell n T] \quad ,$$

$$F_2 = \frac{2}{3} r[\partial_r \partial_\theta \ell n T + \partial_r \ell n(\frac{r^3}{T^2}) \cdot \partial_\theta \ell n(\frac{T}{\sin\theta})] \quad ,$$

$$F_3 = \frac{2}{3} \frac{T^2}{\sin^3\theta} \partial_\theta[\frac{\sin^3\theta}{T^2} \partial_\theta \ell n(\frac{T}{\sin\theta})] \quad ,$$

and

$$F_4 = \frac{2}{3} r \frac{T^2}{\sin^3\theta} \partial_\theta[\frac{\sin^3\theta}{T^2} \partial_r \ell n T] \quad . \qquad (3.25)$$

The boundary condition used at large radius is, as we discussed in section II(d), a Dirichlet condition derived from the lowest order symmetric multipole moments (quadrupole) of equation (2.20). In spherical coordinates, with axisymmetry and equatorial plane symmetry, there are two moments to calculate, D_0 (trace part) and D_2 (tracefree part), namely

$$D_0 = - \int_0^{r_o} \int_0^{\pi/2} dr d\theta \; \sin\theta \; r^3 \; \hat{S}_r \quad , \quad \text{and}$$

$$(3.26)$$

$$D_2 = - \int_0^{r_o} \int_0^{\pi/2} dr d\theta \; \sin\theta \; (\sin^2\theta - 2\cos^2\theta) r^3 \; \hat{S}_r$$
$$- 3 \int_0^{r_o} \int_0^{\pi/2} dr d\theta \; \cos\theta \sin^2\theta \; r^2 \; \hat{S}_\theta \quad ,$$

where r_0 encompasses the support of $\hat{S}_r$ and $\hat{S}_\theta$. The Dirichlet condition at large r_m then becomes

$$\frac{W^r}{r} = \frac{1}{8 r_m^3} \left[(2 D_0 - 3 D_2) + \frac{9}{2} D_2 \sin^2\theta \right] \quad , \quad W^\theta = \frac{3}{8 r_m^3} D_2 \sin\theta \cos\theta \quad .$$

$$(3.27)$$

When the vector potential has been obtained, equation (2.19) gives the longitudinal components of $K^i{}_j$:

$$\hat{\lambda}_L = -2r \left(\frac{W^r}{r} \right) \partial_r \ln T - 2 \frac{\sin\theta}{T} \partial_\theta \left(\frac{T}{\sin\theta} W^\theta \right) \quad ,$$

$$\hat{K}^\phi_{L\phi} = - \frac{2}{3} \frac{r}{T^2} \partial_r \left(T^2 \frac{W^r}{r} \right) - \frac{2}{3} \frac{\sin^2\theta}{T^2} \partial_\theta \left(\frac{T^2}{\sin^2\theta} W^\theta \right) \quad ,$$

$$\frac{\hat{K}^r_{L\theta}}{r} = r \partial_r W^\theta + \partial_\theta \left(\frac{W^r}{r} \right) \quad .$$

$$(3.28)$$

All of the longitudinal components are known, as well as $\hat{\lambda}$ itself, evolved with equation (3.11). We therefore know the single transverse component $\hat{\lambda}_T = \hat{\lambda} - \hat{\lambda}_L$. The second-order tensor Laplacian can now be reduced to a pair of coupled partial differential equations (PDE's) for $\hat{K}^\phi_{T\phi}$ and $\frac{\hat{K}^r_{T\theta}}{r}$ by taking the (r,r) and (r,θ) components of equation (2.27):

$$4T^{2/3}\,\partial_r[\frac{r^2}{T^{2/3}}\,\partial_r\hat{K}^{\phi}_{T\phi}] + \frac{T^{2/3}}{\sin\theta}\,\partial_\theta[\frac{\sin\theta}{T^{2/3}}\,\partial_\theta\,\hat{K}^{\phi}_{T\phi}] + G_1\hat{K}^{\phi}_{T\phi}$$

$$- \frac{r}{T^{5/3}\sin\theta}\,\partial_\theta[\sin\theta\;T^{5/3}\partial_r(\frac{\hat{K}^r_{T\theta}}{r})] + (7 + \frac{r}{3T}\,\partial_rT)\partial_\theta(\frac{\hat{K}^r_{T\theta}}{r}) + G_2(\frac{\hat{K}^r_{T\theta}}{r})$$

$$= 2T^{1/6}\partial_r[\frac{r^2}{T^{1/6}}\,\partial_r\hat{\lambda}_T] + \frac{T^{5/3}}{\sin^2\theta}\,\partial_\theta[\frac{\sin^2\theta}{T^{5/3}}\,\partial_\theta\hat{\lambda}_T] + G_3\,\hat{\lambda}_T \quad , \qquad (3.29)$$

and

$$T^{2/3}\partial_r[\frac{r^2}{T^{2/3}}\,\partial_r(\frac{\hat{K}^r_{T\theta}}{r})] + \frac{T^{2/3}}{\sin\theta}\,\partial_\theta[\frac{\sin\theta}{T^{2/3}}\,\partial_\theta(\frac{\hat{K}^r_{T\theta}}{r})] + G_4(\frac{\hat{K}^r_{T\theta}}{r})$$

$$- T^{7/3}r\partial_\theta[T^{-7/3}\partial_r\hat{K}^{\phi}_{T\phi}] + (-8 + \frac{r}{3T}\,\partial_rT)\partial_\theta\hat{K}^{\phi}_{T\phi} + G_5\,\hat{K}^{\phi}_{T\phi}$$

$$= \frac{r}{\sin\theta\;T^{2/3}}\,\partial_\theta(\sin\theta\;T^{2/3})\partial_r\hat{\lambda}_T - (5 + \frac{2r}{3T}\,\partial_rT)\partial_\theta\hat{\lambda}_T + G_6\,\hat{\lambda}_T \quad , \quad (3.30)$$

and here $\hat{\lambda}_T$ acts as a source. The functions G_i are

$$G_1 = 12r^3\;T^{1/6}\,\partial_r[\frac{1}{r^2}\,\partial_r(\frac{r}{T^{1/6}})] + \frac{T^{5/3}}{\sin\theta}\,\partial_\theta[\frac{\sin\theta}{T^{8/3}}\,\partial_\theta T] \quad ,$$

$$G_2 = \cot\theta(7 + \frac{r}{3T}\,\partial_rT) - \frac{5}{T}\,\partial_\theta T \quad ,$$

$$G_3 = - \frac{6}{rT^{1/6}}\,\partial_r[r^2\;T^{1/6}] + \frac{T^{5/3}}{\sin\theta}\,\partial_\theta[\frac{\cos\theta}{T^{5/3}}] \quad ,$$

$$G_4 = - \frac{6}{T^{1/3}}\,\partial_r(r\;T^{1/3}) + T^{2/3}\,\partial_\theta(\frac{\cot\theta}{T^{2/3}}) \quad ,$$

$$G_5 = r^3 T^{2/3} \partial_r \left[\frac{1}{r^2 T^{5/3}} \partial_\theta T \right] - \frac{3 T^{2/3}}{r} \partial_\theta \left[\frac{1}{T^{1/3}} \partial_r \left(\frac{r^2}{T^{1/3}} \right) \right] \quad , \quad \text{and}$$

$$G_6 = \frac{2}{T} \partial_\theta T - 2 \frac{\cot\theta}{T^{1/3}} \partial_r (r \ T^{1/3}) \quad . \tag{3.31}$$

The asymptotic boundary condition used with this system is the transverse-traceless condition applied to the components of K^i_{Tj}. Thus we set $\hat{K}^\phi_{T\phi} = \frac{1}{2} \hat{\lambda}_T$ (which implies $K^r_{Tr} \approx 0$) and $\frac{\hat{K}^r_{T\theta}}{r} = \mathcal{O}(r^{-2}) \approx 0$. This amounts to the usual rule: differential transversality goes to algebraic transversality for $\omega r \gg 1$, where ω is a characteristic frequency.

With the solution of equations (3.29) and (3.30) the entire extrinsic curvature tensor has now been reconstructed on a new time slice with the evolution of only $\hat{S}_r$, $\hat{S}_\theta$, and $\hat{\lambda}$.

e) Shift Revisited

To treat elliptic systems numerically, we generally desire second order equations. Thus to solve the first order PDE's (3.5) and (3.6) for the shift components, potentials χ and Φ are introduced by

$$\frac{\beta^r}{r} = r \partial_r \chi + \partial_\theta \Phi \quad , \qquad \beta^\theta = r \partial_r \Phi - \partial_\theta \chi \quad . \tag{3.32}$$

With $P = \alpha(2K^r_r + K^\phi_\phi) = \alpha(2\lambda - 3K^\phi_\phi)$ and $Q = 2\alpha \frac{K^r_\theta}{r}$ for the sources, equations (3.5) and (3.6) can be rewritten as separate equations for the potentials,

$$\Delta^f_{(2)} \chi = r^{-2} P \quad , \qquad \Delta^f_{(2)} \Phi = r^{-2} Q \quad , \tag{3.33}$$

where $\Delta^f_{(2)} = r^{-1} \partial_r (r \partial_r) + r^{-2} \partial_\theta \partial_\theta$ is the flat-space two-dimensional Laplacian.

Solution of these equations on the computer requires care (Evans 1984, Evans, Smarr and Wilson 1984a). We give here only the asymptotic boundary conditions. The source for the shift vector is the extrinsic curvature, so both longitudinal and transverse contributions can be expected on the boundary. The longitudinal behavior of the shift can be found from the corresponding behavior of the vector potential in equation (3.27). This gives

$$\frac{\beta^r{}_L}{r} = \frac{1}{r_m^3} \left[\left(\frac{1}{2} D_0 - \frac{3}{4} D_2 \right) + \frac{9}{8} D_2 \sin^2\theta \right] , \qquad \beta^\theta{}_L = \frac{3}{4 r_m^3} D_2 \sin\theta\cos\theta \qquad (3.34)$$

at large radius. The transverse part gives a contribution

$$\beta^r{}_T = -\frac{1}{2} \ln T , \qquad r\beta^\theta{}_T = \mathcal{O}(r^{-2}) \qquad (3.35)$$

for purely outgoing waves in the wave zone. These can be combined to provide suitable boundary conditions for χ and Φ (Evans 1984, Evans, Smarr and Wilson 1984a).

IV. MASS-ENERGY, RADIATION FLUX, AND A COLLAPSE MODEL

One of the main results to be garnered from a collapse calculation is the total energy, wave form, and angular structure of the emitted gravitational radiation. In addition, if a black hole results, the moments of the gravitational field can be followed as the exterior settles down to Schwarzschild. If the core bounces, recoil shocks, jets, and vortices can be followed. Also, various edits can be made to track the accuracy of the calculation. Several of these edits will be discussed below along with results from several oblate model core collapses.

We first consider a collapse calculation which had an initial core taken to be an approximate $\Gamma = 2$ polytrope with a radius $\sim 12M$. The densities were then ellipsoidally deformed to give the star an initial oblateness of 1.5:1 (see Fig. 3a). The internal energy den-

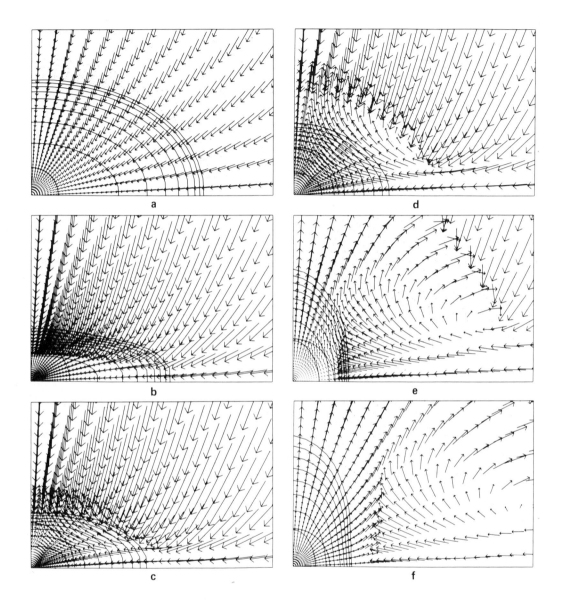

Fig. 3.–Rest energy density contours and velocity field vectors are plotted for one quadrant of the r,θ plane for the core. The vertical axis is the symmetry axis and the horizontal axis represents the equatorial plane. The rest of the core is inferred by axisymmetry and equatorial mirror symmetry. The fiducial circular arc indicates a radius r = 2M. Hydrodynamic milestones in Figures 3a–f are described in the text.

sity was reduced by a factor 0.62 from the equilibrium value, which was known from spherical (1-d) collapse calculations to result in a bounce. Energy was returned in the form of kinetic energy of an initial velocity field. The amount was chosen to give the core roughly zero binding energy, as if it had collapsed from a very large radius. The velocity field in the core was taken proportional to (ellipsoidal) distance and orthogonal to the density contours. The motion was therefore initially homologous. Figures 3a-f show the star at subsequent times in the calculation.

Figure 3a depicts the start of the calculation and indicates the infall phase of the collapse. Figure 3b catches the formation of the primary recoil shock from the oblate bounce. Note that these figures are not produced to the same scale but rather focus on the details of the core. A fiducial circle at radius r = 2M is present, however, and indicates the relative sizes of the core in Figures 3a-f (and the importance of general relativity). Figure 3c shows the shock erupting from the core. Figure 3d is near the times of maximum compression ($r_{star} \approx 4M$) and momentarily vanishing quadrupole moment, I_{zz}. The formation of a secondary shock is shown in Figure 3e resulting from the prolate bounce, and a vortex behind the primary shock in the more tenuous material outside the core is evident. The beginning of the reexpansion phase is displayed in Figure 3f with the secondary shock propagating outward.

One important check on the accuracy of the calculation involves following the total mass-energy of the isolated system. Ideally, the ADM mass (ADM 1962), a conserved quantity, would be calculated at spatial infinity. Secondly, the Bondi mass (Bondi, van der Burg, and Metzner 1962) should be obtained at future null infinity (at late retarded time) for the mass left after passage of the gravitational waves. Unfortunately, a finite difference calculation on spacelike slices is usually confined to a finite region. Therefore the formal mass and flux measures must be replaced with quasi-local indicators carefully chosen to provide meaningful results at the edge of the mesh (Eardley 1979). One such mass indicator, the Hawking mass (Hawking 1968, Eardley 1979, Dykema 1980, Evans 1984), defined on coordinate 2-spheres, has the general form

$$M_H(r) = \left[\frac{A(r)}{16\pi}\right]^{1/2}\left(1 - \int \frac{dA}{2\pi}\,\mu\rho\right) \quad . \qquad\qquad (4.1)$$

Here $A(r)$ is the proper area of the two-surface and μ and ρ are Newman-Penrose spin coefficients (Newman and Penrose 1962). This definition of mass has several nice features (Eardley 1979). One property is that $\lim M_H = M_{ADM}$ as $r \to \infty$ on spacelike slices. Secondly, it also gives $\lim M_H = M_{Bondi}$ as $v = t + r \to \infty$ (i.e., on a cut of null infinity). Since M_{ADM} is conserved, then how well M_H remains constant at the edge of the mesh, prior to the arrival of the wave front, can be regarded as a test of the fineness of the calculation. This mass is plotted versus time in Figure 4 for a second collapse model. Prior to $t = 110M$ this indicator held fixed to within $\pm 0.4\%$. The systematic-looking variations near $t = 40M$ coincide with the bounce phase of this second run and are thought to be due to our use of dynamic gauge conditions introducing coordinate shear on the edit two-surface (Evans 1984). This is the subject of further investigation.

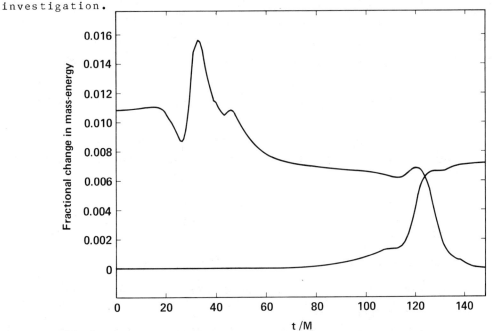

Fig. 4.-Fractional change in the mass-energy of the system (measured by Hawking mass) and integrated energy flux at the edge of the mesh are shown versus time. Mass loss of the system due to radiation-reaction is clearly visible.

Also plotted in Figure 4 is the gravitational radiation energy flux integrated over the same edit two-surface. For the first time we are seeing in these numerical relativity calculations the effect of the radiation-reaction in the expected decrease of the mass-energy of the system! This radiation flux was calculated by taking the derivative of M_H with respect to retarded time along ingoing null rays. In the limit $v = t + r \to \infty$ this corresponds to the Bondi-Sachs flux (Bondi et al. 1962, Sachs 1962). The expression for the flux reduces to

$$\frac{dM_H}{du} = - \frac{1}{4\pi} \int d\mathcal{A} \; |\lambda'|^2 = - \frac{1}{64\pi} \int r^2 d\Omega \; AB\left[\frac{1}{A} \partial_r \ell nT - \lambda\right]^2 \quad , \quad (4.2)$$

where λ' is the Newman-Penrose coefficient (Dykema 1980) and gives the Bondi "news" function at large r. The second half of the expression displays the form in our gauge. Note the very clear appearance of the components which we chose as "dynamical" variables: ℓnT and λ! This quantity is also shown time-integrated (Fig. 2b) for the first collapse calculation displayed in Figure 3. Alternatively, the integrand can be plotted (Fig. 5a-h) to indicate graphically the formation and propagation of the radiation pulses.

Using the simplifying gauge conditions allows the dynamical metric component, ℓnT, to be related in the wave zone to the transverse-traceless amplitude. By an infinitesimal gauge transformation (Evans 1984) we find $h_+^{TT} = \ell nT + \mathcal{O}(r^{-2})$. To lowest order this can be used as a separate measure of the radiation flux:

$$\frac{dE}{dt} = - \frac{dM}{dt} = \frac{1}{16\pi} \int r^2 d\Omega \; AB(h_+^{TT})^2 = \frac{1}{16\pi} \int r^2 d\Omega \; AB \; \lambda^2 \quad . \quad (4.3)$$

This form is very similar to equation (4.2) except that the Bondi-Sachs indicator responds only to outgoing radiation.

Finally, the angular structure of the gravitational waves can be determined by noting that, with the assumed symmetries, the dependence of the metric perturbations at $r \gg M$ (in "cartesian" compon-

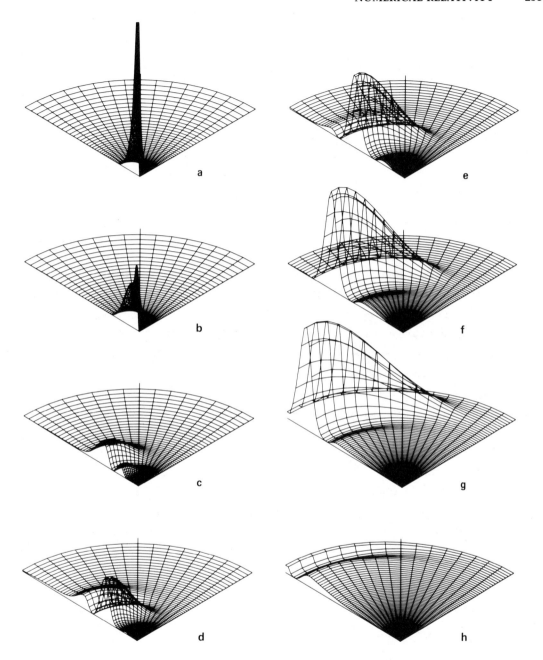

Fig. 5.–Bondi-Sachs flux integrand showing the formation and propagation of the gravitational wave pulse is plotted over one quadrant of
the r, θ plane. The equatorial plane is on the left and the symmetry
axis is on the right. Note the $\sin^4\theta$ radiation pattern. The main
pulse reaches $r \approx \lambda$ in Figure 5f. The main pulse has propagated
cleanly off the mesh in Figure 5h.

ents) will be given by the tensor spherical harmonics $T_{ij}^{E2, \ell 0}$ (Thorne 1980b) for even ℓ. The metric variable ℓnT then has angular structure of the form

$$_2Y^{\ell 0}(\theta) = \left[\frac{2\ell+1}{4\pi} \frac{(\ell-2)!}{(\ell+2)!}\right]^{1/2} \sin\theta \, \partial_\theta \left[\frac{1}{\sin\theta} \, \partial_\theta \, P_\ell(\theta)\right] \qquad (4.4)$$

where $_2Y^{\ell 0}(\theta)$ are spin weight-2 spherical harmonics.

V. CONCLUSIONS

A method has been described for computing fully self-consistent evolutions of general relativistic hydrodynamic systems. Appropriate boundary conditions were given for integration of the elliptic PDE's in a finite region. The method was then shown applied to axisymmetric, nonrotating systems with a presentation of the resulting equations. A computer code to solve these equations has been developed. Important edits during a calculation, such as mass and gravitational radiation flux, were discussed with reference to data from several core collapse and bounce calculations. The code can also follow collapse to a black hole and continue integrating for many dynamical times afterward.

The method produces stable, regular and, we believe, accurate solutions. Work is continuing on producing rigorous calibration tests prior to conducting a survey of strong-field collapse calculations. Future work will also involve the extension to rotating systems and more realistic equations of state. Such a code will then provide insight into relativistic effects, including gravitational radiation production, during collapse of stellar cores and supermassive stars.

ACKNOWLEDGEMENTS

I wish to express my deep gratitude to my mentor, Jim Wilson, for the opportunity to work with and learn from him. In addition, I wish to thank B-division and Lawrence Livermore National Laboratory, where most of this research was conducted, and the Relativity Center at the University of Texas for their hospitality. I also acknowledge financial support from Associated Western Universities as a Laboratory Graduate Participant. My appreciation goes as well to my advisor, Richard Matzner, for his continued support and encouragement. I have also benefitted from discussions with Richard Matzner, Larry Smarr, Jim York, Jim LeBlanc, and especially Pieter Dykema and Joan Centrella. This work was partially supported by NSF grant PHY83-08826. Work performed under the auspices of the U. S. Department of Energy by the Lawrence Livermore National Laboratory under contract No. W-7405-ENG-48.

REFERENCES

Arnowitt, R., Deser, S., and Misner, C. W. 1962, in _Gravitation_, ed. L. Witten (New York: Wiley), p.227 (ADM).

Bardeen, J. M. 1983, in _Gravitational Radiation_, ed. N. Deruelle and T. Piran (Amsterdam: North Holland), p.433.

Bardeen, J. M., and Piran, T. 1983, Phys. Reports, 96, 206.

Bondi, H., van der Burg, M.G.J., and Metzner, A.W.K. 1962, Proc. Roy. Soc. London A, 269, 21.

Cantor, M. 1977, Commun. Math. Phys., 57, 83.

_____. 1979, J. Math. Phys., 20, 1741.

Centrella, J. M., and Wilson, J. R. 1983, Ap. J., 273, 428.

_____. 1984, Ap. J. Suppl., 54, 229.

Choquet-Bruhat, Y., and York, J. W. 1980, in _General Relativity and Gravitation_, ed. A. Held (New York: Plenum), p.99.

Crowley, W. P. 1975, LLNL Publication UCRL-51824.

Dykema, P. G. 1980, "Numerical Simulation of Axisymmetric Gravitational Collapse," Ph.D. thesis, University of Texas at Austin.

Eardley, D. 1979, in _Sources of Gravitational Radiation_, ed. L. Smarr (Cambridge: Cambridge University Press), p.127.

Eardley, D., and Smarr, L. 1979, Phys. Rev. D, 19, 2239.

Epstein, R. 1979, in _Sources of Gravitational Radiation_, ed. L. Smarr (Cambridge: Cambridge University Press), p.69.

Evans, C. R. 1984, "A Method for Numerical Relativity: Simulation of Axisymmetric Gravitational Collapse and Gravitational Radiation Generation," Ph.D. thesis, University of Texas at Austin.

Evans, C. R., Smarr, L., and Wilson, J. R. 1984a, in Radiation Hydrodynamics, eds. K.- H. Winkler and M. Norman (Dordrecht: Reidel), (to appear).

_____. 1984b, in preparation.

Fairbank, W. 1984, personal communication.

Hamilton, W. 1983, personal communication.

Hawking, S. W. 1968, J. Math. Phys., 9, 598.

Lichnerowicz, A. 1944, J. Math. Pures et Appl., 23, 37.

Müller, E. 1982, Astr. Ap., 114, 53.

Müller, E., and Hillebrandt, W. 1981, Astr. Ap., 103, 358.

Newman, E., and Penrose, R. 1962, J. Math. Phys., 3, 566.

Ō Murchadha, N., and York, J. W. 1973, J. Math. Phys., 14, 1551.

_____. 1974, Phys. Rev. D, 10, 428.

Piran, T. 1983, in Gravitational Radiation, ed. N. Deruelle and T. Piran (Amsterdam: North Holland), p.203.

Sachs, R. K. 1962, Proc. Roy. Soc. London A, 270, 103.

Saenz, R. A., and Shapiro, S. L. 1981, Ap. J. 244, 1033.

Shapiro, S. L. 1979, in Sources of Gravitational Radiation, ed. L. Smarr (Cambridge: Cambridge University Press), p.355.

Smarr, L. 1979, in Sources of Gravitational Radiation, ed. L. Smarr (Cambridge: Cambridge University Press), p.245.

Smarr, L., Taubes, C., and Wilson, J. R. 1980, in Essays in General Relativity: A Festschrift for A. Taub, ed. F. Tipler (New York: Academic Press), p.157.

Smarr, L., and York, J. W. 1978, Phys. Rev. D, 17, 2529.

Thorne, K. S. 1980a, Rev. Mod. Phys., 52, 285.

_____. 1980b, Rev. Mod. Phys., 52, 299.

Turner, M. S., and Wagoner, R. V. 1979, in Sources of Gravitational Radiation, ed. L. Smarr (Cambridge: Cambridge University Press), p.383.

Weiss, R. 1979, in Sources of Gravitational Radiation, ed. L. Smarr (Cambridge: Cambridge University Press), p.7.

Wilson, J. R. 1979, in Sources of Gravitational Radiation, ed. L. Smarr (Cambridge: Cambridge University Press), p.423.

York, J. W. 1973, J. Math. Phys., 14, 456.

_____. 1979, in Sources of Gravitational Radiation, ed. L. Smarr (Cambridge: Cambridge University Press), p.83.

_____. 1983, in Gravitational Radiation, ed. N. Deruelle and T. Piran (Amsterdam: North Holland), p.175.

York, J. W., and Piran, T. 1982, in Spacetime and Geometry, ed. R. Matzner and L. Shepley (Austin: University of Texas Press), p. 147.

IV. Cosmology

Semiclassical Formulation of Hawking Radiation in an Inflationary Universe

William H. Press
Harvard University

ABSTRACT

In classical contexts, the fluctuation–dissipation theorem relates damping to thermal "noise" generation. In the inflationary universe, redshift plays the role of a damping, and Hawking radiation can be thought of as the thermal noise. A semiclassical "toy" model is developed to illustrate the analogy.

I. INTRODUCTION

Jim Wilson, whom we rightly celebrate in this volume, has time and again made use of his extraordinary physical good sense to "concretize" problems. By this I mean that he has taken problems which had previously been treated as formal abstractions, from which a few isolated results could perhaps be gleaned, and turned them into honestly computable (though often approximate) physical models, with differential equations that could be evolved on the computer from appropriate initial conditions.

In my opinion, the problem of the origin of cosmological perturbations is on the threshold of just such a concretization. There is a growing sense, among cosmologists and particle physicists alike, that the cosmological epoch of Grand Unified Theories (GUT's) (say, generously, between 10^{10} and 10^{17} GeV) provides a suitable environment for the gestation of cosmological perturbations that, much later, will form galaxies, hence stars, hence heavy metals, hence planets, hence us.

Alan Guth, more than anyone else, is responsible for assembling the key ideas that have forged this breathtaking link between the very smallest scales and the very largest (or, alternatively, between the most arcane aspects of theoretical particle physics and the tangible existence of everyday objects around us). In my talk at the Jim Wilson conference, I reviewed Guth's "inflationary universe" scenario (Guth 1981), its original difficulties (Guth and Weinberg 1982; Hawking and Moss 1982a,b) and its improved version, the "new inflationary universe" which posits a GUT that has the Coleman-Weinberg (1973) shape for its effective potential (Linde 1981, 1982a,b,c,d; Albrecht *et al.* 1982). I will not repeat that review here, since there are a number of good reviews in print, mostly in conference proceedings, e.g., Guth (1983), Turner (1982), Brandenberger (1982).

I also reviewed the various (but mostly similar in conclusions) calculations of the spectrum of perturbations that originates naturally in the inflationary phase, e.g. Guth and Pi (1982), Hawking (1982), Linde (1982a,b,c,d), Starobinsky (1982), Bardeen, Steinhardt, and Turner (1982). These calculations, in the context of the "favorite" SU5 GUT model, obtain a scale-invariant, Zel'dovich (1972) spectrum of perturbations, but unfortunately with amplitude of about 10^2 instead of the required $10^{-3\pm1}$. Various authors have pointed out that the problem is mitigated by positing a potential that derives from a supersymmetric theory (e.g., Albrecht *et al.* 1982; Ellis *et al.* 1982a,b). A rather different calculation is that of Lukash and Novikov (1982), while Hawking and Moss (1982) have a new calculational procedure (not yet fully understood by them or anyone else, but see Brandenberger 1983) which seems to give the "right" answer.

As an outside and somewhat neutral observer of this flurry of activity, I confess to a certain skepticism that the technical details of these calculations are all correct. The issues of coupling the Higgs field to gravitational perturbations in the correct functional way, and then evolving these perturbations gravitationally in a sensible gauge, or in a gauge-independent manner (e.g. Bardeen 1980), have in some cases been given short shrift.

Nevertheless, the general framework "smells" to me exactly right. The most important element in the fragrance is the fact, shown by Gibbons and Hawking (1977; see also Lapedes 1978), that the apparent event horizon in deSitter spacetime (or approximate deSitter spacetime: see Brandenberger and Kahn 1982) has a finite "Hawking" temperature

$$T_{Hawking} = \frac{H}{2\pi},$$
(1.1)

where H is the Hubble expansion rate. (Throughout this paper, we use units with $h = c = 1$, but *not* $G = 1$.) That fact alone, as Steinhardt has pointed out, makes the production of a Zel'dovich perturbation spectrum, or something very close to it, a virtual certainty. During the inflationary phase, the background deSitter metric is very nearly stationary; the quantum fluctuations represented by the Hawking temperature are very nearly stationary; so a nearly stationary set of incipient perturbations are freezing out as they "inflate" across the apparent event horizon. The content of the above-referenced papers on the generation of perturbations is (i) to calculate the *amplitude* of these scale-invariant perturbations, and (ii) to verify that their evolution outside the horizon is such as to bring them back across their horizons, much later, as scale-invariant in the required sense.

So, in some fundamental sense, it all comes down to Hawking radiation, the seemingly paradoxical finite temperature that is ascribed to gravitating systems with event horizons, such as deSitter space or black holes. I don't know a good, general, convincing argument for the inevitability of Hawking radiation in these systems. The argument which seems convincing to many field theorists is that these spacetimes are periodic in Euclidean space (i.e. when $t \to it$ in the metric). Thus, goes the argument, any equilibrium partition function must exhibit this periodicity. Under analytic continuation back to ordinary time such a periodicity turns into a thermal partition function at finite temperature. If you take seriously that our universe really "knows" about its extension into imaginary time (and, if you believe in instantons, then you must perhaps do so), then you might be convinced by this sort of argument. Alternatively, you can fall back on the specific calculations which obtain the same finite Hawking temperatures by a variety of different formalisms.

The key point is that though Hawking radiation is an effect of quantum field theory in a curved spacetime, its temperature follows from entirely classical arguments, namely the classical Euclidean periodicity of the spacetime. I want to show, in this paper, that *knowing only the Hawking temperature, and the fact that the Hawking radiation spectrum is thermal,* we can deduce everything that we need to know to calculate the interaction of the Hawking radiation with a semi-classical field. We are then in a position to "concretize" Hawking radiation in a (perhaps approximate) manner that Jim Wilson might appreciate: we can include it in detailed dynamical calculations of the initiation and evolution of perturbations on an inflationary background. With Brandenberger and Kahn, I am planning to move in just that direction in future work.

The conceptual link between a semiclassical system and a finite temperature bath in which it finds itself is the *fluctuation-dissipation theorem*, which relates the system's classical dissipation to the fluctuating driving term that it must feel from thermal interactions. I will apply the theorem in the most straightforward fashion, exactly in analogy with its application to the simple harmonic oscillator (which we review in §II). In §III, we show how the notion of a stochastic driving term can be fit into a Lagrangian view of the universe, or it least into a Lagrangian view of a "toy" universe. The principal calculation of this paper is in § IV, where the fluctuation-dissipation theorem is applied to the case of a massive scalar field in a deSitter background.

Candelas and Sciama (1977) have previously considered the fluctuation-dissipation theorem in the context of black hole thermodynamics, but from a point of view rather different from this paper.

II. SIMPLE HARMONIC OSCILLATOR

As the simplest possible example of the fluctuation-dissipation theorem, and to see what we can hope to accomplish in the more complicated case of interest, let us consider a single degree of freedom system, the simple harmonic oscillator.

Imagine that we have started with the system's "true" quantum theory, and from that have obtained the usual classical equations of motion, valid in the appropriate limit,

$$\ddot{\phi} + \beta\dot{\phi} + m^2\phi = 0. \tag{2.1}$$

Now suppose that the ϕ field is not free, as equation (2.1) says, but rather interacts with some number of other quantum fields, and that these other fields are well-characterized by thermal equilibrium at some temperature T. The interaction terms can, in detail, themselves be quantum mechanical. We want to ask, however, whether there is a semi-classical modification of (2.1) which summarizes their net effect on the ϕ field.

It is well known that such a modification is possible and unique. The right-hand side of equation (2.1) is replaced by a stochastic driving term $F(t)$,

$$\ddot{\phi} + \beta\dot{\phi} + m^2\phi = F(t), \tag{2.2}$$

characterized by a two-point correlation function (or equivalent power spectrum)

$$\langle F(t)F(t+\tau)\rangle = P\delta(\tau), \tag{2.3}$$

where P is the spectral density of the thermally fluctuating force, which we now compute. The computation is essentially an application of the fluctuation-dissipation theorem for this special case.

In thermal equilibrium at temperature T the ϕ field must have $\frac{1}{2}kT$ energy per degree of freedom, where k_B is Boltzmann's constant. In particular, for its kinetic energy we must have

$$\left\langle \frac{1}{2}\dot{\phi}^2 \right\rangle = \frac{1}{2}k_B T \tag{2.4}$$

Now, ϕ is related to its forcing function $F(t)$ by a Greens function

$$\phi(t) = \int_{-\infty}^{\infty} dt_0 \, G(t - t_0)F(t_0) \tag{2.5}$$

So we have

$$
\begin{aligned}
k_B T = \left\langle \dot{\phi}^2 \right\rangle &= \left\langle \int dt_0 \, \dot{G}(t - t_0)F(t_0) \int dt_1 \, \dot{G}(t - t_1)F(t_1) \right\rangle \\
&= \int dt_0 \int dt_1 \, \dot{G}(t - t_0)\dot{G}(t - t_1)\langle F(t_0)F(t_1)\rangle \\
&= P \int dt_0 [\dot{G}(t - t_0)]^2 = P \int d\tau [\dot{G}(\tau)]^2.
\end{aligned}
\tag{2.6}
$$

The integral multiplying P is seen to depend on the classical Green's function only. If the damping constant β is small,

$$\beta \ll m \tag{2.7}$$

then the time derivative of the Green's function is approximately

$$\dot{G}(\tau) \approx \cos(m\tau)e^{-\beta\tau}. \tag{2.8}$$

So

$$\int \dot{G}^2(\tau)d\tau \approx \frac{1}{2}\int_0^\infty e^{-\beta\tau}d\tau = \frac{1}{2\beta}, \tag{2.9}$$

which, with equation (2.6), implies

$$P = 2\beta k_B T. \tag{2.10}$$

The fluctuation depends linearly on the dissipation and on the temperature, which is the standard result.

Let us, in passing, derive one additional result that we will need in a later section, namely that there is no correlation between ϕ and F:

$$
\begin{aligned}
\langle\phi F\rangle &= \int_{-\infty}^\infty dt_0\, G(t - t_0)\langle F(t_0)F(t)\rangle \\
&= P\, G(0) \\
&= 0,
\end{aligned}
\tag{2.11}
$$

where we have used equations (2.3), (2.5), and the fact the the Greens function for equation (2.1) vanishes at zero lag.

Notice that the term $k_B T$ in equation (2.10) is there because it was put in by fiat in equation (2.4). Had we desired, we could have used "old" (i.e., semiclassical, Planck) quantum theory to derive an occupation number correction to the expected mean energy per degree of freedom. In this case equation (2.10) would instead read

$$P = 2\beta k_B T \frac{m/k_B T}{e^{m/k_B T} - 1}. \tag{2.12}$$

The semiclassical description of the ϕ field at finite temperature is then given completely by equations (2.2), (2.3), and (2.12).

This should, of course, seem straightforward and elementary. We now want to apply the same straightforward and elementary calculation to each degree of freedom of a quantum field $\phi(\mathbf{x}, t)$ in an inflationary deSitter background spacetime that is characterized by a finite Hawking temperature. We will thus be in a position to consider the two processes, *generation* of fluctuations and *evolution* of fluctuations, on a unified semiclassical footing.

III. LAGRANGIAN-BASED FORMALISM

Before we proceed with deriving the fluctuation term for the case of interest, we should perhaps say a few words about how that term should be viewed as fitting into a "universal Lagrangian" that contains all fields of interest (including the gravitational field which generates the deSitter background). It is desirable that our model be based on such a universal Lagrangian, even if the Lagrangian is a "toy" (not the actual GUT), so that we cannot be accused of making up dynamical equations *ad hoc*.

We consider the variational principle

$$\delta S = 0 \tag{3.1}$$

where

$$S \equiv \int L\sqrt{-g}d^4x. \tag{3.2}$$

Here L is the Lagrangian density and g is the determinant of the metric tensor, whose signature is taken to be $(-,+,+,+)$.

For our toy Lagrangian, let us take a Universe with allowed degrees of freedom as follows: a metric constrained to be Robertson-Walker (homogeneous and isotropic), a massive scalar field ϕ, and a thermal bath of unspecified particle composition to which ϕ is coupled. The way to do this is to take

$$L = \frac{1}{16\pi G}R - \frac{1}{8\pi}(\phi_{,\mu}\phi_{,\nu}g^{\mu\nu} + m^2\phi^2 + V_0) + \frac{1}{4\pi}F\phi + U(F). \tag{3.3}$$

Here F stands for all the fluctuating forces which couple to ϕ, the coupling modeled here by the bilinear term $F\phi$. $U(F)$ stands for "unknown functional of F", and represents all the unspecified internal dynamics of the F fields. V_0 is the constant term which generates a cosmological constant. Greek letters are used for spacetime indices: $\mu, \nu = 0, 1, 2, 3$; and ",μ" is $\partial/\partial\chi^\mu$.

In equation (3.3), the scalar R is supposed to connote a Ricci tensor, but it is actually defined as: that functional form which would be the Ricci tensor formed from the *restricted* metric

$$g_{\mu\nu} \equiv \begin{pmatrix} -a^2(t) & & & \\ & a^2(t) & & \\ & & a^2(t) & \\ & & & a^2(t) \end{pmatrix}. \tag{3.4}$$

In other words, the fundamental variables in the Lagrangian are a and α, not R or (for that matter) $\sqrt{-g}$. It is important to notice that a and α are taken to depend on time only. This constrains our toy model to have many fewer gravitational degrees of freedom than the real universe, but imposes that constraint in a formally self-consistent manner. A forthcoming [at the time of the Wilson conference] paper by Brandenberger, Kahn, and Press (1983; hereafter cited as BKP) shows how to extend the formalism and choose a constrained metric with enough degrees of freedom so that the variational equations also contain the growing modes of inhomogeneous cosmological perturbations in a gauge-independent form, with results equivalent to those of Bardeen (1980).

Elementary calculation gives

$$R\sqrt{-g} = -\frac{6a\dot{a}^2}{\alpha} \quad and \quad \sqrt{-g} = a^3\alpha. \tag{3.5}$$

Now we vary with respect to everything in sight: ϕ, a, α, and F.

As is known to relativists familiar with the ADM formalism (Arnowitt, Deser, and Misner 1962; see also Misner, Thorne, and Wheeler 1973, § 21.7), none of the variations will give a dynamical equation for α (the "lapse function"). This means that, *after varying with respect to α*, we can set it equal to unity in all subsequent calculations. Variation with respect to α gives, setting $\alpha = 1$,

$$0 = \frac{\delta S}{\delta \alpha} = \frac{3}{8\pi G}a\dot{a}^2 - \frac{1}{8\pi}\left\langle \dot{\phi}^2 + \frac{1}{a^2}(\nabla\phi)^2 + m^2\phi^2 + 2F\phi + V_0 \right\rangle a^3 + \frac{\delta U}{\delta \alpha}. \tag{3.6}$$

In equation (3.6), the angle brackets denote spatial averaging over a surface of constant time t. Such an average occurs automatically whenever one varies with respect to a quantity (such as α) that depends on t only; for technical discussion see BKP. The term in U is, of course, "unknown" at this point.

Let us define the convenient abbreviations

$$\rho_\phi \equiv \frac{1}{8\pi}\left\langle \dot{\phi}^2 + \frac{1}{a^2}(\nabla\phi)^2 + m^2\phi^2 + 2F\phi + V_0 \right\rangle \tag{3.7}$$

and

$$\rho_U \equiv \frac{\delta(U\alpha)}{\delta \alpha}. \tag{3.8}$$

Then (3.6) takes the form of the familiar Friedmann equation

$$\left(\frac{\dot{a}}{a}\right)^2 = \frac{8\pi G}{3}(\rho_\phi + \rho_U). \tag{3.9}$$

Notice that ρ_ϕ, being spatially averaged, is *not* the local density of mass and energy that the letter ρ usually represents. Rather it is just an abbreviation for that functional combination which couples to the dynamics of the homogeneous expansion factor a.

Variation with respect to a is similar to variation with respect to α, and gives another equation in the familiar Friedmann form,

$$\frac{\dot{a}^2}{a^2} + 2\frac{\ddot{a}}{a} + 8\pi G(P_\phi + P_U) = 0. \tag{3.10}$$

Here, while P_ϕ and P_U connote pressures, they are in fact *defined* as

$$P_\phi \equiv \frac{1}{8\pi}\left\langle \dot{\phi}^2 - m^2\phi^2 - \frac{1}{3a^2}(\nabla\phi)^2 - 2F\phi - V_0 \right\rangle \tag{3.11}$$

and

$$P_U \equiv \frac{\delta U}{\delta a}. \tag{3.12}$$

P_ϕ is manifestly not the pressure of the ϕ field, since that field's stress tensor is, in general, anisotropic. Rather, P_ϕ is that particular projection of the stress tensor, isotropized and homogenized, which couples to the allowed degree of freedom of the Robertson-Walker metric, namely to the expansion factor a. Variation with respect to a restricted metric is a powerful technique for finding just these projections which couple to interesting modes of gravitation; see BKP for further details.

Variation with respect to ϕ gives the familiar massive wave equation, but now with a source term,

$$0 = \frac{\delta S}{\delta \phi} = \phi^{;\mu}_{,\mu} - m^2\phi + F \tag{3.13}$$

or

$$\phi^{;\mu}_{,\mu} - m^2\phi = -F(\mathbf{x}, t), \tag{3.14}$$

where we have emphasized that F, like ϕ, is a function of both space and time. Writing out the covariant derivative; (or just naively doing the variation *after* eliminating g's in favor of a's) gives the explicit form

$$\ddot{\phi} + 3\frac{\dot{a}}{a}\dot{\phi} + m^2\phi - \frac{1}{a^2}\phi_{,jj} = F. \tag{3.15}$$

The term $3(\dot{a}/a)\dot{\phi}$ is not unexpected; it represents the tendency of the scalar field to "redshift away" as the universe expands, and so appears as a damping term with respect to the term $\ddot{\phi}$. In the next section we will see how, from the point of view of the fluctuation-dissipation theorem, this term is precisely the one which requires a corresponding fluctuating source, if thermal equilibrium is to be maintained.

Variation with respect to F gives the dynamical equation for F, but its precise content is hidden in the unknown functional $U(F)$:

$$\frac{\delta U}{\delta F} - \frac{\phi}{4\pi} = 0. \tag{3.16}$$

In the usual textbook treatments of the Friedmann cosmology, one manipulates the two Friedmann equations, like our equations (3.9) and (3.10) above, to obtain the first law of thermodynamics in the form

$$\dot{\rho} = -3(P + \rho)\frac{\dot{a}}{a}. \tag{3.17}$$

In our present scheme, the analogous manipulation gives a relation between the "unknown" matter variables ρ_U and P_U. Calculate as follows: compute the time derivative of $\rho_\phi + \rho_U$ from the definitions (3.7) and (3.8), and simplify the result using equation (3.15) and the fact that the spatial average of a perfect divergence is zero. Next compare this result to $P_\phi + P_U + \rho_\phi + \rho_U$, computed using equations (3.7), (3.8), (3.11), and (3.12). The result is

$$\dot{\rho}_U = -3(P_U + \rho_U)\frac{\dot{a}}{a} - \frac{1}{4\pi}\dot{F}\phi. \tag{3.18}$$

We now have a not-quite-closed set of evolution equations for the five quantities a, ϕ, ρ_ϕ, F, and ρ_U. Equation (3.15) evolves ϕ, while equation (3.7) defines ρ_ϕ. Equation (3.6) evolves a. Equation (3.18) will evolve ρ_U if we posit, as additional information about the unknown fields F, a relation between P_U and ρ_U, i.e. an *equation of state* for the fields F. For the case of modeling Hawking radiation in deSitter (or approximate deSitter) space, we know that the fields F are in a stationary (approximately stationary) thermal equilibrium. This tells us instantly that, with the correct effective equation of state, equation (3.18) must become simply

$$\dot{\rho}_U = 0 \tag{3.19}$$

just so that, when the spacetime is approximately deSitter, we can have the approximate thermal equilibrium density

$$\rho_U \approx \text{constant} \times T^4_{Hawking} \tag{3.20}$$

where the constant can be interpreted as the number of species in F.

[In an earlier paper (Press 1981), I explored the somewhat different choice

$$P_U = -\rho_U \tag{3.21}$$

which leads to a negative definite value of $\dot{\rho}_U$, i.e., a decay of the cosmological constant, "pulled" towards zero by the interaction with the ϕ field. In this paper I am taking the view that the stationarity, or stability, of Hawking radiation in the deSitter background is to be taken as given, hence equation (3.19).]

If we adopt equation (3.19), the only remaining "unknown" equation is (3.16), the dynamical equation for F, which is needed only for the source term in equation (3.15). But this is precisely where the assumption that the F fields are in thermal equilibrium at a particular temperature $T_{Hawking}$, combined with the fluctuation-dissipation theorem, will tell everything that we need to know.

This, then, is the final scheme: all equations come from the variational principle, except that two of them are "unknown". We replace the first unknown equation (Eqn. 3.18, which tracks back to the variation with respect to a) by an assumed equation of state for Hawking radiation. We replace the second unknown equation (Eqn. 3.16) by a fluctuation-dissipation equation, which we now derive.

IV. MASSIVE SCALAR FIELD IN A DE SITTER SPACETIME

Let us make the approximation that $\dot{a}/a$ is only slowly varying, so that

$$\frac{\dot{a}}{a} \approx H, \quad \text{which gives} \quad a \approx e^{Ht}. \tag{4.1}$$

Then equation (3.15) for a single, real scalar field is

$$\ddot{\phi} + 3H\dot{\phi} + m^2\phi - e^{-2Ht}\nabla^2\phi = F(\mathbf{x}, t). \tag{4.2}$$

We need to Fourier analyze equation (4.2) so that we can do field theory mode by mode. Our conventions are:

$$\phi(\mathbf{x}) = V^{1/2} \int e^{i\mathbf{k}\cdot\mathbf{x}} \phi(\mathbf{k}) d^3\mathbf{k} \tag{4.3}$$

and

$$\phi(\mathbf{k}) = \frac{V^{-1/2}}{(2\pi)^3} \int e^{-i\mathbf{k}\cdot\mathbf{x}} \phi(\mathbf{x}) d^3\mathbf{x} \tag{4.4}$$

where V is the volume of some very large imagined box. Then equation (4.2) becomes

$$\ddot{\phi} + 3H\dot{\phi} + (m^2 + k^2 e^{-2Ht})\phi = F(\mathbf{k}, t). \tag{4.5}$$

Since $\phi(\mathbf{x})$ is real, we have

$$\phi(-\mathbf{k}) = [\phi(\mathbf{k})]^* \tag{4.6}$$

where "*" denotes the complex conjugate. The spatial average of ϕ^2 is readily calculated:

$$\langle\phi^2\rangle = \frac{1}{V}\int d^3\mathbf{x}\, V^{1/2}\int d^3\mathbf{k}\, V^{1/2}\int d^3\mathbf{k}'\, e^{i(k+k')\cdot z}\phi(\mathbf{k})\phi(\mathbf{k}')$$
$$= (2\pi)^3\int d^3\mathbf{k}\,\phi(\mathbf{k})\phi(-\mathbf{k}). \tag{4.7}$$

Therefore ρ_ϕ (Eqn. 3.7 above) is given by

$$\rho_\phi = \frac{(2\pi)^3}{8\pi}\int d^3\mathbf{k}\left[|\dot\phi|^2 + m^2|\phi|^2 + e^{-2Ht}k^2|\phi|^2\right]. \tag{4.8}$$

In equation (4.8) we have used the generalization of equation (2.11) to eliminate the term in $\langle F\phi\rangle$.

Equation (4.5) has a Green's function that depends on the five parameters $t, t_0, H, m,$ and k. We can choose H^{-1} as the unit of time, so m will only enter as m/H. Since k is a comoving wavenumber, and since the deSitter background is stationary, k can only appear in the Green's function as $(k/H)e^{-Ht_0}$, while t and t_0 can only occur in the additional combination $H(t-t_0)$. So, from symmetry arguments alone, we know that the Green's function has the form

$$G(t, t_0, H, m, k) = \frac{1}{H}G_0\left(H(t-t_0), \frac{k}{H}e^{-Ht_0}, \frac{m}{H}\right) \tag{4.9}$$

where G_0 is a dimensionless function of its arguments. (We will sometimes suppress the third argument of G_0 as understood.)

Now we want to repeat the argument, based on the fluctuation-dissipation theorem, which we used above in the simple example of the harmonic oscillator. Suppose that we believe the ϕ field to be in a stationary thermal equilibrium. Then the energy in each mode $\phi(\mathbf{k})$ should be stationary and should depend on k only, that is

$$\langle\rho_\phi(k)\rangle = S(k) \tag{4.10}$$

where S is the specified energy in each mode and $\rho_\phi(k)$ denotes the integrand (including, by convention, the outside factor $1/8\pi$) in equation (4.8).

We now can turn equation (4.10) into an integral equation for the fluctuating force term F, analogously with the procedure that led from equation (2.4) to equation (2.10). There is one technical difference, however: the force term F must be stochastic and stationary (and defined by its two-point correlation function) not in comoving coordinates (wavenumbers k) but in *physical* (i.e., proper) coordinates. Let us define

$$k' \equiv ke^{-Ht} \tag{4.11}$$

and

$$F'(k', t) \equiv F(k' e^{Ht}, t).$$ (4.12)

Then F is characterized by its power spectrum $P(k')$,

$$\langle F'(k', t) F'(k', t + \tau) \rangle = P(k') \delta(\tau).$$ (4.13)

One now proceeds to evaluate the left-hand side of equation (4.10), substituting in the various terms in equation (4.8) and their Green's function representation. For example,

$$\langle \phi^2 \rangle = \int dt_0 \int dt_1 G(t, t_0, k, H, m) G(t, t_1, k, H, m) \langle F(k, t_0) F(k, t_1) \rangle$$

$$= \int dt_0 \int dt_1 G(t, t_0, k, H, m) G(t, t_1, k, H, m) P(ke^{-Ht_0}) \delta(t_0 - t_1)$$ (4.14)

$$= \frac{1}{H^2} \int dt_0 G_0^2(t - t_0, \frac{k}{H} e^{-Ht_0}) P(ke^{-Ht_0}).$$

In terms of $\tau \equiv t - t_0$ and k' (Eqn. 4.11), equation (4.14) becomes

$$\langle \phi^2 \rangle = \int d\tau G_0^2(H\tau, \frac{k'}{H} e^{H\tau}) P(k' e^{H\tau}).$$ (4.15)

Evaluating the other terms in like manner, we get the integral equation for P in terms of known functions:

$$S(k') = \frac{1}{8\pi} \int_0^\infty d\tau P(k' e^{H\tau}) \left\{ \dot{G}_0^2(H\tau, k' e^{H\tau}) + \frac{1}{H^2} \left[m^2 + k'^2 e^{2H\tau} \right] G_0^2(H\tau, k' e^{H\tau}) \right\}.$$ (4.16)

Here $\dot{G}_0$ means the derivative of G_0 with respect to its first (τ) argument. We can write equation (4.16) in a simpler form by eliminating the variable τ in favor of $k \equiv k' e^{H\tau}$. The result is

$$S(k') = \frac{1}{8\pi} \int_{k=k'}^\infty \frac{dk}{k} P(k) \left[\dot{G}_0^2(\ln \frac{k}{k'}, k) + \frac{m^2 + k^2}{H^2} G_0^2(\ln \frac{k}{k'}, k) \right].$$ (4.17)

In this form, the integral equation is seen to be upper triangular, and thus very easy to solve numerically. The physical interpretation of this form is that the energy density at a specified wavenumber "now" depends, as we go back on the past light cone, on the source function at higher and higher wavenumbers, those which have by now redshifted to the specified wavenumber of interest.

We now have three remaining tasks: find the Green's function G_0 explicitly (or at least an adequate approximation to it), find $S(k')$ by a semiclassical argument like the one which changes equation (2.10) above to equation (2.12), and solve equation (4.17).

We will do each of these tasks in turn.

a)   The Green's Function

We will content ourselves with deriving a pretty good approximation to the required Green's function. (The meaning of "pretty good" will become apparent in the derivation.)

The Green's function $G(t, t_0, k, H, m)$ satisfies the homogeneous wave equation (Eqn. 4.5 with right hand side equal to zero) for the initial conditions

$$\phi(0) = 0 \quad and \quad \dot{\phi}(0) = 1. \tag{4.18}$$

At early times ϕ approximately satisfies the equation

$$\ddot{\phi} + 3H\dot{\phi} = 0 \tag{4.19}$$

whose solution (with Eqn. 4.18) is

$$\phi = \frac{1}{3H}(1 - e^{-3Ht}). \tag{4.20}$$

This solution remains valid as long as

$$3H\dot{\phi} \gg (m^2 + k^2 e^{-2Ht})\phi. \tag{4.21}$$

A short calculation shows that equation (4.21) holds until

$$t \sim \frac{2}{3H} \ln\left(\frac{3H}{m}\right) \quad or \quad t \sim \frac{2}{H} \ln\left(\frac{3H}{k}\right), \tag{4.22}$$

whichever comes first. At that time,

$$\phi \approx \frac{1}{3H}. \tag{4.23}$$

Subsequently, the evolution satisfies the approximate equation

$$\dot{\phi} + \frac{m^2 + k^2 e^{-2Ht}}{3H}\phi = 0 \tag{4.24}$$

whose solution, incorporating (Eqn. 4.23), is

$$\phi = \frac{1}{3H} \exp\left[-\frac{m^2}{3H}t - \frac{k^2}{6H^2}(1 - e^{-2Ht})\right]. \tag{4.25}$$

A uniform approximation, combining (4.25) with (4.20), is

$$\phi = \frac{1}{3H}(1 - e^{-3Ht}) \exp\left[-\frac{m^2}{3H}t - \frac{k^2}{6H^2}(1 - e^{-2Ht})\right]. \qquad (4.26)$$

Equation (4.26) yields directly the following approximate Green's function, valid at all times:

$$G_0(\tau, y) = \frac{1}{3}(1 - e^{-3\tau}) \exp\left[-\frac{m^2}{3H^2}\tau - \frac{1}{6}y^2(1 - e^{-2\tau})\right], \qquad (4.27)$$

$$\dot{G}_0(\tau, y) = e^{-3\tau} - \frac{1}{9}\left(\frac{m^2}{H^2} + y^2 e^{-2\tau}\right) \exp\left[-\frac{m^2}{3H^2}\tau - \frac{1}{6}y^2(1 - e^{-2\tau})\right] \qquad (4.28)$$

where $\tau \equiv H(t - t_0)$ and $y \equiv (k/H)e^{-Ht_0}$.

b) The Power Density

We turn now to the semiclassical argument that gives $S(k')$, which is straightforward: there are $4\pi\nu^2$ modes of a field per unit volume per Hertz per polarization state, where $\nu \equiv 2\pi k'$. Each mode has, classically, k_B of energy, $\frac{1}{2}k_B$ each in potential and kinetic. *Semi*-classically, this gets multiplied by an occupation number. The black-body energy density for an electromagnetic field, for example, is thus

$$\rho = 2 \int d\nu \, \nu^2 \times (4\pi k_B) \times \text{(occupation number)}. \qquad (4.29)$$

(Here k_B is Boltzmann's constant, not wavenumber. From now on we set it to unity.) So, starting with equation (4.8),

$$\begin{aligned}
\rho_\phi &= (2\pi)^3 \int d^3k' \, \rho_\phi(k') \\
&= (2\pi)^3 \int 4\pi k'^2 dk' \rho_\phi(k') \\
&= \int \nu^2 d\nu \, 4\pi \rho_\phi(k') \\
&= \int \nu^2 d\nu \, 4\pi T \frac{\sqrt{k'^2 + m^2}/T}{\exp(\sqrt{k'^2 + m^2}/T) - 1}.
\end{aligned} \qquad (4.30)$$

Referring to the definition (4.10) and setting

$$T = T_{Hawking} = H/2\pi \qquad (4.31)$$

gives

$$S(k') = H \frac{\sqrt{\left(\frac{k'}{H}\right)^2 + \left(\frac{m}{H}\right)^2}}{\exp\left(2\pi\sqrt{\left(\frac{k'}{H}\right)^2 + \left(\frac{m}{H}\right)^2}\right) - 1}. \tag{4.32}$$

This function is plotted in Figure 1 for several values of m/H from 0 to 1.4. One sees that the equilibrium density of particle states excited by the Hawking temperature approaches unity occupation number for small masses and small wavenumbers, but is cut off by a Boltzmann factor as either the wavenumber or the mass approaches the expansion rate H (DeBroglie wavelength or Compton wavelength becomes smaller than horizon size).

c)   Solution of the Integral Equation

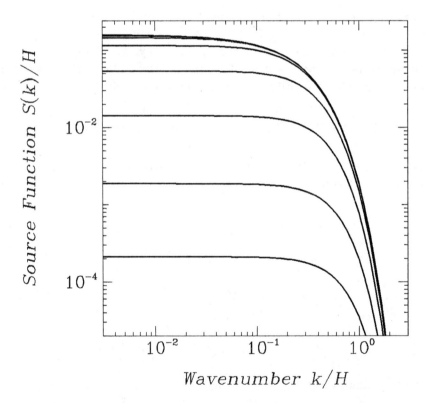

Figure 1. Source function (4.32) which is the inhomogeneous term in integral equation (4.17) and which thus generates the fluctuating power spectrum P(k). The different curves are for different values of particle mass m/H (from the bottom up:) 1.4, 1.0, 0.6, 0.3, 0.1, 0.03, 0.01, 0.

I have solved the set of equations (4.17), (4.27), (4.28), and (4.32) numerically. Figure 2 shows the results, plotting $P(k)$ (power spectrum of the stochastic excitation term F in equations (4.5) and (4.13)) as a function of k and for various values of the scalar particle mass m (in units of the expansion rate). The results are not very surprising: the dominant effect is a Wien cutoff in both m and k. There seems to be a bit of numerical structure for the larger values of m when k is also large, but this is not terribly interesting and may only be an artifact of the approximate Green's function used.

For rough, but quantitative, work, the most useful result from Figure 2 may be that it can be approximated, not too badly, by the simple Wien form

$$P(k) \approx 11 \left[\frac{7.2\sqrt{m^2 + k^2}}{\exp[7.2\sqrt{m^2 + k^2}/H] - 1} \right]. \qquad (4.33)$$

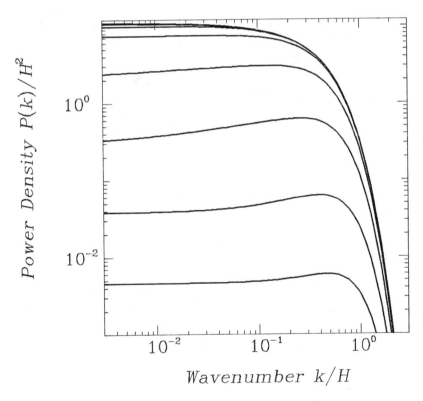

Figure 2. Solution of integral equation (4.17) for the power spectrum of the semiclassical fluctuating force that represents the effect of Hawking radiation. The different curves label different values of particle mass m/H, as in Figure 1.

This function is plotted in Figure 3 for comparison with Figure 2.

V. SUMMARY

We have obtained a closed set of (semi)classical equations that describe the self-consistent evolution of a Friedmann cosmology containing a massive scalar field that is coupled to the background Hawking radiation. The expansion factor a is evolved by equation (3.9), which involves the two densities ρ_ϕ and ρ_U, which are obtained from equations (3.7) and (3.20). The equation of motion of ϕ, the scalar field is equation (3.15), which couples to the semiclassical Hawking fluctuating force F. F is stochastically characterized by its time-correlation function (4.13) and, finally, by its approximate spatial power spectrum (4.33).

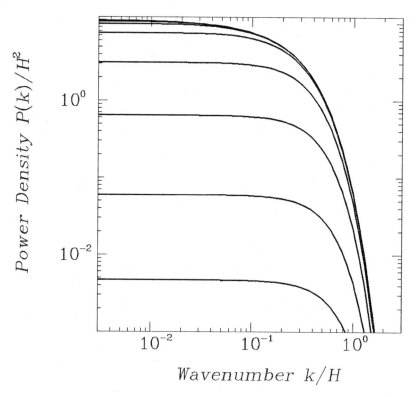

Figure 3. Equation (4.33), a rough-and-ready approximation to the numerical solution shown in Figure 2.

In this paper I have not, of course, coupled the spatial inhomogeneities in the ϕ field back to generate cosmological inhomogeneities. *Without* semiclassical inclusion of Hawking radiation, that problem is the subject of BKP. At some later time, I hope to wed the treatment of Hawking radiation of this paper to the more rigorous formulation of the perturbation problem in BKP. The reader's guess is as good as mine as to how monstrous will be the progeny of such a union.

I thank Robert Brandenberger, Ron Kahn, and Doug Eardley for helpful discussions. This work was supported in part by the National Science Foundation, PHY 80-07351.

REFERENCES

Abbott, L.F., Farhi, E., and Wise, M.B. 1982, *Phys. Lett.*, **117B**, 29.

Albrecht, A., Dimopoulos, S., Fischler, W., Kolb, E.W., Raby, S, and Steinhardt, P.J. 1983, to be published in *Proceedings of the 3rd Marcel Grossman Meeting on General Relativity.*

Albrecht, A., and Steinhardt, P.J. 1982, *Phys. Rev. Lett.*, **48**, 1220.

Albrecht, A., Steinhardt, P.J., Turner, M.S., and Wilczek, F. 1982, *Phys. Rev. Lett.*, **48**, 1437.

Allen, B. 1982, "Phase Transitions in DeSitter Space", preprint.

Arnowitt, R., Deser, S., and Misner, C.W. 1962, in *Gravitation: An Introduction to Current Research*, ed. L. Witten (New York: Wiley).

Bardeen, J.M. 1980, *Phys. Rev. D*, **22**, 1882.

Bardeen, J.M., Steinhardt, P.J., and Turner, M.S. 1982, "Spontaneous Creation of Almost Scale-Free Density Perturbations in an Inflationary Universe", preprint.

Brandenberger, R.H. 1982 "Quantum Field Theory Methods in Cosmology", preprint.

Brandenberger, R.H. 1983, *Phys. Lett.*, **119B**, 75.

Brandenberger, R.H., and Kahn, R. 1982, "Hawking Radiation in an Inflationary Universe", preprint.

Brandenberger, R.H., Kahn, R., and Press, W.H. 1983, *Phys. Rev. D*, **28**, 1809 (cited in text as BKP).

Candelas, P., and Sciama, D.W. 1977, *Phys. Rev. Lett.*, **38**, 1372.

Coleman, S., and Weinberg, E. 1973, *Phys. Rev. D*, **7**, 1888.

Ellis, J., Nanopoulos, D.V., Olive, K.A., and Tamvakis, K. 1982a, (CERN, September, 1982) preprint.

Ellis, J., Nanopoulos, D.V., Olive, K.A., and Tamvakis, K. 1982, (CERN, October, 1982) preprint.

Gibbons, G.W., and Hawking, S.W. 1977, *Phys. Rev. D*, **15**, 2738.

Guth, A.H. 1981, *Phys. Rev. D*, **23**, 347.

Guth, A.H. in *The Very Early Universe: Proceedings of the Nuffield Workship on the Very Early Universe*, ed. G.W. Gibbons, S.W. Hawking, and S. Siklos, Cambridge: (Cambridge University Press).

Guth, A.H. and Pi, S-Y 1982, *Phys. Rev. Lett.*,**49**, 111.

Guth, A.H. and Weinberg, E.J. 1982, preprint.

Hawking, S.W. 1982, *Phys. Lett.*, **115B**, 295.

Hawking, S.W. and Moss, I.G. 1982a, *Phys. Lett.*, **110B**, 35.

Hawking, S.W. and Moss, I.G. 1982b, preprint.

Lapedes, A.S. 1978, *J. Math Phys.*, **19**, 2289.

Linde, A.D. 1982a, *Phys. Lett.*, **108B**, 389.

Linde, A.D. 1982b, *Phys. Lett.*, **116B**, 340.

Linde, A.D. 1982c, *Phys. Lett.*, **114B**, 431.

Linde, A.D. 1982d, *Phys. Lett.*, **116B**, 335.

Lukash, V.N. and Novikov, I.D. 1982, "Generation of the Primordial Perturbations in the Early Universe" (IKI-ANSSSR preprint).

Misner, C.W., Thorne, K.S., and Wheeler, J.A. 1973, *Gravitation* (San Francisco: Freeman).

Petschek, R.G. 1981, "Particle Emission by Non-Equilibrium Quantum Absorbers", preprint.

Press, 1981, in *Cosmology and Particles*, Proceedings of the Sixteenth Rencontre de Moriond Astrophysics Meeting, ed. J. Audouze, P. Crane, T. Gaisser, D. Hegyi, and J. Tran Thanh Van, (Dreux: Editions Frontieres).

Starobinsky, A.A. 1982, *Phys. Lett.*, **117B**, 175.

Turner, M.S. 1982, "The Origin of Density Fluctuations in the New Inflationary Universe", preprint.

Zel'dovich, Ya. B. 1972, *M.N.R.A.S.*, **160**, 1P.

Neutrino Astrophysics

David N. Schramm
University of Chicago

Katherine Freese
University of Chicago

ABSTRACT

Several aspects of neutrino astrophysics are reviewed,
including the problem of solar neutrinos and the role of
neutrinos in cosmology. Cosmological constraints on
neutrino masses, lifetimes, and the number of neutrino
species are emphasized. A possible resolution to the
solar neutrino problem involves a new measurement of
the ^{7}Be (p,γ) ^{8}B cross section. With both internal
and external errors taken into account (opacities may
fall into this category), the current theoretical
estimate is 5.0 ± 2.0 SNU's, $\lesssim$ 1.5 standard deviations
away from the observed 2.0 ± 0.3 SNU.

I. INTRODUCTION

In this article we review two interesting branches of neutrino
astrophysics. The recent coupling of cosmology to particle physics
has yielded some powerful constraints on the properties of neutrinos.
In Section II we review the constraints from Big Bang nucleosynthesis
(Schramm and Wagoner 1977 and references therein), namely that the
number of neutrino species cannot exceed four (probably only three;
Yang et al. 1983 and references therein) and that the density of
baryons in the universe cannot exceed $\Omega_b \lesssim 0.14$. [Here Ω_b is the
ratio of baryonic matter density ρ_b to critical density

$$\rho_c = \frac{3H_o^2}{8\pi G} = 1.88 \times 10^{-29} h_o^2 \text{ gm/cm}^3 = 8.1 \times 10^{-11} h_o^2 \text{ eV}^4$$

where the Hubble parameter $H_o = 100 h_o$ km s^{-1} Mpc^{-1}. We will also use the notation Ω_ν to represent the ratio of neutrino density ρ_ν to critical density and simply Ω for the ratio of total energy density ρ of the universe to critical density.]

Since a neutrino species gives a contribution $\Omega_{\nu_i} = \frac{m_{\nu_i}}{97 \text{ eV}} h_o^{-2}$ (see Equation (3.2) below) to the cosmological density parameter, neutrinos more massive than a few eV would be the dominant matter in the universe. They may solve the "missing mass" problem, the unanswered riddle of dark matter on large scales (Cowsik and McClelland 1972, Marx and Szalay 1972, Schramm and Steigman 1981). In Section III we review the constraints on the masses of stable long-lived neutrinos (following Freese and Schramm 1983). Independently of galaxy formation arguments and with only the most conservative limits on the age of the universe, the neutrino mass is restricted to two ranges, $3 \text{ eV} \lesssim m_\nu \lesssim 100 \text{ eV}$, or $m_\nu \gtrsim 6$ GeV. More model dependent constraints and consistency with globular cluster determinations of the age of the universe further restrict the lower mass branch to $10 \text{ eV} \lesssim m_\nu \lesssim 25 \text{ eV}$, with only one massive neutrino species allowed and $\Omega = 1$ only possible for $m_\nu \approx 25$ eV. In Section IV we show that the constraints on unstable massive neutrinos are remarkably rigorous; no matter what the lifetime, the mass must satisfy either $m_\nu \lesssim 100 \text{ eV}$ or $m_\nu \gtrsim 10$ MeV (Turner 1981 and references therein). In Section V we discuss the solar neutrino problem following Filippone and Schramm (1982) and the recent work of Filippone et al. (1983). The ^{37}Cl experiment is probably incapable of resolving the issue of whether or not there is a real discrepancy between theory and experiment; hence we emphasize the need for experiments with a gallium detector. Other interesting aspects of neutrino astrophysics, such as the neutrinos from gravitational collapse and high energy background neutrinos, have been discussed in detail elsewhere (see e.g., Schramm 1983) and will not be presented here.

II. PRIMORDIAL NUCLEOSYNTHESIS

The prediction of element abundances from Big Bang nucleosynthesis that are in good agreement with observations is one of the great successes of the hot Big Bang model. Approximately three minutes after the Big Bang, when the temperature of the universe has dropped to $\sim 10^9$ K, neutrons and protons can bind together stably as deuterium. Through a variety of reactions the deuterium is converted primarily into ^{4}He, with a smattering of ^{7}Li and other elements as well. The dependence of various primordial element abundances on the amount of baryonic matter in the universe (Schramm and Wagoner 1977 and references therein) is plotted in Figure 1. A lower limit on the

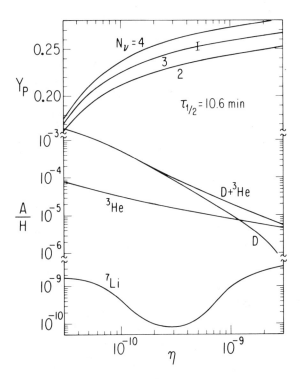

Fig. 1. Mass fractions of elements from primordial nucleosynthesis as functions of baryon-to-photon ratio $\eta = n_b/n_\gamma$, where $\tau_{1/2}$ is neutron halflife, Y_p is mass fraction of ^{4}He, N_ν is number of neutrino species, and A/H indicates abundances of other elements relative to hydrogen. This plot is taken from Yang et al. (1983).

baryonic density can be derived from the combined D and ^{3}He abundances. This comes from the fact that no significant amount of D has been produced since nucleosynthesis (Epstein et al. 1976); much of the original deuterium has been converted to helium in stellar burning. The amount of ^{3}He, on the other hand, has increased in normal stellar processes. Hence the sum of their abundances D + ^{3}He today gives an upper limit on D + ^{3}He at nucleosynthesis and a lower limit on nucleonic matter, $\Omega_b h_o^2 \gtrsim 0.01$ (Yang et al. 1983). The observed abundances of ^{4}He (mass fraction $Y \lesssim 0.25$), D, and ^{7}Li result in an upper limit to baryonic matter density, $\Omega_b h_o^2 \lesssim 0.034$. These arguments restrict baryonic matter to the range

$$0.01 \lesssim \Omega_b \lesssim 0.14. \qquad (2.1)$$

A recent measurement of ^{7}Li abundance by Spite and Spite (1982) in low metallicity Population II stars yielded a ^{7}Li mass fraction of $\sim 10^{-10}$, again in perfect concordance with other element abundances and Equation (2.1).

Helium abundances from Big Bang nucleosynthesis also constrain the number of neutrino species. In Figure 2 the mass fraction Y_p of ^{4}He synthesized in the Big Bang is plotted as a function of baryon-to-photon ratio η for several different values of the number of neutrino species, N_ν = 2, 3, 4. The greatest uncertainty in the plots is due to the neutron halflife, which is somewhere between 10.4 and 10.8 minutes. We can see that at most four low mass ($\lesssim 1$ MeV), long-lived neutrino species are compatible with $Y \lesssim 0.26$, and only three with the best observational limit of $Y \lesssim 0.25$ (Kunth 1981, Pagel 1982, Kunth and Sargent 1983). We know two of these species experimentally, namely the ν_e where $m_{\nu_e} \lesssim 60$ eV and the ν_μ where $m_{\nu_\mu} \lesssim 570$ keV. The experimental mass limit on the ν_τ is $m_{\nu_\tau} \lesssim 250$ MeV (Bacino et al. 1979). Note, however, that if there is some type of particle in the early universe that interacts more weakly than the neutrino (Olive, Schramm, and Steigman 1981) and thus decouples at a temperature $\gtrsim 100$ MeV, the cosmological limit on the numbers of species of this particle is some number greater than three. Further studies of the properties of the Z^0, the neutral weak-current vector boson, at high energy particle accelerators will test the validity of these cosmological arguments, since the width of the Z^0 is proportional to the number of neutrino channels and hence will tell us the number of neutrino species. Thus colliding-beam machines will test the Big Bang theory to earlier times than any other technique to date.

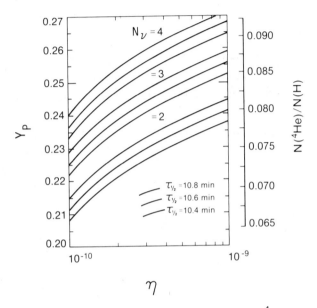

Fig. 2 Dependence of mass fraction of ^{4}He on baryon-to-photon ratio $\eta = n_b/n_\gamma$ for several values of the number of neutrino species, where $N(^4He)/N(H)$ is the ratio of helium abundance to hydrogen abundance. This plot is taken from Yang et al. (1983).

III.   NEUTRINO MASSES

a)   The Missing Mass (Light) Problem.

More and more nonluminous matter seems to exist on larger and larger scales in the universe. Dividing the mass of a bound system (obtained by application of the virial theorem) by its luminosity, one can obtain mass-to-light ratios (M/L) and estimates of matter contributions on different scales. Many authors (e.g., Press and Davis 1982) find evidence for M/L increasing linearly with scale, e.g., M/L ~ (1-4) for stars to M/L ~ (300-800)h_0 for rich clusters (see Table 1, drawn largely from Faber and Gallagher 1979).

Multiplying M/L on a given scale by an average luminosity density (uncertain by a factor of two) for the universe (Kirshner et al. 1979)

$$\mathcal{L} \simeq 2 \times 10^8 \, h_o \, (L_\odot \, \text{Mpc}^{-3}), \qquad (3.1)$$

one obtains a mass density and hence a value of Ω (also listed in Table 1) implied by assuming M/L on that scale applies to the average light of the universe. Davis et al. (1980) have suggested that the M/L curve may be approaching an asymptotic limit (perhaps at $\Omega = 1$) on the scales of superclusters, while other authors (Gott and Turner 1977) believe that the curve flattens already on scales of binaries and small groups. In any case the consensus is that some form of dark matter dominates the dynamics of objects on scales larger than 100 kpc.

Table 1

Mass-to-Light Ratios

Object	$\frac{M}{L} / (\frac{M}{L})_\odot$	Ω
stars	1–4	$(0.7\text{–}2.9) \times 10^{-3} h_o^{-1}$
spiral galaxies	$(8\text{–}12)h_o$	$(5.7\text{–}8.6) \times 10^{-3}$
elliptical and S0 galaxies	$(10\text{–}20)h_o$	$(0.7\text{–}1.4) \times 10^{-2}$
binaries and small groups	$(60\text{–}180)h_o$	$(0.4\text{–}1.3) \times 10^{-1}$
clusters of galaxies	$(280\text{–}840)h_o$	$0.2\text{–}0.6$

From the arguments of the previous section we have seen that the contribution of baryonic matter to the density of the universe cannot exceed $\Omega_b \lesssim 0.14$. Hence a universe with $\Omega \gtrsim 0.15$, as indicated by the matter on scales of clusters of galaxies, must be dominated by nonbaryonic matter. Massive neutrinos (or other neutral, weakly-interacting particles) are ideal candidates for the dark matter on large scales. With this objective in mind, let us now review the thermodynamics of neutrino number densities and cosmological constraints on neutrino masses (this discussion is taken from Freese and Schramm 1983).

b)   Neutrino Densities and Masses.

The equilibrium neutrino number density is given by

$$n_\nu = \frac{1}{2\pi^2} \int dp \; p^2 / [\exp\{(p - \mu_\nu)/T_\nu\} + 1] \qquad (3.2)$$

(throughout we take $\hbar = c = k_B = 1$). The neutrinos fall out of chemical equilibrium at temperature T_D when the reaction rates for their production (e.g., $e^+ e^- \to f\bar{f}$) can no longer keep up with the expansion of the universe. The fermion distribution continues to be described by Equation (3.1), with momentum p and temperature T_ν simply redshifting with the expansion. We shall consider only the case where the chemical potential μ_ν and hence the lepton number are zero, as favored by the usual Grand Unified Theories (GUTs) scenarios (for a discussion of galaxy formation and neutrino mass limits with $\mu_\nu \neq 0$, see David and Reeves 1979, Freese et al. 1983). Since neutrinos decouple at $T_D \simeq 3$ MeV, they cannot participate in the heating due to $e^+ e^-$ annihilation at $T \simeq 0.5$ MeV. By entropy conservation it can be shown (Weinberg 1972) that neutrino (T_ν) and photon (T_γ) temperatures after $e^+ e^-$ annihilation are related by $T_\nu = (4/11)^{1/3} T_\gamma$.

The value of the number density in the present epoch for a species of neutrinos which are relativistic at decoupling is given by $n_{\nu_i} = 109 \; [\frac{T_{\gamma 0}}{2.7}]^3 \; cm^{-3}$ (i = e, μ, τ and $T_{\gamma 0}$ is the photon temperature in °K today), and the energy density in units of the closure density by

$$\Omega_{\nu_i} = \frac{\rho_{\nu_i}}{\rho_c} = \frac{m_{\nu_i}}{97} \; h_0^{-2} \; [\frac{T_{\gamma 0}}{2.7}]^3 \qquad (3.3)$$

where m_{ν_i} is the mass in eV of a neutrino species. If the sum of the masses of different neutrino species exceeds $\sim 100 \; h_0^2$ eV the universe is closed ($\Omega > 1$). Requiring $\Omega \lesssim 4$ (Tammann, Sandage, and Yahil 1979) and $h_0 \lesssim 1$ gives only the weak limit, $\sum m_\nu \lesssim 400$ eV; we will see that constraints on the age of the universe can strengthen this limit. The ratio of neutrino to baryonic matter is given by

$$\frac{\Omega_\nu}{\Omega_b} \gtrsim \frac{\sum\limits_i m_{\nu_i}}{2.4 \text{ eV}}$$

where the equality sign corresponds to the largest value of baryonic matter density consistent with element abundances from primordial nucleosynthesis, $\Omega_b h_o^2 \lesssim 0.034$ Hence, as mentioned earlier, if the sum of the neutrino masses exceeds a few eV, neutrinos are the dominant matter in the universe and must play an important role in galaxy formation.

The above discussion of fermion number densities assumes the fermions are relativistic at decoupling. For neutrinos more massive than a few MeV or for other fermions whose mass exceeds their decoupling temperature, this obviously does not hold. Lee and Weinberg (1977) as well as Dicus, Kolb, and Teplitz (1978) showed that because of annihilation prior to decoupling, the mass density of very massive neutrinos would fall roughly as $m_\nu^{-1.85}$. Thus the total density limit $\Omega \lesssim 4$ can be satisfied for sufficiently massive ($m_\nu \lesssim 1$ GeV) particles, while if $\sum_i m_{\nu_i} \gtrsim 20$ GeV the density has fallen so low that neutrinos cannot be the dominant matter. Krauss (1983) and Goldberg (1983) have recently shown that for certain supersymmetric particles the annihilation rates can be slower than those for neutrinos. Thus the mass density corresponding to a given mass will be larger than the Lee and Weinberg value, and the mass limits are pushed to even higher values. These very massive neutrinos, however, cluster on small scales and hence could explain the dark matter on the scales of binaries and small groups but not on the largest scales.

Figure 3 is a plot of Hubble parameter ($0.5 \lesssim h_o \lesssim 1$) vs. total energy density in the universe ($\Omega \lesssim 4$). The total energy density is the sum of baryon density ($\Omega_b h_o^2 \lesssim 0.01$) and neutrino density ($\Omega_{\nu_i} h_o^2 \simeq m_{\nu_i}/97$); we have plotted this sum for several values of total neutrino mass. We have also plotted curves for several values of the age of the universe, which can be parametrized (for cosmological constant $\lambda = 0$) as $t_u = f(\Omega)H_o^{-1}$, where $f(\Omega)$ is a monotonically decreasing function of Ω with values between 1 and 1/2 in the range of interest. Several arguments (Symbalisty and Schramm 1981) have been used to restrict the age of the universe: certainly it must exceed the age of the solar system, so $t_u > 4.6$ Gyr (1 Gyr $= 10^9$ yr); dynamical arguments ($h_o \gtrsim 0.5$) restrict $t_u \lesssim 20$ Gyr; the age of the

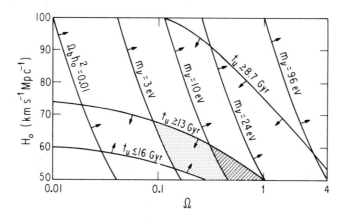

Fig. 3   On a plot of Hubble parameter H_o vs. energy density Ω we have drawn curves for several values of the age of the universe ($t_u = f(\Omega)H_o^{-1}$), for the energy density in baryons ($\Omega_b h_o^2 \gtrsim 0.01$), and for the total energy density of the universe with several values of

the neutrino mass $\Omega_{total} = \Omega_b + \Omega_\nu \gtrsim (0.01 + \dfrac{\sum m_\nu}{97})h_o^{-2}$

(for $T_{\gamma o} = 2.7$K).   this plot is taken from Freese and Schramm 1983. The firm lower limit to the age of the univese $t_u > 8.7$ Gyr restricts $\sum m_\nu \lesssim 100$ eV, while an age range consistent with dynamics and globular clusters 13 Gyr $< t_u$ requires $\sum m_\nu \lesssim 25$ eV. The dotted region indicates the range of neutrinos massive enough to serve as the dark matter in clusters (massive species satisfies $m_\nu \gtrsim 3$ eV) yet consistent with all the age arguments. The smaller hatched region indicates the range of neutrinos which may be responsible for the formation of large-scale structure in the adiabatic picture (single massive species satisfies $m_\nu \gtrsim 10$ eV, cf. §4).

globular clusters combined with an upper limit of ^{4}He fraction $Y \lesssim 0.26$ restricts 13 Gyr $\lesssim t_u \lesssim 19$ Gyr (Schramm 1982); and nucleocosmochronology requires 8.7 Gyr $\lesssim t_u \lesssim 19$ Gyr. The range (13-16) Gyr is simultaneously consistent with all arguments, while the widest range allowed by the most stringent limits is (8.7 - 19)Gyr. Consistency with the widest range allowed as well as the restrictions $\Omega \lesssim 4$ and $h_o > 1/2$ requires

$$\sum_i m_{\nu_i} \lesssim 100 \text{ eV} \quad (8.7 \text{ Gyr} < t_u). \qquad (3.4)$$

Consistency with the "best fit" range of ages restricts

$$\sum_i m_{\nu_i} \lesssim 25 \text{ eV} \quad (13 \text{ Gyr} < t_u) \tag{3.5}$$

(see also Steigman 1981a, 1981b; Joshi and Chitre 1981), where $\Omega = 1$ is achieved only for $\sum_i m_{\nu_i} \simeq 25$ eV. As Schramm (1982) noted, this best fit age also limits $h_o < 0.7$ to have concordance. By the inversion of this age argument, an actual neutrino mass gives an upper limit to the age of the universe. For example, if Lubimov et al. (1980) are correct and $m_{\nu_e} \gtrsim 30$ eV, then the universe must be younger than 12 Gyr.

Tremaine and Gunn (1979) have used phase space arguments to obtain a restriction on neutrino masses. The smaller the scale on which neutrinos are confined, the larger the velocity dispersion, and the easier it is for neutrinos to escape from the region. A necessary (but not sufficient) condition for trapping neutrinos of a particular species on the scale of clusters is the requirement on the mass of the species, $m_\nu \gtrsim 5h_o^{1/2}$ eV, on the scale of binaries and small groups $m_\nu \gtrsim 14 h_o^{1/2}$ eV, and in galaxies $m_\nu \gtrsim 20$ eV. If massive neutrinos are to solve the missing mass problem they must be trapped at least on scales of clusters of galaxies, i.e., $m_\nu \gtrsim 3$ eV. Of course, actually to trap them requires some cluster formation scenarios. Possibilities will be addressed in the next section, where it will be shown that this lower limit can probably be strengthened for any realistic scenario.

c) Adiabatic Perturbations.

The formation of galaxies requires the clumping of baryons; i.e. enhancements $\delta_b = \dfrac{\delta\rho_b}{\rho_b} = \dfrac{\rho_b - \rho_{\bar{b}}}{\rho_{\bar{b}}}$ in the baryon density over the background value must grow from small values in the early universe to nonlinearity $(\delta_b > 1)$ by the present day to achieve the formation of bound structures. In the adiabatic mode the baryon perturbations δ_b are accompanied by radiation perturbations δ_γ, whereas in the isothermal mode initially $\delta_\gamma \ll \delta_b$. In general any primordial fluctuation scheme for galaxy formation can be treated as a superposition of these two independent modes. Thus in the adiabatic theory of galaxy formation, initially $\delta_\gamma = \delta_\nu = \delta_{\bar\nu} = \frac{4}{3}\delta_b$ (where $\delta_i = \frac{\delta\rho_i}{\rho_i}$ describes the density enhancement of particle species i in a perturbation over the background value). These fluctuations grow together outside the horizon, and once inside the horizon their evolution depends on the value of the Jeans mass.

The Jeans mass is the smallest mass unstable to gravitational collapse. It is given by the rest mass of particles in a sphere of radius equal to the Jeans length λ_J, the scale on which radiation pressure forces just balance gravitational forces. Objects larger than the Jeans mass are unstable to gravitational collapse while smaller ones are stable and merely oscillate as sound waves.

In Figure 4 we have plotted the evolution of neutrino ($M_{J\nu}$) and baryon (M_{Jb}) Jeans masses in a neutrino-dominated universe. While

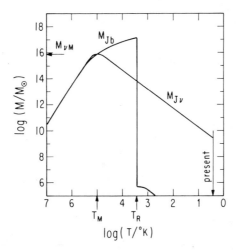

Fig. 4. Neutrino and baryon Jeans masses as a function of temperature for a neutrino species of mass $m_\nu \simeq 20$ eV. During the radiation-dominated era, the Jeans mass is approximately the comoving mass inside the horizon and grows as $(1 + z)^{-3}$. The neutrino Jeans mass peaks at $M_{\nu M} \simeq 1.8\ m_{pl}^3/m_\nu^2 \simeq 7.5 \times 10^{15} M_\odot$ for $m_\nu = 20$ eV and thereafter falls as $(1 + z)^{3/2}$. The exact shape of $M_{J\nu}$ near its peak value has been calculated by Bond, Efstathiou, and Silk (1980) and is merely approximated here. M_{Jb} drops at recombination ($T_R \simeq 2700$ K) to $\simeq 5 \times 10^5 M_\odot$.

the neutrinos are relativistic, the universe is radiation-dominated with sound speed $v_s \simeq \frac{c}{3^{1/2}}$, and the Jeans mass is simply (up to factors O(1)) the rest mass of the particles contained within the horizon, $M_J \propto (1 + z)^{-3}$, where z is the redshift of the epoch. At the temperature where the average neutrino momentum $\simeq$ rest mass, $\langle p_\nu \rangle \simeq m_\nu$, neutrinos become nonrelativistic and at about the same time begin to dominate the energy density of the universe. The neutrino Jeans mass reaches its peak value (Bond, Szalay, and Turner 1982),

$$M_{\nu M} \simeq 1.8 \ m_{pl}^{\ 3}/m_\nu^{\ 2} \simeq 3 \times 10^{18} \ M_\odot/m_\nu^{\ 2} \qquad (3.6)$$

at $z_M \simeq 1900 \ m_\nu$ (eV), where $m_{pl} = G^{-1/2} = 1.2 \times 10^{19}$ GeV is the Planck mass. Subsequently, $v_s \simeq \langle p_\nu \rangle / m_\nu \propto T_\gamma$ and the neutrino Jeans mass falls as $M_{J\nu} \propto (1 + z)^{3/2}$. The baryon Jeans mass continues to rise although more slowly until recombination, where it drops from a peak value of $\simeq 10^{17} \ M_\odot$ down to $\simeq 5 \times 10^5 \ M_\odot$. Prior to recombination the baryonic matter is ionized and hence closely coupled to the radiation. In the adiabatic theory, as photons diffuse out of over-dense regions they drag the baryons with them, smoothing out any structure (Silk damping) on scales less than a critical mass (Silk 1974; Bond, Efstathiou, and Silk 1980),

$$M_S \simeq 3 \times 10^{13} \ \Omega_B^{\ -1/2} \ \Omega_\nu^{\ -3/4} \ h_o^{\ -5/2} \ M_\odot \qquad (3.7)$$

It is the perturbations in the neutrinos, the dominant matter in the universe, that determine the formation of structure. Neutrino perturbations on scales $\gtrsim M_{\nu M}$ can grow once the neutrinos become the dominant matter. However, Bond et al. (1980) have shown the neutrino perturbations on scales smaller than $M_{\nu M}$ are strongly damped by free streaming of the neutrinos out of dense regions (Landau damping). Only perturbations on scales larger than $M_{\nu M}$ can survive and grow to nonlinearity (Bond and Szalay 1981). To enable the formation of large-scale structure, we require this damping scale to be smaller than the largest structure observed, superclusters of mass $\simeq 10^{16} \ M_\odot$ (Oort 1981 and references therein), i.e., $M_{\nu M} \lesssim M_{sc} \simeq 10^{16} \ M_\odot$. Equation (3.6) is only approximate; folding an initial power spectrum $|\delta_k|^2 \propto k^n$ with a transfer function to describe damping by neutrino

diffusion, Bond, Szalay, and Turner (1982) obtained an n-dependent
power spectrum. Although the peak of the power spectrum is the scale
on which perturbations first go nonlinear, significant power may
exist on somewhat smaller or larger scales. We take the least
restrictive limit, the smallest mass for physically plausible values
of n that has significant power, and find that

$$M_{\nu M} \simeq \frac{9 \times 10^{17} \, M_\odot}{m_\nu^2} \lesssim 10 \text{ eV}. \qquad (3.8)$$

In a universe with one massive neutrino species this requires

$$m_\nu \gtrsim 10 \text{ eV}.$$

If there are three species of neutrinos with equal mass, the mass of
each species must satisfy $m_{\nu_i} \gtrsim 16$ eV, giving a sum of masses
$\sum_i m_{\nu_i} \lesssim 48$ eV. This is not compatible with the requirement
$\sum_i m_{\nu_i} \lesssim 25$ eV from consistency of all the arguments restricting
the age of the universe. A "best fit" model does not allow all the
neutrino masses to be equal. Of course, if we relax our age constraint to $t_u > 8.7$ Gyr then equal masses are allowed. If larger
scales than $M_{\nu M}$ in Equation (3.8) reach nonlinearity first and
tidally strip the smaller scales, the limit on the masses only
becomes more restrictive. In this adiabatic picture with massive
neutrinos, the smallest scales to form initially are large clusters,
and smaller scales come from later cooling and fragmentation (see the
articles by Centrella and Melott and Bond, Centrella, Szalay, and
Wilson in this volume).

Synthesizing all the arguments we find that in the adiabatic
picture preferred by GUTs, all of the independent constraints can
only be met in a "best fit" model with 10 eV $\lesssim m_\nu \lesssim 25$ eV for the
most massive neutrino eigenstate, where the upper limit may be pushed
as high as 100 eV. Freese and Schramm (1983) also discuss massive
neutrinos in the isothermal mode and show that for these one can
obtain 3 eV $\lesssim m_\nu \lesssim 20$ eV (see also Schramm and Steigman 1981).

IV.   NEUTRINO LIFETIMES

Remarkably, the astrophysical mass constraints on unstable
neutrinos of finite lifetimes (Cowsik and McClelland 1972; Dicus,
Kolb, Teplitz, and Wagoner 1978; Falk and Schramm 1978; Gunn et al.
1978; Turner 1981) are quite general and extremely rigorous: for a
massive species, $m_\nu \lesssim 100$ eV or $m_\nu \gtrsim 10$ MeV. Figure 5 (taken from
Turner 1981) summarizes the mass limits for different lifetimes.
Constraints on neutrinos with lifetimes 10^4s $\lesssim \tau \lesssim 10^{12}$s come from
the lack of distortion of the microwave background, and for lifetimes
$\tau \gtrsim 10^{12}$s from upper limits on diffuse photon backgrounds. For
10^{-3}s $\lesssim \tau \lesssim 10^4$s, Falk and Schramm (1978) have shown that supernovae
can be used to obtain constraints. The bulk of the energy of the
core collapse in forming a neutron star ($\approx 10^{53}$ ergs) is released in

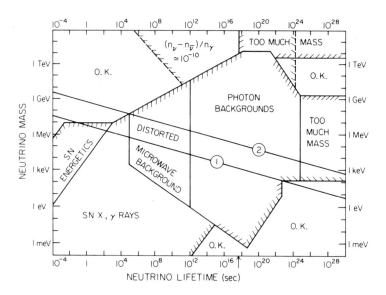

Fig. 5. Mass constraints on unstable neutrinos of
various lifetimes (plot taken from Turner 1981).
The cross-hatched regions are forbidden. Lines 1
and 2 represent mass-lifetime estimates from Turner
(1981).

the form of neutrinos of average energy ~ 10 MeV. Neutrinos decaying
too quickly would contribute too much energy associated directly with
supernovae, which are known to have total energies $\lesssim 10^{51}$ ergs.
Those neutrinos decaying on slightly longer time scales than the
escape times would contribute to diffuse photon backgrounds and are

constrained by observed limits on these backgrounds. For more detailed discussion of these and other astrophysical constraints on unstable neutrinos see Turner (1981) and references therein.

V. SOLAR NEUTRINOS

The basic reactions in the p-p chain of nuclear reactions that are thought to take place in the sun are illustrated in Figure 6, taken from Filippone (1982). The properties of the neutrinos that would be emitted are also illustrated. For the past fifteen years theoretical estimates of electron neutrino fluxes from the sun have

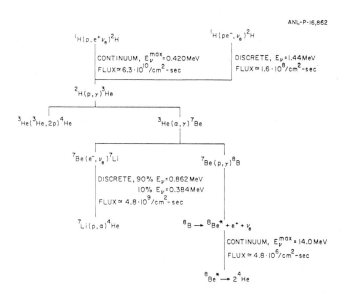

Fig. 6.   Proton-proton chain of nuclear reactions (plot taken from Filippone 1982). Neutrino energies and fluxes are for a mean standard model (Filippone and Schramm 1982).

differed from experimental results by factors ranging between two and ten. The recently updated models of Bahcall et al. (1980) obtained a best-estimate capture rate of 7.3 SNU (solar neutrino unit; 1 SNU $\equiv 10^{-36}$ ν captures/(target atom sec)) in a ^{37}Cl detector, while the experimental capture rate above background in Davis' (1983) detector (see also Davis 1978, 1980) was only 2.0 ± 0.3 SNU. By calculating the effects of individual uncertainties on the mean standard model and summing these errors in quadrature, an uncertainty of about ± 1 SNU is quoted by Bahcall et al. (1980) for the ^{37}Cl detector. However, since many of the parameters enter in a highly nonlinear and correlated manner, the effect of a particular parameter on the capture rate could change significantly with a slight departure from the mean model. Hence Filippone and Schramm (1982) reevaluated the uncertainties by using a Monte Carlo treatment to allow parameters to vary simultaneously, and found a capture rate of 7.0 ± 3.0 SNU for ^{37}Cl.

In addition to the Monte Carlo treatment, Filippone and Schramm (1982) also tried to take into account external as well as internal errors in the input data. This is particularly important for situations where different groups measure the same cross section and obtain results outside of each other's formal statistical errors. Another difficult area of error estimation involves the opacities, where the two leading groups making such calculations yield results which are a full 1 SNU off from each other. Also, due to nonlinear effects, the shape of the Monte Carlo is not a symmetric Gaussian. Thus the use of such a distribution for errors $\gtrsim$ 1 standard deviation is peculiar.

Several explanations for the discrepancy between theory and experiment have been proposed, among them new treatments of turbulent mixing in the sun (Schatzman and Maeder 1981) and neutrino oscillations (Pontecorvo 1968; Gribov and Pontecorvo 1969; Bahcall and Frautschi 1969). In particular, since the detectors are sensitive only to electron neutrinos, if a neutrino oscillates to another species by the time it reaches the earth it would go undetected.

The only detector that has been used to look for solar neutrinos uses ^{37}Cl. We want to emphasize the importance of running the proposed ^{71}Ga experiment. Both detectors use neutrino capture from a stable to a radioactive nucleus (^{37}Cl → ^{37}Ar, ^{71}Ga → ^{71}Ge) which can then be detected. The response of the ^{37}Cl detector is mainly due to the high energy neutrinos from ^{8}B decay. Large uncertainties in the rate of formation of ^{8}B (rate $\propto T^{14}$) carry over to large uncertainties in the neutrino capture rate. The ^{71}Ga detector, however, with its lower energy threshold is sensitive to the low energy neutrinos at much higher fluxes from the ^{1}H(p, e$^+\nu_e$)^{2}H reaction.

The neutrino fluxes and hence the capture rate should be much higher, with much lower uncertainties.

There has been an important recent development in experimental nuclear physics relevant to solar neutrino calculations. Filippone et al. (1983) obtained new measurements of the ^{7}Be(p,γ) ^{8}B reaction. Using the new value in the Filippone and Schramm (1982) solar model code, they found an expected neutrino capture rate in ^{37}Cl of 5.0 ± 2.0 SNU, only $\leq$ 1.5 standard deviations away from the experimental value. Perhaps the solar neutrino problem is nearing resolution. The proposed ^{71}Ga experiment, with its higher fluxes and lower uncertainties, is very important in determining a capture rate and finding out whether or not a problem still exists.

REFERENCES

Bacino, W. et al. 1979, Phys. Rev. Lett., **42**, 749.

Bahcall, J. N. and Frautschi, S. C. 1969, Phys. Letters, **29B**, 623.

Bahcall, J. N., Lubow, S. H., Heubner, W. F., Magee, N. H., Jr.,
    Merts, A. L., Argo, M. F., Parker, P.D., Rozsnyai, B., and
    Ulrich, R. K. 1980, Phys. Rev. Lett., **45**, 945.

Bond, J. R., Efstathiou, G., and Silk, J. 1980, Phys. Rev. Lett.,
    45, 1980.

Bond, J. R., and Szalay, A. S. 1981, in Proc. Neutrino '81,
    ed. R. J. Cence, E. Ma, and A. Roberts (Honolulu: High Energy
    Physics Group, University of Hawaii), p. 59.

Bond, J. R., Szalay, A. S., and Turner, M. S. 1982, Phys. Rev. Lett.,
    48, 1636.

Cowsik, R., and McClelland, J. 1972, Phys. Rev. Lett., **29**, 669.

David, Y., and Reeves, H. 1979, Les Houches Proc. '79, ed. R. Balian
    et al. (Amsterdam: North Holland Publishing Co.), p. 444.

Davis, M., Tonry, J., Huchra, J., and Latham, D. W. 1980, Ap. J.,
    238, L113.

Davis, R., Jr. 1978, Brookhaven National Laboratory Report No. 50879,
    Vol. **1**, p 1.

_____ 1980, in Proc. of the International DUMAND Symposium,
    ed. V. J. Stenger, Vol. **2**, p. 103.

_____ 1983, in Proc. of the Los Alamos Workshop on Underground
    Science (American Institute of Physics).

Dicus, D. A., Kolb, E. W., and Teplitz, V. L. 1978, Ap. J., **221**, 327.

Dicus, D. A., Kolb, E. W., Teplitz, V. L., and Wagoner, R. V. 1978,
    Phys. Rev. D, **17**, 1529.

Epstein, R., Lattimer, J., and Schramm, D. N. 1976, Nature, **263**, 198.

Faber, S. M., and Gallagher, J. S. 1979, Ann. Rev. Astr. Ap.,**17**, 135.

Falk, S. W., and Schramm, D. N. 1978, Phys. Lett. **79B**, 511.

Filippone, B. W. 1982, Ph. D. Thesis, University of Chicago.

Filippone, B. W., and Schramm, D. N. 1982, Ap. J., **253**, 393.

Filippone, B. W., Elwyn, A. J., Davids, C.N., and Koetke, D. D.
    1983, Phys. Rev. Lett., **50**, 412.

Freese, K., Kolb, E. W., and Turner, M. S. 1983, Phys. Rev. D, **27**
    1689.

Freese, K. and Schramm, D. N. 1983, "Cosmological Constraints on the
    Masses of Neutrinos and Other Inos", Univ. of Chicago preprint.

Goldberg, H. 1983, Northeastern University preprint No. 2592.

Gott, J. R., and Turner, E. L. 1977, Ap. J., **213**, 309.

Gribov, V., and Pontecorvo, B. 1969, Phys. Letters, **28B**, 493.

Gunn, J. E., Lee, B. W., Lerche, I., Schramm, D. N., and Steigman, G.
    1978, Ap. J. **223**, 1015.

Joshi, P. S., and Chitre, S. M. 1981, Nature, **293**, 679.

Kirshner, R. P., Oemler, A., and Schechter, P. L. 1979,
    Astron. Jour., **84**, 951.

Krauss, L. M. 1983, Harvard Univ. preprint No. 83/A009.

Kunth, D. 1981, in Proc. First Morond Astrophysics Meeting:
    Cosmology and Particles, ed. J. Audouze, P. Crane, T. Gaisser,
    D. Hegyi, and J. Tran Thanh Van, p. 241.

Kunth, D., and Sargent, M. 1983, Ap. J.. **273**, 81.

Lee,B. W. and Weinberg, S. 1977, Phys. Rev. Lett., **39**, 165.

Lubimov, V. A., Novikov, E. G., Nozik, V. Z., Tretyakov, E. F.,
    and Kosik, V. S. 1980, Phys. Rev. Lett., **B94**, 266.

Marx, G., and Szalay, A. S. 1972, in Proc. Neutrino '72 (Budapest:
    Technoinform), p. 123.

Olive, K., Schramm, D. N., and Steigman, G. 1981, Nucl. Phys., B**180**,
    497.

Oort, J. H. 1981, Astr. Ap., **94**, 359.

Pagel, B. E. J. 1982, Phil. Trans. R. Soc. Lond. A, **307**, 19.

Pontecorvo, B. 1968, Soviet Phys. [JETP **26**, 984].

Press, W., and Davis, M. 1982, Ap. J. **259**, 449.

Schatzman, E., and Maeder, A. 1981, Astr. Ap., **96**, 1.

Schramm, D. N. 1982, Phil. Trans. R. Soc. Lond. A, **307**, 43.

_____ 1983, "Underground Neutrino Astronomy", in Proc. of the
    Los Alamos Workshop on Underground Science (American Institute
    of Physics).

Schramm, D. N. and Steigman, G. 1981, Ap. J. **243**, 1 (see also
    Gravity Award Essay 1980).

Schramm, D. N., and Wagoner, R. V. 1977, Ann. Rev. Nucl. Sci., **727**,
    37.

Silk, J. 1974, in In Confrontation of Cosmological Theories with
    Observational Data,, ed. M. S. Longair (Dordrecht: Reidel),
    p. 175.

Spite, M., and Spite, F. 1982, Nature, **297**, 483.

Steigman, G. 1981a, in Proc. Europhys. Study Conference "Unification of the Fundamental Interactions", eds. J. Ellis, S. Ferrara, and P. van Nieuwenhuizen (New York: Plenum).

_____. 1981, in Proc. Neutrino '81, ed. R. J. Cence, E. Ma, and A. Roberts (Honolulu: High Energy Physics Group, Univ. of Hawaii).

Symbalisty, E. M. D., and Schramm, D. N. 1981, Rep. Prog. Phys., **44**, 293.

Tammann, G. A., Sandage, A., and Yahil, A., 1979, in Les Houches 1979, ed. R. Balian, J. Audouze, and D. N.Schramm (Amsterdam: North-Holland Publishing Co.), p. 53.

Tremaine, S., and Gunn, J. E. 1979, Phys. Rev. Lett., **42**, 407.

Turner, M. S. 1981, in Proc. Neutrino '81, ed. R. J. Cence, E. Ma, and A. Roberts (Honolulu: High Energy Physics Group, Univ. of Hawaii).

Weinberg, S. 1972, Gravitation and Cosmology (New York: Wiley).

Yang, J., Turner, M. S., Steigman, G., Schramm, D. N., and Olive, K. A. 1983, University of Chicago preprint.

A Computation of Nucleosynthesis in a 1-D Inhomogeneous Cosmology

Richard Matzner
University of Texas at Austin

Joan Centrella
University of Texas at Austin

Tony Rothman
University of Texas at Austin

James R. Wilson
Lawrence Livermore National Laboratory

ABSTRACT

We present a discussion of a computer code designed to evolve a 1-dimensional inhomogeneous cosmology and its matter content, including the nuclear evolution of the isotopes H through ^{4}He. We describe the result of one such computation. The initial data consist of a strongly inhomogeneous model at temperatures $T_\gamma \gtrsim 2 \times 10^{10}$, with the initial entropy per baryon set to a standard value corresponding to a value of the baryon mass density $\rho \sim 4 \times 10^{-31}$ gm/cm^3 now.

Evolution continues until the temperature T_γ has dropped below 2×10^8K, at which time all the nucleosynthetic evolution has stopped. We find spatial variations in the mass fraction of the final ^{4}He between extremes $Y = 0.216$ and $Y = 0.278$ (the mass weighted average is 0.25), spatial variations of the fraction of ^{2}H between extremes $X(^2H) = 3 \times 10^{-5}$ and $X(^2H) = 4 \times 10^{-5}$, and almost homogeneous ^{3}He with fraction $X(^3He) = 1.5 \times 10^{-5}$.

I. INTRODUCTION

A remarkable coincidence exists between the theoretical predictions of light element cosmic abundances, calculated in a hot big bang model, and observations. On the observational side, Schramm and Wagoner (1977) quote "standard" observed abundances (using mass fraction X):

$$Y = X(^4He) : \quad 0.20 - 0.25 \quad ,$$

$$X(^3He) : \quad \sim 3 \times 10^{-5} \quad , \quad \quad (1.1)$$

$$X(^2H) : \quad \sim 2.5 \times 10^{-5} \quad .$$

Because it is difficult to conceive of an astrophysical process that destroys ^4He, a secure measurement of low ^4He presumably puts an upper bound on the primordial production. Extragalactic objects pose substantial difficulties in determination of the ^4He mass fraction Y. Occasionally reports in the literature give quite low values, e.g., $Y \gtrsim 0.18$ in I Zw 18 (French 1980). This particular observation may have been defective, and both older and recent (Shields 1983) measurements tend to give more "standard" ($Y \sim 0.21 - 0.22$) results for this low ^4He object. It is interesting to note, however, that when considering different objects of essentially the same low metallicity, French finds variations in ^4He that are larger than the probable observational uncertainties.

In attempting to understand these observations theoretically, one first considers the computational results of Wagoner, which we show in Fig. 1 via the ^4He - ^3He and ^4He - ^2H contours for homogeneous and isotropic (Robertson-Walker) cosmologies. The ^4He increases to the right as the baryon number density at fixed temperature increases. [This figure is plotted from data in Wagoner (1973).]

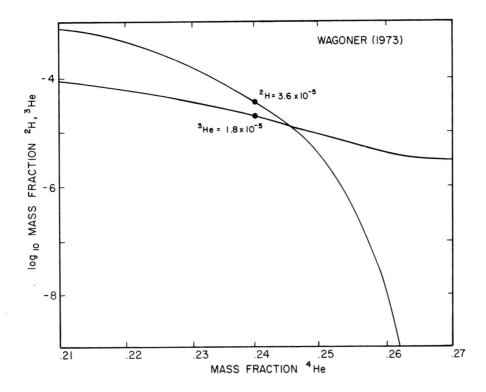

Fig. 1. Results of a computer determination of the final mass fractions of deuterium and of ^{3}He plotted as a function of final ^{4}He mass
fraction. These results are plotted from Wagoner (1973). They are for
homogeneous isotropic (i.e., Robertson-Walker) cosmologies. These
results are usually given as a function of baryon density ρ at the
present epoch - when the photon temperature $T_\gamma \simeq 2.7$ K. Increasing
the present baryon density moves the system to higher ^{4}He and conversely. The points marked give the ^{4}He (= 0.24), ^{2}H and ^{3}He fractions corresponding to $\rho \sim 4 \times 10^{-31}$ gm/cm^3, and they are consistent
with astrophysical observations of these quantities. We take this
particular model as our fiducial Robertson-Walker model. This model
has <u>two</u> flavors of massless neutrinos: ν_e and ν_μ.

Figure 2 is a diagram showing the time evolution of the abundances in one such cosmology (set to give baryon density $\rho = 4 \times 10^{-31}$
gm/cm^3 at the present time when the electron-neutrino temperature is
$T_{\nu_e} = 1.9$K). The results presented here are from a computer program
by Rothman (1981); they are very similar to those of Wagoner (1973).
See also Schramm and Freese, this volume.

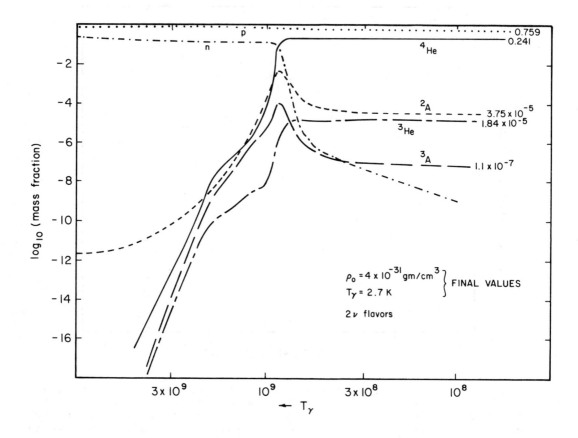

Fig. 2. Dynamical evolution of the isotopes p (protons, i.e. H), n (neutrons), ^{4}He, ^{2}H, ^{3}H and ^{3}He, plotted here as a function of photon temperature T_γ. (T_γ decreases as time increases.) This calculation is from Rothman (1981). Its parameters are chosen to correspond to the fiducial model of Figure 1.

The coincidence to which we alluded above is that for a particular value of the present baryon density ($\rho \sim 4 \times 10^{-31}$ gm/cm^3 now), agreement with the observed values quoted in (1.1) is possible for all three species ^{2}H, ^{3}He, ^{4}He. This is a remarkable coincidence between prediction and observation. However, we must still consider the obvious fact that the universe is not exactly spatially homogeneous and, in light of French's (1980) data, the possibility that this inhomogeneity may be reflected in the element abundances.

To that end, we have developed a code which calculates nuclear abundances in an inhomogeneous hot big bang model (Centrella et al. 1984). The cosmology is evolved using a 1-dimensional code developed by Wilson and Centrella. It is described in detail elsewhere (Centrella and Wilson 1983, 1984), but we will give an abbreviated summary below. The nucleosynthesis calculation is adapted from a code written for homogeneous cosmologies by Tony Rothman (1981) which has been extensively checked for agreement with results published by Wagoner (e.g., 1973). The combined, or merged, code calculates the light element abundances in each zone on every time step of the inhomogeneous cosmology. Most of the developmental work on the merged code was done on the University of Manchester CDC7600 (accessed through the Oxford ICL 2900). The code now runs on a Cray at Livermore and on the CDC dual-Cyber system at the University of Texas.

II. THE COSMOLOGY

The geometry portion of the code, described elsewhere (Centrella and Wilson 1983, 1984), is based on a 3 + 1 decomposition (York 1979 and this volume). The 3-metric variables (coordinates ordered 1,2,3 = x,y,z) are chosen to be

$$^{3}g_{ij} = diag(A^2, A^2h^2, A^2) \quad , \tag{2.1}$$

where A and h, like all the variables in this problem, are functions of the coordinates t (time) and z, only. The diagonality of the metric, and the equality of two of the metric components, is assured by using the equations for the shift vector components β^x, β^z to maintain these coordinate conditions (cf. below). The time coordinate is defined by the demand that t = constant surfaces be surfaces of constant mean curvature (i.e., $K \equiv tr \ K^i_{\ j} = K(t)$ only). This is the simplest generalization of the maximal slicing choice which is made in asymptotically flat situations; this choice determines the lapse function α in this problem.

To avoid difficulties at the edge of the spatial grid, the code is made periodic in z; this requires not only that identifications be made at the end grid zones, but also that physical quantities be single-valued in space. This latter requirement is the large-amplitude version of the "linearization stability" condition (Moncrief 1975, 1976; Brill 1982) and means that an extra iterative process must be used in the solution of the elliptic equations in the code (Centrella and Wilson 1984).

This metric contains an overall expansion variable A, and an anisotropy variable h. From work by York (this volume; also 1979) we expect that A can be found as a solution to an elliptic equation, the Hamiltonian constraint. For the symmetry and metric form here this equation, which obviously also involves h, is in fact linear in h. Hence the Wilson-Centrella code solves for h from this constraint and evolves A hyperbolically.

The situation with regard to the momentum variables is as follows: $^3g_{yz} = 0$ with $\beta^y = 0$ requires $K^y_z = 0$; $^3g_{xy} = 0$ requires $K^x_y = 0$. The symmetry of the metric, and the assumption of vanishing y-components of the matter current, give $K^y_z = 0$ via the y-component of the momentum constraint. The only remaining off-diagonal nonzero K^i_j is $K^z_x \neq 0$. Of the three diagonal elements of K^i_j, one is already determined because $K = K(t)$. The two remaining momentum-constraint equations are solved for K^z_z and K^z_x. Hence A and $K_1 = K^x_x - K^y_y$ remain as the dynamical conjugate coordinate and momentum variables for this integration. Such a scheme is called a fully constrained evolution, because only the minimum number of quantities are dynamically evolved, and the rest are obtained from the elliptic constraint equations. This method has been used in numerical relativity by Wilson (see, e.g., Wilson 1979) and produces substantial improvements in the stability of the numerical evolution.

The matter content of the universe is described as a perfect fluid:

$$T_{\mu\nu} = (\rho + \varepsilon + P)u_\mu u_\nu + Pg_{\mu\nu} \ , \qquad (2.2)$$

where u_μ is the fluid 4-velocity, ρ is the (conserved) particle mass density, ε is the energy density, and P is the pressure. All these objects are local quantities as measured by comoving observers. The variables used in the code are:

$$w \equiv \alpha u^t \quad ,$$

$$D \equiv w\rho \quad ,$$

$$E \equiv w\varepsilon \quad ,$$

$$\sigma \equiv \rho + \varepsilon + P \quad ,$$

$$S_\mu \equiv \sigma w u_\mu \quad ,$$

$$v^i \equiv u^i/u^t = S^i/S^t \quad (\text{ordinary 3-velocity}) \quad . \qquad (2.3)$$

The geometry code as written can accommodate nonzero S_x as well as S_z, but S_y vanishes by symmetry [see above]. For the present we are only interested in $S_x = 0$ models.

With these definitions and restrictions, the matter equations are simply the conservation of particle number

$$(\rho u^\mu)_{;\mu} = 0 \qquad (2.4)$$

together with the energy momentum conservation equation

$$T^{\mu\nu}{}_{;\nu} = 0 \quad . \qquad (2.5)$$

Here, ; denotes the covariant derivative in the full 4-dimensional spacetime. For the explicit form of the equations being considered, see Centrella and Wilson (1983, 1984).

III. THE NUCLEOSYNTHESIS

Cosmic nucleosynthesis occurs while the universe passes through the temperature range from (just above) 10^{10}K to 10^8K or so; a typical temperature for nucleosynthesis thus is $T_9 \equiv T(^\circ K)/10^9 = 1$. In a Robertson-Walker cosmology, one expects at late times a relation between the temperature of photons T_γ and the temperature of neutrinos T_ν:

$$T_\gamma = \left(\frac{11}{4}\right)^{1/3} T_\nu = 1.401 \ T_\nu \quad . \tag{3.1}$$

At late times T_γ and T_ν differ by this factor ~ 1.4 even though the photons and neutrinos were in thermal equilibrium (and therefore at a common temperature) at high temperature, because the entropy formerly contained in positron-electron pairs all appears finally in the photons (Weinberg 1972). In the Robertson-Walker cosmology the neutrinos evolve adiabatically, hence their temperature obeys RT_ν = constant. The density of baryons (i.e., the number density times the mass per baryon) in the system obeys ρR^3 = constant. Hence we can set the initial (high temperature) ratio of neutrino energy density to baryon number density consistently with current observations, if we know the baryon density today. As a fiducial value, and because for Robertson-Walker cosmologies it gives results close to the observations, we take our standard model to have ρ(now) = 4×10^{-31} gm/cm^3; T_γ(now) = 2.7K, T_ν(now) = 1.93K. Thus, for instance, if $T_9 = 10$, $\rho = 0.056$ gm/cm^3, while $\varepsilon_{\nu_e} = \frac{7}{8} aT^4 = 7.4 \times 10^4$ gm/cm^3. Throughout nucleosynthesis, the baryon density plays a negligible role in the dynamics of the universe, though of course it represents the essential players in the nuclear evolution.

Nuclear processes occurring by different mechanisms have very different rates. Strong and electromagnetic interactions occur so rapidly prior to, during, and just after nucleosynthesis that reactions via them are effectively in equilibrium, with the cosmology providing only a slowly varying background which adiabatically shifts the equilibrium abundances. The weak interactions, however, have (at these energies) cross sections σ_w proportional to T^2. Since the relevant parameter determining equilibrium is the ratio $t_{collision}/$ $t_{universe}$, consider $t_{collision}^{-1} \sim \sigma_w n_{scatt} \propto T^2 T^3$ where n_{scatt} is the number density of the interacting neutrons and protons. Now, in a Robertson-Walker universe, $t_{universe}^{-1} \propto \varepsilon_\nu^{\frac{1}{2}} \propto T_\nu^2$. Hence $t_{collision}/$ $t_{universe} \propto T^{-3}$ and weak interactions become very slow as the temperature drops. This occurs at roughly the same temperature range as nucleosynthesis ($T_9 = 10$ to 0.1), and the largest effect is the so-called freeze-out of neutrons: neutrons are maintained at a level above their equilibrium abundance with protons because the isotopic-spin changing weak reactions become so slow. This important feature is what effectively determines the endpoint ^{4}He abundance, because essentially all neutrons finally end up in ^{4}He. Adding further interesting complication to the physics is the fact, alluded to above, that the electron-positron annihilation is going on at the same time. This complicated interplay of reactions and reactants makes nucleosynthesis much more sensitive to variations in the geometry than is, say, baryosynthesis (which occurs at much higher temperatures but follows from a less complicated set of interactions (Kolb and Wolfram 1980)).

From Figure 2, one can see that early effects on nucleosynthesis may change the n/p freeze-out ratio, which will change the ^{4}He and all the other abundances. Late effects mainly change the eventual evolution of the intermediate species ^{3}He and ^{2}H, after the essentially "standard" ^{4}He abundance has been produced.

The lack of equilibrium via weak interactions means that yet another complication enters the nucleosynthesis computation. The neutrino-neutrino cross sections and the neutrino-electron cross sections are dropping, so that the neutrinos are no longer a collisional system; they are going out of equilibrium with the electron-positron pairs and hence out of equilibrium with the photons. In Robertson-Walker cosmologies the neutrinos stay in a thermal distribution anyway, though one that eventually has a different temperature from the photons. This will not be the case if inhomogeneities or anisotropies are present. In such a case we would expect that the neutrinos would contribute Landau damping, and their anisotropic stresses would generate shear, and oscillations in the shear, of the matter flow. Anisotropic expansion can also lead to differential redshifts, and can further raise the neutrino average energy above the photon temperature T_γ, thereby altering the weak interactions in the problem, specifically the ratio n/p. For homogeneous anisotropic cosmologies these effects have been investigated by Matzner and Rothman (1984). The net effect is generally to raise the ^{4}He abundance above that for isotropic models. However, here we have not yet included these effects. A general kinetic theory description of the neutrinos would "break the gauge" used in the cosmology code, requiring the addition of extra terms in the metric and field equations. However, for special symmetry ($h = 1$, $K_1 = 0$), these terms can be and have been written into the geometry code (Wilson 1984). We have not yet attempted this in the nucleosynthesis calculation. For the purpose of the present investigation, the neutrinos are considered to be a fluid comoving with the photons and having the equation of state $p_\nu = \varepsilon_\nu/3$. (We take two flavors of neutrinos for the calculations reported here.)

The nuclear reactions follow the scheme of Wagoner (1973) and Peebles (1971). Besides the weak reactions tending to equilibriate neutrons and protons, we consider the following reactions leading to ^{4}He:

$$n + p \rightleftharpoons {}^2H$$

$$^2H + {}^2H \rightleftharpoons {}^3He + n$$

$$^2H + {}^2H \rightleftharpoons {}^3H + p$$

$$^3He + n \rightleftharpoons {}^3H + p$$

$$^3H + {}^2H \rightleftharpoons {}^4He + n$$

$$^2H + p \rightleftharpoons \gamma + {}^3He$$

$$^2H + {}^3He \rightleftharpoons p + {}^4He$$

$$^3He + {}^3He \rightleftharpoons 2p + {}^4He$$

$$^2H + {}^2H \rightleftharpoons \gamma + {}^4He$$

$$^3H + {}^3H \rightleftharpoons {}^4He + n + n$$

$$^3He + \,^3H \; \rightleftarrows \; ^4He + n + p$$

$$^3He + \,^3H \; \rightleftarrows \; ^4He + \,^2H$$

$$n + \,^3He \; \rightleftarrows \; ^4He + \gamma$$

$$n + \,^2H \; \rightleftarrows \; ^3H + \gamma$$

$$p + \,^3H \; \rightleftarrows \; ^4He + \gamma \; . \tag{3.2}$$

We use Wagoner's (1973) reaction rates and equilibrium constants. We thus have six coupled nonlinear equations for the six relative abundances Y_i, ($Y_1 = n$, $Y_2 = p$, $Y_3 = \,^2H$, $Y_4 = \,^3He$, $Y_5 = \,^3H$, $Y_6 = \,^4He$). A recent paper (Dicus et al. 1982) considers a variety of physical processes, including plasma effects, Coulomb corrections and ν_e-heating during $e^{\pm}$ annihilation, occurring during nucleosynthesis. The fractional shift in abundances due to these effects is small, of order one percent, and for simplicity we consider none of them here. We take the mean neutron lifetime to be 926 seconds (halflife ~ 10.7 min.).

A typical rate equation is

$$\frac{dY_1}{dt} = LY_2 - L_B Y_1 - NPD(Y_1 Y_2 - GNP \; Y_3)$$

$$+ \; DD3(\tfrac{1}{2} \, Y_3 Y_3 - GN3 \; Y_1 Y_4) - N3T(Y_1 Y_4 - GQTP \; Y_5 Y_2)$$

$$+ \; TD4(Y_3 Y_5 - GN4 \; Y_6 Y_1) + TT4(Y_5 Y_5 - G2N4 \; Y_1 Y_1 Y_6)$$

$$+ \; T34NP(Y_4 Y_5 - GNP4 \; Y_1 Y_2 Y_6) - DN(Y_1 Y_3 - GTG \; Y_5)$$

$$- \; N34(Y_1 Y_4 - G4G \; Y_6) \; , \tag{3.3}$$

which describes the evolution of the fractional abundance of neutrons. The first term on the right gives the gain from protons via the weak interaction, the second gives the loss from neutrons to protons via the weak interaction (including free decay of neutrons). The remaining terms give the change in neutron number via strong reactions involving neutrons. Each term is written as the algebraic sum of a reaction and its back reaction; if the abundances have their thermal-equilibrium value then each of the terms in parentheses on the right of equation (3.3) separately vanishes. Because we have only six isotopes, we are allowed the luxury of individually naming the rates (cf. Peebles 1971); Wagoner (1973), who considered reactions up to oxygen, was forced to use a subscript formulation for the rates we call NPD, GNP, etc.

Note that the multi-baryon rates are strong interaction rates. Thus DD3, for instance, is roughly the inverse of a strong interaction time. Hence equilibrium involving the interactions containing DD3 and the other strong reaction constants is very sharply defined; a small deviation in one of the Y_i's gives large derivatives dY_i/dt. This leads to a classic difficulty in numerically integrating these equations; a classic solution--implicit differencing--works brilliantly (Laasonen 1949, Richtmeyer and Morton 1967). This point was first noted in this context by Peebles (1971) and by Wagoner (e.g. 1973).

Consider a simple, linear, two component model with constant coefficients:

$$\frac{d}{dt}\begin{bmatrix} Y_a \\ Y_b \end{bmatrix} = \begin{bmatrix} -(Y_a \to Y_b) & (Y_b \to Y_a) \\ (Y_a \to Y_b) & -(Y_b \to Y_a) \end{bmatrix} \begin{bmatrix} Y_a \\ Y_b \end{bmatrix} , \qquad (3.4)$$

where, for example, $(Y_a \to Y_b)$ is the constant positive rate for a single particle of species a to be transformed to species b. The Y_a are species fractions, and are positive. Notice that the matrix appearing in equation (3.4) is singular, as it must be if the equation is to admit equilibrium, $\frac{d}{dt}\begin{bmatrix} Y_a \\ Y_b \end{bmatrix} = 0$.

An explicit first-order difference scheme for equation (3.4) with time step Δt has

$$\begin{bmatrix} Y_a \\ Y_b \end{bmatrix}_{new} = [1 + Q] \begin{bmatrix} Y_a \\ Y_b \end{bmatrix}_{old} , \qquad (3.5)$$

where Q is Δt times the 2 × 2 matrix that appears in equation (3.4). We can investigate the numerical stability of equation (3.5) by considering the properties of the matrix $1 + Q$. It is straightforward to show that the eigenvalues $\lambda_{1,2}$ of $1 + Q$ are:

$$\lambda_1 = 1 \quad ,$$

$$\lambda_2 = 1 - [(Y_a \rightarrow Y_b) + (Y_b \rightarrow Y_a)]\Delta t \quad . \tag{3.6}$$

The eigenvalue $\lambda_1 = 1$ <u>must</u> be present to allow for equilibrium. The second eigenvalue dictates the approach to equilibrium. We see that if Δt is greater than roughly twice the inverse of a typical matrix element $(Y \rightarrow Y)$, then λ_2 is negative and of modulus greater than unity. This shows that increasing the timestep sufficiently then leads to instabilities (growing cycle-to-cycle oscillations) and must eventually cause the code to crash (typically by producing a negative value for an intrinsically positive quantity).

In contrast we can write a first-order implicit difference scheme:

$$[1 - Q] \begin{bmatrix} Y_a \\ Y_b \end{bmatrix}_{new} = \begin{bmatrix} Y_a \\ Y_b \end{bmatrix}_{old} \quad , \tag{3.7}$$

where Q has the same meaning as before. To solve for $\begin{bmatrix} Y_a \\ Y_b \end{bmatrix}_{new}$ we must invert $[1 - Q]$; the stability of this system is thus determined by the eigenvalues $\tilde{\lambda}$ of $[1 - Q]^{-1}$. One finds:

$$\tilde{\lambda}_1 = 1 \quad ,$$

$$\tilde{\lambda}_2 = \frac{1}{1 + [(Y_a \rightarrow Y_b) + (Y_b \rightarrow Y_a)]\Delta t} \tag{3.8}$$

As before, the eigenvalue unity describes equilibrium while the eigenvalue λ_2 describes the approach to equilibrium. In this case a larger Δt gives a faster approach to equilibrium, and it makes sense to take the largest Δt possible. (In a more realistic system one would allow the rates to vary. Errors would then be generated if the time step were so large that significant changes in the rates occurred in one cycle. This criterion would then be used for time step selection.)

In the nucleosynthesis calculation the implicit differencing scheme seems to work well. In the simple scheme computed here, we must invert a 6 × 6 matrix. Two points complicate the analysis. The rates are not constant but rather are functions of T_γ and of ρ. And the equations are not linear!

The nonlinearity is approached simply by straightforward linearization in the difference $Y_{new} - Y_{old}$, in a way introduced by Wagoner (1973). For instance, equation (3.3), when differenced and linearized, becomes:

$$
\frac{1}{\Delta t}(Y_{1new} - Y_{1old}) \simeq LY_{2new} - L_B Y_{1new}
$$

$$
- \frac{1}{2} NPD(Y_{1new}Y_{2old} + Y_{1old}Y_{2new} - 2GNP\ Y_{3new})
$$

$$
+ \frac{1}{2} DD3(Y_{3new}Y_{3old} - GN3\ Y_{1new}Y_{4old} - GN3\ Y_{1old}Y_{4new})
$$

$$
- \frac{1}{2} N3T(Y_{1new}Y_{4old} + Y_{1old}Y_{4new} - GQTP\ Y_{5old}Y_{2new} - GQTP\ Y_{5new}Y_{2old})
$$

$$
+ \frac{1}{2} TD4(Y_{3new}Y_{5old} + Y_{3old}Y_{5new} - GN4\ Y_{6new}Y_{1old} - GN4\ Y_{6old}Y_{1new})
$$

$$
+ TT4\ Y_{5old}Y_{5new} - \frac{1}{3} TT4\ G2N4(Y_{1old}Y_{1old}Y_{6new} + 2\ Y_{1new}Y_{1old}Y_{6old})
$$

$$
+ \frac{1}{2} T34NP(Y_{4old}Y_{5new} + Y_{5old}Y_{4new})
$$

$$
- \frac{1}{2} DN(Y_{1old}Y_{3new} + Y_{1new}Y_{3old} - 2GTG\ Y_{5new})
$$

$$
- \frac{1}{3} T34NP\ GNP4(Y_{1old}Y_{2old}Y_{6new} + Y_{1old}Y_{6old}Y_{2new} + Y_{1new}Y_{2old}Y_{6old})
$$

$$
- \frac{1}{2} N34(Y_{1old}Y_{4new} + Y_{1new}Y_{4old} - 2G4G\ Y_{6new}) \quad . \tag{3.9}
$$

This can be written in the form of equation (3.7), where now Q depends on Y_{old}, among other things.

Original development of this code at Texas used an IMSL routine LEQT2F to invert this matrix. The code as developed at Oxford used a NAG library routine FØ4ATF. Both these versions had, for obscure reasons, difficulty in inverting the matrix, and required that we maintain $|\Delta Y/Y| \lesssim 10^{-2}$ per evolution step. (Wagoner's work used $|\Delta Y/Y|$ ~ 0.2 to 0.4.) When the program was transferred to Livermore and to Texas, the matrix inversion problem was again tackled. At Texas, excellent results were obtained by a 6 × 6 matrix inverter (i.e., one explicitly written for this dimension matrix) which uses a lower-triangular, upper-triangular inversion method (Gerald 1980). At Livermore, the inversion routines (which also work very well) are Cray-adapted programs called DEC and SOL. The Texas program currently running uses <u>no</u> library routines. Typical runs in our programs use $|\Delta Y/Y|$ ~ 0.2 or larger per evolution step.

IV. INTERFACING THE CODES

The rates appearing in equations (3.3) depend on the baryon density ρ, the photon temperature, the neutrino temperature, and the rates at which these parameters change compared to the rates themselves. (The neutron freeze-out already discussed in III is an example of this latter dependence.) The chemical rate equations, like equation (3.3), contain no spatial derivatives. So, if the geometry program can supply these quantities as functions of (proper) time, then a nucleosynthesis program written for a 0-dimensional, i.e. homogeneous, situation will run and can be used to calculate the abundances in each zone on every cycle. In order to evolve the physical quantities, the geometry code requires an equation of state. This is provided by a look-up table generated by the nucleosynthesis program. If the code can accurately follow the history of a particular fluid element, then the nucleosynthesis of that fluid element can be accurately described. This scheme explicitly excludes diffusion of chemical abundances out of the fluid element. Macroscopic matter transport is accounted for explicitly, as we now show. The form of the nucleosynthesis equations is

means that the abundances "arrive" at the later time slice offset from the grid zones on that slice. The advection then carries the

$$\frac{dY}{d\tau} = f \ (Y, \text{local thermodynamic variables}) \quad , \qquad (4.1)$$

where now we explicitly write the time dependence as a proper-time derivative.

Now rewrite equation (4.1) as

$$u^t \frac{dY}{dt} = f - u^i \frac{\partial Y}{\partial x^i} = f - u^z \frac{\partial Y}{\partial z} - u^x \frac{\partial Y}{\partial x} \quad . \qquad (4.2)$$

The last term vanishes because we have chosen the system to be homogeneous in the x-direction. Then:

$$\frac{dY}{dt} = \frac{f}{u^t} - \frac{u^z}{u^t} \frac{\partial Y}{\partial z} \quad . \qquad (4.3)$$

(The code variable is $v^z = u^z/u^t$.) We use an operator splitting approach (Wilson 1979, Centrella and Wilson 1984), first evaluating the change in Y due to the f/u^t term, then performing the advection represented by the spatial gradients. The situation is described in Figure 3. Two geometry time slices are shown.

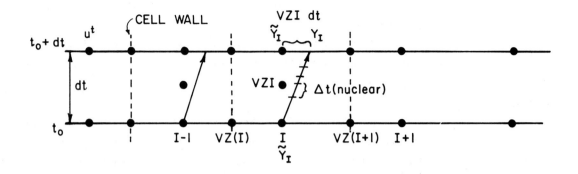

Fig. 3. Representation of the computational grid. Scalar hydrodynamical variables, ρ, E, D, etc. - and the nuclear abundances Y - are defined at each time slice (t_0, $t_0 + dt$, $t_0 + 2dt$ ...) at grid cell centers; other quantities, S_z, V^z, β^z, are defined at cell walls. The geometrical and hydrodynamical evolution first advances all quantities <u>except</u> the abundances from time slice t_0 to time slice $t_0 + dt$. The nuclear evolution is then computed following the motion of a material element, and the nucleosynthesis code can if necessary take small timesteps Δt (nuclear) as it evolves from t_0 to $t_0 + dt$. Hydrodynamical quantities (e.g., densities and temperatures) which are needed by the nucleosynthesis are obtained by linear interpolation. Finally mass densities $\rho_i = \rho Y_i$ are constructed, and their fluxes are advected along with the other fluxes in the hydrodynamical problem, to bring the abundances back to the appropriate grid positions.

As noted above, nucleosynthesis requires densities and temperatures from the geometry. Evolution of the geometry returns these objects on the later time slice. The values of the variables on the earlier time slice are stored in memory; any object required by the nucleosynthesis is obtained by linear interpolation between the slices. Any particular world line is assumed to start at a geometry zone node on the old slice, and evolve along a path given by the 4-velocity associated with that node, eventually crossing the surface $t = t_{new}$. Because V^z is typically nonzero, we have a time-dilation as discussed below. In addition, as Figure 3 shows, the nonzero V^z

abundances back to the proper grid zones on the new slice.

Notice that the Courant condition (see, for instance, Roache 1976) requires that all evolution remain within one of the time slice grid zone rectangles. So, as far as the nucleosynthesis is concerned, we have a "warped rectangle" as our local approximation to the space-time.

The time dilation factor $1/u^t$ multiplying f in equation (4.3) simply reflects the fact that clocks run at different rates for the world lines of the fluid elements. During the proper time that evolves between two geometry slices, the nucleosynthetic conditions may change so much that multiple nucleosynthesis steps are appropriate. Hence we let the nucleosynthesis run asynchronously. The only condition is that the final nucleosynthesis time step should end at the "new" geometry time slice. The total proper time interval along the matter world line is $(t_{new} - t_{old})/u^t$, and this effect is taken into account in the computation. An average dilation is taken by time averaging u^t between the two geometry slices.

In actual runs we rarely find more than a few instances of the nucleosynthesis taking more than one step to evolve between geometry time slices. On the contrary, because the geometry must satisfy stability conditions, we typically have the nucleosynthesis time step "bumping up against" the geometry slicing. In the model displayed below, there was exactly one nucleosynthesis step per geometry slice.

The final step in the evolution of the abundances is to account for the advection described by the spatial gradient terms. For consistency with the transport in the remainder of the coding, we use a technique due to Wilson (1979) which is a mixture of upwind first order and second order differencing. This is applied to the mass densities $\rho_i = Y_i \rho$ (recall that ρ is the baryon density), calculating individual gradients for each species. This transport is carried out in the same subroutine in which the hydrodynamical transport is effected (hence outside of the ELEMENT subprogram). This approach minimizes unintentional numerical diffusion in the element transport and allows the consistent, simultaneous modification of all transport coding, should new schemes become desirable (Centrella and Wilson, 1984).

V. THE INITIAL DATA PROBLEM

The Wilson-Centrella cosmology code uses constant-K slicing and thus decouples the solution of the momentum and Hamiltonian constraints (York 1979). The initial data are specified by giving in each grid zone the value of E, D, K_1, A. (Values are typically fed in by giving a Fourier sum over sines and cosines on the periodic grid.) The lapse, shift, and Hamiltonian equations are solved repetitively (~ 50 times) to produce consistent initial data for this scheme (Centrella and Wilson 1984). As noted above, the baryon density is irrelevant for the dynamics. So, after this step, the baryon-photon ratio is still adjustable.

The most straightforward way to use the code is to take the data for the geometry to correspond to a high temperature ($T_9 = 50$, say). At such temperatures neutrons and protons are typically in thermal equilibrium, and other species are very sparse. We therefore take Y_1, Y_2 in their thermal abundances, $Y_3 = Y_4 = Y_5 = Y_6 = 0$, and let the program go. Unfortunately, the results produced by this technique are usually uninteresting. The reason is that the expansion of the cosmology tends to damp inhomogeneities and irregularities, and so by the time that nucleosynthesis is in full swing (an expansion decade or so later), the geometry has relaxed to roughly homogeneous behavior.

The following solution to this problem, due to Wilson, is used in the results resented here. First the geometry data are initialized as described above. Then the geometry code is run backwards to an arbitrarily chosen time using a simple $P = \varepsilon/3$ equation of state, thereby enhancing the inhomogeneities. In the results presented here, the initial inhomogeneities are inserted into the matter variables only, so the timescale of the universe is _roughly_ that of a Robertson-Walker universe. In such cases we know that deviations from the equilibrium n/p ratio actually occur only for $T_9 \lesssim 15$. Hence we make the assumption at the restart temperature ($T_9 \sim 20$) that $n/p = (n/p)_{thermal}$. From the restart temperature the model evolves forward performing the nucleosynthesis and using the correct nucleosynthesis equation of state.

By considering the curves in Figure 2, one can see that starting as low as $T_9 \sim 5$ may be possible, but would require that the non-equilibrium values of Y_1 and Y_2 be used initially. The other Y_i could still be set to zero initially. Starting at such a low temperature would also require that the ratio T_γ/T_ν and the electron-positron number densities be correctly set.

A further refinement would be to evolve the geometry initially back in time until each grid zone is one horizon size. Then, by investigating the expansion and shear in each grid zone, we can identify each grid zone with a Type I homogeneous cosmology (Ryan and Shepley 1975), which is how that grid zone has evolved from the big bang up to that time. This will mean that matter and wave modes can be put into such a cosmology. We will have such a program working in the near future.

VI. IMPLEMENTATION

Because the nucleosynthesis and the geometry were both working codes, we attempted to minimize disruptions in either. The nucleosynthesis program is treated strictly as an equation of state routine by the geometry evolution. The only modification to the geometry code was the inclusion of the element abundance advection alluded to above.

ELEMENT integrates the abundances, choosing its own timestep. In a computation for a homogeneous cosmology, ELEMENT would also numerically integrate the homogeneous geometry. Here, those homogeneous geometry routines are replaced by KLUGE, which returns the same variables, but obtains them by interpolation on the inhomogeneous cosmology results as outlined above. (KLUGE first checks the nucleosynthesis timestep to reset it if ELEMENT would overshoot the "new" geometry slice.)

VII. RESULTS

Figures 4a-d show the degree of the initial perturbation in the baryon density and its subsequent evolution. This figure uses a relative scale which, if read in gm/cm^3, gives a typical evolution.

This inhomogeneity is definitely <u>not</u> a small perturbation. The density variation starts out with a large spike (and some net momentum).
This spike "evolves through" the grid; some of this motion is shown
in Figures 4b,c. By the end of the evolution, the variation in the
baryon density is ~ 20% (note the broken vertical scale in Fig. 4c),
though one does see a clear trend toward homogeneity.

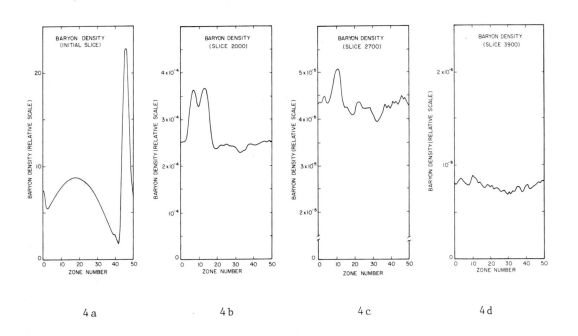

4 a   4 b   4 c   4 d

Fig. 4. Evolution of the structure in the baryon density ρ shown on
the first slice after the code begins its forward evolution, and on
subsequent slices. Because the baryon density is small compared to
the total energy density, its dynamical effect is small, so it can be
reset or rescaled as desired. Such rescaling does change the nucleosynthesis results. For the nucleosynthesis reported here, this baryon density was scaled so that the entropy per baryon corresponds to
that of the fiducial model of Fig. 1 (and is everywhere the same).
"Typical" or "representative" values of the baryon density can be
obtained by reading Fig. 4 in gm/cm^3.

Figures 5a-d show similar graphs for $\frac{8\pi G}{3} E = \frac{8\pi G}{3} \varepsilon w$; the baryon density and E roughly follow one another, though they in fact evolve independently.

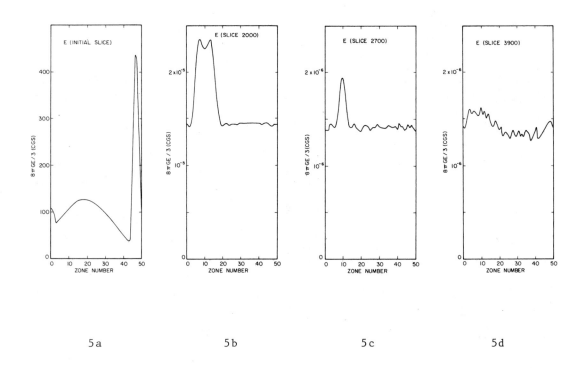

5a   5b   5c   5d

Fig. 5.   Evolution of the quantity $E = \varepsilon w$, where ε is the local energy density.   Initial data with $\delta E/E \gtrsim 5$ shows a propagating pulse structure, which eventually evolves toward smaller wavelengths and smaller amplitudes.   The time slices correspond to those in Fig. 4.

Finally, Figures 6a,b give the ^{4}He variation from zone to zone for an intermediate and a late time slice, and Figures 7a,b give the ^{2}H and ^{3}He variations (tritium in this model is $\sim 10^{-2}$ times the ^{3}He abundance at the end of the run).

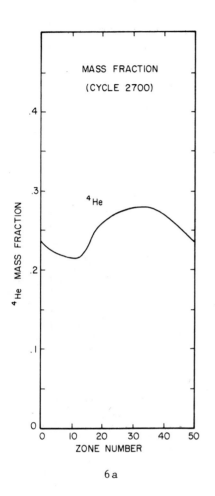

6a

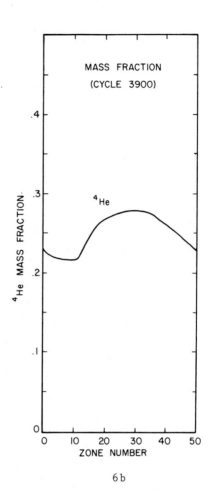

6b

Fig. 6. Inhomogeneous ^{4}He production. The abundance of ^{4}He as a function of zone for a moderately late (cycle 2700) and a very late
(cycle 3900) siice. It can be seen that very little evolution of ^{4}He
occurs after cycle 2700. The small difference between Figs. 6a,b is
due to macroscopic transport (advection) of the ^{4}He; see section 4.

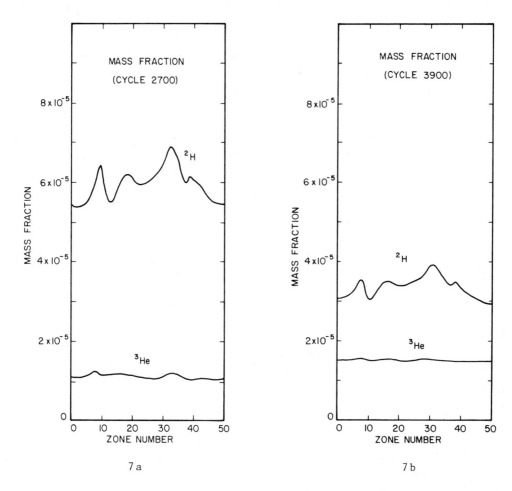

7a   7b

Fig. 7. The zone-to-zone variation of ^{2}H and of ^{3}He on cycle 2700 and on cycle 3900. It can be seen that considerable nucleosynthetic evolution is still affecting these abundances at cycle 2700. By cycle 3900, when the photon temperature $T_{9\gamma} \gtrsim 0.28$ across the grid, the nucleosynthesis has ceased. The spatial averages of the final abundances are: ^{2}H: 3.4×10^{-5}; ^{3}He: 1.5×10^{-5}, ^{4}He: 0.25. This model overproduces ^{4}He relative to lighter isotopes, when compared to isotropic homogeneous models. If the light abundances here had been computed in a homogeneous isotropic model, they would have required a final ^{4}He abundance of 0.24.

From Figure 6 we see that the ^{4}He resulting from the evolution varies from a minimum of 0.216 to a maximum of 0.278, which is comparable to the range French (1980) reports for low-metal extragalactic objects. Again we make the comparison to homogeneous cosmologies: this would correspond to a range of models (Wagoner 1973) with present densities $\sim 7 \times 10^{-32}$ gm/cm^3 to $\sim 3 \times 10^{-29}$ gm/cm^3. The mass weighted ^{4}He average density is ~ 0.25. The ^{3}He and ^{2}H abundances vary also, but by an amount corresponding to a much smaller variation in ρ. This is consistent with the sensitivity of these isotopes to the late evolution, when the inhomogeneity has become much weaker, and is especially apparent when comparing Figures 6a,b to Figures 7a,b. The nuclear evolution has essentially ceased by slice 3900 ($T_9 \lesssim .28$ across the grid). Even though the baryon-entropy ratio was initially set, entropy is produced in this model. Hence comparing ^{2}H and ^{3}He to ^{4}He, which eliminates the uncertain parameter ρ, is the best approach. It is clear from such a comparison that a significant effect of the inhomogeneity is to break the simple relations of Figure 1 between ^{3}He and ^{4}He and between ^{2}H and ^{4}He. In fact, because the evolution reported here takes place well within a horizon size, one must expect spatial averaging of the abundances to take place. Had we plotted in Figure 1 the average from our inhomogeneous model of the endpoint abundances of ^{2}H (3.4×10^{-5}) and ^{3}He (1.5×10^{-5}) against average ^{4}He (0.250), they would have lain above the lines predicted by Wagoner's homogeneous code. They in fact correspond in homogeneous models to a ^{4}He fraction ~ 0.240.

From this preliminary run, we see that the requirement that at least the observed deuterium abundance should have been produced primordially (Schramm and Wagoner (1977) give a review of possible processes that could produce the deuterium; they conclude that astrophysical production is unlikely, but astrophysical destruction is more believable) no longer requires a low ^{4}He universe. Additionally, it suggests that we should consider lower overall density initial situations, which will presumably produce lower ^{4}He average abundances. Finally, in view of the small spatial scale of these variations, we again note the large scatter in observed ^{4}He in extragalactic objects (French 1980, Shields 1983).

Compared to previous calculations of these effects, this work has included much more of the physics, particularly the hydrodynamics involved. Work by Hawking and Taylor (1966) and by Thorne (1967) showed that ^{4}He final abundance is raised by anisotropic speedup of the timescale; here we have computed the complete nucleosynthesis chain in the context of anisotropic, inhomogeneous models. Barrow

(1977), and Gisler, Harrison and Rees (1974) calculated models in which variations in nucleosynthesis are calculated on the basis of varying parameters in homogeneous models that represent parts of the universe, while our hydrodynamics correctly reflects the causal connections between parts of our models. In a recent paper, Barrow and Morgan (1983) assume a log-normal distributed density fluctuation spectrum, and find that only very small inhomogeneities are allowed if agreement with observation is to be achieved. Our calculation shows instead that a particular kind of perturbation can be consistent with observations; more computer experiments are under way to map out the acceptable parameter span for these models.

ACKNOWLEDGEMENTS

This work was supported in part by NSF grant PHY81-07381, by the SERC (UK), and by the National Geographic Society. We are also grateful for the generous support of the University of Manchester, and for computation support at Oxford University. RAM thanks the Aspen Center for Physics for support in 1981, 1983. This project was also supported at Lawrence Livermore National Laboratory by DOE contract number W-7405-ENG-48.

REFERENCES

Barrow, J. D. 1977, M.N.R.A.S., 178, 625.

Barrow, J. D., and Morgan, J. 1983, M.N.R.A.S., 203, 393.

Brill, D. 1982, in "Spacetime and Geometry," ed. R. A. Matzner and L. C. Shepley (Austin: University of Texas Press).

Centrella, J., and Wilson, J. R. 1983, Ap. J., 273, 428.

_____. 1984, Ap. J. Supp., in press.

Centrella, J., Matzner, R. A., Rothman, T., and Wilson, J. R. 1984 (to be submitted to Ap. J.).

Dicus, D. A., Kolb, E. W., Gleeson, A. M., Sudarshan, E.C.G., Teplitz, V. L., and Turner, J. S. 1982, Phys. Rev. D26, 2694.

French, H. B. 1980, Ap. J., 246, 41.

Gerald, C. F. 1980, "Applied Numerical Analysis" (New York: Addison Wesley).

Gisler, G. R., Harrison, E. R., and Rees, M. J. 1974, M.N.R.A.S. 166, 663.

Hawking, S. W. and Taylor, R. J. 1966, Nature, 209, 1278.

Kolb, E., and Wolfram, S. 1980, Nucl. Phys., B172, 224.

Laasonen, P. 1949, Acta Math., 81, 309.

Matzner, R. A., and Rothman, T. 1984, Phys. Rev. D (submitted, 1984).

Moncrief, V. 1975, J. Math. Phys., 16, 493.

_____. 1976, J. Math. Phys., 17, 1893.

Peebles, P.J.E. 1971, "Physical Cosmology" (Princeton: Princeton University Press).

Richtmeyer, R. D., and Morton, K. M. 1967, "Difference Methods for Initial Value Problems" (New York: Interscience Publishers).

Roache, R. J. 1976, "Computational Fluid Dynamics" (Albuquerque, New Mexico: Hermosa Publishers).

Rothman, T. 1981, Ph.D. Thesis, University of Texas at Austin.

Ryan, M. P., and Shepley, L. C. 1975, "Homogeneous Relativistic Cosmologies" (Princeton: Princeton University Press).

Schramm, D. N., and Wagoner, R. V. 1977, Ann. Rev. Nucl. Sci., 27, 37.

Shields, G. 1983, private communication.

Thorne, K. S. 1967, Ap. J., 148, 51.

Wagoner, R. V. 1973, Ap. J., <u>179</u>, 343.

Weinberg, S. 1972, "Gravitation and Cosmology" (New York: Wiley).

Wilson, J. R. 1979, in "Sources of Gravitational Radiation," ed. L. L. Smarr (Cambridge: Cambridge University Press).

Wilson, J. R. 1984, in "Astrophysical Radiation Hydrodynamics," ed. M. L. Norman and K. H. Winkler (Dordrecht: Reidel).

York, J. 1979, in "Sources of Gravitational Radiation," ed. L. L. Smarr (Cambridge: Cambridge University Press).

Massive Neutrinos and Cosmic Matter Collapse*

James R. Wilson
Lawrence Livermore National Laboratory

J. R. Bond
Stanford University

J. M. Centrella
University of Texas

A. S. Szalay
Eotvos University

ABSTRACT

Calculations have been made of the collapse of pancake-like perturbations in the late universe driven by massive neutrinos. The fraction of baryonic mass cool enough for galaxy formation is found to be
small and short-lived for likely neutrino masses.

One hypothesis of the formation of galaxies and clusters of galaxies is pre-
dicated on the idea that the gravitational field responsible for the coalescence
of matter is mainly due to weakly interacting particles of nonzero rest mass. The
authors have written a computer program to study the one-dimensional (planar)
collapse of ordinary matter (photons, baryons and electrons) together with low

*Work performed under the auspices of the U. S. Department of Energy by the
Lawrence Livermore National Laboratory under contract No. W-7405-ENG-48.

mass particles that interact by gravity only (Bond et al. 1984). The present
report is restricted to considering the weakly interacting particles to be neutrinos having rest masses of a few electron volts in a flat Friedmann universe
(for a review see Schramm and Freese, this volume). The principal results of
this study are that if heat conduction is ignored during collapse a sizeable
fraction, 5-20%, of the baryonic matter cools by radiation losses to temperatures
of the order of 10^4 °K. This temperature is low enough that further aggregation
of the cool matter into galaxies is plausible. If heat is allowed to flow as it
would in a plasma containing no magnetic field then cool matter is formed briefly.
Heat conduction would seem to make galaxy formation difficult in a standard
Friedmann universe if massive ordinary neutrinos are responsible for the collapse.

Our computer program is based on the Zel'dovich pancake model for cosmic
perturbation growth (Zel'dovich 1970; Bond, Efstathiou, and Silk 1980). Only
the last hundred-fold decrease in red shift is followed in our calculation so we
treat the neutrinos in the Newtonian limit. Numerically they are represented by
about one thousand discrete mass points. The baryonic matter is calculated using
a more or less standard Eulerian hydrodynamical scheme; however, electrons and
ions are allowed to have different temperatures. The shock heating energy is put
into the ions only and the electrons are heated by Coulomb collisions. The electrons cool by Compton collisions with the microwave background, bremsstrahlung
radiation, and recombination radiation. The matter is assumed to be 75% hydrogen
and 25% helium for the purposes of evaluating the radiation losses. Heat conduction is calculated for both electrons and ions by the usual plasma formulae except
that the conduction velocity is limited to the sound speed of the particles. The
degree of ionization is calculated by equating the recombination rate by radiation
to the ionization rate by particle Coulomb collisions.

First we will impose some constraints on the models we study to reduce the
number of parameters. We assume the standard Friedmann $\Omega_o = 1.0$ model where the
total density is $(\dot{R}/R)^2$ 3/8πG. Here "." denotes time derivative, R is the scale
factor, and Ω_o is the ratio of the present total density to the density required
to close the universe. We consider neutrinos to have unit statistical weight and
come in f varieties all of equal mass m_ν. We require that the neutrinos be in
equilibrium at a temperature of one MeV and that the universe evolve such that the
present radiation temperature is 2.7°K. Let t_o be the present age of the universe
in billions of years. Then the results of these constraints may be roughly
summarized by the following formulae (cf. Schramm and Steigman 1981):

$$m_{max} = 44(10/t_0)^2 \text{ eV} \quad ,$$

$$B/P = 2.8 \times 10^{-10}(m_{max} - m) \quad ,$$

$$\Omega_B = \rho_B/(\rho_B + \rho_\nu) = 1 - m/m_{max}$$

where $m = fm_\nu$, m_{max} is the largest allowable value of m, B/P is the ratio of the numbers of baryons to photons, and ρ_B and ρ_ν are respectively the baryon and neutrino densities. B/P, ρ_B and ρ_ν are present day values. The present age of the universe is 10 to 20 billion years (Berman 1982; Symbalisty and Schramm 1981; Schramm and Freese, this volume) so the neutrino masses are small. The baryon to photon ratio is thought to be about 3×10^{-10} within a factor of a few, which restricts m to be close to m_{max}. For a Friedmann universe, element production requires that Ω_B be around one tenth or less (Yang et al. 1979). Again this requires that m be close to m_{max}.

To set the scale for our perturbations we use the neutrino length scale $\lambda = 4 \times 10^{27}/(f^{1/2}m_\nu(1+z))$, where z is the redshift. This λ is the dominant wavelength for neutrino perturbations at the time the neutrinos become non-relativistic and gravitationally unstable (Bond et al. 1980). Below this scale, waves are highly damped. The neutrino perturbation is taken to be of the cosine form, peaking at the origin. The amplitude is selected to be such that neutrinos start crossing through the origin at a redshift z_c. We usually take $z_c = 5.0$ except where indicated below.

As an example we will consider a run with a universe age of 15 billion years with one type of neutrinos of mass 19 eV. The masses inferred from the perturbation length scale are 4.7×10^{14} $M_\odot$ for the baryons and 1.6×10^{16} $M_\odot$ for the neutrinos. The calculation is started at a redshift of 65 with a small perturbation. At the redshift of 5 the perturbation has grown and distorted to such a degree that neutrinos start passing through the origin. Up to this time the baryonic matter has such a low pressure that it stays in step with the neutrinos. Since ordinary matter cannot pass through itself, a shock wave is formed shortly after the neutrinos start passing through the origin and each other. The velocity of matter increases somewhat linearly away from the origin; hence, the temperatures behind the shock wave are initially small but rise rapidly as the wave progresses outward. In Figure 1a the temperatures for three times after the neutrinos start crossing the origin are shown. Shortly after $t/t_c = 1.40$ (t is time and t_c is neutrino crossing time) the heat conduction wave reaches the

central plane and no more cool matter exists. The heat flow from the hot material
has overwhelmed the radiation losses of the cold material. The cold material only
exists for a short time and encompasses at most only 6% of the baryonic matter.
In Figure 1b the results of running the same initial model without heat flow are
given. Here the cold region continues to grow, reaching 18% of the total matter
by the present epoch. The peak ion temperatures are quite hot, 4 x 10^7 °K. In
Figure 2 the ion temperatures for the models with and without conduction are
compared at the same time. We see that the temperature distribution is flattened
out to about 10^7 °K by the heat flow.

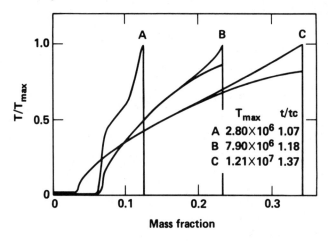

Fig. 1a - Ratio of ion temperature (upper curve) and electron temperature (lower
curve) to maximum ion temperature versus baryon mass fraction at selected times,
for the calculation with full heat flow.

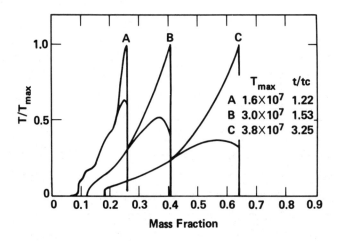

Fig. 1b - Same as Fig. 1a, for the case with no heat flow.

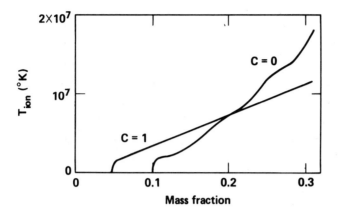

Fig. 2. - The ion temperatures for the case of full heat conduction and no heat conduction (C=1, C=0) are shown as functions of mass fraction at the same time, t/t_c = 1.30.

TABLE 1

Summary of Results

t_0	m_ν	f	Ω_B	C	z_c	M16	t/t_c	Cool Fraction
15	19	1	0.03	1.0	5.	1.6	1.40	0.06
15	19	1	0.03	0.0	5.	1.6	14.2	0.18
10	43	1	0.03	1.0	5.	0.42	14.7	0.10
20	10.7	1	0.03	1.0	5.	6.0	1.22	0.048
15	19	1	0.03	1.0	10.	2.0	1.5	0.07
15	19	1	0.03	1.0	20.	2.0	13	0.16
15	18	1	0.09	1.0	5.	2.2	1.75	0.09
15	6.3	1	0.03	1.0	5.	9.	1.14	0.037
15	6.3	1	0.03	0.0	5.	9.	14.7	0.17

In Table 1 we summarize the results of a number of calculations. The notation is as follows: t_0 is the present age of the universe in billions of years, m_ν is the rest mass of the neutrinos in electron volts, f is the number of neutrino types, Ω_B is the baryon mass fraction of the universe, C is the heat conduction multiplier, Ml6 is the total associated mass in units of 10^{16} $M_{\odot}$, t_c is the time neutrinos start crossing through the origin, t is the time at which all matter has become hot, and cool fraction is the maximum fraction of matter that is cool ($T < 10^6$ °K). Note that the time of maximum cool fraction is less than t. From the table we observe that if heat flow is not inhibited the amount of material that cools sufficiently to condense into galaxies is sometimes small, and, further, the relative time the matter is cool is short. Our constraints on the models that $\Omega_o = 1.0$ and ρ_B/ρ_ν be small leads to small neutrino masses and large total masses. It is, of course, these large total masses that release so much gravitational energy and lead to the high temperatures and high heat flow. In calculations with no heat flow a modest amount, 5-20%, of cold material is formed. The temperature of the cool matter is about 10^4 °K. It cools until recombination slows the radiation losses. The spectrum from the bremsstrahlung emission is calculated. While the peak temperatures may be several tens of keV, the radiation density in the keV region is always less than the observed diffuse X-ray background. This is due to the low baryon density in the hot region and also to red shifting of the X-rays.

In our restricted survey it appears to be difficult to form galaxies in the neutrino-driven pancake model unless thermal heat conduction is suppressed by perhaps a tangled magnetic field. Another possibility is that fragmentation into galaxies occurs almost immediately, within a Hubble time, after crossing and before conduction has a chance to heat up the cool layer. Studies of heat flow in laser generated plasmas have indicated a suppression of heat flow compared to the usual formulas by a factor of 10 to 30 in the case that the thermal gradients are large over one electron mean free path (Max 1982). A large volume fraction of the gas in our models has relatively large mean free paths. We choose the eighth model from Table 1 to study how sensitive our models are to the magnitude of the heat conductivity. Write the heat flux schematically as:

$$F = \frac{C \nabla T}{1 + L \nabla T / T}$$

where C = L = 1 corresponds to standard heat flow. Tables 2 and 3 give results of varying the coefficients away from unity. The results are only weakly dependent on the magnitude of the limiter coefficient L. The results are strongly dependent on the overall conductivity coefficient C, but a drastic alteration of C is required to make an appreciable change in the cool fraction. The peak ion temperature is sensitive to L; it rises by 40% over the L variation in Table 3.

In these numerical calculations it is difficult to have sufficiently fine zoning in mass to represent the temperature well at low temperatures (10^4 to 10^5 °K) where the cooling rate is a strong function of the temperature. The question is, have we exaggerated the evaporation of the cold gas by our coarse zoning? As noted in Bond et al. (1984), behind the shock the pressure is nearly constant. If the pressure is assumed constant, then there can be a steady state temperature

<table>
<tr><td colspan="3">TABLE 2</td><td colspan="3">TABLE 3</td></tr>
<tr><td colspan="3">Variation of C</td><td colspan="3">Variation of L</td></tr>
<tr><td>C</td><td>t/t_c</td><td>Cool Fraction</td><td>L</td><td>t/t_c</td><td>Cool Fraction</td></tr>
<tr><td>1.00</td><td>1.14</td><td>0.037</td><td>1.0</td><td>1.14</td><td>0.037</td></tr>
<tr><td>0.32</td><td>1.25</td><td>0.040</td><td>3.2</td><td>1.15</td><td>0.037</td></tr>
<tr><td>0.10</td><td>1.9</td><td>0.050</td><td>10</td><td>1.16</td><td>0.038</td></tr>
<tr><td>0.032</td><td>14</td><td>0.070</td><td>32</td><td>1.18</td><td>0.041</td></tr>
<tr><td>0.010</td><td>14</td><td>0.17</td><td></td><td></td><td></td></tr>
</table>

mass profile for which heat flow just balances radiation losses. This temperature obeys the equation

$$\frac{\partial}{\partial x} \left(k_o \, T^{5/2} \frac{\partial T}{\partial x} \right) = n^2 \dot{E}(T)$$

where $k_o T^{5/2}$ is the heat conductivity, n is electron number density, and $\dot{E}(T)$ is the volume radiation loss rate. This equation defines a critical heat flux F_c, and F_c/P is a unique function of T, where P is electron pressure. Figure 3 shows a solution of the above equation. For the high temperatures behind the shock the critical flux becomes insensitive to the details of the radiation losses at low temperatures. The heat flux at high temperatures ($T > 10^6$ °K) is accurately calculated in the numerical model. The fractional change of temperature per zone is small and the initial post shock temperatures depend only on the gravitational potential. In Figure 4 we show how this critical flux of Figure 3 correlates with the evaporation of cold gas in an actual dynamic calculation. When the flux F/P is less than F_c/P the cool region grows; when F/P is larger than F_c/P the cool region shrinks. In the dynamic calculation there is a time delay so that the flux greatly exceeds the critical flux by the time the cold region has completely evaporated.

For full heat conduction not to be destructive to the cold matter we estimate the total mass must be as low as $10^{15} M_\odot$, which requires the universe have a

short life. The massive noninteracting particle pancake model has many possibilities. These present calculations just illustrate a possible difficulty. For
more general surveys of the model using this computer program see Bond, Centrella,
Szalay, and Wilson (1984).

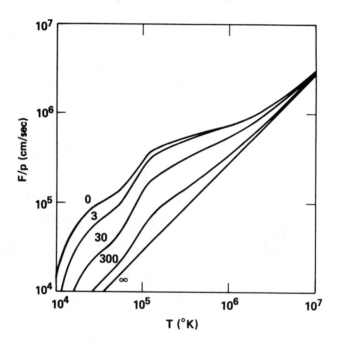

Fig. 3. - Steady state flux divided by electron pressure versus temperature. In
order to illustrate how recombination radiation affects the critical flux, the heat
loss has been modified as:

$$E = E_{recom}\; T/(T+T_0) + E_{brem}\; .$$

The labels on the curves correspond to values of T_0 in units of 10^4 °K.

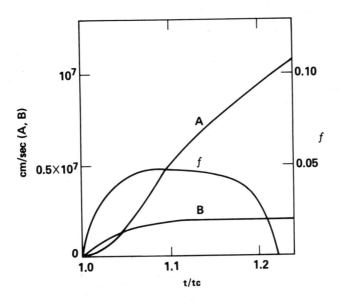

Fig. 4. - For the fourth model calculation of Table 1 we have plotted the mass fraction of cold gas (curve f), the heat flux divided by electron pressure behind the shock wave (curve A), and the critical heat flux/pressure (curve B), evaluated at the same place. The time is t, and t_c is the neutrino crossing time.

REFERENCES

Berman, B. L. 1982, in Energy and Technology Review (Lawrence Livermore National
    Laboratory UCRL-52000-82-12).

Bond, J. R., Centrella, J., Szalay, A. S., and Wilson, J. 1984, M.N.R.A.S.,
    submitted.

Bond, J. R., Efstathiou, G., and Silk, J. 1980, Phys. Rev. Lett., 45, 1980.

Max, C. E. 1982, "The Physics of Laser Fusion", Vol. I (Lawrence Livermore
    National Laboratory UCRL-53107).

Schramm, D. N., and Steigman, G. 1981, Ap. J., 243, 1.

Symbalisty, E. M. D., and Schramm, D. N. 1981, Rep. Prog. Phys., 44, 293.

Yang, J., Schramm, D. N., Steigman, G., and Rood, R. T. 1979, Ap.J., 227, 697.

Zel'dovich, Ya.B. 1970, Astr. Ap., 5, 84.

The Large-Scale Structure of the Universe:
Three-Dimensional Numerical Models*

Joan M. Centrella
University of Texas at Austin

Lawrence Livermore National Laboratory

Adrian L. Melott
University of Chicago

ABSTRACT

Galaxies and clusters of galaxies have been observed to lie in
large flattened or filamentary systems known as superclusters. We have
studied the development of this large-scale structure of the universe
using three-dimensional numerical simulations. Our computer code calculates the motion of collisionless matter acting under the force of
gravity in an expanding universe. The code was optimized to take
advantage of the vector processing capabilities of the Cray-1 supercomputer on which these simulations were run. The resulting models
clearly show the formation of clusters and superclusters as the
universe evolves.

I. INTRODUCTION

Our understanding of the universe we live in is grounded in observations.
Detailed mapping of the distribution of galaxies by measurements of their

* Part of this work was performed under the auspices of the U. S. Department of
Energy by the Lawrence Livermore National Laboratory under contract No.
W-7405-ENG-48.

redshift velocities gives us information about the three-dimensional (3-D) structure of the universe. Our current picture is one in which the galaxies and
clusters of galaxies lie in even larger associations known as superclusters of
galaxies (de Vaucouleurs 1981; Oort 1983). Superclusters are typically either
flattened pancake-like systems, or elongated filamentary systems several tens of
megaparsecs (Mpc) in extent (1 Mpc $\sim$ 3 x 10^6 light years). The galaxy distribution also contains large holes or voids where no galaxies are observed. The largest such region found so far is in the constellation Boötes and contains a spherical volume of diameter 62 h^{-1} Mpc that is devoid of galaxies (Kirshner et al.
1983). Here the parameter h is related to Hubble's constant H_o by

$$H_o = 100 \ h \ km \ sec^{-1} \ Mpc^{-1} \ , \tag{1}$$

where h lies in the range 0.5 $\leq$ h $\leq$ 1 (Peebles 1971). These observations of the
occurrence of galaxies in supercluster filaments and pancakes and the absence of
galaxies from large voids lead us to envision a "Swiss cheese" structure in the
universe: the galaxies lie in an interconnected web of superclusters that surrounds vast regions devoid of galaxies (Einasto, Joeveer, and Saar 1980).

The task of theory is to explain how this large scale structure developed.
In the standard Big Bang cosmological models the universe began in a state of
extreme density and temperature and then expanded into the form we observe today.
These models can be characterized by a density parameter Ω_o given by

$$\Omega_o = \frac{\rho_o}{\rho_{crit}} \ . \tag{2}$$

Here, $\rho_o = \rho(t_o)$ is the total mass density in the universe at the present
epoch t_o and

$$\rho_{crit} = \frac{3H_o^2}{8\pi G} = 1.8 \times 10^{-29} \ h^2 \ g \ cm^{-3} \tag{3}$$

is the critical density above which the universe will recollapse. Here G is the
Newtonian gravitational constant. Thus, if $\Omega_o \leq 1$ the universe will expand forever; if $\Omega_o > 1$ the universe will eventually halt its expansion and recollapse.

The value of Ω_o can in principle be deduced from observations; current work places it in the range

$$0.1 \lesssim \Omega_o \lesssim 1 \tag{4}$$

(Peebles 1979; Davis and Huchra 1982; Ford et al. 1981; Szalay and Silk 1983).
However, theoretical studies of the synthesis of light elements in the early
history of the universe show that the ratio of the present density in baryons
alone to the critical density Ω_b must fall in the range

$$0.01 \lesssim \Omega_b \lesssim 0.1 \tag{5}$$

in order to agree with observations of the primordial abundances of these elements
(Schramm and Steigman 1981; Olive et al. 1981). Taken together, equations (4) and
(5) imply that the universe could be dominated by dark, i.e. nonluminous, nonbaryonic matter.

What is this nonbaryonic dark matter composed of? The most promising candidates are elementary particles such as neutrinos with rest masses in the range
10-100 eV and other, more speculative, particles such as axions and gravitinos
(Freese and Schramm, this volume; Primack and Blumenthal 1984). Such particles
decouple from the baryons and photons very early in the history of the universe.
The spectrum of wave perturbations in the distribution of these particles suffers
from collisionless damping due to directional effects in both the relativistic and
nonrelativistic regimes, and due to velocity-dispersion effects in the nonrelativistic regime only. The temperature at which each type of particle decouples
selects out a length scale below which collisionless damping is effective in
erasing structure. In this way the dark matter candidates are distinguished by
their respective perturbation spectra and are classified as being of the hot or
large-scale damping, warm or intermediate-scale damping, or cold or no damping
type (Bond, Centrella, Szalay and Wilson 1984a; Shapiro 1984). All such particles
are collisionless after they decouple, interacting with other matter only gravitationally, and thus deserve the name "dark matter".

Numerical modeling provides the arena in which these theoretical considerations are developed and brought to confront the observations. In this work we
study the development and evolution of structure in dark matter from an input
spectrum of small perturbations using numerical simulations. Our calculations
follow the time evolution of structure in a 3-D cosmological model from the linear
regime

$$\left(\frac{\delta\rho}{\rho}\right)_{rms} \ll 1 \tag{6a}$$

into the nonlinear regime

$$\left(\frac{\delta\rho}{\rho}\right)_{rms} \gtrsim 1 \quad . \tag{6b}$$

Here the density contrast is $\frac{\delta\rho}{\rho}$ is defined by

$$\frac{\delta\rho}{\rho} = \frac{\rho - \tilde{\rho}}{\tilde{\rho}} \tag{7}$$

where $\tilde{\rho}$ is the average density in the model. The subscript "rms" signifies the root mean square value. For the case of hot dark matter, such as that consisting of massive neutrinos, the simulations show a Swiss cheese structure of interconnected dense objects, identified as superclusters, surrounding vast empty regions or voids (Centrella and Melott 1983; Matzner 1984; Klypin and Shandarin 1983; Shandarin 1983; Frenk, White and Davis 1983).

The plan of this paper is as follows. The physical model which underlies our calculations is presented in Section II. Section III contains a discussion of our numerical model and the resulting computer code. These simulations were run on a Cray-1 supercomputer. We optimized the code to take advantage of the vector processing capabilities of that machine, and this is discussed in Section IV. The results of our simulations are presented in Section V.

II. THE PHYSICAL MODEL

Modern scientific cosmology began with Hubble's (1929) discovery of the recession of galaxies. From observations of the spectra of galaxies, Hubble found that the galaxies at distances r are traveling away from us with velocities $v = H_o r$, where H_o is Hubble's constant. This discovery tells us that the universe is expanding and, running the expansion backwards in time, implies that the universe began with an explosion from a very dense state.

The second great discovery of modern cosmology occurred in 1965 when Penzias and Wilson detected a cosmic radiation field with a temperature of about 3 K (Penzias and Wilson 1965; Dicke, Peebles, Roll, and Wilkinson 1965). This microwave background radiation field is very highly isotropic (Gorenstein and Smoot 1981; Lubin et al. 1983a, b; Fixsen et al. 1983). The conventional interpretation (Peebles 1971; Weinberg 1972) of this radiation field is that it is the relic of the hot fireball stage of the universe at the Big Bang. In this standard cosmo-logical model, the universe started out in a very hot, dense state and cooled as it expanded. When the temperature of the universe reached about 10^4 K, the matter and radiation decoupled. Since the matter in the universe is transparent to radi-ation after decoupling, the observations of the microwave background provide us with direct observations of the physical conditions at that period. In partic-ular, the isotropy of the microwave background tells us that the universe was highly isotropic at decoupling.

This condition of isotropy, coupled with the Copernican belief that we do not occupy a privileged location in the universe, leads us to expect the universe to be spatially homogeneous as well. This means that there should exist some scale in the universe above which the average properties of the universe are uniform. However, the observational evidence for homogeneity is slim at best (Peebles 1980). In particular we know from the work of de Vaucouleurs and others that the universe is inhomogeneous at least out to the scales of superclusters of galaxies, some tens of Mpc (de Vaucouleurs 1981; see also Oort 1983 for a survey). Nevertheless, spatial homogeneity on scales larger than this, say larger than 100 Mpc or so, is a widely used assumption and we will adopt it here.

The basis of our physical model is therefore a homogeneous, isotropic expand-ing universe. This uniform universe acts as a "background" universe in which structures smaller than the scale of homogeneity form and evolve. The basic evolution equation for such a uniform model is

$$\frac{1}{R}\frac{dR}{dt} = \frac{R_o H_o}{R}\left(1 - \Omega_o + \Omega_o \frac{R_o}{R}\right)^{\frac{1}{2}} \tag{8}$$

where $R(t)$ is the expansion scale factor of the universe, $R_o = R(t_o)$, and t is cosmic time. Hubble's constant is defined to be $H_o = H(t_o)$, where

$$H(t) = \frac{1}{R}\frac{dR}{dt} \ . \tag{9}$$

Equation (8) is valid during the post-decoupling, matter-dominated regime in which the pressure is negligible and the mass density of the universe obeys

$$\frac{\rho}{\rho_0} = \left(\frac{R}{R_0}\right)^{-3} \quad ; \tag{10}$$

it is the only nontrivial field equation of general relativity for a homogeneous, isotropic universe (assuming the cosmological constant $\Lambda = 0$). It can also be derived from Newtonian considerations of a large, expanding gas cloud (Weinberg 1972).

The density parameter Ω_0 plays a key role in the evolution of this model universe. As noted in Section I, Ω_0 is the ratio of the present density of matter in the universe to the critical density above which the universe will recollapse. In Newtonian terms, this is equivalent to the statement that Ω_0 is the ratio of the potential energy to the kinetic energy of the universe. So, if the potential energy exceeds the kinetic energy, the universe will recollapse; otherwise it will expand forever.

Since the mass density of the universe plays such a key role in its evolution, it is important to know what this matter is composed of. As discussed in Section I, both observational and theoretical considerations suggest that the mass density of the universe is dominated by nonluminous, nonbaryonic matter. From equations (4) and (5) we see that this dark matter will dominate the gravitational dynamics of the universe, in particular the processes of gravitational collapse and clustering important in the evolution of structure. Therefore, as a first step in understanding the development of structure in the universe, we take our model to contain only collisionless matter. Our calculations follow only the gravitational dynamics of this dark matter. Since we do not follow the hydrodynamical evolution of the luminous matter, we cannot study shocks and other dissipative effects, heat flow or radiation losses. These processes have been included in 1-D models (Bond, Centrella, Szalay and Wilson 1984a, b; Wilson, Bond, Centrella and Szalay, this volume; Shapiro, Struck-Marcell and Melott 1983) and will be included in multidimensional models later.

We will study the evolution of this dark matter within the framework of Newtonian cosmology (Weinberg 1972). This means that the gravitational field and the equations of motion for the particles moving under its influence will be given using the Newtonian expressions. In other words, the matter will evolve via the Newtonian force laws in an expanding background universe governed by equation (8) in which the average density of matter is decreasing according to equation (10). This approach is valid for velocities $v \ll c$, where c is the speed of light, and for length scales $\lambda \ll L_H$, where $L_H \sim ct$ is the horizon size. The second condition means that the structures which form do not couple to the curvature of the universe itself, and so our use of a uniform expanding background universe is valid. Typical values of these quantities for galaxies in clusters and super-clusters are $v \lesssim 10^3$ km/sec and $\lambda \lesssim 10^2$ Mpc; the conditions of Newtonian cosmology are thus satisfied in these simulations.

We therefore know that the particle distribution function f for this colli-sionless dark matter evolves according to the Vlasov equation

$$\frac{\partial f}{\partial t} + \nabla f . \vec{v} + \left(\vec{F} . \frac{\partial}{\partial \vec{v}} \right) f = 0 \tag{11}$$

where $\vec{v}$ represents the particle velocities. The force $\vec{F}$ is determined from Poisson's equation

$$\nabla . \vec{F} = -4\pi G \rho \quad . \tag{12}$$

We will find it useful to rewrite these equations using the following trans-formation of variables (Melott 1983; 1981):

$$\vec{x}' = \frac{R_0}{R} \vec{x} \quad , \tag{13}$$

$$dt' = \left(\frac{R_0}{R} \right)^2 dt \tag{14}$$

where the particle coordinates are written in Cartesian coordinates $\vec{x}$. The velocities $\vec{v}'$ with respect to the primed system $(\vec{x}', t')$ are

$$\vec{v}' = \left(\frac{R_0}{R} \right)^{-1} (\vec{v} - H\vec{x}). \tag{15}$$

Substituting the primed variables into equation (11) and using equation (8), we get

$$\frac{\partial f}{\partial t'} + \nabla' f \cdot \vec{v}' + \left(\vec{F}' \cdot \frac{\partial}{\partial \vec{v}'} \right) f = 0 \quad , \tag{16}$$

where

$$\vec{F}' = \left(\frac{R_0}{R} \right)^{-3} (\vec{F} + 4\pi G\rho \vec{x}) \quad . \tag{17}$$

Thus,

$$\nabla' \cdot \vec{F}' = -4\pi G' \rho' \quad , \tag{18}$$

where

$$\rho' = \left(\frac{R_0}{R} \right)^{-3} (\rho - \bar{\rho}) \quad , \tag{19}$$

$\bar{\rho}$ is proportional to the density of the background universe, and

$$G' = \left(\frac{R_0}{R} \right)^{-1} G \quad . \tag{20}$$

The primed coordinates are known as "comoving coordinates" and are useful because they allow us to calculate the dynamics of particles relative to the expanding background universe. For example, the average density in a large volume of the universe is constant in comoving coordinates. Also, two particles at rest in the uniform expansion will remain stationary in comoving coordinates. Density inhomogeneities produce gravitational forces; particles moving under these forces have velocities relative to the background known to astronomers as "peculiar velocities". Bound structures will shrink with time in comoving coordinates, since we are observing them in an expanding background.

To complete our physical model we need a cosmic energy equation which gives the time evolution of energy over volumes of the universe larger than any condensation that forms (Irvine 1961; Layzer 1963; Dimitriev and Zel'dovich 1964). First define, in comoving coordinates, kinetic energy

$$K' = \frac{1}{2} \int \rho'(v')^2 \, dV' \tag{21}$$

and potential energy

$$U' = -\frac{G'}{2} \iint \frac{\rho'_1 \rho'_2}{|\vec{x}'_1 - \vec{x}'_2|} \, dV'_1 \, dV'_2 \quad , \tag{22}$$

where the volume element $dV' = d\vec{x}'$. Then the total energy is

$$E' = K' + U' \quad , \tag{23}$$

and the cosmic energy equation giving its time evolution is

$$\frac{dE'}{dt'} = H' \, U' \quad . \tag{24}$$

Equation (24) will be used to test energy conservation in the numerical computation as discussed in Section III below.

III.   THE NUMERICAL MODEL

We now turn to the task of converting the physical model outlined in Section II into a numerical model suitable for evolution on a computer. Our discussion follows Hockney and Eastwood (1981). We begin by considering the Vlasov equation which gives the evolution of the particle distribution function $f(\vec{x},\vec{v},t)$. The quantity $f(\vec{x},\vec{v},t)d\tau$ gives the probability that the infinitesimal phase space volume $d\tau = d\vec{x} \, d\vec{v}$ is occupied at time t. If there is a particle in this cell at time t, then there will be a particle in the cell at $(\vec{x}_1, \vec{v}_1)$ at time t_1 where we find $(\vec{x}_1, \vec{v}_1)$ from $(\vec{x}, \vec{v})$ using the equations of motion for the particle. Thus we can replace the Vlasov equation by the particle equations of motion and the relation

$$f(\vec{x}_1, \vec{v}_1, t_1) = f(\vec{x}, \vec{v}, t) \quad .$$

That is, f is constant along the particle trajectories given by the equations of motion. If we knew the value of f in every infinitesimal phase space volume at time t, we could evolve it forward to any later time t_1 using the equations of motion.

Even with the power of modern computers it is clearly impossible to map the distribution function f for every such cell. We therefore choose a set of sample points in $(\vec{x}, \vec{v})$ phase space, with each point representing an element of phase fluid corresponding to a large number of particles. We then follow the orbits of these sample points through phase space using the equations of motion. If we use a sufficiently large number of sample points in this discrete model then we need make no explicit reference to the distribution function f (Hockney and Eastwood 1981).

Since these sample points in phase space represent many particles, we can regard them as finite-sized clouds of particles. The position of one of these "superparticles" is the center of mass of the cloud, while its velocity is the mean velocity of the cloud. In modeling gravitational dynamics in a universe dominated by dark matter, one superparticle typically corresponds to many billions of elementary particles such as neutrinos.

In our numerical model we therefore replace the Vlasov equation with the superparticle equations of motion. For Newtonian gravitational fields in an expanding background universe these equations are, in comoving coordinates,

$$\frac{d\vec{x}_i'}{dt'} = \vec{v}_i' \tag{25}$$

and

$$\frac{d\vec{v}_i'}{dt'} = \vec{F}_i' \quad . \tag{26}$$

These equations describe the trajectory $\vec{x}_i$ (t) for the ith particle moving under the force of gravity; the subscript i is the superparticle label.

Another restriction that must be introduced to study the evolution of large scale structure on a computer is that the computational box or the volume of space enclosed by the simulation model is finite. Since we are working in Cartesian coordinates, we take our computational box to be a cube; furthermore, since these coordinates are comoving with the expanding background, the coordinate size of this box remains fixed. We also impose periodic boundary conditions on this box to approximate a region in an infinitely periodic universe. Thus, superparticles which leave through one face of the cube reenter through the opposite face and the total mass within the cube remains constant. These restrictions should pose no problem as long as the size of the cube is much smaller than the horizon size of the expanding background universe and much larger than the typical sizes of the structures which form. In particular, we will not be able to see clustering on scales larger than the size of the box.

Having thus set up our region of computation, we now turn to the equations for the fields within this space. The Newtonian gravitational field is given by Poisson's equation (18) in comoving coordinates. We set up a uniform Cartesian mesh within the computational box; the density and the gravitational potential are assigned to the nodes of the mesh with the forces centered between them.

These considerations form the basis for a class of numerical methods known as "particle-mesh" methods (Hockney and Eastwood 1981). The field quantities are defined on a calculational mesh. The matter is represented by superparticles, hereafter called simply particles, which move through this mesh under the action of the fields. In order for this numerical model to be a good representation of our physical model, the particles must behave as a collisionless fluid and the forces must be smooth, allowing us to study the collective effects of many particles. There are several particle-mesh methods which differ in the way the density is assigned to the mesh and the way the forces on the particles are calculated. To satisfy the requirements of accuracy and computational efficiency, we have chosen the Cloud-in-Cell or CIC method (Hockney and Eastwood 1981).

The CIC method can be compared with the direct N-body codes used in similar simulation work (Frenk, White and Davis 1983). In such codes the force is calculated directly as a summation over all particles. Direct N-body methods are computationally expensive and allow the use of only a relatively small number of particles, say 10^3. In addition, the force due to near neighbors must be important in this method; density fluctuations on the interparticle separation scale exist and may grow. This manifests itself in the growth of unphysical small clumps in the models (see Frenk, White and Davis 1983). Two-body scattering will exist in these clumps. Varying the initial arrangement of particles (White, Frenk and Davis 1983) does not constitute a valid test of the validity of this method, as all such arrangements possess this interparticle noise. Hybrid code methods, such as the P^3M method (Hockney and Eastwood 1981), also suffer from these noise features.

In contrast, the CIC method is ideal for simulating our physical model. It is computationally efficient and allows the use of many particles, typically 10^5 to 10^6. "Quiet start" techniques (Potter 1973) can be used to minimize interparticle noise in the initial conditions; evolution by the CIC method then explicitly suppresses the growth of such small-scale fluctuations. The price we pay for this suppression is that the resolution of the model is limited to the resolution of the mesh; however, the scale at which the resolution becomes bad is the interparticle separation scale. We thus gain speed by sacrificing untrustworthy information. Some gain in effective resolution is possible by varying the physical scale.

The first step in actually computing the evolution of our model is to assign the density to the mesh. The particles or "clouds" are taken to have a cubical shape and the same size as a grid zone. A typical particle at position $\vec{x}$ with velocity $\vec{v}$ will overlap eight zones. In the CIC method the fraction of the mass of a particle assigned to each of these eight zones is given by the volume of the overlap of the particle in each zone. For this reason the CIC method in 3-D is often called the volume-weighting scheme.

Now that the density is defined everywhere on the mesh, Poisson's equation (18) is solved for the gravitational potential. Poisson's equation is solved on the mesh using a fast Fourier transform (FFT) method (Potter 1973) which is computationally efficient. Once we have the potential in each zone we can take its gradient using centered differences to get the gravitational force.

We are now ready to "push the particles" with this force. The equations of motion (25) and (26) are solved using the standard leapfrog scheme (Potter 1973) to update the coordinates and velocities. The force on each particle is interpolated from the forces in the zones which it overlaps, using the same volume-weighting method used to compute the density. This gives us a new distribution of particles. The new density is assigned to the mesh and the cycle is repeated until the model has evolved into a state which can be compared with observations of the present universe; see Section V.

Implicit in this discussion is the discret representation of the continuous time variable t' by a set of time levels separated by a small timestep. For stability the timestep must be small compared to both the time for the fastest moving particle to cross a zone and the dynamical time for the densest condensation. Since condensations form and grow denser as the model evolves, the timestep decreases as the calculation proceeds. This varying timestep is kept dynamically centered for the leapfrog evolution.

Energy conservation is monitored on each timestep using the cosmic energy equation (24). Typically, energy is conserved to within a few percent as the model evolves into the nonlinear regime. Energy ceases to be conserved when dense clumps shrink within a cubical zone; structures on scales smaller than a zone are not resolved.

IV. OPTIMIZING THE COMPUTER CODE

When large 3-D problems are run on a computer, careful attention must be paid to efficiency. There are two components to this efficiency: memory usage and calculational speed. Moreover, these two components are related and depend on the type of computer used. In our case, initial code development and some preliminary runs were done on a DEC-20; production runs with higher resolution were done on a Cray-1. In this section we describe the memory and speed considerations that led us to use the Cray and the steps we followed to take advantage of its vector processing capabilities.

The most severe problem for 3-D calculations is memory overflow. The particle simulations described here require a minimum of about $2N^3$ words of computer memory, where N is the number of grid zones along one edge of the computational box. This requirement is based on keeping both the density and gravitational potential arrays in central memory to allow vectorization, as described below. Adequate resolution of the structures which form during a calculation requires a minimum of N=32, with N=64 needed for runs which allow a more detailed study of the structures. These grid sizes translate into minimum central memory requirements of about 7×10^4 and 6×10^5 words, respectively. Of course, additional memory is needed for particle positions and velocities.

Such memory requirements make the relatively slower DEC-20 or VAX computers, which contain large virtual memories, a better choice than faster computers such as the Cyber 175/750 which have much smaller memories. However, these smaller computers are really very slow. In fact, our optimized code runs about 100 times faster on a Cray with two million words of central memory than it does on a VAX. These considerations, plus the trend toward even larger supercomputer central memories (McMahon 1982), led us to choose supercomputers for our work.

Once memory constraints have been satisfied, attention is turned to computational speed. The basic rule for optimizing a computer code is to work first on that part of the code where the computer spends most of its time (Higbie 1978). Optimizing this time-consuming central portion of the code will produce the largest increase in speed. This is especially important for vector processors like the Cray in which the increase in the speed of a code is a rapidly increasing function of the percent of the code vectorized (LeBlanc, this volume; Rodrigue, Giroux, and Pratt 1980).

Particle-mesh calculations like the CIC method described here break naturally into two parts: the particle-pusher and the Poisson solver. As its name implies, the particle-pusher updates the coordinates and velocities of the particles using the equations of motion (25) and (26). It includes the computation of the force on each particle and the updating of the density when the particles are moved. The Poisson solver computes the potential from equation (18). Since the particle-pusher is the most time-consuming part of the code, we can best increase the speed of the code by optimizing the particle-pusher first. Once this has been done we can turn attention to the Poisson solver.

In a particle-mesh method particles move through a grid under the action of the fields. This basic feature leads to two distinct levels of subscripting of variables in the code. The particles themselves are identified by the particle label I. The Ith particle is located at position $(X(I), Y(I), Z(I))$ and has velocity $(VX(I), VY(I), VZ(I))$. The particle subscript runs over $I = 1, 2 \ldots$ NTOT, where NTOT is the total number of particles in the simulation. The grid is labeled using a separate set of subscripts. A node on the grid is denoted (J, L, K) and grid quantities such as the density are subscripted DENS (J, L, K), where $J, L, K = 1, 2 \ldots N$. Calculating the density over the grid for a distribution of particles or pushing a particle using the forces requires a mapping between the particle labels and the grid subscripts. This is accomplished by finding the zones (J, L, K) corresponding to the Ith particle at $(X(I), Y(I), Z(I))$. As will be shown below, this mapping poses special problems for vectorization.

As noted above, supercomputers are vector processors (Levine 1982). For our purposes we consider a vector to be an array of data stored in the memory of a computer with a fixed increment in storage location between its successive elements. A vector processor then is a computer with a set of instructions which operate on vectors. Vector processors are well-suited to scientific computation; in fact, many equations in physics are usually written in vector form. On a scalar computer such equations must be converted to scalar form by programming them as DO loops in FORTRAN. The vector statement of the problem is not only simpler but, when the vector instructions are executed directly, is also much more efficient because a single vector instruction replaces a loop of scalar instructions (Higbie 1983).

There are three distinct ways of producing efficient vector coding. The simplest and most attractive is to have the compiler automatically vectorize the FORTRAN code. As compilers improve, it is possible to rely more on them to do the job automatically (Higbie 1978). However, there are typically a few operations that are common in the code but that are not yet automatically recognized as vector operations by the compiler. In these cases special vector syntax can be substituted into the program. Finally, there are some operations which are outside the scope of the particular computer's hardware vector instruction set. In these cases some efficient coding can still be achieved by using special vector functions written in machine language (Levesque 1982). In the CIC calculation described here, all three methods of vectorization were employed.

Since the particle-pusher is the most time-consuming part of our CIC code, accounting for about 75% of all the operations performed, we first began work to vectorize it. The Cray FORTRAN compiler (CFT) automatically vectorized the basic particle-pushing operations, e.g.

$$X(I) = X(I) + TSN * VX(I) \quad , \tag{27}$$

and similarly for Y and Z, where TSN is the timestep. That is, CFT recognized equation (27) as a vector operation over the subscript I and performed it using vector instructions.

The periodic boundary conditions required the substitution of special vector syntax. For example, consider the statement

$$IF \ (X(I) \ .LT. \ SBOUND) \ \ X(I) = X(I) + N \quad . \tag{28}$$

This expression checks to see if the x-coordinate of particle (I) is below the lower bound of the computational box and, if it is, puts the particle back into the box from the other side. CFT does not recognize this as a vector operation, and the presence of statements such as this which contain "IF" will inhibit vectorization of the entire DO loop in which they occur (Higbie 1978). We could simply place the boundary conditions in a separate unvectorized loop, allowing the basic particle-pushing operation (27) to be vectorized. However, we can do better than that by substituting the vector merge operation

$$X(I) = CVMGM(X(I) + N, \ X(I), \ X(I) - SBOUND) \tag{29}$$

for operation (28). The built-in function F = CVMGM(A,B,C) is defined to be

$$F = A \qquad\qquad if \ C < 0 \tag{30a}$$

and

$$F = B \qquad\qquad otherwise \tag{30b}$$

(CFT manual 1978). Similar functions are defined for C > 0 and C = 0. The boundary conditions in the form of statement (29) are now recognized as vector operations.

After vectorizing the basic operations such as (27) and (29) we found that the particle-pusher was still doing most of its operations in scalar mode. This is because the calculations of the density on the mesh and the force on any particle require that we compute the subscripts of certain arrays. Such computed subscripts are not supported directly by the hardware vector instruction set on the Cray (Higbie 1978). To optimize this part of the code we therefore used STACKLIBE (McMahon 1983a), which is a library of vector operations for the Cray implemented in optimal machine code. The vector functions in STACKLIBE can be called directly in FORTRAN programs and complement the vector operations implemented in hardware.

One example of a situation in which a STACKLIBE subroutine dramatically improved the speed of the code is in the calculation of the force on a particle. The force is the volume-weighted sum of the forces in the cells the particle overlaps; each partial force is calculated from the gradients of the potential. This procedure involves computing the appropriate subscripts in the potential array and "gathering" these values of the potential for each particle. This "gather" operation is not vectorizable either automatically or by the substitution of vector syntax on the Cray-1. However, it can be accomplished by calling the STACKLIBE subroutine QVTILS.

This routine QVTILS performs an operation called "transmit index list" (McMahon 1983a). An index list array IL is first filled with the subscripts of the zones in the potential array which the particle overlaps. QVTILS is then given IL, the potential array A from which the values are to be gathered, and an array B in which they are to be stored. The subroutine is then simply called in the FORTRAN program:

$$\text{CALL} \quad \text{QVTILS(B, IL, A, NI)}. \tag{31}$$

Schematically,

$$B(M) = A(IL(M)). \tag{32}$$

where M = 1, 2, ... NI (McMahon 1983a). The power of this method can be seen from the fact that we can take NI = 8NTOT; in other words, we can "gather" the

contributions from each of the 8 zones involved for all NTOT particles. The
force components are then calculated by taking the gradients of the potential
using the values stored in arrays such as B.

Another case in which computed array subscripts cause standard vectorization
techniques to fail is in the calculation of the density from the distribution of
particles on the mesh. Once the position of a particle has been updated using
operations (27) and (29), we then update the density in the eight cells it overlaps using the volume-weighting method described in Section III. The particle
position arrays are subscripted by particle label, whereas the density array DENS
is subscripted by zones on the mesh. Therefore, to update the density due to the
contribution of any particle we must calculate the subscripts of the zones which
it overlaps using its position on the mesh. In standard FORTRAN this becomes

$$
\begin{aligned}
&DENS(J,L,K) = DENS(J,L,K) + VOL1 \\
&DENS(J,L,KO) = DENS(J,L,KO) + VOL2 \\
&DENS(JO,L,K) = ...
\end{aligned}
\tag{33}
$$

where (J,L,K) is the subscript of the zone in which the center of the cloud is
located. The cloud also overlaps neighboring zones such as (J,L,KO) where
KO = ± 1. The quantities VOL1, VOL2 ...VOL8 are the contributions to the eight
zones in question. Expression (33) must be calculated for each particle on each
cycle and is not vectorizable either automatically or by substitution of vector
syntax.

However, expression (33) can be replaced by calling the STACKLIBE subroutine
QVILAO once for all particle subscripts I:

$$
CALL\ QVILAO(DENS,IL,V,NI) \ .
\tag{34}
$$

Here the array IL contains the subscripts or "index list" of the eight zones to
be incremented for all particle subscripts I, the array V contains the partial
volumes VOL1, VOL2, etc. to be added to each of these zones, and NI = 8NTOT is
the dimension of the arrays IL and V. Schematically,

$$
DENS(IL(M)) = DENS(IL(M)) + V(M)
\tag{35}
$$

(McMahon 1983a). This operation is known as "index list accumulate" because an
array accumulates contributions in zones given by an index list of subscripts.

Note that the slots in the density array to be filled are in general not evenly spaced in memory since particles which were originally neighbors can move in different directions on the mesh at different speeds, depending on the gravitational field. This process cannot be vectorized using ordinary vector syntax on the Cray. The STACKLIBE routine QVILAO, however, is coded in machine language and makes optimal use of the existing hardware vector instruction set to do this operation efficiently.

Having thus optimized the particle-pusher, we turned our attention to the Poisson solver. As discussed in Section III, Poisson's equation is solved using FFT's. The FFT of a 3-D array is a triple sum over the three subscripts of the array. We transform each of these subscripts in turn, holding the other two constant. For each of these three 1-D Fourier transforms we use a Cray optimized library FFT subroutine. Since the Poisson solver transforms one mesh quantity, the density, into another, the potential, this part of the code was vectorized in a simple way.

The result of all this optimization is that the code ran three times as fast as it did in pure scalar mode (McMahon 1983b). Since the particle-pusher is dominated by operations involving computed subscripts, most of this speed increase is due to the use of STACKLIBE routines. Optimization of the code required about one month of work; given the speed increase achieved, it was a month well spent.

Two final remarks about memory constraints and optimization are in order. The memory requirements mentioned at the beginning of this section were based on the requirement that both the potential and density arrays, each having dimension N^3, remain in central memory while the particle-pusher is executing. This is necessary to take advantage of the STACKLIBE routines which need access to zones in these arrays unknown in advance. However, we do not require that the six position and velocity arrays reside wholly in central memory; we can break them into subsets or chunks. One set of chunks, and thus one group of particles, resides in central memory while it is being updated; the other ones are stored on disk. When the update is finished the chunks are written out to disk and the next set is read in. Since such input/output (I/O) operations are very slow, while the particle-pusher is very fast, we fit as many particles as possible into central memory and minimize disk access. For example, on a grid with N=64 and one particle per cell on average, we use two chunks on a Cray-1 with two million words of central memory. Such a simulation requires about 30 minutes of CPU time and 30 minutes of I/O time to run, not including the setup of the initial particle spectrum.

V.   RESULTS

Our program of simulating the development of structure in cosmological models
containing collisionless matter is now in the production stage. A computer code
has been written and optimized based on the considerations in the preceding sections; this code is now being used to run a set of models designed to determine
the effect of the type of initial perturbation spectrum and the density parameter
Ω_o on the structures which develop. In this section we present the results
of two such models and discuss qualitative comparisons between them. Further
details of these and other models, as well as quantitative comparisons among them
and with the observations, will be presented elsewhere (Bushouse, Centrella,
Gallagher and Melott 1984; Centrella, Melott and Shapiro 1984).

The two models presented here were both run with the density parameter
$\Omega_o = 1$; they differ in the initial input spectrum of density perturbations and
therefore in the type of dark matter they represent. The first model has an input
spectrum pertaining to hot dark matter such as massive neutrinos. This spectrum
has a cutoff at a wavelength corresponding to the scale of collisionless damping.
The model was run on a grid with N = 64, a cutoff wavelength chosen to be 16
zones, and NTOT = 2.6×10^5 particles or one particle per cell on average. The
second model features a Poisson initial spectrum with the particles placed at
random. Such a spectrum, with all wavelengths down to the grid scale present,
pertains to some kind of cold dark matter. This model was run on a grid with
N = 32 and NTOT = 8.8×10^5 particles or 27 particles per cell on average.
Both models were started after decoupling with an root mean square density
contrast (equation (7))of less than one percent, i.e., in the linear perturbation
regime. As the models evolve, different types of structures form as the density
contrast grows into the nonlinear regime.

The aim of this work is to compare the results of the models with observations of the universe. Therefore we must have criteria for recognizing the state
in the models that best corresponds to the present universe. For the neutrino
model we use the two-point correlation function (Peebles 1980). Observations
tell us that the two-point correlation function for galaxies has a power-law
form; the correlation function of the particles in the neutrino model also takes
a power-law form, with a time-dependent exponent. We thus stop the neutrino
model when the power law matches that given by the observations, and call that

state the present time (Centrella and Melott 1983; Klypin and Shandarin 1983; Shandarin 1983; Frenk, White and Davis 1983). The amplitude of the correlation function, when compared to that given by the observations, gives the spatial scale of the model; in this case, our computational box with N = 64 corresponds to about 100 Mpc. Life is not so simple for the Poisson model, since in this case the correlation function never matches the power law given by the observations (Efstathiou and Eastwood 1981). We therefore used velocity dispersion arguments (Bushouse, Centrella, Gallagher and Melott 1984), and in this case the box with N = 32 corresponds to about 30 Mpc.

Having thus decided on an appropriate "final state" for each model, we are now ready to begin comparing them with each other and with the observations. Figure 1 shows 3-D contour plots in comoving coordinates of the density contrast in the models in their final states. The contours have been drawn at the root mean square value of the density contrast in each model, i.e., the surfaces enclose regions in which the density contrast is greater than the root mean square value. Figure 1a shows the neutrino model, in which the dense regions are connected in a "Swiss cheese" structure. Note the large holes or voids. These structures are on scales of several tens of Mpc, which is in agreement with observations of the large-scale structure (deVaucouleurs 1981; Oort 1983; Kirshner, Oemler, Schechter, and Shectman 1983). In contrast, the Poisson model in Figure 1b shows no such large-scale connected structure and is dominated by clumps.

Figure 2 shows contour plots of these same two models where the contours have been drawn at twice the root mean square value to display the denser regions. The stringy character of the neutrino model is very apparent in Figure 2a. The dense regions, which correspond to rich clusters of galaxies, are filamentary and are again in line with the observations (Batuski and Burns 1984; Bahcall and Soneira 1983). In contrast, the Poisson model is even more strongly dominated by unconnected clumps at this level of density contrast.

Another method of displaying the structures present in these models is to plot the positions of the particles in a series of 2-D slices taken from the full 3-D models. This has been done in Figures 3 and 4 for the neutrino and Poisson models, respectively. A set of 4 slices from each model has been taken out of the grid, and the particles in each slice have been plotted. The slices are labeled by the third grid subscript K, where K = 1,2....64 for the neutrino model and K = 1,2...32 for the Poisson model. Each particle is marked by an "x" which has been scaled to be approximately the size of one grid zone in each model. For the neutrino model each particle in a slice has been plotted, whereas for the

a)

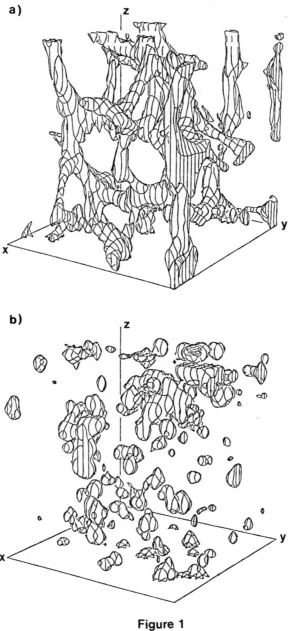

b)

Figure 1

Fig. 1. - The density contrast in the final state of the neutrino model (a) and of the Poisson model (b) is shown. The 3-D contours have been drawn at the root mean square value of the density contrast.

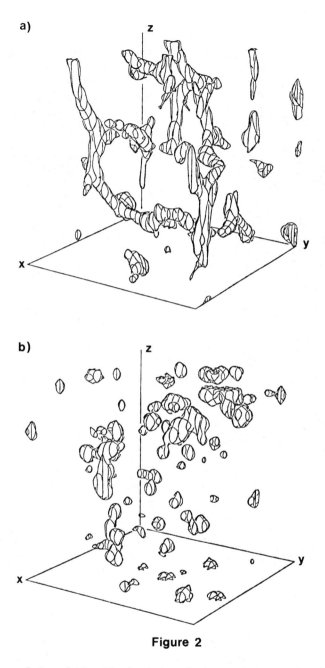

Figure 2

Fig. 2. - Contour plots of the final state of the neutrino model (a) and the of Poisson model (b) are shown. The contours have been drawn at twice the root mean square value of the density contrast.

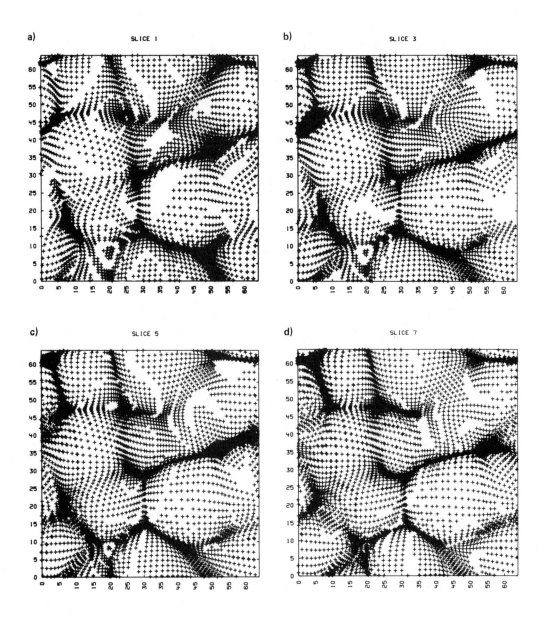

Fig. 3. - A set of four slices from the neutrino model is shown. All the
particles in each slice have been plotted.

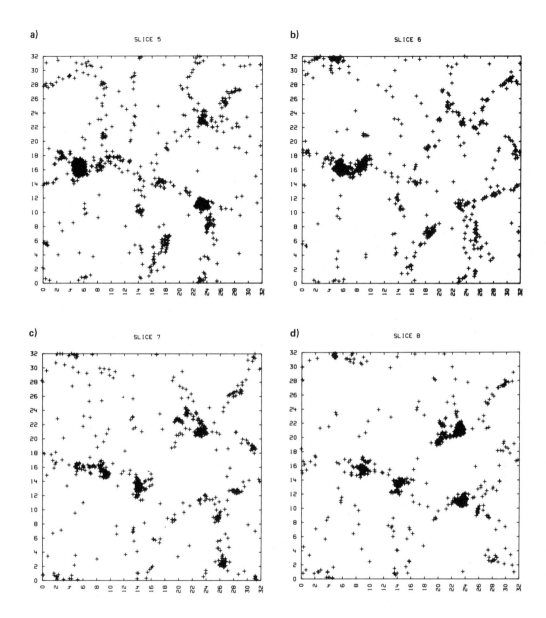

Fig. 4. - A set of four slices from the Poisson model is shown. Only one of every nine particles has been plotted.

Poisson model only one of every nine particles is shown.

Note the cellular structure in the neutrino model of Figure 3. The linear features across a slice are also present on neighboring slices over a large region; in three dimensions these structures are therefore actually flattened pancakes which intersect in even denser filaments. Such pancakes, with their relatively low density contrast, are difficult to see in 3-D contour plots. The Poisson model by comparison is dominated by dense clumps and shows no large scale filaments or pancakes.

Our qualitative conclusion is that the neutrino or hot dark matter model is better than the Poisson model in representing the major features of the observed large-scale structure. We note that the neutrino model has problems in producing galaxies themselves, because not enough of the matter in the model has collapsed to such high densities as to have been able to form galaxies. However, it may be naive to expect dark matter to account for all structures from superclusters down to individual galaxies; the galaxies may well have formed from some other process with dark matter accounting for their large-scale distribution (Rees 1982; Bushouse, Centrella, Gallagher, and Melott 1984). Or perhaps several different types of dark matter are present and account for different scales of structure (Schramm 1983). Our current work is aimed at understanding the constraints on such processes by evolving different types of input spectra and making quantitative comparisons with the observations (Bushouse, Centrella, Gallagher, and Melott 1984; Centrella, Melott, and Shapiro 1984).

We would like to thank Jim Wilson for many stimulating discussions throughout the course of this work. His indomitable stamina and questing spirit have been a continued source of inspiration and encouragement. This work would also not have been possible without the advice and instruction of Jim LeBlanc and Frank McMahon on the mysteries of supercomputers and without the generous support of Lawrence Livermore National Laboratory.

REFERENCES

Bahcall, N. A., and Soneira, R. M. 1983, Ap.J., **270**, 20.

Batuski, D. J., and Burns, J. O. 1984, M.N.R.A.S., submitted.

Bond, J. R., Centrella, J., Szalay, A. S., and Wilson, J. R. 1984a, in "The Proceedings of the 1983 Moriond Conference", ed. J. Audouze (Dordrecht: Reidel).

_____ 1984b, M.N.R.A.S., in press.

Bushouse, H., Centrella, J., Gallagher, J., and Melott, A. 1984, in preparation.

Centrella, J., and Melott, A. L. 1983, Nature, **305**, 196.

Centrella, J., Melott, A., and Shapiro, P. 1984, work in progress.

Cray-1 FORTRAN (CFT) Reference Manual 1978, Cray Research, Inc., #2240009, Rev. C.

Davis, M., and Huchra, J. 1982, Ap.J., **254**, 437.

de Vaucouleurs, G. 1981, Bull. Astr. Soc. Ind., **9**, 1.

Dicke, R., Peebles, P., Roll, P., and Wilkinson, D. 1965, Ap.J., **142**, 414.

Dimitriev, N. A., and Zel'dovich, Ya.B. 1964, Soviet Physics - J.E.T.P., **18**, 793.

Efstathiou, G., and Eastwood, J. W. 1981, M.N.R.A.S., **194**, 503.

Einasto, J., Joeveer, M., and Saar, E. 1980, M.N.R.A.S., **193**, 353.

Fixsen, S., Cheng, E., and Wilkinson, D. 1983, Phys. Rev. Lett., **50**, 620.

Ford, H. C., Harms, R. J., Ciardullo, R., and Bartko, F. 1981, Ap.J., **245**, L53.

Frenk, C. S., White, S., and Davis, M. 1983, Ap.J., **271**, 417.

Gorenstein, M., and Smoot, G. 1981, Ap.J., **244**, 361.

Higbie, L. 1978, "CRAYVECTOR: Speeding Up Fortran (CFT) Programs on the Cray-1",
    Cray Research, Inc., #2240207.

_____. 1983, Datamation, **29** (No. 8), 180.

Hockney, R. W., and Eastwood, J. W. 1981, "Computer Simulation Using Particles"
    (New York: McGraw - Hill).

Hubble, E. 1929, Proc. Nat. Acad. Sci. **15**, 169.

Irvine, W. M. 1961, Ph.D. Thesis, Harvard University.

Kirshner, R. P., Oemler, A., Schechter, P. L., and Shectman, S. A. 1983, in
    "Early Evolution of the Universe and its Present Structure" (IAU Symposium
    #104), ed. G. O. Abell and G. Chincarini (Dordrecht: Reidel).

Klypin, A. A., and Shandarin, S. F. 1983, M.N.R.A.S., **204**, 891.

Layzer, D. 1963, Ap.J., **138**, 174.

Levesque, J. M. 1982, Cray Channels, **4** (No. 2), 7.

Levine, R. D. 1982, Scientific American, **246**, 118.

Lubin, P., Epstein, G., and Smoot, G. 1983a, Bull. A.A.S., **28**, 30.

_____. 1983b, Phys. Rev. Lett., **50**, 616.

Matzner, R. A. 1984, P.A.S.P., **96**, 189.

McMahon, F. H. 1982, private communication.

_____. 1983a, "Stacklibe: Vector Function Library for the Cray-1" (Lawrence
    Livermore National Laboratory, UCID-30083).

_____. 1983b, private communication.

Melott, A. L. 1981, Ph.D. Thesis, University of Texas at Austin.

_____. 1983, Ap.J., **264**, 59.

Olive, K. A., Schramm, D. N., Steigman, G., Turner, M. S., and Yang, J. 1981, Ap.J.,**246**, 557.

Oort, J. H. 1983, Ann. Rev. Astr. Ap., **21**, 373.

Peebles, P. J. E. 1971, "Physical Cosmology" (Princeton: Princeton University Press).

_____. 1979, Astr. J., **84**, 730.

_____. 1980, "The Large Scale Structure of the Universe" (Princeton: Princeton University Press).

Penzias, A., and Wilson, R. 1965, Ap.J., **142**, 419.

Potter, D. 1973, "Computational Physics" (New York: Wiley).

Primack, J., and Blumenthal, G. 1984, in "Proceedings of the Fourth Workshop on Grand Unification", ed. P. Longacker, in press.

Rees, M. 1982, private communication.

Rodrigue, G., Giroux, E., and Pratt, M. 1980, Computer, **13** (No. 10), 65.

Schramm, D. N., and Steigman, G. 1981, Ap.J., **243**, 1.

Schramm, D. N. 1983, preprint (University of Chicago).

Shandarin, S. F. 1983, in "The Origin and Evolution of Galaxies", ed. B. J. T. Jones and J. E. Jones (Dordrecht: Reidel).

Shapiro, P. R., Struck-Marcell, C., and Melott, A. L. 1983, Ap.J., **275**, 413.

Shapiro, P. R. 1984, preprint (University of Texas at Austin).

Szalay, A. S., and Silk, J. 1983, Ap.J., **264**, L31.

Weinberg, S. 1972, "Gravitation and Cosmology" (New York: Wiley).

White, S., Frenk, C., and Davis, M. 1983, Ap.J., **274**, L1.

V. Supernovae

Introduction to the Physics of Supernovae

Gordon Baym
University of Illinois at Urbana-Champaign

ABSTRACT

This paper describes the basic physics governing the gravitational collapse of massive stars, the formation of a shock in the rebound of the collapsing core, and the mechanism of ejection of the stellar mantle and envelope by the shock to produce a supernova explosion, with creation of a neutron star.

It is a particular pleasure for me to give here a short overview of the physics of supernovae -- whose details will be filled out in the following talks -- because of the crucial role that Jim Wilson has played in its development. His beautiful and detailed numerical simulations of the gravitational collapse and rebound of massive stars has provided, over the years, much of the basis of our current knowledge of the mechanism of this fundamental phenomenon.[*]

The essential problem is to understand the final dynamical stages of massive single hot young stars, believed to be the progenitors of Type II supernovae, to see how they can form a neutron star in their cores while at the same time energetically ejecting the rest of their mass to produce a supernova remnant. The mass of the neutron star left behind, as indicated by timing measurements on binary

---

[*] A complete description of the physics and numerical techniques of the present collapse code as developed by Wilson and coworkers is given by Bowers and Wilson (1982) and is summarized by Bowers in his paper here.

x-ray sources, as well as the binary pulsar PSR 1913+16, is expected to be of order 1.4 $M_\odot$. The total energy ejected in the remnant is expected to be of order 10^{51} ergs, to explain observations in Type II remnants (reviewed in Trimble 1982) of: kinetic energy of expansion, at velocities $\lesssim 10^4$ km/sec, corresponding to energies $\sim 10^{50-51}$ erg/$M_\odot$; visible light $\sim 10^{49-50}$ erg over one year; and cosmic and x-rays, possibly of order 10^{50} erg. We shall focus on seeing the extent to which one can understand the basic aspects of such super-novae in terms of the evolution of a centrally symmetric non-rotating star, with magnetic effects neglected, and mass ejection caused by an outward-moving shock wave, formed in the collapse. The shock ejec-tion mechanism, although a distance away from being a definitive success in calculations thus far, appears nonetheless to be the most promising as well as appealing candidate to explain Type II supernova explosions.

Stars of mass greater than the Chandrasekhar mass $M_{Ch} = 5.76 \, Y_e$ $M_\odot^2 = 1.4 \, M_\odot$ (for Y_e = mean number of electrons per nucleon in the matter = 1/2) cannot simply settle down to become stable cold ob-jects, but rather must do something interesting in their evolution. Single stars of initial mass below $\sim 8 \, M_\odot$ are expected, during their evolution, to lose enough mass to end up below M_{Ch}. On the other hand, stars more massive must have violent fates, either undergoing a supernova explosion or collapsing entirely into a black hole.

Massive stars evolve hydrostatically to become red supergiants with iron cores supported by electron degeneracy pressure. The suc-cess of the shock mechanism for mass ejection (on rapid 0.01 - 0.1 s time scales) depends sensitively, as the papers here discuss, on the structure of the pre-supernova core -- its temperature, density, com-position, and total mass -- as well as on the structure of the region outside the core. As emphasized by Bludman and Lichtenstadt's in their paper (see also Arnett 1982) these quantities are in turn sen-sitive to electron capture processes, and accompanying neutrino cooling, during hydrostatic evolution. Recent improved estimates of electron capture rates by Fuller, Fowler and Newman (1982), which generally are more rapid for the nuclei present before collapse (and slower during infall) than previously assumed, are currently being employed in recalculating pre-supernova stellar models; results for

stars of 20 and 25 $M_\odot$ are described in detail in the accompanying
paper by Weaver, Woosley and Fuller. They find, at an early moment
in the collapse when the central density is 1×10^{10} g cm^{-3}, that Y_e
in the center is ~ 0.42, rising with increasing radius (and generally
~ 0.02 lower than in the earlier Weaver, Zimmerman and Woosley (1978)
models). The initial core entropies s_i are remarkably low, ~ 0.7
units per nucleon in the center, comparable to that in air at room
temperature. The corresponding central temperature is $\sim 8 \times 10^9$ °K
or 0.7 MeV. As a consequence of the increased neutrino cooling the
entropy is significantly lower than the values $s_i \sim 1.2$ found earlier
by Weaver et al. (1978) and ~ 0.9 by Arnett (1977). The smaller Y_e
and s_i lead to smaller degenerate core masses, $\sim 1.35-1.4$ $M_\odot$, than
previously found.

Once the core exhausts its nuclear fuel it undergoes further
contraction and heating, which causes partial dissociation of the
core nuclei, e.g.,

$$^{56}Fe \rightarrow 13\alpha + 4n, \qquad \alpha \rightarrow 2p + 2n. \qquad (1)$$

The energy required for dissociation is taken from the kinetic energy
of the electrons, which reduces their support pressure, and initiates
dynamical collapse; in other words, the effective electron "cooling"
caused by dissociation reduces the Chandrasekhar mass, for the Y_e
present, to below that of the core. Once collapse begins, electron
captures, e.g.,

$$e^- + {}^{56}Ni \rightarrow {}^{56}Co + \nu_e, \qquad e^- + {}^{56}Co \rightarrow {}^{56}Fe + \nu_e , \qquad (2)$$

further reduce the electron support against gravity, and the effec-
tive adiabatic index $\Gamma = (\partial \ln P / \partial \ln \rho)_s$ (where P is the pressure, ρ the
density and s the entropy per nucleon) of the core material falls
below the minimum value 4/3 for which stable configurations exist;
inexorable collapse ensues.

Neutrinos, produced by electron capture, play a very remarkable
role in the physics of collapse. In the neutrino mass ejection
mechanism initially proposed by Colgate and White (1966), neutrinos
flowing out of the core were expected to transmit enough momentum to

the outer layers to reverse their infall and cause explosion. Neutrino capture by neutrons and neutrino-electron scattering are too
weak, however, to make this process work. With the advent of neutral
weak currents, Freedman (1974) pointed out that the electron capture
neutrinos, of relatively low energy ($\lesssim$ 10 MeV) and hence long wavelengths ($\gtrsim$ 20 fm), would scatter coherently from nuclei (cross-
section proportional to number of nucleons squared) and hence very
effectively transfer their outward momentum to the nuclei. The
problem is that this process is too effective for it to produce mass
ejection; the neutrinos produced in the core scatter so much there
that they never reach the outer layers on collapse timescales.
Rather they become trapped in the core. For a Weinberg angle given
by $\sin^2\theta_W$ = 1/4, close to the experimental value 0.23, coherent
scattering of neutrinos by nuclei takes place only on neutrons, not
protons, and, as derived by Lamb and Pethick (1976), the mean free
path for elastic scattering of a neutrino of energy ε_ν assumes the
simple form:

$$\lambda_\nu = \frac{10 \text{ km}}{\left(\frac{\varepsilon_\nu}{10 \text{MeV}}\right)^2 \rho_{12} \left(\frac{N^2}{6A} x_h + x_n + \frac{5}{6} x_p\right)} , \qquad (3)$$

where ρ_{12} is the mass density in units of 10^{12} g cm^{-3}, N is the mean
neutron number and A the mass number of the heavy nuclei (assumed to
have spin 0), and x_h, x_n and x_p are the mass fractions of heavy
nuclei, free neutrons and free protons. Neutrino trapping sets in
when the density rises to about 10^{12} g cm^{-3}, for then $\lambda_\nu \gtrsim$ 1 km,
which is small compared with the core radius $\sim$ 80 km. The neutrinos
once trapped soon become degenerate, filling Fermi seas.

One immediate consequence of neutrino trapping is that the Pauli
principle inhibits further electron capture processes, since all
available neutrino states (below the neutrino Fermi energy) are
essentially occupied. Because electron capture is the principal
source of entropy generation during infall, the entropy remains low,
with $\sim$ 0.2 units per nucleon produced in the collapse. To a good
approximation the collapse can be treated as adiabatic. Small capture also implies that the electron fraction Y_e remains high, falling
by only $\sim$ 0.07 in the collapse. At such low entropy and high Y_e the

matter remains primarily in the form of heavy nuclei, since large not overly neutron-rich nuclei have a sufficiently large density of excited states to absorb their share of the entropy without appreciable dissociation (Bethe et al. 1979). As described by the Lamb, Lattimer, Pethick and Ravenhall (1981) equation of state, discussed in the accompanying paper by Pethick and Ravenhall, the nuclei become heavier with increasing matter density, while the fraction of free nucleons, primarily neutrons, falls.

The pressure of the matter in the core during this phase of collapse arises primarily from the relativistic electrons and neutrinos, and so P on adiabats with low s has a dependence close to $\rho^{4/3}$; the free nucleons and nuclei contribute negligibly to the pressure. [Because Y_e decreases somewhat with density, the adiabatic index is, in fact, $\sim 0.01\text{-}0.03$ smaller than 4/3.]

This simple form of the equation of state produces an enormous simplification of the collapse dynamics. A typical view of the infall velocity u in the core as a function of radius r is shown in Figure 1 (Arnett 1977), together with the local sound speed in the matter. The absence of a length scale in the equation of state (for $\Gamma=4/3$)

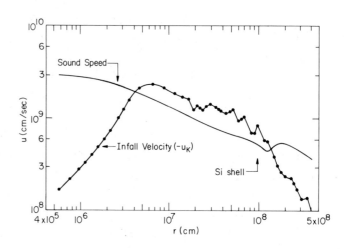

Fig. 1 – Magnitude of infall velocity and sound speed as functions of radius during, core collapse.

implies that the core collapses homologously, $u \propto r$, over the region that remains in pressure communication with itself, i.e., where the infall velocity is subsonic (in Fig. 1 for $r \lesssim 40$ km). Beyond the "sonic" point, where the infall speed equals the local sound speed, the infall is supersonic and resembles a quasi-free fall, under a reduced effective gravity, with $u \sim r^{-1/2}$.

Dynamical scaling solutions for the infall for $\Gamma = 4/3$ were first given by Goldreich and Weber (1980); extensions of these solutions to $\Gamma < 4/3$ (and $> 6/5$) by Yahil (1983) encompasses very clearly the separation of the iron core into homologously collapsing and quasi-free fall regions, as first found in detailed computer simulations of the collapse (Wilson 1980, Arnett 1977). The mass of the homologous core lies in the range $1.04\ M_{Ch} < M_{hc} < 1.25\ M_{Ch}$ for $4/3 > \Gamma > 1.30$, where M_{Ch}, the Chandrasekhar mass for the core material (the mass that would have zero binding energy) is essentially of the form (Burrows and Lattimer 1983)

$$M_{Ch} \sim 0.8\ \left(\frac{Y_L}{0.4}\right)^2\ M_\odot\ ,\tag{4}$$

where Y_L is the electron fraction at the time of neutrino trapping; typically $M_{hc} \sim 0.8\text{-}0.9\ M_\odot$.

Collapse continues until the nuclei begin to crush together to form a nuclear matter core, as the central density rises above nuclear matter density $\rho_o \sim 2.8 \times 10^{14}\ g\ cm^{-3}$. Because nuclear matter is substantially stiffer (initially $\Gamma \sim 2.5$) than the nuclei plus lepton system, outwardly propagating pressure waves are generated by the nuclei banging together, and the homologous infall is disrupted. Actually, the matter in undergoing the transition from nuclei to nuclear matter liquid passes through an unusual "bubble" phase, around $\rho_o/2 < \rho < \rho_o$, containing roughly spherical bubbles of low density nuclear vapor in otherwise uniform nuclear matter (Ravenhall, Pethick and Wilson 1983; Lamb et al. 1983). The transition through the bubble region, which is described more fully in the paper by Pethick and Ravenhall, smooths out the otherwise abrupt change in the compressibility of the matter at ρ_o.

The pressure signal from the center travels outward in space until it reaches the sonic point at the edge of the homologous core. Because beyond the sonic point the "sound cones" tilt inward (as do the light cones inside the event horizon of a black hole), the pressure disturbance can travel no further, and builds up just inside the sonic point soon forming a discontinuity. This is the start of the shock. Figure 2, a plot of radial velocity versus radius at several successive times, from Wilson's renowned "Munich" calculation (1980),

illustrates clearly how the shock
is formed at the sonic point. The
curve labelled 0 is at the last
moment that the inner core collapses homologously; we see here
the homologous and the quasi-free
fall regions. The sonic point in
this calculation is at 28 km. In
curve I, 0.37 ms later, a discontinuity is beginning to form at
the sonic point, and in curve II,
0.86 ms after curve 0, we see a
fully formed discontinuity there;
the inner material is now moving
outward, while the outer material
still rains in rapidly. During
the shock formation the relatively
slow motion of the sonic point in

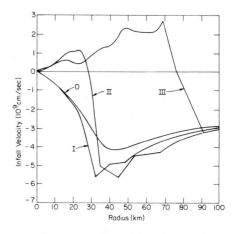

Fig. 2 - Radial velocity vs. radius at several successive moments after core bounce.

space can be neglected. The inner core material transfers its
kinetic energy on a ms timescale, through "PdV work," to the shock
(Brown, Bethe and Baym 1982), and the inner core comes into hydrostatic equilibrium, eventually becoming self-bound; in curve III,
1.81 ms after curve 0, we see the decided deceleration of the inner
core, and also the outward propagation of the shock to ~ 76 km. [The
core motion damping is shown in detail in Cooperstein's paper.]

     It is important to note that the shock forms at the outer edge
of the homologous core. Consequently the bulk of the homologous core
material never undergoes shock heating and acceleration, and the core
becomes gravitationally bound. This means that the gravitational
collapse leaves a condensed remnant. The crucial question is whether
enough energy can be transferred to the outer layers to expel them,
or whether the entire star collapses to a black hole.

     One can estimate the energy put into the shock by noting that
the material that forms the hydrostatic core has essentially zero
energy per unit mass (with respect to dispersed iron nuclei) before
collapse. To a good approximation, the energy transferred to the
shock initially is simply the binding energy B of the hydrostatic

core, neglecting heating near its surface occurring in the formation
of the shock (Yahil and Lattimer 1982; J. Lattimer, private communication). For an equation of state with $P \propto (Y_L \rho)^{4/3}$ below ρ_0, the
energy of a core with central density not too much above ρ_0 scales as
$Y_L^{10/3}$; as Yahil and Lattimer estimate,

$$B \sim 8 \left(\frac{Y_L}{0.4}\right)^{10/3} \times 10^{51} \text{ erg,} \qquad (5)$$

in good agreement with shock energies $\lesssim 10^{52}$ erg seen in computer
simulations (Brown et al. 1982). Initially the shock energy is more
than ample to produce a good explosion; the crucial question is how
the shock degrades on the way out.

While additional material falling through the shock provides it
with further energy, neutrino radiation and nuclear dissociation tend
to dissipate the shock. The neutrinos trapped behind the shock front
contribute pressure to drive the shock; however, as the shock propagates to larger radii the mean free paths for these neutrinos to
escape through the unshocked material increase, and by a certain
radius, r_ν, the "neutrino-sphere," the neutrinos behind the shock
become able to leave freely. Typically $r_\nu \sim 80$ km. Further losses
occur from neutrino pair creation behind the shock, as well as neutrinos produced in electron captures. The total loss of shock energy
by neutrino emission is, however, bounded, since the temperature
behind the shock falls with increasing shock radius; an estimate by
Bethe, Applegate and Brown (1980) indicates that the loss in neutrinos increases from 0.5 to 6×10^{51} erg for initial shock energy
increasing from 3 to 10×10^{51} erg. Neutrino losses alone appear not
to knock the shock out of commission.

More serious is the further loss of immediately useful shock
energy caused by dissociation of nuclei as they pass through the
shock front and are heated to post-shock temperatures ~ 7 MeV. Dissociation of heavy infalling nuclei requires ~ 8 MeV energy per
nucleon, which translates into a rather large 1.5×10^{51} erg per
tenth of a solar mass. Although the total loss from nuclear dissociation is self-limited -- cooled post-shock material can no longer
dissociate -- the shock cannot tolerate dissociating more than a few

tenths of a solar mass before it becomes too weak to cause an explosion on rapid time scales. Instructive is the example given in
Cooperstein's paper of a briskly propagating shock which stalls and
is last seen as a standing accretion shock.

Let us put aside for the moment the question of the conditions
needed for the shock to be successful, and look at mass ejection by
an outwardly propagating shock. Material in passing through the
shock receives an outward acceleration (Brown et al., 1982)

$$\Delta u \sim \left(\frac{3}{2\pi} \frac{\Gamma-1}{\Gamma+1} \frac{E_s}{\rho(r_s)r_s^3} \right)^{1/2} \tag{6}$$

where Γ is the adiabatic index behind the shock, E_s is the total
shock energy, r_s is the shock radius and $\rho(r_s)$ the unshocked density
there. Taking conditions appropriate to $r_s \sim 10^3$ km, with $\rho \sim r^{-3}$,
one finds $\Delta u \sim 1.7 \times 10^9 (E_s/10^{51} \text{ erg})^{1/2}$ cm s^{-1}, independent of r_s.
When the post-shock velocity exceeds the escape velocity of the
matter (if we neglect other acceleration effects),

$$v_{esc} = \left(\frac{2GM(r_s)}{r_s} \right)^{1/2} \simeq 1.6 \times 10^9 \left(\frac{M(r_s)}{M_\odot} \right)^{1/2} / \left(\frac{r_s}{10^3 \text{ km}} \right)^{1/2} \text{ cm s}^{-1} , \tag{7}$$

the matter is ejected. The total rest mass of matter left behind
falls with increasing shock energy, and ranges from $\sim 1.5 - 1.6$ M$_\odot$
for final E_s ranging from $4 - 2 \times 10^{51}$ erg (Brown et al. 1982). The
condensed remnants are produced with $Y_e \sim 0.3 - 0.4$; electron captures with neutrino emission turn these remnants into highly bound
neutron stars on a one second time scale. With general relativistic
gravitational binding effects included, the masses of the neutron
stars created in the supernova are ~ 1.4 M$_\odot$, a quite satisfactory
result.

What then does it take to have a successful shock? The larger
the lepton fraction Y_L is at trapping, the more effective will be the
shock (Burrows and Lattimer 1983), for not only is the mass of the
homologous core $\propto Y_L^2$ [see eq. (4)] then larger, reducing the amount
of material in the iron core that the shock must pass through before
causing ejection, but the initial shock energy, $\propto Y_L^{10/3}$ [eq. (5)], is

increased strongly. Higher final entropies s_f after electron capture
in collapse also help to increase the core mass as well as its final
binding energy, through increase in the Chandrasekhar mass (eq. 4).
The key to having large Y_L is to have a low entropy s_i before collapse, since the cooler the initial configuration the fewer the electron captures that take place during collapse. Use of more accurate
capture rates (Fuller et al. 1982) during collapse also increases Y_L
above older estimates. Although smaller s_i leads to smaller s_f, the
increase in shock energy and core mass from the larger Y_L it produces
by far outweighs the loss of benefit from larger s_f. Lower s_i also
has the effect of reducing the mass of the initial degenerate iron
core, through decrease of the support pressure of the matter, again
reducing the amount of material to be dissociated before the shock
reaches the more diffuse matter outside the core.

Understanding the facets of pre-supernova evolution that affect
the shock propagation is one of the principal concerns of the accompanying papers. As shown by Weaver et al., fuller inclusion of electron capture processes in pre-supernova evolution significantly
decreases the entropy and electron fraction and hence the iron core
mass at the start of the collapse. The influence of the initial
entropy on the final shock dynamics is discussed in detail by Cooperstein, as well as Bludman and Lichtenstadt, who work out models to
show the importance for the success of the shock mechanism of
smaller, cooler initial iron cores, and suppression of electron
captures in the collapse.

The prompt shock ejection mechanism may turn out to be inadequate to explain supernovae. But on the other hand it makes use of
only a small fraction of the total energy, $\sim 10^{53}$ erg, released in
gravitational collapse. Because of neutrino trapping only $\sim 10\%$ of
the total energy released becomes available to the shock on short
time scales. The remaining 90% is released as the core slowly neu-
tronizes, and the question is how such energy could be utilized to
generate an explosion. Fortunately, we have Jim Wilson still working
on the problem; carrying out collapse simulations for far longer
times (0.5 - 0.8 s) than previously done, as described in his paper,
he finds that for a certain period neutrinos from the core produce a
net heating behind the shock. This heating has the effect of

starting up an otherwise stalled shock, after ~ 0.5 s, which goes on to cause an explosion. While the explosions Wilson presently finds are weaker that expected for Type II, neutrino-driven late time shocks could well be the crucial mechanism of successful Type II supernovae.

This research has been supported in part by NSF Grant DMR81-17182.

REFERENCES

Arnett, W. D. 1977, Ap. J., **218**, 815.

Arnett, W. D. 1982, Ap. J., **263**, 55.

Bethe, H. A., Brown, G. E., Applegate, J., and Lattimer, J. M. 1979, Nucl. Phys., **A324**, 487.

Bethe, H. A., Applegate, J., and Brown, G. E. 1980, Ap. J., **241**, 343.

Bowers, R. L., and Wilson, J. R. 1982, Ap. J. Suppl., **50**, 115.

Brown, G. E., Bethe, H. A., and Baym, G. 1982, Nucl. Phys., **A375**, 481.

Burrows, A., and Lattimer, J. M. 1983, Ap. J., **270**, 735.

Colgate, S. A., and White, R. H. 1966, Ap. J., **143**, 626.

Freedman, D. Z. 1974, Phys. Rev., **D9**, 1389.

Fuller, G. M., Fowler, W. A., and Newman, M. 1982, Ap. J. Suppl., **48**, 279.

Goldreich, P., and Weber, S. 1980, Ap. J., **238**, 991.

Lamb, D. Q., and Pethick, C. J. 1976, Ap. J. Lett., **209**, L77.

Lamb, D. Q., Lattimer, J. M., Pethick, C. J., and Ravenhall, D. G. 1981, Nucl. Phys., **A360**, 459.

Lamb, D. Q., Lattimer, J. M., Pethick, C. J. and Ravenhall, D. G. 1983, Nucl. Phys. **A411**, 449.

Ravenhall, D. G., Pethick, C. J., and Wilson, J. R. 1983, Phys. Rev. Lett., **50**, 2066.

Trimble, V. 1982, Rev. Mod. Phys., **54**, 1183.

Weaver, T. A., Zimmerman, G. D., and Woosley, S. E. 1978, Ap. J., **225**, 1021.

Wilson, J. R. 1980, Proc. N. Y. Acad. Sci., **336**, 358.

Yahil, A. 1983, Ap. J., **265**, 1047.

Yahil, A., and Lattimer, J. M. 1982, in "Supernovae: A Survey of
    Current Research," ed. M. J. Rees and R. J. Stoneham
    (Amsterdam: Reidel), p. 53.

Electron Capture and the Final Evolution of Massive Stars

Thomas A. Weaver
Lawrence Livermore National Laboratory

S. E. Woosley
University of California, Santa Cruz

Lawrence Livermore National Laboratory

G. M. Fuller
University of Chicago

Lawrence Livermore National Laboratory

ABSTRACT

The final evolution of 20 and 25 $M_\odot$ stars is presented. The inclusion of accurate electron capture rates during all stages of nuclear burning from core oxygen burning onwards, more stringent time step and zoning criteria, and a new series of reactions for burning silicon that has already become partly neutronized all result in iron core masses and central entropies at collapse that are considerably decreased from our previous calculations.

I. INTRODUCTION

In an earlier paper (Weaver, Zimmerman, and Woosley 1978; hence WZW) we presented the complete evolutionary histories of 15 $M_\odot$ and 25 $M_\odot$ stars. These stars end their lives as red supergiants with cores of neutronized heavy elements that collapse owing to the photodisintegration instability (Fowler and Hoyle 1964). Unfortunately, subsequent calculations of these models through core collapse and bounce (eg. Bowers and Wilson 1982) have failed to yield outwardly propagating shock waves with strength adequate to eject the overlying mantle and envelope and produce an optical supernova display. This dismal state persists even though simulated explosions in these stars (Weaver and Woosley 1980) produce light curves in excellent accord with those observed in Type II supernovae and nucleosynthesis that bears striking similarity to solar abundances. A number of authors (eg. Hillebrandt 1982a; Arnett 1982; Woosley and Weaver 1982a) have called attention to the fact that explosion would be favored by a smaller iron core mass at the time of collapse. Then if the "homologous" core mass (i.e., that region that stays in sound communication throughout the collapse and bounce) does not vary greatly, the work that must be done by the shock in photodisintegrating and reversing the momentum of infalling material is substantially reduced. A smaller initial entropy also favors explosion. Lower entropy means that less energy is stored in nuclear excited states as the collapse proceeds, so that the inner core can collapse to higher density and generate a stronger bounce and reflected shock wave (Bethe 1983). Lower entropy also implies a smaller abundance of free protons, hence less electron capture and a higher value of Y_e at bounce. This makes the homologous core mass larger, again giving the shock greater energy as well as less matter to photodisintegrate (Burrows and Lattimer 1983). It is noteworthy that Hillebrandt (1982b) gets an energetic explosion in a 10 $M_\odot$ star (Weaver and Woosley 1979; Woosley, Weaver, and Taam 1980) using the same physics that failed to produce supernovae in our larger models. The chief differences are the smaller core mass ($\sim$ 1.40 $M_\odot$) and lower entropy per baryon (central value $\sim$ 0.85 with an inversion to $\sim$ 0.65 at $\sim$ 0.5 $M_\odot$).

In this paper we present results from an improved numerical study of the complete evolution of 20 $M_\odot$ and 25 $M_\odot$ stars. A recalculation of a 15 $M_\odot$ star is also currently underway and will be reported elsewhere. We find core masses and entropies that are substantially smaller than in our earlier models (WZW). Core masses of 1.41 $M_\odot$ and 1.35 $M_\odot$; central entropies per baryon of 0.69 and 0.73; and electron mole numbers, $Y_e = \Sigma X_i Z_i / A_i$, of 0.422 and 0.423 respectively are found for the 20 and 25 $M_\odot$ stars. Both entropy and Y_e have substantial radial gradients.

II.   IMPROVEMENTS IN PHYSICS

Unless otherwise specified the physics employed in this series
of calculations is the same as described in WZW. Major
improvements centered on a more realistic treatment of nuclear
physics, especially electron capture, although there were also
important modifications to time step and zoning criteria. A total
of 300 mass shells was carried throughout the final stages of
evolution although automatic and continuous mass rezoning and the
parasitizing of outer, slowly evolving surface zones gave in effect
a much finer zoning than this might indicate. At the time of
collapse, for example, the inner 1.5 $M_\odot$ of the 25 $M_\odot$ star
contained 72 zones. More stringent time step criteria were also
employed. Roughly twice as many models were generated in the
present study as compared to WZW. In the 25 $M_\odot$ study more than
8,500 models were generated between core oxygen depletion and the
onset of iron core collapse.

As was first pointed out by Woosley, Arnett, and Clayton
(1972), substantial electron capture may already begin to occur
during the oxygen burning stage of the evolution of a massive
star. The captures occur on relatively rare species, ^{31}P, ^{33}S,
^{35}Cl, and ^{37}Ar (and, to a lesser extent, on abundant species
like ^{32}S and ^{36}Ar), that have small endoergic Q-valves for
electron capture, Woosely et al. found, for example, that core
oxygen burning at "balanced power" (neutrino emission balancing
nuclear energy generation) gave, for temperatures below 1.8 billion
degrees and densities greater than 5 x 10^6g cm^{-3}, Y_e less
than 0.49 at oxygen depletion. Later, Woosely and Weaver (1982b)
studied isotopic nucleosynthesis in their 25 $M_\odot$ model using a 135
isotope network and weak interaction rates from Hansen (1966) and
Mazurek (1973). They found the captures occurring during shell
oxygen burning, i.e., during that time between oxygen core
depletion and silicon ignition, to be even more important. The
distribution of Y_e with mass for the inner 2 $M_\odot$ resulting from
that earlier study is shown in Figure 1 at times corresponding to
oxygen ignition, oxygen core depletion (X_{16} = 0.01), and silicon
ignition. Since the isotopic nucleosynthesis was calculated by

"post-processing" a stellar evolutionary calculation that employed a much smaller network (see WZW) and did not include electron capture prior to silicon ignition, the results obtained in Figure 1 are not entirely self-consistent. Such large changes in Y_e can be expected to alter the stellar structure prior to silicon ignition. Therefore a proper structure calculation must include the effects of electron capture at least from the time of oxygen depletion onwards.

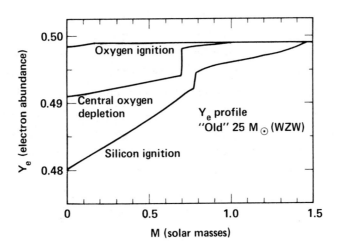

Fig. 1.-The distribution of electron mole number, Y_e, is shown for the inner 1.5 $M_\odot$ of the 25 $M_\odot$ model of WZW at three times as indicated. Adapted from Woosley and Weaver (1982b).

In order to do so, we modified the quasiequilibrium network employed in our earlier study (WZW) so as to function at much lower temperatures. The group of isotopes from magnesium to nickel was subdivided into two large quasiequilibrium clusters, one including isotopes up to scandium, the other all heavier nuclei. These two clusters were separated by non-equilibrium link at ^{46}Ti which was allowed to bring the two disparate clusters into equilibrum on a time scale $t_{qe} = 1.8 \times 10^{-20}$ exp(176.3/T_9) s (Woosley, Arnett, and Clayton 1973) where T_9 is temperature in billions of degrees. Such a prescription enables the program to calculate approximately the abundances of important rare isotopes such as ^{33}S, ^{35}Cl, and ^{37}Ar even for the low temperatures that exist in the core following oxygen depletion ($T_9 \sim 2.0$). The transition to this cluster equilibrium network was made when the oxygen abundance in the given zone had declined below 1%. The small amount of remaining oxygen was not discarded but was coupled by the oxygen burning reaction into the network. The transition between networks (see WZW for a full description of the 19 isotope network employed at lower temperatures) was made smoothly and no anomaly in the nuclear energy generation rate was experienced.

Also very important to the revised calculations was the choice of weak interaction rates. Fuller, Fowler, and Newman (1982ab) have recently published tabulations of rates in which discrete nuclear resonances are included where known and the Gamow-Teller streangth properly accounted for. These rates, in addition to being generally more reliable and accurate than past estimates, are also usually considerably faster, a factor of 5 increase over the rates of Mazurek (1973), for example, being typical. Rates from Fuller et al. were employed for all isotopes included in the cluster equilibrium network (Table 1). The effect of the accelerated rates as well as the capture at early times is to give a smaller value of Y_e at each point in the late evolution.

TABLE 1

Isotopes Included in Quasi-equilibrium Network

Element	A Range	Element	A Range	Element	A Range
n	1	Al	26-28	Sc	43-49
H	1-3	Si	28-30	Ti	44-52
He	3-5	P	30-33	V	47-54
Li	5	S	31-34	Cr	48-56
C	12	Cl	35-37	Mn	51-58
O	16	Ar	36-40	Fe	52-62
Ne	20	K	39-43	Co	54-64
Na	23	Ca	40-44	Ni	56-66
Mg	24-26		46-48	Zn	60

Owing to the substantial decrease of Y_e prior to silicon ignition, the composition that eventually burns is not one overwhelmingly dominated by ^{28}Si. Instead we find, at the time of silicon ignition in the core, comparable amounts of ^{28}Si and ^{30}Si. This has two consequences. First, because of the general increase in the abundance of all neutron-rich isotopes, the species ^{25}Mg and ^{26}Mg exist in sufficient quantities to offer an alternate means of burning silicon. Traditionally it has been assumed (Bodansky, Clayton, and Fowler 1968) that the rate of silicon burning will be determined by the reaction $^{24}Mg(\gamma,\alpha)^{20}Ne$ which bridges the gap between the quasiequilibrium group and lighter species that can be stripped into α-particles by the photon bath. We find here that the reactions $^{24}Mg(n,\alpha)^{21}Ne$, $^{25}Mg(n,\alpha)^{22}Ne$, and especially, $^{26}Mg(p,\alpha)^{23}Na$ compete favorably with photodisintegration. In fact, for typical conditions at the center of the star, roughly 5 times more flow passes though the neutron-rich isotopes than through ^{24}Mg. Second, owing to the larger binding energy per nucleon of the more neutron-rich isotopes, the abundance of free α-particles is reduced. Since the abundance of magnesium isotopes relative to those of silicon is inversely proportional to this α-particle abundance, the concentration of these "bottleneck" nuclei is raised correspondingly. Both these modifications are difficult to calculate without the use of a large quasiequilibrium network (such as the one we employ), since they depend upon accurate knowledge of the α-particle and nucleonic abundances and not just upon the temperature as in the case of photodisintegration reactions. Combined, they have the effect of accelerating the rate of silicon burning at a given temperature by roughly an order of magnitude. As a result, silicon burns at a slightly lower temperature than would have been calculated using the traditional algorithm.

Other minor modifications to the physics of WZW include the use of a Cameron (1973) set of initial Population I abundances (WZW used Cox and Steward 1970ab); the ability of the code to back up and take smaller time steps when an unacceptably large change in abundance occurs during any step in any zone; and an improved

treatment of nuclear screening corrections. WZW used screening
corrections from Graboske et al. (1973) and did not screen
photodisintegration reactions. Here we employ the prescription of
Alastuey and Jancovici (1978) as formulated by Wallace, Woosley and
Weaver (1982) for strong screening, Graboske et al. (1973) for weak
screening, and an average for intermediate cases (see Wallace,
Woosley and Weaver 1982). We also screen both forward and reverse
reactions symmetrically.

III.   RESULTS OF THE CALCULATIONS

Initial models for 20 and 25 $M_\odot$ stars were generated by
allowing dense clouds of solar (Cameron 1973) composition to relax
and commence nuclear burning. The evolution of both stars through
successive stages of hydrogen, helium, carbon, and neon burning
transpired in a manner very similar to our previous calculations
(WZW for the 25 $M_\odot$ star; the 20 $M_\odot$ star was previously
unpublished). Details will be published elsewhere. Important
evolutionary modifications were noted from the point of central
oxygen depletion onwards. One interesting change, brought about by
the inclusion of electron capture at these earlier times, is the
existence of a new "burning stage" powered by the energy liberated
as a quasiequilibrium distribution centered about α-particle
nuclei is transformed into a more tightly bound distribution of
neutron-rich nuclei. A portion of this energy is, of course, lost
to neutrinos, but since the captures, for the most part, proceed to
excited states, considerable energy may be deposited locally. The
binding energies of ^{28}Si and ^{30}Si, for example, are 8.448 MeV
and 8.521 MeV per nucleon respectively. The difference corresponds
to 7.0×10^{16} erg g^{-1}, somewhat less considering the fact that
the silicon is only partly neutronized. When liberated on a
timescale of several months this implies an energy generation rate
of $\sim 10^9 - 10^{10}$ erg g^{-1} s^{-1}, which aids in supporting the

star during this period of preliminary neutronization and keeps its entropy from decreasing quite as much as it might have. A second, rather obvious modification is the shrinking of the core mass in response to the diminished Y_e. At equivalent stages, eg. silicon core ignition, the new models have higher values of central density and less mass enclosed by the oxygen burning shell. However, the final iron core mass is not set simply by scaling the effective Chandrasekhar mass for the modified Y_e. Rather the core mass is determined by a more complicated interplay of convective burning shells and entropy gradients.

At the time of core silicon depletion (i.e., $X_c(Si) = 0.001$) the mass interior to the oxygen burning shell is 1.08 $M_\odot$. The value of Y_e is close to 0.46 throughout this "core" while the electron degeneracy parameter ((Fermi energy - $m_e c^2$)/kT) ranges from 2.87 to 2.33 and the entropy from 1.38 to 1.44. The mass fraction of silicon at the outer edge of this 1.08 $M_\odot$ is 0.013. Even if the core were totally degenerate, and it is not, the Chandrasekhar mass for this value of Y_e is still $\sim$ 1.22 $M_\odot$. Obviously the core is far from collapse at this point. It does contract, however, and the accompanying heating first depletes the small residual silicon abundance in the core, then burns out the oxygen shell to about 1.37 $M_\odot$. At this time the remaining oxygen begins to burn in a convective shell extending from 1.37 $M_\odot$ to 1.68 $M_\odot$. The location of this oxygen burning shell is critical, as it sets up the entropy profile that will subsequently determine the extent of the silicon burning shell and, therefore, of the final collapsing iron core. Unfortunately this mass cannot be estimated from simple first principles since it depends upon the thermodynamic structure of the star established by previous burning stages. The entropy within the convective oxygen shell is, of course, nearly constant. Moving from the inside of the star out, however, one experiences a sharp increase in entropy, from about 2.0 at 1.3 $M_\odot$ to 2.7 at 1.35 $M_\odot$ to 3.25 in the convective shell itself (values are sampled at a time when the oxygen abundance within the convective shell is almost depleted).

As evolution and contraction continue, oxygen is exhausted in the convective shell and burning and convection cease. Further contraction, however, leads to the ignition of a silicon convective shell burning in the region 1.06 $M_\odot$ to 1.35 $M_\odot$. At a time when the mass fraction in this convective shell is 0.39 (roughly half burned) the entropy within this shell is 2.0. The mass interior to the silicon shell has become quite degenerate, (Fermi energy $-m_e c^2$) ranging from roughly 7 kT at the center to 4 at 0.65 $M_\odot$, but within and around the silicon shell the degeneracy is not so great. Typically the Fermi energy is only 1 to 2 times kT. The star therefore does not collapse until the silicon convective shell has burned out. At that time the core mass, as determined by discontinuous changes in entropy, density, and composition, is 1.35 $M_\odot$. The presupernova model is summarized in Figures 2 through 5 which give the state of the star at that time when the collapse velocity first reaches 1000 km s^{-1} in any zone.

This work has been supported by the National Science Foundation (AST-81-08509) and the Department of Energy (W-7405-ENG-48) at the Lawrence Livermore National Laboratory.

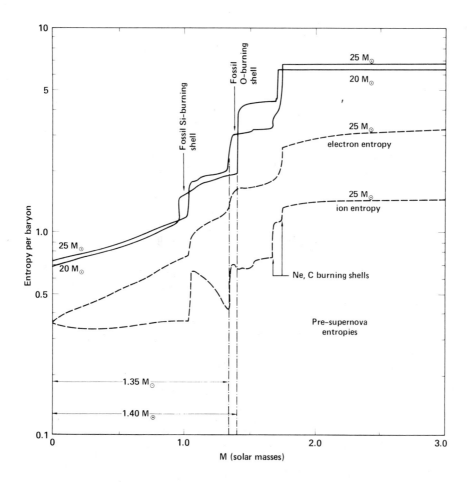

Fig. 2. - The distribution of dimensionless entropy is given for the inner 3 $M_\odot$ of the 20 $M_\odot$ and 25 $M_\odot$ (solid lines). The dashed lines show the partial contributions in the 25 $M_\odot$ model from ions and electrons. A smaller contribution, included in the total but not plotted separately, comes from the radiation field. Not included in this graph (nor in the numbers given in the text) is a small contribution from entropy stored in nuclear excited states. Excited states were included in the calculation but their entropy was not edited. Arrows at sudden increases in total entropy indicate the location of what were, until fuel was exhausted, the bases of convective oxygen and silicon burning shells. Carbon and neon burning shells are still active. The entropy is sampled at a time when the collapse velocity first reaches 1000 km s^{-1} (the most rapidly collapsing zones are those located at the edge of the iron core).

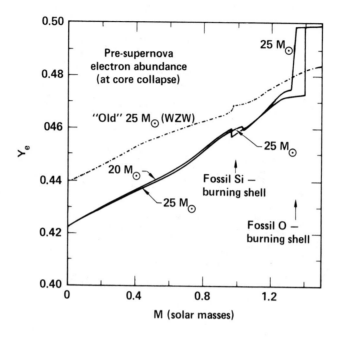

Fig. 3 - The distribution of electron mole number, Y_e, with mass is shown for the inner 1.5 $M_\odot$ of the new 20 and 25 $M_\odot$ models (solid curves) and compared to the distribution obtained by WZW (broken line). The locations of (now exhausted) oxygen and silicon burning shells are indicated. Snapshot is at the same time defined in Fig. 2.

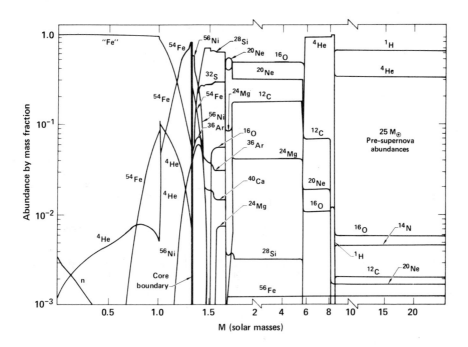

Fig. 4. - Composition by mass fraction is given for the 25 $M_\odot$ model. The dark line at 1.35 $M_\odot$ bounds the collapsing core and may be the locus of mass bifurcation following core bounce. "Implosive" silicon burning is in progress in the region 1.35 $M_\odot$ to 1.40 $M_\odot$ and has already produced some ^{56}Ni. The abundance of carbon in the carbon burning convective shell ($X_C = 0.17$) is significantly larger than obtained by WZW, presumably owing to a more careful treatment of convection and zoning in the current model. Note scale breaks at 2 $M_\odot$ and 10 $M_\odot$. Sampling time is as in Fig. 2.

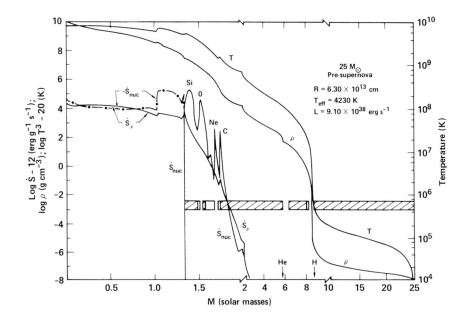

Fig. 5. - Thermodynamic conditions and energy generation at the time of core collapse are given for the new 25 M$_\odot$ model. Quantities are plotted logarithmically with the indicated scale factors. Temperature may be read either T^3 (left scale) or T (right scale). In regions where density is proportional to T^3 the curves for ρ and T are parallel. The central density at this time is 7.90 x 10^9 g cm^{-3} and the central temperature 7.84 x 10^9 K. Exterior to the collapsing core (1.35 M$_\odot$) nuclear energy is positive and is plotted as a solid line. Active burning shells are apparent and are labelled with the appropriate fuel (hydrogen and helium burning shells are off-scale). Neutrino losses are inherently negative and are always indicated by a solid line. Within the core, nuclear energy is being absorbed by photodisintegration leading to a negative energy generation (dash-dot line). Owing to the higher density and faster capture rates of Fuller, Fowler, and Newman (1982ab) electron capture is of comparable importance to photodisintegration in initiiating the collapse (unlike WZW where photodisintegration grossly dominated). Stellare surface conditions also indicated as are convective (cross-hatched), semiconvective (open block), and radiative (open space) stellar zones. Note scale breaks at 2 M$_\odot$ and 10 M$_\odot$. Sampling time is as in Fig. 2.

REFERENCES

Alastuey, A., and Jancovici, B. 1978, Ap. J., 226, 1034.

Arnett, W. D. 1982, Ap. J. Lettr., 263, L55.

Bethe, H. C. 1983, private communication.

Bodansky, D., Clayton, D. D., and Fowler, W. A. 1968,
    Ap. J. Suppl., 16, 299.

Bowers, R. L., and Wilson, J. R. 1982, Ap. J., 263, 366.

Burrows, A., and Lattimer, J. 1983, preprint; see also
    Bull. AAS, 14, 937.

Cameron, A. G. W. 1973, Space Sci. Rev., 15, 121.

Cox, A. N., and Stewart, J. N. 1970a, Ap. J. Suppl., 19, 243.

_____. 1970b, Ap. J. Suppl., 19, 261.

Fowler, W. A., and Hoyle, F. 1964, Ap. J. Suppl., 9, 201.

Fuller, G. M., Fowler, W. A., and Newman M. 1982a,
    Ap. J. Suppl., 48, 279.

_____. 1982b, Ap. J., 252, 715.

Graboske, H. C., DeWitt, H. E., Grossman, A. S., and Cooper, M. S.
    1973, Ap. J., 181, 457.

Hansen, C. J. 1966, PhD Thesis, Yale University.

Hillebrandt, W. 1982a, in Supernovae: A Survey of Current Research,
    ed. M. J. Rees and R. J. Stoneham (Dordrecht: D. Reidel).

_____. 1982b, Astron. and Ap., 110, L3.

Mazurek, T. 1973, PhD Thesis, Yeshiva University.

Wallace, R. K. Woosley, S. E., and Weaver, T. A. 1982,
    Ap. J., 258, 696.

Weaver, T. A., Zimmerman, G. B., and Woosley, S. E. 1978,
    Ap. J., 225, 1021 (WZW).

Weaver, T. A., and Woosley, S. E. 1979, Bull. AAS., 11, 724.

_____. 1980, Ann. N. Y. Acad. Sci., 336, 335.

Woosley, S. E., Arnett, W. D., and Clayton, D. D. 1972,
    Ap. J., 175, 731.

_____. 1973, Ap. J. Suppl., 231, 26.

Woosley, S. E., Weaver, T. A., and Taam, R. E. 1980,
    in Type I Supernovae, ed. J. C. Wheeler (Austin: University of
    Texas Press), p. 96; and Ap. J., in preparation.

Woosley, S. E., and Weaver, T. A. 1982a, in Supernovae:
    A Survey of Current Research, ed. M. J. Rees and R. J. Stoneham
    (Dordrecht: D. Reidel), p. 79.

_____. 1982b, in Essays on Nuclear Astrophysics, ed. C. A.
    Barnes, D. D. Clayton, and D. N. Schramm (Cambridge:
    Cambridge University Press), p. 377.

Supernova Explosions: Entropy and the Equation of State[*]

J. Cooperstein and G. E. Brown
State University of New York, Stony Brook

ABSTRACT

The influence of the equation of state of hot dense matter on Type II supernova explosions is examined. Numerical simulations of collapse indicate a high sensitivity
to the entropy of the initial pre-collapse model. If
$S \gtrsim 1$, the energy available to the shock wave is decreased because of heat going into the thermal excitation of large nuclei in the inner unshocked core. This
heat energy is not useful for the shock, because it does
not produce any pressure. For successful explosions on
short time scales (within a few milliseconds after the
bounce of the inner core), an entropy $S < 1$ is desirable.

I. INTRODUCTION

Type II supernovae have long been thought to be linked to the
gravitational collapse and subsequent explosion of large stars
(Burbidge, Burbidge, Fowler, and Hoyle 1957). However, theoretical
calculations of the process are inherently complex and include
fluid dynamics, radiative transport by neutrinos, and the equation
of state of hot dense matter. Each of these is rich in physics
and difficult when considered by itself. Together, their coupling
is highly nonlinear. Several talks at this meeting have focussed on
the highly detailed (and sometimes elegant) methods that have been
used to tackle each of these, utilizing the power of the large computers. Jim Wilson has made contributions in all of these areas.
The calculations reported here use some simplifications and do not
attempt to include all the ingredients of these detailed calculations.

The main features of the supernova progenitor have been well
established (Weaver, Zimmerman, and Woosley 1978, WZW; Arnett 1977).
Surrounded by onion-skin shells of lighter elements, a central region

*Supported in part by USDOE under Contract No. DE-AC02-76 ER 13001.

of about 1.5 M , roughly the Chandrasekhar mass, evolves to the end
point of nuclear burning, with the ashes being the iron peak nuclei.
This innermost core evolves on a millisecond dynamical time scale.
Thus it decouples from the more slowly evolving overlying mantle,
permitting separate investigation of the central region. Photodisintegration of nuclei initiates the collapse, using up thermal energy
of the electrons, thereby decreasing the pressure. The implosion is
reversed only when the innermost region achieves supranuclear densities.
Then a sudden stiffening of the equation of state halts implosion and
launches a hydrodynamical shock wave (Bethe, Brown, Applegate, and
Lattimer 1979, BBAL). The shock wave proceeds outward and eventually
is required to provide the energetic input that ejects the overlying
mantle, thereby powering the fiery display of Type II supernovae.

Such a scenario seems clear enough. Yet numerical simulations
by many workers have not achieved explosions that eject matter, when
the input physics has been considered as most realistic. The two
principal villains have been the energetic price the shock pays in
dissociating heavy nuclei and in furnishing escaping neutrinos.

This report will comment principally on the role of the equation
of state. In particular, a low entropy ($S < 1$) seems essential for
the homologously collapsing inner core to produce ejection of matter
through a fluid-dynamical shock wave in the first few milliseconds
after bounce. For longer time scales it has been suggested that
neutrinos radiated from the inner core and nuclear recombination can
help promote mass ejections; this possibility is not considered here.
See the contributions of Jim Wilson and Richard Bowers elsewhere in
this volume.)

The numerical calculations reported here were carried out at
Brookhaven National Laboratory on the CDC 7600. They all fail to
eject mass. A variety of initial models has been examined, but we
concentrate on one particular calculation. This uses for input the
WZW 15 M star, which has an inner iron core of $\sim$ 1.5 M . The fluid
dynamics is explicit, energy conservative, and Lagrangian, and
employs pseudoviscosity to represent shocks. The innermost 1.6 M
is divided into 115 zones, with 12 zones per 0.1 M through the
region of shock formation and propagation. Neither general
relativistic effects nor rotation has been included.

Figures 1 and 2 show the evolution of the radius and density with
time for selected mass elements. The shock forms at about 0.875 M
and a radius of 13 km. Within a few milliseconds it stalls and becomes an accretion shock.

Neutrino transport is treated quite minimally. On short time
scales neutrinos lower the odds for a successful explosion. First,
their escape during the infall epoch reduces the size of the homologous core by lowering the effective Chandrasekhar mass. This
directly increases the amount of mass the shock needs to dissociate
(at a cost of about 1.5×10^{51} ergs for each 0.1 M). Second, the
neutrinos simply drain energy away even before the bounce. As a
simplification, we adopt the use of a trapping density below which
neutrinos are assumed to escape freely, and above which they are
completely trapped. The trapping density is chosen to be 3.3×10^{11} gm/
cm^3, the value being determined by comparison with earlier calculations performed using more elaborate transport schemes (Mazurek,
Cooperstein, and Kahana 1980; Cooperstein 1982). Such a simple
scheme will tend to underestimate the neutrino losses. Because investigations in which neutrino losses are turned off after bounce
have indicated dissociation losses alone can be sufficient to kill
the shock (Mazurek, Cooperstein, and Kahana 1981; Hillebrandt 1981),
such simplification permits a focus on the other problems. Full
transport calculations can be done upon their successful resolution.

II. THE IMPORTANCE OF ENTROPY

The collapse of the inner core is almost adiabatic; only when
neutrinos escape at low densities will heat be exchanged with other
regions (BBAL). However, the motion will not be entirely isentropic,
because it takes some time for the weak interaction processes to come
to equilibrium. In general the collapse will modify the entropy
through only three mechanisms:

First, during the free escape era the neutrinos produced extract
heat. If the electron capture proceeds on free protons (as in the
calculations reported here), the entropy is decreased. This is because the free protons converted to neutrons have to be replaced from
the nuclei, and this uses up energy. The process is similar to the
cooling of the skin by evaporation of water. (Capture on heavy nuclei

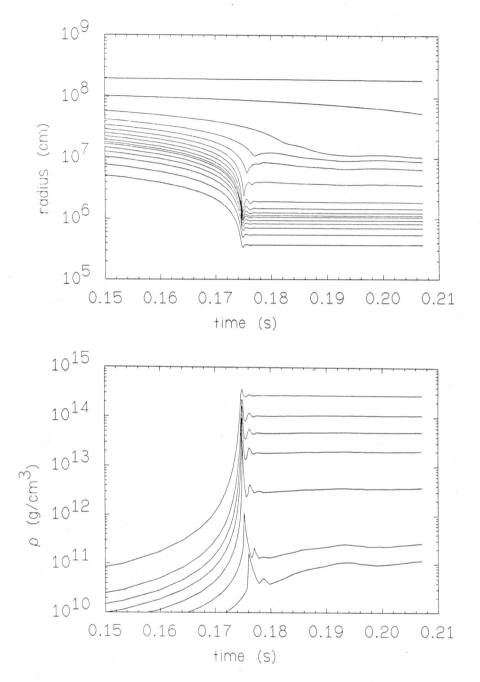

Figures 1 and 2. - The radius and density of Lagrangian mass
elements are given as a function of time from the beginning of the
collapse phase. Each line represents 0.1 M , and most zones have
not been displayed.

tends to increase the entropy, since the neutrinos escaping will be less energetic as heat goes into the thermal excitation of large nuclei.) Second, after the neutrinos are trapped, the approach to beta equilibrium will produce entropy as the "out-of-whackness" in the chemical potentials is converted into heat (BBAL), according to

$$TdS = -(\mu_e - \mu_{\nu_e} - (\mu_n - \mu_p)) \ dY_e = -(\mu_e - \mu_{\nu_e} - \hat{\mu}) \ dY_e \qquad (1)$$

where Y_e is the fractional proton charge. Note that at low entropies (or temperatures) this effect produces more entropy than at high entropies. Thus, even with a low initial entropy, some entropy increase is unavoidable. Finally we note that numerical errors and thermodynamical inconsistencies can alter the entropy. Except as may result from these three considerations, entropy generation does not occur until the inner core bounces, generating a shock. Thus the entropy is an important "constant" of the motion.

Figure 3 displays the initial entropy profile and that after the inner core has bounced and expanded to its hydrostatic configuration. The entropy has deviated only slightly from its initial value in the innermost regions, with the slight increase coming from the adjustment to beta equilibrium after trapping. In the region from 0.6 M to 0.87 M there is some increase in entropy due to the details of the shock formation (as well as some "pseudoviscous spillage").

Whereas the entropy of the inner core is determined by its history, the way in which this entropy is divided up among the nuclei, leptons and drip particles depends on the equation of state. Each of these contributes to the pressure and the internal energy density of the core in a distinct manner, as we now discuss.

III. EQUATION OF STATE

The equation of state must cover a broad range of density, composition, and temperature. Fortuitously, near nuclear matter density, where the nuclei begin to fill up all of space, the matter remains unshocked. This is because the shock forms, not at the center of the stellar core, but near the edge of the inner core (more precisely, at the mass point which has the highest infall velocity, which becomes the sonic point where pressure waves radiating from the

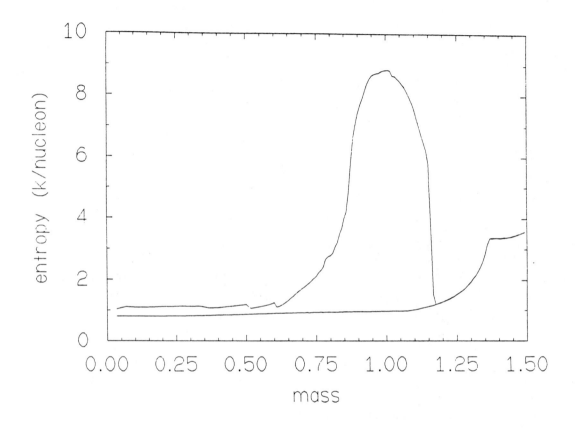

Figure 3. - The initial and post-shock entropic profiles are given, the latter at the point where the inner core has become hydrostatic and the shock is becoming an accretion shock. The entropy in the inner core has risen slightly from its initial value due to neutrino equilibration following trapping.

center accumulate and launch the shock.)

Thus we will not need to consider $S \gtrsim 2$ for $\rho \gtrsim 5 \times 10^{13} \mathrm{gm/cm^3}$. The equation of state in this region of densities has been included in a simplified fashion, easily adapted to numerical hydrodynamics, in a recent paper (Bethe, Brown, Cooperstein, and Wilson 1983, BBCW). The BBCW equation of state is used in these calculations, together with a straightforward extension to subnuclear regimes and arbitrary entropy as reported in detail elsewhere (Cooperstein 1982). The main features of BBCW are as follows:

First, for low entropies (and high densities) the protons prefer to reside within the large nuclei because $\hat{\mu}$, the neutron-proton chemical potential difference, is large. Thus we need only consider a mixture of free neutrons and heavy nuclei.

Second, because the nuclei become rather large ($A \sim 1000$), translational effects in the nuclear free energy can be neglected.

Third, the nuclear entropy is that of the bulk plus a surface entropy which will disappear (with the surface disappearing) as the system approaches the nuclear matter phase. The surface contributions can be taken into account by an effective mass which decreases with increasing density, as given by BBCW:

$$m^*/m - 1 = 10.67 \ (1-Y_e)^{4/3} \ Y_e^{\ 2} (1 - \frac{3}{2} u^{1/3} + \frac{1}{2} u) \qquad (2)$$

where u is the fraction of the total volume occupied by nuclei.

Fourth, the phase transitions, from nuclei to the bubble phase, discussed by Chris Pethick elsewhere in this volume, and from there to nuclear matter, can be handled in a simplified interpolative fasion. Such an approximation is roughly equivalent to making a Maxwell construction, and demonstrates easily the rapid increase in the pressure at the nuclear matter transition. Figures 4 and 5 (taken from BBCW) give the pressure per nucleon and the temperature as calculated by this procedure. The temperature in the nuclear matter phase is lower below nuclear matter density because the entropy is enhanced by the "loosening up" of the nuclei. This demonstrates the value of considering the entropy as the important quantity, rather than the temperature.

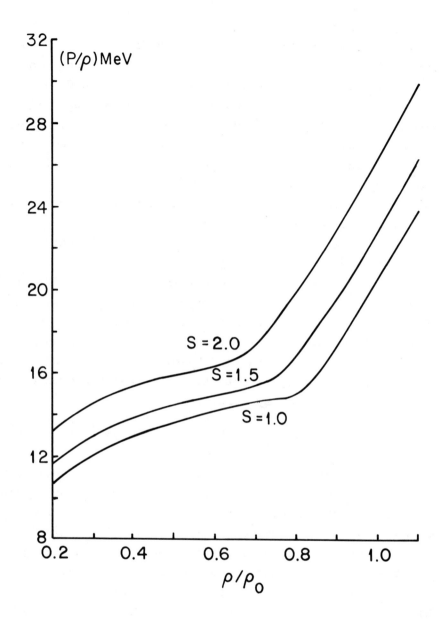

Figure 4.- Pressures per nucleon are given along the isentropes
S = 1.0, 1.5, and 2.0. The rapid increase in the pressure is due
to the phase transition to nuclear matter, which occurs at lower
densities at higher entropies. The nuclear matter density ρ_0 is
taken to be 0.145 fm^{-3}. (Taken from BBCW.)

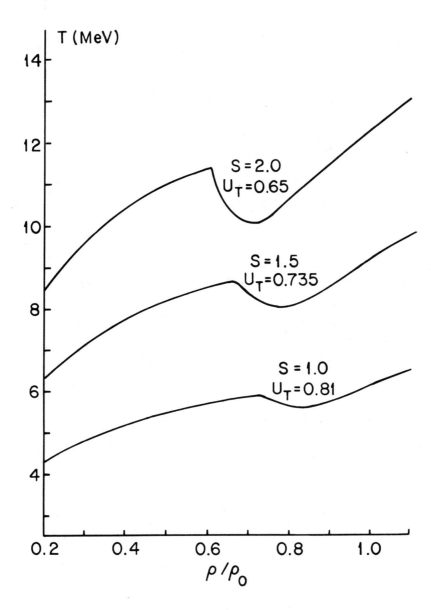

Figure 5.- Temperatures along the isentropes S = 1.0, 1.5, and 2.0 are given near the transition to nuclear matter. U_t is the density (relative to nuclear matter) of the transition at each entropy. The temperature is seen to decrease in the nuclear matter phase. (Taken from BBCW.)

Finally, one notes that the electrons are extremely relativistic. Thus the leptonic equation of state has an elementary form.

One important simplification accompanies the recognition that because the nuclei are so large, the neutrons inside the nucleus will behave as if they are in nuclear matter. One can then introduce the approximations

$$\mu_n = -2 - \frac{\pi^2 T^2}{12 \, \varepsilon_F} \text{ MeV} ,\tag{3}$$

where $\varepsilon_F = 37$ MeV. Here the -2 gives the correct binding energy for neutrons in nuclear matter at $Y_e \sim 0.30$ (BBAL), and the second term is the usual finite temperature correction for a degenerate Fermi gas. Since μ_n should be identical in the drip vapor and heavy nucleus phases, so that no chemical instabilities arise from the transfer of a neutron across the nuclear surface, this equation also yields the properties of the drip neutrons. As a result, one sidesteps the self-consistent solution of the thermodynamic constraint that X_d, the amount of drip, be chosen so as to minimize the free energy. Abandonment of this requirement introduces minor thermodynamic inconsistencies but permits the use of a noniterative, computationally easy, analytical equation of state.

Entropy will reside in nuclei, free neutrons, and leptons:

$$S_{nuc} = (1-X_\alpha) \left(\frac{\pi^2 T}{2 \varepsilon_F} \frac{m^\star}{m} \right) ,\tag{4a}$$

$$S_{drip} = X_d \left(\frac{5}{2} - \mu_n/T \right) ,\tag{4b}$$

$$S_{lept} = \pi^2 T \left(Y_e/\mu_e + Y_{\nu_e}/\mu_{\nu_e} \right) .\tag{4c}$$

The effective mass factor $m^\star/m$ is given in equation (2) and is near unity in the region near nuclear density.

The entropy in free nucleons and leptons contributes thermal pressure; the entropy in nuclei does not. The latter goes into internal degrees of freedom through the population of excited states. The drip entropy per neutron is quite large, typically about 3. Thus, the nuclei soak up most of the entropy and there is little neutron drip.

IV. EFFECT ON THE SHOCK

As emphasized by Yahil and Lattimer (1981), the supernova process is primarily one of energy transfer, from the innermost core·to the external regions. The inner core rebounds and then relaxes, quickly becoming hydrostatic. Figure 6, tracing the velocity evolution of various mass elements, shows this quick damping of the core motion.

A net decrease in the energy of the inner core (an increase in the binding energy) is needed to provide energetic input for the shock. Thus, if the post-shock hydrostatic innermost core is not tightly enough bound, the shock cannot succeed in ejecting the envelope on short time scales (but how much is "enough" is debatable; see Burrows and Lattimer 1983; Brown, Bethe, and Baym 1982; and Burrows, Yahil and Lattimer 1984). At any rate, at least several times 10^{51} ergs of binding energy would be required if the shock is to have a chance to eject the mantle. The inner (hydrostatic) core of the model reported here has about zero energy and the shock does not propagate into the overlying mantle.

The thermal excitation energy per nucleon of the large nuclei is given by

$$E_{th} = \frac{1}{2} TS_{nuc} = 4S_{nuc}^2 \, \text{MeV/particle}$$

$$= 8 \times 10^{51} \, S_{nuc}^2 \, \text{erg/M} \qquad (5)$$

(as first shown to us by Hans Bethe). For a core mass of 0.875 M and a change in S_{nuc} from 1.0 to 10.5, about 8×10^{51} ergs can thus be deposited in thermal excitation.

This energy is associated with the internal degrees of freedom of the nuclei, so it cannot provide pressure for the shock. Equivalently, one notes that a lower entropy core will provide the same pressure and interface with the external regions as a higher entropy core. Hence the binding energy of the core is lessened and the shock weakened.

Details such as the effect of entropy on the size of the inner core, and thus on the envelope mass which would be dissociated by the shock, have not been considered. In particular, one notes that it is only the nuclear entropy that is wasteful. The leptonic and drip components do contribute thermal pressure. (The size of the unshocked core increases with its entropy. Thus the amount of matter external to it which needs to be dissociated is decreased.) This mitigates somewhat the effect of an increased entropy, but the increase in the nuclear entropy outweighs this gain. Burrows and Lattimer (1983) have considered these effects and find that for $Y_e \sim 0.4$ at trapping, the entropy may have to be as low as 0.5 to give a successful explosion. This may be overly pessimistic. They assume all the energy paid for dissociation is lost, but eventual recombination may be important.

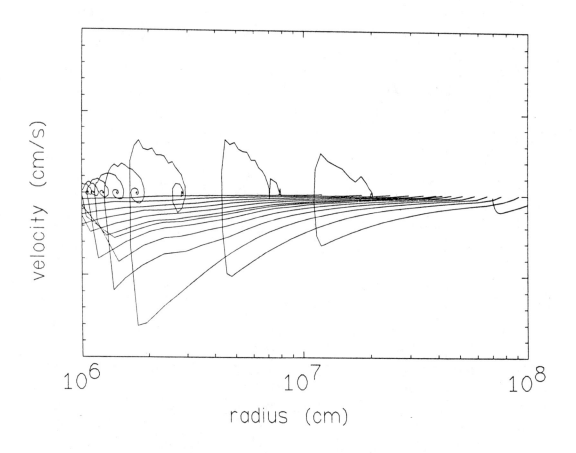

Figure 6.- The rapid damping of the core motion is shown by the motion of selected Lagrangian mass elements. After the initial expansion, the inner core quickly comes to rest, with little oscillation.

V. CONCLUSION

Thus we are left with the conclusion that it will be difficult to achieve success (within the first few milliseconds after bounce) with one-dimensional, nonrotating models, unless the core is quite cool (regardless of whatever scheme is used for neutrino transport), with any equation of state that correctly incorporates both nuclear dissociation and thermal excitation.

Whether such cores can be evolved to the pre-collapse phase depends on the details of the silicon-burning stage and the treatment of convection, by no means closed subjects. One must also ask if such cases can be evolved to bounce, without weak interaction processes providing too much of an entropy increase. We are now investigating exactly what entropy is required for success. Preliminary studies indicate that perhaps only a very narrow range of rather low entropies can be successful.

We would like to acknowledge extensive discussions with H.A. Bethe. J. Lattimer provided us with recent results. Sidney Kahana and the Nuclear Theory Group at Brookhaven National Laboratory graciously provided the computing facilities.

REFERENCES

Arnett, W.D. 1977, *Ap. J.*, 218, 815.

Lattimer, J., Burrows, A., and Yahil, A. 1984, to be published.

Bethe, H.A., Brown, G.E., Applegate, J., and Lattimer, J. 1979, *Nucl. Phys.*, A324, 487 (BBAL).

Bethe, H.A., Brown, G.E., Cooperstein, J. and Wilson, J. 1983, *Nucl. Phys. A.*, 403 (1983) 625 (BBCW).

Brown, G.E., Bethe, H.A., and Baym, G. 1982, *Nucl. Phys.*, A375, 481.

Burbidge, E.M., Burbidge, G.R., Fowler, W.A., and Hoyle, F. 1957, *Rev. Mod. Phys.*, 29, 547.

Burrows, A., and Lattimer, J.M. APJ 270 (1983) 735.

Cooperstein, J. 1982, Ph.D. Thesis, State University of New York at Stony Brook.

Hillebrandt, W. 1981, unpublished.

Mazurek, T.J., Cooperstein, J., and Kahana, S. 1980, *Proc. Workshop, Dumand*, ed. V.J. Stengler (Honolulu: University of Hawaii Press).

_____. 1981, *Proc. NATO Advanced Study Inst., on Supernovae*, ed. M. Rees (Cambridge: Cambridge University Press).

Weaver, T.A., Zimmerman, G.B., and Woosley, S.E. 1978, *Ap. J.*, 225, 1021 (WZW).

Yahil, A., and Lattimer, J. 1981, *Proc. NATO Advanced Study Inst. on Supernovae*, ed. M. Rees (Cambridge: Cambridge University Press).

Iron Core Collapse Models of Type II Supernovae

Richard L. Bowers
Los Alamos National Laboratory

ABSTRACT

Results of recent numerical, one-dimensional core collapse calculations for $1 \circ M_\odot$, $15 M_\odot$ and $20 M_\odot$ population I stars are reviewed. The physics model is discussed, including recent improvements in the nuclear equations of state, and nuclear binding energies. None of the models produces prompt explosions as a direct result of core collapse and bounce.

I. INTRODUCTION

The physics of gravitational collapse of iron cores and its relation to Type II supernovae has been reviewed in this volume by Baym, and by Weaver and Woosley. The physics needed to model core collapse spans more than fifteen orders of magnitude in density ($\rho \lesssim 5 \times 10^{14}$ g/cm^3) and requires temperatures as high as 30 MeV. For nearly fifteen years, Jim Wilson has played a major role in advancing the frontier of computational work on this problem. During this period, substantial improvements have been made in our understanding of the conditions under which Type II supernovae are believed to occur (these include improved models of massive stars following silicon burning), and in our understanding of the physics which is important under these new conditions, particularly neutrino interactions with dense matter and the equation of state of nuclear matter.

With each new development, Jim Wilson has modified the one-dimensional (1-D) code to include new physics or improved numerical methods, or to check and calibrate the methods against known results. The collapse code has been discussed by Bowers and Wilson (1982a), who include a complete description of the physics models and numerical algorithms. The evolution of the $10M_\odot$, $15M_\odot$ and $20M_\odot$ iron cores of Weaver, Zimmerman and Woosley (1978) and of Woosley, Weaver and Taam (1980) as described by the 1-D supernova code has been discussed by Bowers and Wilson (1982b). In this article, the physics in the 1-D supernova code will be summarized, including several modifications which were developed subsequent to the discussions of Bowers and Wilson (1982b). Next, the status of prompt explosions from the iron core collapse of stars in the mass range $10M_\odot$ to $20M_\odot$ as described by our most recent calculations will be reviewed. The emphasis here is on prompt explosions, that is, mass ejection immediately following core bounce. In the next article Jim Wilson will discuss the late time behavior of these models.

At the onset of core collapse, the star has an onion-skin structure consisting (from the surface inward) of concentric shells of hydrogen, helium, nuclei of intermediate atomic weight, silicon, and finally iron group nuclei. The latter constitute the iron core. In the recent models of Weaver, Zimmerman and Woosley, and of Woosley, Weaver and Taam, the density in the iron core at the onset of dynamical collapse is a few times 10^9 g/cm^3. The density drops rapidly across the iron core-silicon boundary (containing $1.27M_\odot$ to $1.58M_\odot$) to values of order 10^5 g/cm^3. The dynamic time scale at a point in the star at density ρ is proporportional to $\rho^{-1/2}$. Thus, although the region outside of the iron core contains most of the stellar mass, the ratio of the dynamic time scale in the core to that in the mantle is of order $(\rho_{mantle}/\rho_{core} \approx 10^{-2})$. Consequently, the core evolution can be considered to be essentially decoupled from the remainder of the stellar model. For our initial model we typically take of the order of $2M_\odot$, which contains the evolved iron core and several tenths $M_\odot$ of the overlying stellar mantle. In all of our calculalations, the outer $0.1M_\odot$ or so remains nearly stationary well beyond core bounce.

II.   IRON CORE COLLAPSE CODE

Our most recent numerical models of core collapse have been constructed using Lagrangian hydrodynamics coupled with the multi-group transport of neutrinos (ν_e, ν_μ, ν_τ and their antiparticles). Analytic and numerically calculated equations of state describe matter for $\rho \lesssim 5 \times 10^{14}$ g/cm^3 and $T \lesssim 30$ MeV. Thermonuclear burn of carbon, oxygen and silicon are approximated by simple analytic energy release rates. Also included are the emission, absorption, pair production, electron scattering, and coherent nuclear and elastic nucleon scattering of ν_e, ν_μ, and ν_τ and their antiparticles. A simple multigroup model is also used to describe electron capture by an average heavy nucleus. Finally, relativistic corrections in post-Newtonian approximation are included in the momentum equation. The spectral distribution of each neutrino type is calculated dynamically and need not be in thermal equilibrium.

A complete discussion of the numerical algorithms used here can be found in Bowers and Wilson (1982a). The remainder of this section will focus on the physics and the differential equations in the code.

The time rate of change in material energy density results from compression, thermonuclear energy release, and neutrino-matter coupling:

$$\rho\frac{d\varepsilon}{dt} = \frac{P}{\rho}\frac{d\rho}{dt} + \sum_i \rho \varepsilon_i^N X_i + \sum_\alpha \left(\frac{dF^\alpha}{dt}\right)_{collision} \tag{1}$$

where ρ is the mass density, ε the specific energy, and P the material pressure; ε_i^N are the thermonuclear energy release rates (erg g^{-1} sec^{-1}) due to carbon, oxygen and silicon burning, X_i are the abundances of carbon, oxygen and silicon, and F^α include the neutrino-matter coupling for all neutrino types (antiparticles included).

The time rate of change of the velocity v is described by

$$\frac{dv}{dt} = -\frac{1}{\rho}\frac{\partial P}{\partial r} + a_G + a_{rot} + a_{rad} \tag{2}$$

where the gravitational acceleration is

$$a_G = -\frac{m(r)G}{r^2}\left[1 + \frac{1}{c^2}\left\{\varepsilon + P/\rho + \frac{4\pi r^3 P}{m(r)}\right.\right. \tag{3}$$

$$\left.\left. + \frac{2m(r)G}{r} + \frac{1}{m(r)}\int_0^r[\varepsilon - \frac{m(r')G}{r'}]dm(r')\right\}\right].$$

This last expression contains in curly brackets the post-Newtonian correction to the gravitational field of a spherically symmetric mass distribution. Note that m(r) is the baryon mass inside radius r (Zel'dovich and Novikov 1971). The term a_{rot} allows for one-dimensional effects due to rotation, but is not used here. The neutrino radiation acceleration is

$$a_{rad} = \sum a_{rad}^\alpha = -\frac{1}{\rho}\sum_\alpha \int\left(\frac{D_\nu}{\lambda_\nu c}\right)_\alpha \frac{\partial F_\nu^\alpha}{\partial r} d\nu \tag{4}$$

where the sum is over all neutrino types. For each neutrino type, F_ν^α represents the spectral energy density, and ν is in energy units. The quantity in parentheses reduces to 1/3 in matter which is optically thick to neutrinos, and is included to handle the transition to the optically thin regime properly (see Bowers and Wilson 1982a).

Finally, mass conservation requires that

$$\frac{d\rho}{dt} + \rho\frac{1}{r^2}\frac{\partial}{\partial r}r^2 v = 0 . \tag{5}$$

The time rate of change of each neutrino distribution includes spacial transport and neutrino-matter coupling:

$$\frac{\partial F_\nu^\alpha}{\partial t} = \frac{1}{r}\frac{\partial}{\partial r}\ rD_\nu^\alpha\ \frac{\partial F_\nu^\alpha}{\partial r} + \left(\frac{\partial F_\nu^\alpha}{\partial t}\right)_{collision} . \tag{6}$$

Spacial transport of each neutrino type is described by flux limited spacial diffusion with the diffusion coefficient for neutrinos of type α and energy ν:

$$D_\nu^\alpha = \frac{c}{3k_\nu^\alpha + \xi_\nu^\alpha} . \tag{7}$$

Here $k_\nu^\alpha \equiv 1/\lambda_\nu^\alpha$ is the specific opacity, and ξ_ν^α is the flux limiter. The flux limiter is constructed such that $\xi_\nu^\alpha \ll k_\nu^\alpha$ in the diffusion regime. In the optically thin regime $\lambda_\nu^\alpha \gg F_\nu^\alpha\ |\partial r/\partial F_\nu^\alpha|$, ξ_ν^α is chosen such that neutrino energy is transported through matter at the speed of light.

The neutrino mean free paths are given in Bowers and Wilson (1982a). The electron neutrino and antineutrino mean free paths contain contributions for electron-neutrino scattering, neutrino-nucleon scattering, and neutrino coherent scattering off heavy nuclei. The latter process includes finite nuclear structure effects and ion-ion correlation effects. Analytic approximations to the cross-sections (Tubbs and Schramm 1975) are used for all processes. The muon and tau neutrino (and antineutrino) mean free paths include contributions from electron scattering, coherent scattering off heavy nuclei, and scattering off free nucleons. Coherent scattering includes ion-ion correlations and finite nucleon structure effects.

In addition to spacial transport, each neutrino spectral energy distribution will change as a result of the coupling between the neutrinos and matter. These are included in the last term on the right hand side of equation (6). For electron neutrinos and antineutrinos these terms correspond to electron capture by heavy

nuclei, electron scattering, emission and absorption by free nucleons, compressional work done on the neutrino fields when the
matter is optically thick, and finally energy loss associated with
radiation acceleration of matter described by equation (4). For
muon and tau neutrinos and their antiparticles, the last term on
the right hand side of equation (6) includes contributions due to
electron scattering, thermal and plasma pair production, compressional heating, and energy changes due to radiation acceleration
of matter.

All electron scattering energy exchange processes are described in the Fokker-Planck approximation, which has been cali-
brated to the Monte Carlo results of Tubbs et al. (Tubbs, Weaver,
Bowers, Wilson and Schramm 1980):

$$\left(\frac{\partial F^{\alpha}_{\nu}}{\partial t}\right)_{F.P.} = \nu \frac{\partial}{\partial \nu} \left\{ K^{\alpha}_{\nu} \left[F^{\alpha}_{\nu}(1-f^{\alpha}_{\nu}) + kT\left(\frac{\partial F^{\alpha}_{\nu}}{\partial \nu} - \frac{3F^{\alpha}_{\nu}}{\nu}\right)\right]\right\} \tag{8}$$

with

$$f^{\alpha}_{\nu} \equiv 2\pi^2\left(\frac{\hbar c}{k}\right)^3 \frac{F^{\alpha}_{\nu}}{\nu^3} \ ;$$

ν has units of energy, and k is Boltzmann's constant. The analytic approximations to the cross-sections used in the diffusion coefficient K^{α}_{ν} are discussed in Bowers and Wilson (1982a).

In steady state, equation (8) can be used to show that F^{α}_{ν} reduces to the usual Fermi-Dirac distribution $F^{\alpha}_{\nu,eq}$, whose chemical
potential μ_{ν} is fixed by the constraint

$$n(\mu_{\alpha}) = \int F^{\alpha}_{\nu,eq} \, d\nu/\nu.$$

The change in F_ν^α for electron neutrinos due to emission and absorption by an average heavy nucleus is described by the simple model

$$\left(\frac{dF_\nu^e}{dt}\right)_A = n_e c n_p^* \sigma_e(\nu)(1-f_\nu^e) - \frac{cF_\nu^e}{\nu^3} n_n^* \sigma_e(\varepsilon_e)(1-f_e) \; . \tag{9}$$

Here f_e is the electron distribution function, ε_e the electron energy, n_e the electron number density, and σ_e the electron capture cross-section. Finally, n_p^* and n_n^* represent the effective number densities of protons and neutrons, respectively, in the average heavy nucleus which is capable of capturing neutrinos. We have not included capture of $\bar\nu_e$.

Similarly, the emission and absorption of electron neutrinos by free nucleons is given by

$$\left(\frac{dF_\nu^e}{dt}\right)_{ea} = n_e c \sigma_{pe} \, n_p \nu(1-f_\nu^e) - c\sigma_{n\nu} \frac{F_\nu^e}{\nu} n_n(1-f_e)\nu \tag{10}$$

where n_p and n_n are the number densities of free protons and neutrons. A similar expression is used for electron antineutrinos.

The change in F_ν^α due to radiation acceleration is given by

$$\left(\frac{dF_\nu^\alpha}{dt}\right)_{rad} = \nu \frac{\partial}{\partial \nu} \left[F_\nu^\alpha \frac{1}{r} \frac{\partial}{\partial r} \left(\frac{D_\nu^\alpha}{\lambda_\nu^\alpha c} \right) r^2 v \right] \; . \tag{11}$$

The quantity in parentheses has been discussed above for equation (6). The change in F_ν^α above has been constructed to conserve the sum of material kinetic energy and neutrino energy per unit volume, to conserve neutrino number for each species, and to conserve total momentum.

The thermal and plasma pair production for muon and tau neutrinos is based on a simple phenomenological model discussed in detail by Bowers and Wilson (1982a).

The neutrino radiation-hydrodynamic equations discussed above require the equations of state

$$P = P(\rho, \varepsilon, X_i, Y_e) \tag{12}$$

and

$$T = T(\rho, \varepsilon, X_i, Y_e), \tag{13}$$

where Y_e is the number of electrons per baryon, and the thermonuclear energy release rates

$$\varepsilon_i^N = \varepsilon_i^N(\rho, T, X_i). \tag{14}$$

The stellar composition includes baryons in the form of free nucleons, and a distribution of atomic nuclei. We assume for simplicity that the baryonic composition can be parametrized by free nucleons, helium nuclei, and an average heavy nucleus of atomic number A and charge Z. The mass fractions of free nucleons, X_B, helium, X_{He}, and heavy nuclei, X_A, satisfy

$$X_B + X_{He} + X_A = 1. \tag{15}$$

For the purposes of thermonuclear reactions, the average heavy nucleus is represented by a distribution of carbon, oxygen, silicon and iron group nuclei of mass fractions X_C, X_O, X_{Si} and X_{Fe}, respectively:

$$X_A = X_C + X_O + X_{Si} + X_{Fe}.$$

The ratio of free protons to free nucleons is given by

$$Z_B = \frac{n_p}{n_p + n_n} \cdot \qquad (16)$$

Changes in composition due to electron capture and to emission and absorption are described by

$$n_A \frac{dZ}{dt} = -\int \left(\frac{dF^e_\nu}{dt}\right)_{ec} \frac{d\nu}{\nu} \qquad (17)$$

and

$$-\frac{dn_n}{dt} = \frac{dn_p}{dt} = -\int \left(\frac{dF^e_\nu}{dt}\right)_{ep} \frac{d\nu}{\nu} + \int \left(\frac{dF^{\bar{e}}_\nu}{dt}\right)_{p\bar{\nu}} \frac{d\nu}{\nu} . \qquad (18)$$

The subscript ep above indicates that the quantity in parentheses is the first term on the right hand side of equation (10); subscript $p\bar{\nu}$ indicates that the quantity in parentheses is the corresponding contribution from the change in $\bar{F}^e_\nu$ due to proton capture of an electron antineutrino.

$\bar{F}^e_\nu$ is the spectral distribution of electron antineutrinos, $n_A = \rho X_A / A m_H$ is the number density of average heavy nuclei, and $n_e = Y_e \rho / m_H$ is the free electron number density, with

$$Y_e = (Z/A)X_A + (1/2)X_{He} + Z_B X_B . \qquad (19)$$

The mass of the hydrogen atom is denoted by m_H.

Finally, the distribution of baryons between heavy nuclei, helium and free baryons is determined by the Saha equation corresponding to the processes

$$(A,Z) \rightarrow \frac{1}{2} Z \ He + (A - 2Z)n,$$

$$He \rightarrow 2n + 2p.$$

The collapse code uses less than fifty thousand words of memory on a CDC 7600, with an average run time of about 10^{-2} seconds per zone-cycle. Run time to bounce is about five minutes. Following core bounce, the time step drops to several times 10^{-6} seconds and only a few tens of milliseconds can be followed with the fully explicit calculations.

III.   RECENT PHYSICS MODIFICATIONS

The equation of state discussed in Bowers and Wilson (1982a, b) has recently been modified, and new collapse models have been calculated. The new models and their effect on core collapse are summarized in this section.

a)   Nuclear Equation of State

The numerical equation of state for matter near nuclear density which has been developed by Wilson for core collapse calculations (see Bowers and Wilson 1982b) has been modified to reproduce the analytic results of Bethe, Brown, Cooperstein and Wilson (1983). In this model, the density of nuclear matter $\rho_n = 2.4 \times 10^{14}$ g/cm^3 is about 20% higher than that used in Bowers and Wilson (1982b). The pressure increase due to nuclear repulsion above ρ_n has also been modified such that

$$\delta P_{repulsion} = 7 \times 10^4 \rho(\rho - \rho_n) \ dyne/cm^2 . \qquad (20)$$

Figure 1 shows the new equation of state for $Y_e = 0.30$ and an

entropy per baryon s = k, where k is Boltzmann's constant.   The
crosses correspond to the analytic model of Bethe, Brown,
Cooperstein and Wilson (1983).

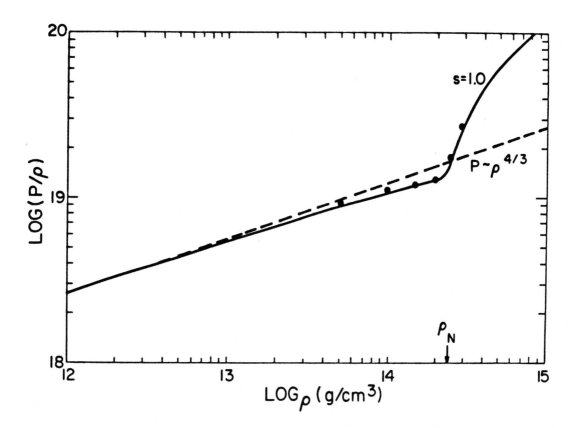

Fig. 1.- Nuclear equation of state (solid) including
repulsive pressure from equation (20) for the isentrope
s = 1.0 in units of Boltzmann's constant. The pressure
is in dyne/cm^2. The dashed line corresponds to
$P \approx \rho^{4/3}$, and the (·) denote values from Bethe, Brown,
Cooperstein and Wilson (1983). The arrow shows nuclear
matter density.

b)   Energy of Nuclear Dissociation

The energy needed for thermal dissociation of nuclei is an important parameter affecting the strength of the shock when it reaches the mantle. We consider the photodissociation of iron group nuclei into helium nuclei and free neutrons:

$$(A,Z) \rightarrow (Z/2)He + (A - 2Z)n .$$

The value for the dissociation energy per baryon for helium, Q_{He}, used previously has been found to be too large. A better value can be obtained by noting that changes in density lead to variations in Z and A for our average heavy nucleus. A model for Q_{He} which includes these effects is

$$Q_{He} = 1.7 + 95(0.464 - Z/A)^2 \text{ MeV} , \qquad (21)$$

where the last term takes into account the change in reaction energy with nuclear type. This form gives a pressure which grows less rapidly with the charge on the average heavy nucleus Z than does the earlier (linear) form. This results in less dissociation of He in the lower density regime outside the homologous core. Consequently, the shock will lose less energy as it traverses the infalling material from the stellar mantle.

c)   Results Near Core Bounce

The core model from the Weaver and Woosley $15M_\odot$ star was rerun with the modifications in equation of state and Q_{He} discussed above. The new form of the nuclear equation of state leads to an increase in the sonic mass of $0.02\ M_\odot$, and modification of Q_{He} leads to an additional increase of $0.04M_\odot$. Thus, for the $15M_\odot$ star

$$M_{sonic} \simeq 0.60\ M_\odot. \qquad (22)$$

We note that if general relativistic corrections to the hydrodynamics are turned off, the sonic mass increases to $0.78\ M_\odot$ in agreement with the analytic models of Bethe, Brown, Applegate and Lattimer (1979).

IV.   CORE COLLAPSE, BOUNCE AND SHOCK PROPAGATION--PROMPT EXPLOSIONS

Core bounce and shock propagation into the stellar mantle involve essentially all of the physics discussed in Section II. Whether or not the shock can deliver enough energy to the mantle to eject it depends on the net (small) difference between the energy available in the shock and the energy losses as the shock propagates outward.

The initial (gravitational potential) energy of the core at the onset of dynamic infall is of order 10^{49} erg for most evolved stellar models. The binding energy of the homologous core plus the additional mass which falls in through the shock following bounce is of order 10^{53} erg. Observations of Type II supernovae indicate that the energy release in the stellar core is of order 10^{50} to 10^{51} erg. Thus, only about 1% of the energy change available from collapse is needed to produce an explosion.

Analytic models using the results of extensive numerical cal- culations have been used to clarify the physics of core collapse (see, for example, Brown, Bethe and Baym 1982, and Yahil 1983). In the remainder of this section we consider simple order of magnitude arguments in an attempt to focus on the basic issues of core collapse models.

Consider the energetics of iron core collapse for low entropy- systems such as the Weaver-Woosley models. The initial collapse results in a quasistatic unshocked core of radius $R_c \approx 7 \times 10^6$ cm and mass $M_H \approx 0.6 M_\odot$ (these values are nearly constant for initial stellar masses in the range 10-20 $M_\odot$). Additional material, primarily in the form of heavy nuclei, continues to flow onto the core. The kinetic energy per baryon of this material at $r_c \approx R$ is of order

$$\frac{1}{2}v_{in}^2 \approx \frac{M_H G}{R_c} \approx 10^{19} \text{ erg/g,} \qquad (23)$$

which gives v $\approx$ 5 x 10^9 cm/sec. The shock, which forms just above the surface of the homologous core, must traverse about $\Delta M \approx 0.4 M_\odot$ of overlying material before it can reach the neutrino-sphere. The infall energy of this mass ΔM is, to order of magnitude,

$$E_{infall} \approx \frac{1}{2} \Delta M v_{in}^2 \approx 10^{52} \text{ erg.} \qquad (24)$$

The kinetic energy of material falling through the shock front goes partly into thermal energy (which helps drive the shock) and partly into neutrino radiation. To order of magnitude the infall energy going into the shock is

$$E_{shock} \approx E_{infall} \approx 10^{52} \text{ erg.} \qquad (25)$$

Assuming that this energy goes into particle motion of the matter in ΔM, the energy per baryon is of order $E_{infall}/\Delta M$, the particle velocity is

$$v \approx (2 \times 10^{52} \text{erg}/0.8 \times 10^{33} \text{g})^{1/2} \approx 3 \times 10^9 \text{ cm/sec,}$$

and the shock moves outward with velocity $\approx 0.1c$.

The binding energy per nucleon in heavy nuclei, ε_B, is about 8 MeV. Matter falling through the shock at a radius r_D defined roughly by

$$r_D \approx \frac{m_H GM}{\varepsilon_B}$$

will be heated to temperatures sufficient to thermally dissociate helium and heavy nuclei. For $M \approx M_\odot$, this gives a value $r_D \approx$ 2 x 10^7 cm. Thus the infall energy of matter reaching radii of order r_D or less goes into nuclear thermal dissociation rather than into maintaining the shock's outward motion, and E_{shock} is less than the value given by equation (25). To order of magnitude the shock energy dissipated in this way is

$$E_{diss} \approx \frac{\Delta M}{m_H} \left(\frac{8MeV}{baryon} \right) \approx 6 \times 10^{51} \text{ erg,} \qquad (26)$$

or about 0.8×10^{19} erg/g. This corresponds to a fractional reduction in the shock velocity of order

$$[(E_{shock} - E_{diss})/E_{shock}]^{1/2} \approx v \approx 0.6.$$

Nuclear recombination subsequently could release this energy, but that is expected to occur on much longer time scales than are of interest for prompt explosions.

Once the shock is within a neutrino mean free path λ_ν of the neutrinosphere, the shock-heated matter efficiently converts shock energy into neutrino energy at a rate which is strongly temperature sensitive. At this point the neutrino luminosity changes across the shock front by $\Delta L_\nu \approx 10^{54}$ erg/sec. The time spent by the shock within a distance λ_ν of the neutrinosphere is of order

$$\Delta t_\nu \approx \lambda_\nu / v_s \approx (10^7 \text{cm})/(3 \times 10^9 \text{cm/sec}) \approx 3 \times 10^{-3} \text{ sec,} \qquad (27)$$

where v_s is the shock velocity near the neutrinosphere. Therefore, the energy radiated as neutrinos by the shock is of order

$$E_{rad} \approx \Delta L_\nu \Delta t_\nu \approx 3 \times 10^{51} \text{ erg,} \qquad (28)$$

or about 0.4×10^{19} erg/g.

Neutrino damping of the shock is seen in all of our recent calculations. For example, Figure 2 shows the change in neutrino luminosity L_ν across the shock, and the shock luminosity

$$L_H = 2 \pi r^2 \rho v^2 v_s \qquad (29)$$

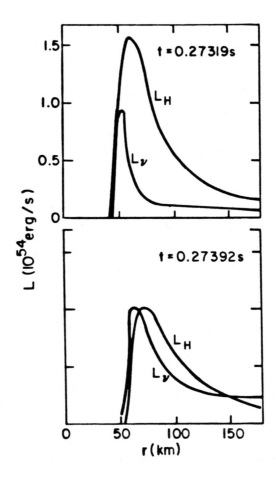

Fig. 2.- Neutrino damping of shock. a) The neutrino
luminosity L_ν and the shock luminosity L_H just
before the shock reaches the neutrinosphere.
b) L_ν and L_H when the shock is about λ_ν outside
the neutrinosphere.

before the shock reaches the neutrinosphere, and when it is a mean free path beyond the neutrinosphere. Here v is the material velocity, and v_S is the shock velocity.

A prompt explosion appears to be possible only if the shock energy outside the neutrinosphere exceeds 10^{50} to 10^{51} erg. From the discussion above we see that, to within the accuracy of our estimates above,

$$E_{shock} - E_{diss} - E_{rad} \approx 10^{52} - 6 \times 10^{51} - 3 \times 10^{51} \text{ erg} \approx 0. \quad (30)$$

The message contained in equation (30) is simple: although core collapse leads to the prompt release of about 10^{52} erg of gravitational potential energy, it appears to be difficult to convert more than 1% of it into mass motion of the stellar mantle as a direct result of core bounce.

A crude estimate of the shock velocity outside the neutrinosphere can be made by noting that $L_H \approx 10^{54}$ erg/sec there; using equation (29) with $v \approx v_S$,

$$v_S \approx (L_H/2\pi r_\nu^2 \rho_\nu)^{1/3} \approx 1.0 \times 10^9 \text{ cm/sec}$$

for $\rho_\nu \approx 10^{12}$ g/cm^3 and $_\nu r \approx 10^7$ cm. The escape velocity for matter at r_ν is

$$v_{esc} \approx [(M_H + \Delta M)G/r_\nu]^{1/2} \approx 3.5 \times 10^9 \text{ cm/sec,}$$

which exceeds v_S.

In order to optimize the chances of an explosion, it might be considered sufficient to increase E_{shock} and reduce E_{diss}. Decreasing the stiffness of the nuclear equation of state near core bounce will increase the extent to which the core overshoots its quasi-equilibrium radius. This could impart more energy to the shock. A decrease in leptonization rates during infall can result

in an increased homologous core mass. This has two important
effects: first, a larger core drives a larger shock at bounce;
and second, the greater the mass in M_H, the less overlying mass
of heavy nuclei there will be for the shock to photodissociate.
Finally, in initial models having higher specific entropy outside
the homologous core, less shock energy will be needed to dissociate the heavy nuclei there.

Unfortunately, in all of our calculations we see very little
change in the final shock energy due to moderate changes in equation of state, leptonization rates and specific entropy. Although
these changes do increase the shock strength, the accompanying
increase in shock heating produces an increased rate of neutrino
pair production near the neutrinosphere. The net result in all
cases that we have investigated is to rob the shock of the extra
strength it acquired at bounce.

The absence of a prompt explosion in a core collapse model
does not mean that an explosion at later times is not possible.
For example, if the core bounce shock can ultimately reach radii
greater than a few times 10^7 cm, no further nuclear thermal dissociation will occur. Furthermore, because of the reduced temperature at larger radii, the neutrino radiative losses will decrease. If energy can be supplied to the shock at this stage, an
explosion may be possible (see Wilson, this volume).

V.   IRON CORE COLLAPSE MODELS

Core collapse calculations have been completed for the $10M_\odot$,
$15M_\odot$ and $20M_\odot$ models which include the nuclear equations of state
and binding energy for helium discussed in Section III; the procedure follows that of Bowers and Wilson (1982b). The principal
difference between the $15M_\odot$ results of Bowers and Wilson (1982b)
and the new model were summarized in Section III above.

None of the models shows any indication of a prompt explosion. In all cases, the shock wave, which is reasonably strong
before it reaches the neutrinosphere, turns into what appears to
be an accretion shock. The original calculations, which were run
out to about 0.03 sec after bounce, give no indication that the

shock has sufficient energy to accelerate the overlying matter to escape velocities. The results are insensitive to zoning, the exact form of the nuclear equation of state, and the modification in Q_{He} for the $15M_0$ model (see Bowers and Wilson 1982b for a discussion of these details).

REFERENCES

Bethe, H.A., Brown, G., Applegate, J., and Lattimer, J.M. 1979, Nucl. Phys. A, 324, 487.

Bethe, H.E., Brown, G., Cooperstein, J., and Wilson, J.R. 1983, Nucl. Phys. A, 403, 625.

Bowers, R.L., and Wilson, J. 1982a, Ap. J. Suppl., 50, 115.

_____. 1982b, Ap. J., 263, 366.

Brown, G., Bethe, H.A., and Baym, G. 1982, Nucl. Phys. A, 375, 481.

Tubbs, D.L., and Schramm, D.N. 1975, Ap. J., 201, 467.

Tubbs, D.L., Weaver, T.A., Bowers, R.L., Wilson, J., and Schramm, D.N. 1980, Ap. J., 239, 271.

Weaver, T.A., Zimmerman, G.B., and Woosley, S.C. 1978, Ap. J., 225, 1021.

Woosley, S.C., Weaver, T.A., and Taam, R.E. 1980, in Type I Supernovae, ed. J.C. Wheeler (Austin: University of Texas Press), p.96.

Yahil, A. 1983, "The Energetics of Type II Supernovae", in Stellar Nucleosynthesis, (Dordrecht: Reidel).

Zel'dovich, Ya.B., and Novikov, I.D. 1971, Relativistic Astrophysics, Vol. 1, "Stars and Relativity", ed. K. Thorne and W.D. Arnett (Chicago: University of Chicago Press).

Supernovae and Post-Collapse Behavior*

James R. Wilson
Lawrence Livermore National Laboratory

ABSTRACT

After the collapse of heavy stars (10-25 $M_\odot$) at the end of their nuclear burning phase a hot neutron star is formed. It has been found that a few tenths of seconds after the neutron star has formed, the neutrino emission from this star is sufficient to heat matter a few hundred kilometers out in radius and produce an explosion with energies of a few times 10^{50} ergs.

For many years there has been an extensive effort in the astrophysics community to try to make a connection between the collapse of iron cores of highly evolved massive stars and type II supernova explosions. A considerable fraction of this effort in supernova research has concentrated on the shock propagation immediately after core collapse bounce. The prospects for the immediate propagation of the shock outward in an explosive manner seem dim at present (Bowers and Wilson 1982b and Bowers in this volume). Hildebrandt (1982) recently carried out hydrodynamic calculations of the collapse of Weaver and Woosley's 10 $M_\odot$ model. He found that the shock propagated out rapidly and led to an explosion energy of 5 x 10^{50} ergs about 40 milliseconds after bounce. When I reran the Weaver and Woosley 10 $M_\odot$ model out to 40 milliseconds, no material behind the shock had escape energy at the end of the calculation. However, it was noted that matter behind the shock at the end of the calculation had started slowly increasing its entropy. Neutrino interactions behind the

---

*This work was performed under the auspices of the U.S. Department of Energy by Lawrence Livermore National Laboratory under contract No. W-7405-Eng-48.

shock had changed from matter heat losers to heat gainers. The calculation of the 10 $M_\odot$ model was carried out to 500 milliseconds after bounce, and an explosion, albeit weak, was found. The pursuit of these late time explosions will be the subject of this paper.

The computer code of Bowers and Wilson (1982a) is used for these calculations. The equation of state for nuclear matter is now modified to be in substantial agreement with that of Bethe et al. (1983). In order to carry out the calculations to the late times necessary for these problems, the hydrodynamics in the central core is modified 10 milliseconds after bounce so that the Courant time step limit does not apply there. This was accomplished by using the local Courant condition time step for hydrodynamics for those zones in the central core far from the shock wave. In Table 1 the collapse calculations for three precollapse models are summarized. Final core mass is the baryon mass of the core. The neutron star masses were estimated from the baryon mass by averaging the gravitational mass

TABLE 1

Summary of Calculations

Model Mass $M_\odot$	Energy of Explosion, ergs	Heating Time after bounce, ms	Final Core Mass	Mass Neutron Star	BE, ergs	Efficiency
10	1.8×10^{50}	250	1.475	1.25	2.7×10^{53}	0.067%
15	3.4×10^{50}	450	1.76	1.55	3.8×10^{53}	0.090%
25	4.5×10^{50}	550	1.66	1.46	3.6×10^{53}	0.125%

curves for several nuclear matter equations of state. In Figures 1, 2, and 3 the radius versus time graphs show a different hydrodynamical behavior for the 10 $M_\odot$ model from that of the other two models. In particular, the shock wave in the 10 $M_\odot$ model progresses outward in a continuous manner, while the shock in the other two models retreats in radius sometimes. The 10 $M_\odot$ calculation will be discussed first and then the 25 $M_\odot$ case will be analyzed.

From Figure 4 it is seen that during the first 100 ms after bounce the shock wave is progressing outward at a rate much lower than free fall speed. This is due to both the high losses by neutrinos and the high compression across the shock resulting from nuclear dissociation. As the shock wave moves out, the neutrino losses decrease because of their strong temperature dependence. From Figure 1 it is seen that matter passing through the shock for the first 50 ms rapidly continues its infall. At 30 ms after bounce the hydrodynamic luminosity $L_h = 2\pi r^2 \rho v^3$

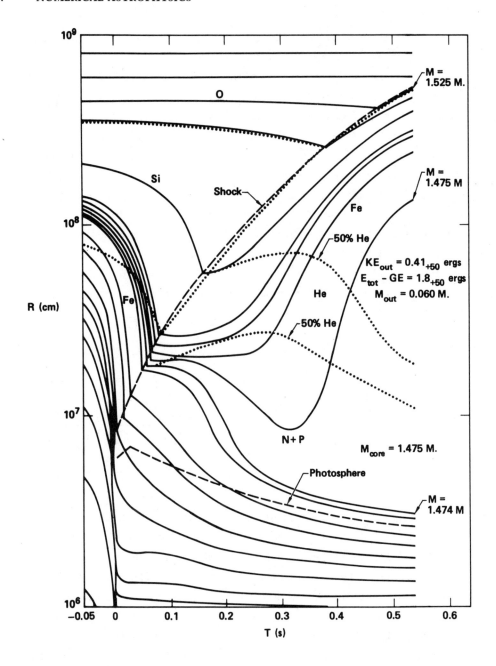

Fig. 1. - Radius versus time trajectories of selected mass points for the collapse of the 10 M$_\odot$ model. The upper dashed line is the shock front and the lower dashed line is the electron neutrino photosphere. The dotted lines between the dashed lines are the positions where the helium abundance is 50%. Above the helium region is iron and below are free neutrons and protons. Above the dashed shock line the dotted lines separate Si from Fe and O. Curves are labeled by mass in units of the solar mass.

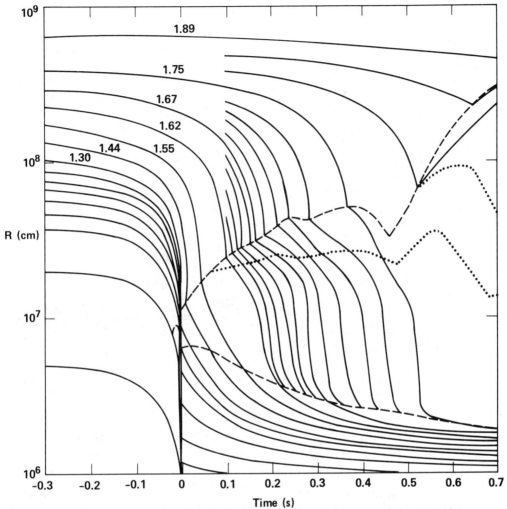

Fig. 2. - Radius versus time trajectories of selected mass points for the collapse of the 15 M$_{\odot}$ model. See Fig. 1 caption for details.

is about equal to the jump in neutrino luminosity from the photosphere out.

The matter below the shock and well outside the photosphere is moderately transparent, and one can estimate the radiation heat exchange rate in a simple manner by assuming that the opacity is proportional to temperature squared as follows:

$$\dot{\varepsilon} = K_{abs}(T_m)\left[\left(\frac{T_{ph}}{T_m}\right)^2 \frac{L_e}{4\pi r^2} - ac\, T_m^4\right] \quad , \tag{1}$$

where T_{ph} is the temperature of the photosphere, T_m is the matter temperature

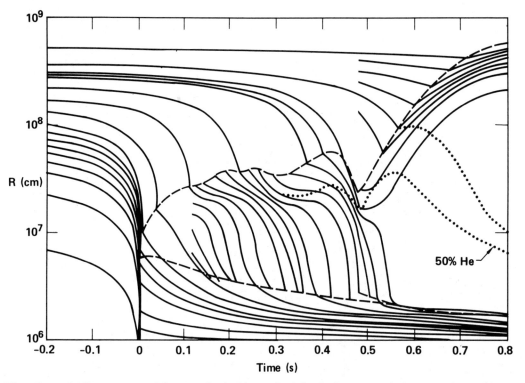

Fig. 3. - Radius versus time trajectories of selected mass points for the collapse of the 25 $M_\odot$ model. See Fig. 1 caption for details.

behind the shock at radius r, L_e is the luminosity in electron-positron neutrinos, K_{abs} is the absorption opacity, and 4ac is the Stefan-Boltzmann constant. The photospheric temperature is constant in time and the luminosity drops slowly with time, but T_m drops rapidly as the shock moves outward. The outward shock velocity is small compared to free fall (see Fig. 4) before the energy deposited becomes appreciable. The thermal energy increase across the shock is only a little different from free fall energy before 250 ms. At a time of 250 ms after bounce the temperature behind the shock is found to be approximately $T_m = 9 \times 10^4/r^{2/3}$ MeV, the luminosity is 4.5×10^{52} ergs/sec, and $T_{ph} = 4.5$ MeV. From equation (1) it can be seen that for a radius greater than about 4×10^6 cm the matter behind the shock has a net heating by neutrinos. The density in the region of interest can be fit by $\rho = 6 \times 10^{22}/r^2$ (for radii above the shock, density is better fitted by a $1/r^3$ law). Integrating equation (1) over mass gives the net neutrino heating for radii greater than 4×10^6 cm of about 1.4×10^{51} ergs/sec. This condition persists for about a tenth of a second; thus, this heating can account for the explosion energy.

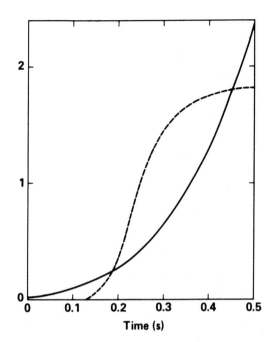

Fig. 4. - Ratio of coordinate shock speed to free fall speed for 10 $M_\odot$ model (solid curve). Dashed curve is energy above escape energy of outward bound matter in units of 10^{50} ergs.

How did the envelope get into a situation where heating is important? As time progresses, the matter crossing the shock front has a lower density. The entropy behind the shock increases, so the matter coasting down below the shock has a higher entropy but a lower pressure. The pressure (density) falls fast enough to make up the increase of entropy, and the temperature at fixed radius ($\sim 10^{7}$ cm) falls with time (see Fig. 5). About 150 ms after bounce neutrino heating starts to take effect and the entropy begins rising rapidly (at radius = 10^{7} cm, S goes from 12 per baryon (in units of Boltzmann's constant) at t = 150 ms to 28 at t = 300 ms). All the while the temperature and density are falling. The net heating is limited by the expansion of the matter out from the heating region. The energy of explosion must be proportional to the heating rate and to the confining density.

We now pass on to a discussion of the 25 $M_\odot$ model, which for all appearances is similar to the 15 $M_\odot$. The basic explosion mechanism is the same as in the 10 $M_\odot$ model, but how the star gets into a situation where neutrino heating can occur is subtle. From Figure 3 we note first of all that the outward progress of the shock wave is not monotonic. The matter that passes through the shock

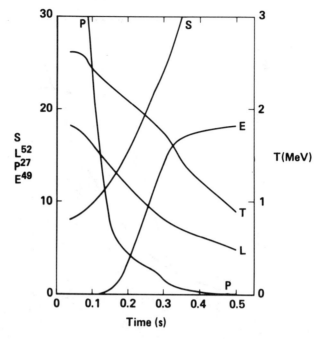

Fig. 5. - Curves labeled T, L, P, and S are the temperature in Mev, luminosity in units of 10^{52} ergs/sec, pressure in units of 10^{27} dynes/cm^2, and entropy per baryon in units of Boltzmann constant for the 10 M$_\odot$ model at a radius of 10^7 cm. Curve labeled E is the explosion energy in units of 10^{49} ergs.

continues to fall onto the core for a much longer time after bounce than does the matter in the 10 M$_\odot$ model. Comparing Figures 5 and 6, we note that the 10 M$_\odot$ makes a smooth transition from fall-in to explosion, but the 25 M$_\odot$ has oscillations of the shock wave position and in the structure of the sub-shock region before the explosion starts. In particular, a collapse of the sub-shock region at a time of 450 ms gives rise to a burst in luminosity as the accretion onto the core increases. Figure 7 gives details of the shock front around the time of shock collapse. The matter underneath the shock is radiatively unstable in time. The net radiative heating of matter in the region around 10^7 cm changes sign twice (the last change in sign is shown in Fig. 8) before it finally becomes positive and stays positive. In Figure 9 it can be seen how matter that has passed through the shock at first continues to increase its entropy; then as it reaches a lower radius the heating turns to cooling and the matter collapses onto the opaque core. Mass cuts 1.66 and 1.67 have very similar initial behavior, and then at a time of 550 ms a parting of the ways occurs (see Figs. 9, 10).

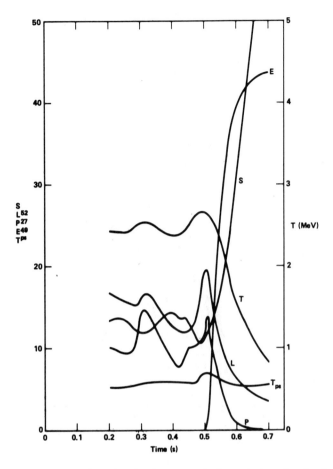

Fig. 6. - Same as Fig. 5 except the electron neutrino photospheric temperature, T_{ps}, is added for the 25 $M_\odot$ model.

A bootstrapping effect takes place at late times that helps the explosion a little. As the entropy rises, the number of electron-positron pairs per nucleon increases. The cross-section for electron scattering is much smaller than the nuclear absorption cross-section, so most of the time nuclear absorption is the principal heating mechanism; but as can be seen in Figure 11, at late times neutrino electron scattering becomes the dominant heating process. Unfortunately, it occurs a little too late to add much energy to the explosion. The greater efficiency of the higher mass models has two possible sources. The luminosity is higher for the heavier cores and so the heating, when it starts, can proceed faster. Also the heavier cores have higher density envelopes falling in, which prevents the hot matter from expanding as quickly out of the heating region.

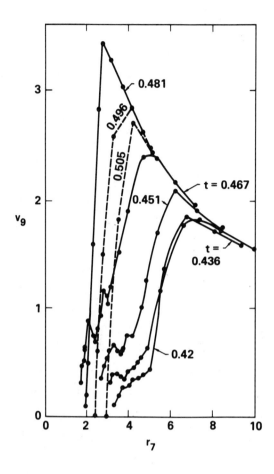

Fig. 7. - Inward velocity in units of 10^9 cm/sec versus radius in units of 10^7 cm of the individual mass points (heavy dots) in the calculation for times near the time of the last retreat of the shock front for the 25 $M_\odot$ model. The numbers near the curves are the times in seconds after bounce that the curve represents. The dashed curves are the velocity curves after the shock wave starts out again.

A new possible mechanism has been found for supernova explosions; however, the energy produced is a bit small compared to the energy thought to exist in a supernova explosion. The computer code used was not designed for these late time calculations and has several defects that we must cure before we can give a definitive discussion of the explosions. The hydrodynamics has faults at present. First, it uses a Lagrangian representation, but since matter falls so far it needs a great deal of zoning and dezoning (more than a thousand rezones, dezones per run). An attempt has been made to dezone and rezone only relatively inactive

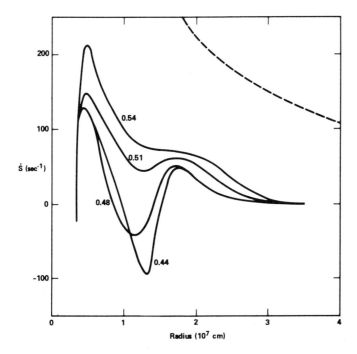

Fig. 8. - The net rate of entropy change per second for selected times versus
radius for the 25 M$_\odot$ model. The numbers by the curves are the times in seconds.
The dashed curve is the S from absorption only, emission not included.

zones, but an appreciable amount of numerical error may be introduced. Second,
the computer program uses a post-Newtonian acceleration force. At the end of the
calculation the central force thus calculated is 68% larger than the Newtonian
force. A proper relativistic treatment of the dynamics should be used. The
material in the critical heating region is near the boundary between helium and
free nucleons. It is necessary that the equation of state represent this composition very well, because there is little neutrino interaction with helium. At late
times the inner core becomes convectively unstable due to the neutronization of
the outer portions of the core (Epstein 1979, Colgate and Petschek 1979, Smarr
et al. 1981). The resulting convective heat flow should augment the explosion
energy, but it will be very difficult to model this effect quantitatively.

I would like to acknowledge the enthusiastic help and criticism of James
LeBlanc on the supernova project for almost 15 years and more recent help on the
program by H. Bethe, R. Bowers, and G. Brown.

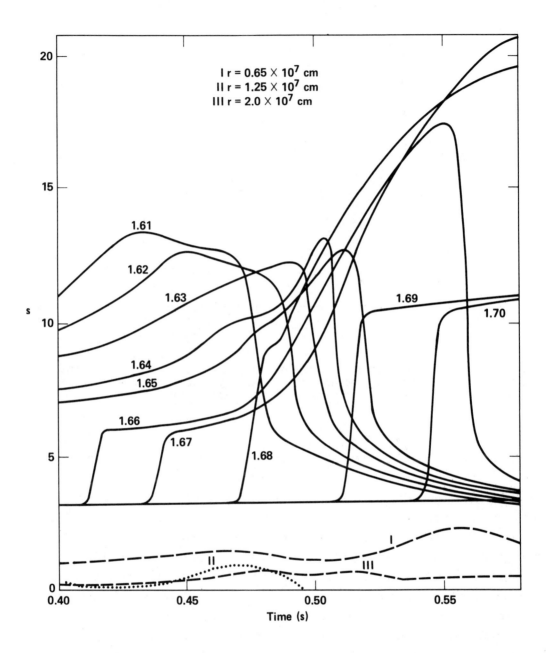

Fig. 9. - Entropy versus time trajectories of selected mass points for 25 M⊙ model. Mass in solar masses is indicated by the numbers by the curves. Curve I is S/100 sec⁻¹ for the inner peak of S. See Fig. 8. Curve II is the negative of the outer minimum of S/100 as long as the minimum is negative. Curve III is S/100 for the outer peak in S.

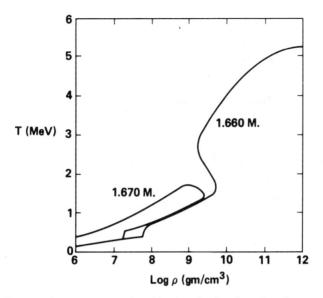

Fig. 10. - Temperature versus density trajectories for two mass points, one (1.67 M$_\odot$) just above and one (1.66 M$_\odot$) just below the mass cut between the exploding interior and the final inner core.

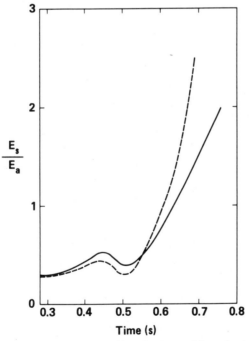

Fig. 11. - The solid curve is one tenth of the ratio of the number of electrons plus positrons to the number of protons for the 25 M$_\odot$ model, versus time in seconds. Dashed curve is the ratio of heating by neutrino scattering on electrons to the heating by neutrino absorption on free baryons. The electron scattering heating includes the mu and tau neutrinos.

REFERENCES

Bethe, H. A., Brown, G., Cooperstein, J., and Wilson, J. R. 1983, Nucl. Phys., A 403, 625.

Bowers, R., and Wilson, J. 1982a, Ap. J. Suppl., 50, 115.

————. 1982b, Ap. J., 263, 366.

Colgate, S., and Petschek, A. 1979, Ap. J. (Letters), 236, L115.

Epstein, R. 1979, M.N.R.A.S., 188, 305.

Hildebrandt, W. 1982, Astr. Ap., 110, L3.

Smarr, L., Wilson, J., Barton, R., and Bowers, R. 1981, Ap. J., 246, 515

Adiabatic Collapse and Explosion of Low Mass Iron Stellar Cores[*]

S. A. Bludman
University of Pennsylvania

I. Lichtenstadt[†]
University of Pennsylvania

ABSTRACT

We investigate the adiabatic collapse of 1.7 and 1.5 $M_\odot$ iron cores using the LLRP equation of state and Fermi gas electron capture rates. For a variety of initial and configurations, infall deleptonization leaves a homologous core of only 1 $M_\odot$; the large overlay mass that the shock must penetrate and dissociate then prevents significant ejection of mass and kinetic energy. If all electron capture is artificially suppress, we do obtain ejection of 0.1 $M_\odot$ with 5×10^{50} and 2×10^{52} ergs kinetic energy for the 1.7 and 1.5 $M_\odot$ initial cores respectively. In these mass stars, neutrino processes are not responsible for supernova explosion but instead kill the otherwise efficient thermal stiffening mechanism. The initial iron core configuration needed for a supernova explosion must be cooler, and therefore lighter and more isentropic, then those cores heretofore considered. Such a cooler pre-supernova configuration can evolve if hydrostatic electron capture leads to greater neutrino cooling before the contraction becomes dynamic.

I. INTRODUCTION: EQUATION OF STATE

In this paper we report on the collapse of a number of more-or-less realistic iron cores, using the Illinois equation of state (LLPR) for warm nuclear matter below nuclear saturation density (Lamb et al. 1978, 1981). We assume Newtonian gravity and

---

[*]Dedicated to J. R. Wilson on his 60th birthday. Supported in part by the U.S. Department of Energy under Contract EY-76-C-02-3071.

[†]Permanent address: Racah Institute of Physics, Hebrew University, Jerusalem, Israel.

complete neutrino trapping at all times (adiabatic hydrodynamics).
Because neutrino losses can only increase the deleptonization during
collapse and the shock dissipation during rebound, there is little
purpose in including the dilatorious effects of neutrino transport
until after an explosion is obtained in the adiabatic case. We are
thus using state-of-the-art initial core configurations, equations of
state and hydrodynamics to find necessary (but not sufficient) conditions for supernova explosion.

The four initial configurations we considered were those of
Weaver et al. (1978) for M = 1.7 $M_\odot$ and those of Arnett (1978, 1982)
of Woosley and Weaver (1982), and of our own construction for $M/M_\odot$ =
1.53, 1.48, and 1.45 respectively.

Wherever possible, we used the LLPR equation of state (LATEOS) in
tabular form as kindly furnished us by J. M. Lattimer. For $\rho < 10^8$g
cm^{-3}, T < 4 x 10^9K, where the LLPR table ends, we used our own equation of state (ZIGEOS) in which four nuclear species (n, p, α, an
average heavy nucleus) are included in the Saha equation (Epstein
and Arnett 1975) and the internal partition function for the heavy
nucleus was taken from Tubbs and Koonin (1979). This simple analytic
equation of state agrees well with the LLPR tables, so long as nuclear interactions are small ($\rho < 10^{13}$g cm^{-3}). The join-up between
ZIGEOS and LATEOS, which we effected at low ρ and T, presented no
problems.

We corrected the LLPR table for the semi-relativity of the electrons (important at low densities) and for one density entry at
ρ = 1.6 x 10^{14}g cm^{-3}, where the bubble phase had inadvertently been
omitted from the table. Except in the narrow density region of this
bubble phase transition at about half nuclear density, the LLPR equation of state, which is derived from the liquid-drop models of the
nucleus with effective Skyrme potential, agrees well with the equation of state of Bonche and Vautherin (1981), which is derived from
the Hartree-Fock approximation. Because, at these densities, the
core collapse is already in rapid free-fall, any of these small
changes in the equation of state over a narrow density range have
negligible effect on the hydrodynamics. In fact, the correction to
the LLPR table at the density entry ρ = 1.6 x 10^{14}g cm^{-3} had no
significant effect on the hydrodynamics.

As described earlier (Lichtenstadt et al. 1980), we used 100 mass zones, the inner 30 equally spaced in mass, the outer 70 with geometrically decreasing mass content, so as to produce fine zoning where mass ejection is expected. Our numerical time step was chosen to allow a maximum 2% density change in each mass zone, leading to overall energy unbalance less than 2-3% of the initial energy, internal plus kinetic plus gravitational. This makes the uncertainty in ejected kinetic energy about 4×10^{50} ergs. An explosion weaker than this is probably not significant numerically nor typical of type II supernovae.

With the LLPR equation of state, Van Riper and Lattimer (1981) and Van Riper (1982) had already shown for a 1.61 $M_\odot$ iron core that incuding electron capture led to a small (0.9 $M_\odot$) homologous core and no explosion; without electron capture, a larger (1.2 $M_\odot$) homologous core formed and a weak explosion was obtained. Our own results for a 1.7 $M_\odot$ core are compared with Van Riper and Lattimer's in Table 1 and show remarkably good agreement. [M_{hc} is the mass of the homologous core formed in collapse, defined by where v/R departed from constancy by 20% or more, ρ_b the highest central density reached, $(S/kN_b)_{peak}$ and $(S/kN_b)_{sh}$ the maximum entropy per baryon reached and the entropy per baryon of the material just behind the shock front, M_{sh} the mass of the shock material, v_{sh} the approximate speed of the shock front, K_{ej} the kinetic energy of the ejected matter.] So far as we know, this is the first time independent workers, using the same realistic equation of state and initial configuration, have checked one another's hydrodynamics to this extent. (With a schematic equation of state and an initial polytropic configuration Van Riper's and our calculations had previously checked in the A. Yahil "tournament".) This gives confidence in our hydrodynamics and handling of the equation of state, and permitted us to proceed to investigate a variety of lower mass initial configurations in which an explosion might be obtained, at least in the absence of neutrino transport.

II. PRE-SUPERNOVA CONFIGURATIONS

We studied three low mass initial configurations: A, the 1.53 $M_\odot$ fore Arnett (1978, 1982) evolved from a 4 $M_\odot$ helium core; W, the

TABLE 1

Collapse of a High-Mass Initial Configuration Calculated
with the LLPR Equation of State, Assuming Complete Neutrino Trapping

	Van Riper	Present Calculation
Initial Core Mass ($M_\odot$)	1.61	1.7
With Electron Capture		
Run number	15 (includes GR)	20
$M_{hc}/M_\odot$	0.9	1.0
$\rho_b/10^{14} \text{g cm}^{-3}$	NA	> 3.4
Without Electron Capture		
Run number	19	19
$M_{hc}/M_\odot$	1.2	1.2
$\rho_b/10^{14} \text{g cm}^{-3}$	6	3.4
$(S/kN_b)_{PEAK}$	15	16
$v_{sh}/10^9 \text{cm sec}^{-1}$	2	2
$K_{ej}/10^{50} \text{erg}$	4.5	5
$M_{sh}/M_\odot$	1.53	1.55
$(S/k N_b)_{sh}$	8	10

1.48 $M_\odot$ core Woosley et al. (1980), Woosley and Weaver (1982) evolved
from a 10 $M_\odot$ Main Sequence star; and S, the 1.45 $M_\odot$ core we constructed by assuming constant entropy. The mechanical structure, shown in
the lower half of Figure 1, is in all three cases practically that of
an n = 3 polytrope. This mechanical structure is fixed by the hydrostatic equilibrium of the pre-supernova under nearly relativistic
partially degenerate electron pressure support.

The pre-supernova thermal structure is determined in a more complicated and theoretically more questionable way: for the burned out
core, by the earlier convective mixing and hydrostatic electron capture during the late stages of evolution; for the silicon-burning
shell, by equilibrium between nuclear energy generation and neutrino

losses. This leaves A and W with a 50-100% positive entropy gradient from M = 0 to 1.4 $M_\odot$. The thermal structure is decisive for the ultimate fate of the core: by fixing the initial nuclear excitation and dissociation, it determines the infall deleptonization and therefore the size of the homologous core and how far out the bounce shock forms. For a 1.5 $M_\odot$ iron core, 0.3 $M_\odot$ above the Chandrasekhar limit, the mass-averaged entropy per baryon must be $<S/k\ N_b> = 1.4$. Our isentropic initial configuration S represents the limit of convective stability and, for a given mass, is cooler (hotter) than A and W for mass shells outside (inside) M = 0.6 $M_\odot$. Since the lower entropy allows neutron shell blockage to set in sooner and yields fewer free protons, this is most favorable for propagation of the reflected shock.

The upper half of Figure 1 shows the thermal structure, under the LLPR equation of state, for the three initial configurations considered. Because A and W were evolved with their own equations of state, their temperatures might need to be adjusted to yield the hydrostatic pressure needed for their configurations. In the case of W, this temperature adjustment is insignificant and too small to show in any of the figures. With Arnett's configuration, the unadjusted and adjusted profiles are marked by A and A' respectively in Figures 1, 2 and 8. The temperature adjustment is confined to the mass zones 1.15 - 1.35 $M_\odot$, where the initial densities and temperatures are $\rho = 10^8 - 10^9 g\ cm^{-3}$ and T = 0.6-0.7 Mev, and has almost no effect on subsequent hydrodynamic developments. (Although we ran with both A and A' initial configurations, in Figures 3-7 we show results for A only.) Nevertheless, this does suggest that in a relatively low density - low temperature regime, where the equation of state should be very well known, Arnett's equation of state is a little softer than LLPR.

On the whole, however, Figure 1 shows how well the three initial configurations agree: they are all roughly isothermal, A and W showing a 24% and S showing a 32% temperature gradient per solar mass out to M - 1.3 $M_\odot$.

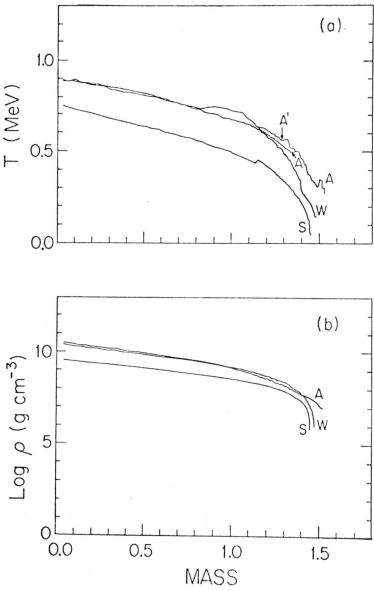

Fig. 1-Comparison of W, A, and S initial density and temperature profiles. (The abscissae are in all cases the included mass in solar
mass units.) The curve A' shows the temperature adjustment to A
necessary to obtain the LATEOS pressure with this configuration. The
adjustment to W is imperceptible. The isentropic configuration S is
shown at an earlier stage in the collapse than are W and A. All
configurations are approximately isothermal out to the silicon-burning shell at 1.4 $M_\odot$ where the density reduces precipitously.

III.   HOMOLOGOUS COLLAPSE

We now initiated the collapse for A, W, and S by a small inward
velocity and allowed electron capture to take place on free protons
and, until neutron shell blockage, on average heavy nuclei at rates
determined by the Fermi gas approximation for nuclei (Bludman et al.
1982). In addition, for the initial configuration W (which is nearly
the same as A or A') we turned off all electron capture and allowed
the collapse and rebound to proceed without any deleptonization.
This case is designated W-Ad hereafter.

The ensuing pressure profiles are shown in Figure 2 at moments
when the central density has reached $\rho_c = 10^{11}$ and 10^{13}g cm^{-3}. At
each moment and at all mass zones, A, A', and W have produced least,
and W-Ad has produced most pressure. Besides thermal dissociation,
electron capture produces a most important additional pressure deficit, even though all neutrinos are being kept always trapped. For
the different initial configurations W, A, and A' the pressure profiles evolving are not much different. The isentropic initial configuration S initially reduces electron capture over most of the star.
By the time higher densities and entropies are reached, however, the
pressure deficit with S approaches that with A or W.

In Figure 3, we show density profiles for about 20 instants during
the collapse for the three initial confiturations A, W, and S, and
for W-Ad, the case with electron capture entirely suppressed. The
similarity shows that the mass out to $M_{hc} = 1.0 M_\odot$ collapses homologously for A, W, and S, but that $M_{hc} = 1.2 M_\odot$ for W-Ad. The edge of
homology is marked by a vertical arrow in each figure. Because the
complete nuclear dissociation of 0.5 $M_\odot$ will cost 8 x 10^{51} ergs, and
the shock will be formed at the edge of homology with about 6 x 10^{51}
ergs, deleptonization has already fixed the ultimate fate of the
shock!

IV.   SHOCK FORMATION AND PROPAGATION

In Figure 4 we show electron capture profiles and in Figure 5,
mass shell trajectories both before and after the bounce. The formation of the shock at the homology edge and its outward propagation

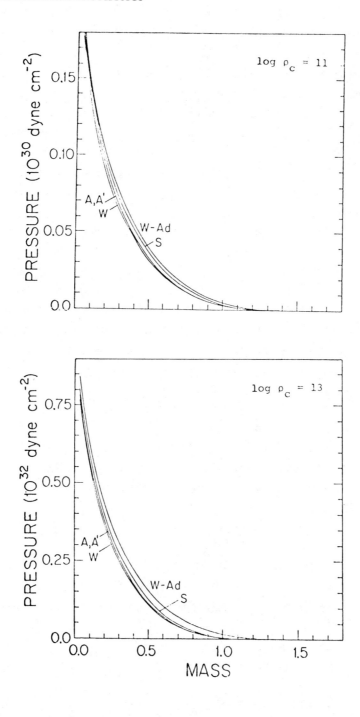

Fig. 2–Pressure profiles for five different runs at two moments during the infall, when the central density has reached $\rho_c = 10^{11}$ gcm^{-3} and when it has reached $\rho_c = 10^{13}$ gcm^{-3}.

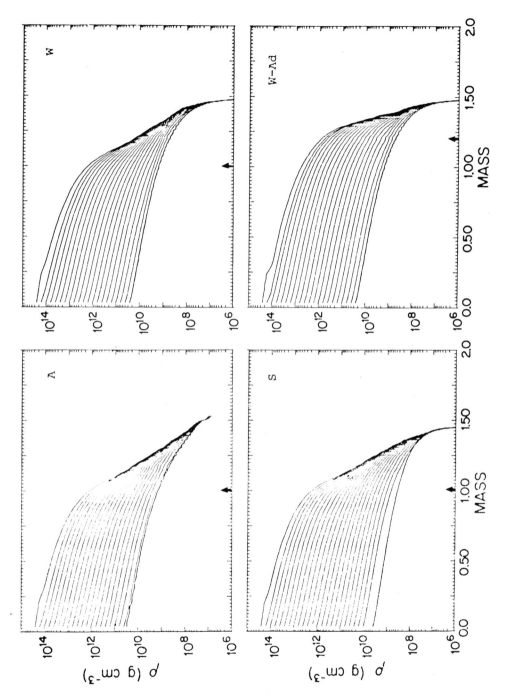

Fig. 3-Density profiles at 22 moments during the collapse for four
different runs. The vertical arrows show the edge of the homologous
core, at which the shock wave forms. Only in the absence of electron
capture (W-Ad) is this far out enough to permit the shock to propagate through the (0.28 $M_{\odot}$) overlap.

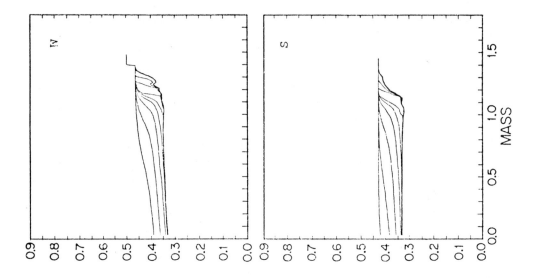

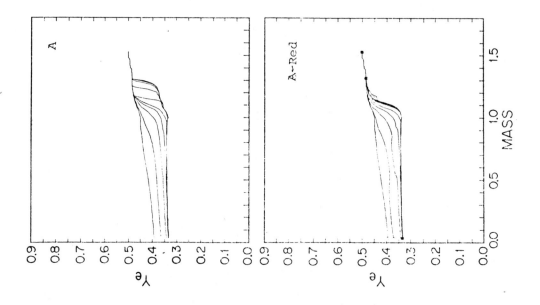

Fig.4-Electron capture profiles at 11 moments during the collapse for three different initial configurations. Note the waves of neutroni- zation accompanying the propagating shock. In A-Red, the initial con- figuration A was used but the electron capture rate on free protons was artificially reduced by a factor 100.

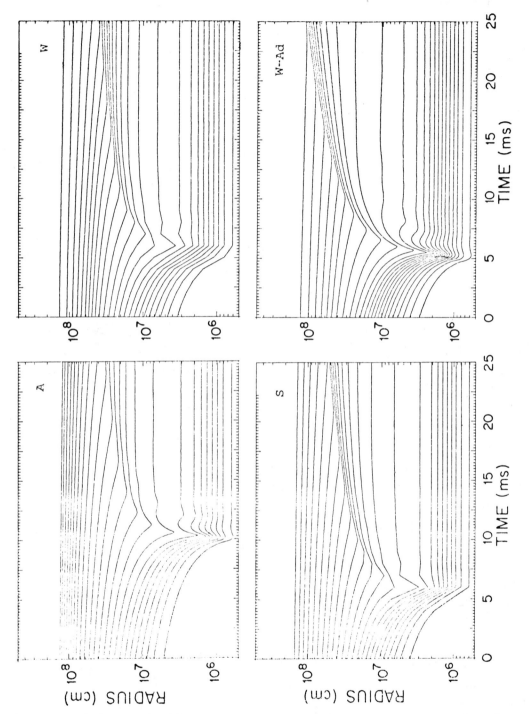

Fig. 5–Positions of different mass shells as a function of time for four different runs 10 ms after bounce. The success or failure of the shock to propagate is already apparent immediately after bounce.

are clear.

In case A-Red of Figure 4 we ran the A initial configuration with
the capture rate on free protons, but no on heavy nuclei, artificially reduced by a factor 100. We did this to compare with Arnett,
whose equation of state has negligible capture on free protons. The
deleptonization, which, until neutron shell blocking is mostly by
heavy nuclei, is the same as in A or W up to the formation of the
shock wave. Thereafter, the shock falters even sooner than in those
cases where electron capture on protons is appreciable. This shows
the positive role of the fast free proton processes in keeping the
out-of-whackness Δ_H close to equilibrium, so that the energy loss by
electron capture on heavies ($\sim \Delta_H^6$) can be moderated.

In Figure 6, already in the first few milliseconds after bounce,
it is clear that a fast-propagating shock forms only when all electron capture is entirely suppressed.

The infall velocity profiles at 10-12 instants are shown in Figure 6. For A and W the shock forms near 0.95 $M_\odot$ and is practically
dissipated after passing through about 0.4 $M_\odot$, at radius 260-270 km.
Because the collapse deleptonization of overlying material is almost
the same for S, the shock again forms at 0.95 $M_\odot$. But because for S
the overlying material is cooler than for A and W, less electron capture takes place during shock penetration and the shock just arrives
at the core edge. Only when there is no electron capture at all
(W-Ad) does the shock commence further out at 1.1 $M_\odot$, allowing a
powerful shock to reach the edge of the core.

Most revealing about the shock propagation are the successive entropy profiles in Figure 7. The shock again starts at the homology
edge, fizzles at 1.3 $M_\odot$ for A and W, and just makes it to the core
edge for S. Only for W-Ad does it reach the edge of the core in
strength. The final entropies for A (and A'), W, S, and W-Ad are
superimposed in Figure 8 and the results are summarized in Table 2.

In all cases, core bounce takes place 20% above nuclear density.
Ten milliseconds after bounce, the shock has reached 350 km for S
and 570 km for W-Ad. While 0.1 $M_\odot$ is nominally ejected in both cases,
the kinetic energy (5 x 10^{50} ergs) is marginal for S and decisive
(2 x 10^{51} ergs) only for W-Ad.

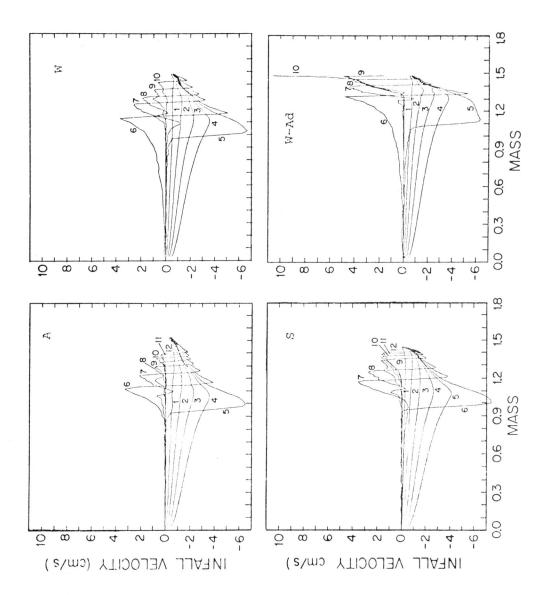

Fig.6-Velocity profiles at ten or twelve moments for four different runs. The bounce takes place near time 5 in runs A, W and W-Ad, and near time 6 in run S. Only in the absence of electron capture does the shock reach the edge of the core.

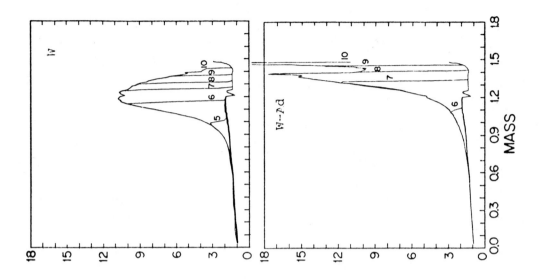

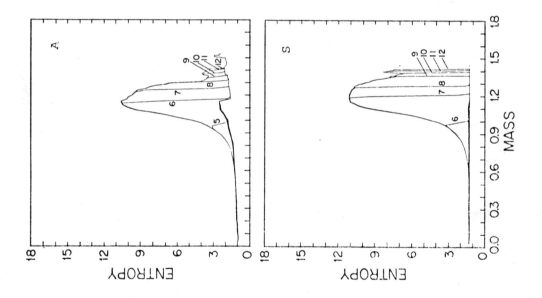

Fig. 7-Entropy profiles at 10-12 different moments during the shock propagation for four different runs. In runs A, W, and S, the shock starts out about M = 0.95 $M_\odot$ and falters about M = 1.3 $M_\odot$. Only in the absence of electron capture (W-Ad) does the shock, starting further out at M = 1.1 $M_\odot$, succeed in propagating to the edge of the core.

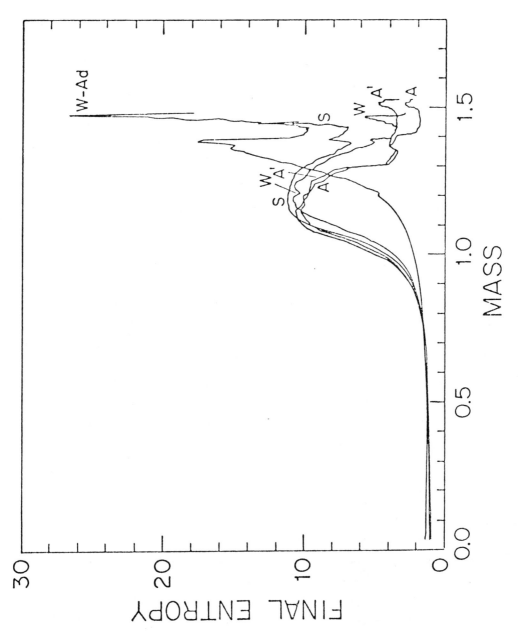

Fig.8-Comparison of the final entropy profiles at the end of five runs. (A and A' refer to the Arnett initial configuration without and with the (small) pressure fix-up.) In runs A, W, and A', electron capture kills the shock at about 1.3 $M_\odot$. With the isentropic initial configuration S, a marginal shock survives out to M=1.42 $M_\odot$. In the absence of electron capture (W-Ad), the shock starts further out and survives the nuclear dissociation losses about M = 1.34 - 1.43 $M_\odot$.

TABLE 2

Three Low-Mass Initial Configurations Collapsed with the
Corrected LLPR Equation of State

Initial Configuration	$\frac{M}{M_\odot}$	Job No.	$\frac{M_{hc}}{M_\odot}$	$\frac{\rho_b}{10^{14} \, \text{gcm}^{-3}}$	$\frac{R_{sh}(10)}{km}$	$\frac{M_{ej}}{M_\odot}$	$\frac{K_{ej}}{10^{51} \, \text{erg}}$
A	1.53	52	1.0	3.4	260	-	-
W	1.48	48	1.0	3.4	270	-	-
W	1.48	50	1.2	3.4	570	0.11	20
S	1.45	40	1.0	3.5	350	0.1	0.5

V.   CONCLUSIONS

Our low mass results are summarized in Table 2, always assuming complete neutrino trapping. The last two columns of the table give the mass and kinetic energy ejected; only in the absence of electron capture was a significant explosion obtained. For the isentropic initial configuration (S) the shock was already marginal at 350 km. Recall that our energy balance to 5×10^{50} ergs makes any lesser kinetic energy ejection numerically insignificant. This warning applies to the weak explosions obtained by other authors as well (Hillebrandt 1982; Arnett 1982) unless it can be demonstrated that their energy balance is appreciably better than ours. Even if numerically significant, such weak explosions do not produce a typical type II supernova which requires at least 2×10^{51} ergs.

We also stress once again that the fate of the shock is already determined during implosion and at densities below the bubble phase transition. The hydrodynamics is insensitive to small changes in the equation of state at higher densities. On the other hand, the equation of state at lower densities should no longer be in dispute. We believe that the mild explosion Arnett (1982) obtained for a low mass core, if energetically significant, results from the practical suppression of free protons in his equation of state, as well as from additional inhibition of electron capture on heavy nuclei.

Our principal conclusion, based on the LLPR equation of state, is that even for iron cores as small as 1.45 $M_\odot$ and even neglecting neutrino losses, "Electron Capture Kills the Shock" (Sack et al. 1980). The powerful explosion we obtained when all electron capture was suppressed, and the marginal explosion we obtained for our isentropic configuration in the presence of electron capture, suggest that a type II supernova may still be just possible, even after neutrino transport is included. This would require a cooler ($<S/k\ N_b>$<1) and therefore smaller ($M \sim 1.35\ M_\odot$) and more isentropic initial core. Such a pre-supernova configuration is massive enough to have burned silicon and for collapse to be still started by thermal dissociation, rather than by electron capture. This per-supernova configuration may evolve if hydrostatic electron capture leads to greater neutrino cooling before core collapse, either because the theoretical capture rates (Fuller et al. 1982) are now higher than previously believed or because better theoretical treatments of convection prolong the last hydrostatic stages of stellar evolution.

We wish to acknowledge useful discussions with our colleagues at the Stellar Collapse Workshop of the Aspen Center for Physics, July, 1982. We are grateful to J. M. Lattimer, who furnished the original table of the LLPR equation of state, and to S. Colgate for the hospitality of the Los Alamos National Laboratory.

REFERENCES

Arnett, W. D. 1978, Ap. J., 219, 1008.
————, 1982, private communication.
Bonche, P., and Vautherin, D. 1981, Nucl. Phys. A, 327, 496.
Bludman, S. A., Lichtenstadt, I., and Hayden, G. 1982, Ap. J., 261, 661.
Epstein, R. I., and Arnett, W. D. 1975, Ap. J., 201, 202.
Fuller, G., Fowler, A. W., and Newman, M. J. 1982, Ap. J. Suppl., 48, 279.
Hillebrandt, W. 1982, Astron. Astrophysics, 110, L3.
Lamb, D. Q., Lattimer, J. M., Pethick, C. J., Ravenhall, D. G. 1978, Phys. Rev. Lett., 41, 1623.
————, 1981, Nucl. Phys., A360, 459.
Lichtenstadt, I., Sack, N., and Bludman, S. A. 1980, Ap. J., 237, 903.
Sack, N., Goldberg, I., Bludman, S. A., and Lichtenstadt, I. 1980, Abhand. Akad. Wiss, Gottingen, Math-Physik Kl. III, Nr. 33, 257.
Tubbs, D. L., and Koonin, S. E. 1979, Ap. J., 232, 59.
Van Riper, K. A., and Lattimer, J. M. 1981, Ap. J., 249, 232.
Van Riper, K. A. 1982, Ap. J., 249, 270.

Weaver, T. A., Zimmerman, G. B., and Woosley, S. E. 1978, Ap. J.,
    225, 1021.
Woosley, S. E., Weaver, T. A., and Taam, R. E. 1980, in "Type I
    Supernovae", ed. J. C. Wheeler (Austin: University of Texas Press).
Woosley, S. W. and Weaver, T.A. 1982, private communication.

The LeBlanc-Wilson Jet Revisited

Eugene M. D. Symbalisty
Harvard-Smithsonian Center for Astrophysics

ABSTRACT

A numerical model of a jet that is similar to the LeBlanc-Wilson
jet of 1970 is examined using a modern magnetorotational stellar
collapse code. The model allows 0.007 $M_\odot$ of matter to escape, but
requires very strong magnetic fields.

The LeBlanc-Wilson (1970, hereafter LW) jet evolution driven by
magnetorotational stellar collapse first explicitly demonstrated the dramatic role
that the combination of rotation and magnetic fields can play in collapsing stars.
It also provided a possible site for the r-process (Schramm and Barkat 1972, Meier
et al. 1976). Their 7 $M_\odot$ star was initially endowed with 0.25% rotational energy
and 0.025% magnetic energy, normalized to the gravitational energy, and collapsed
to a central density of 10^{11} gm/cc, producing a polar jet that it was estimated
would eject 0.06 $M_\odot$ Field strengths of 10^{15} gauss were reached during the
evolution. In contrast, both their spherically symmetric and rotation-only models
collapsed to 10^{13} gm/cc and no matter achieved escape energy, though some matter
did leave the computational grid in the rotational case.

A magnetorotational stellar collapse code was written (Symbalisty 1984,
hereafter Paper I) under the guidance of J. LeBlanc and J.R. Wilson for the purpose
of searching for a possible r-process site and a possible ingredient in the more
general supernova problem. The code is a Newtonian, Eulerian, adaptive mesh
scheme written in spherical coordinates. It assumes symmetry about the rotation
axis and through the equator.

The code incorporates improvements made since 1970 in the equation of state
of nuclear matter, the physics of neutrino transport, and the initial configuration
of the core. Spherically symmetric test evolutions were found to track the one-

dimensional evolution of Bowers and Wilson (1982). The physical and numerical details of the code are reported in Paper I. The implications of the rotation-only models as possible r-process sites have been discussed elsewhere (Symbalisty et al. 1984). In this paper I discuss how to evolve a LeBlanc-Wilson jet today.

The starting point for the collapse evolution is the inner 2.7 $M_\odot$ of the 15 $M_\odot$ model of Weaver et al. (1978), taken at a time when the central density is 6 x 10^9 gm/cc, the core is principally ^{56}Fe, and the onset of collapse due to the photodisintegration of the iron has begun. From Weaver et al. profiles of density, temperature, and radial velocity vs. radius are obtained. To the 2.7 $M_\odot$ is added rotational and magnetic energy via the following technique:

$$\Omega(r,\theta) = \Omega(r) = k_\phi \, f(r),$$
$$A_\phi(r,\theta) = -k_m \, r \, \sin\theta/(1+(r/r_c)^3).$$

The constants k_ϕ and k_m are chosen such that the desired initial rotational and magnetic energies are obtained. The function $f(r)$ is obtained by evolving the model of Weaver et al. from an earlier time with uniform angular velocity Ω and allowing it to evolve assuming local conservation of angular momentum. The constant r_c is chosen such that the field derived from the vector potential A_ϕ is nearly polar and uniform over the inner 1 $M_\odot$ and falls off like a dipole field for $r \gg r_c$.

The density is then scaled, via the virial theorem, so that the core is still in a state of collapse. The quantities k_ϕ, k_m, $f(r)$, and r_c therefore represent our parametrization of the rotational energy, magnetic energy, angular velocity profile, and magnetic field profile. In the numerical explorations only k_ϕ and k_m were varied so that the evolutions can be characterized by their initial rotational/gravitational energy ratio, β_ϕ, and initial magnetic/gravitational energy ratio, β_H.

It was found through a parameter search in β_ϕ (β_H set equal to zero) that models collapsing with initial β_ϕ less than 1% do not explode and do not eject any matter. Models with β_ϕ equal to 4.5% also do not explode but do allow some mass to be ejected (Paper I). Then β_ϕ was set to 4.5% and β_H was varied. Initial β_H less than 0.053% produced evolutions dynamically indistinguishable from rotation-only models, though field strengths reached 10^{15} gauss. When β_H is pushed to 0.56% (about 20 times the LW value) a jet-like explosion ensues (see Figs. 1 and 2). The figures are truncated at 1000-1500 km because, even though the grid extends to 10,000 km, there is little action beyond 1500 km. The core first collapses to a rotational quasi-equilibrium stage. The rotation-only (and small β_H) models would evolve to this point and then develop an expanding circulation region. In this case the quasi-equilibrium persists for only 6 ms. The magnetic pressure is able (1) to turn the vortex expansion into the jet-like explosion outside the quasi-equilibrium radius of 50 km, and (2) to break the quasi-equilibrium and allow the core to collapse sightly beyond nuclear matter density. In contrast, the LW collapse was halted at a central density of 10^{11} gm/cc, a factor of 100 less than their spherically symmetric and rotation-only evolutions.

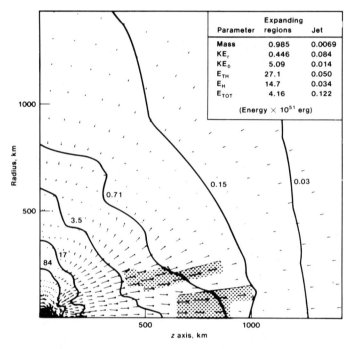

Parameter	Expanding regions	Jet
Mass	0.985	0.0069
KE_r	0.446	0.084
KE_ϕ	5.09	0.014
E_{TH}	27.1	0.050
E_H	14.7	0.034
E_{TOT}	4.16	0.122

(Energy $\times\ 10^{51}$ erg)

Fig. 1 - Velocity vector profile in the RZ-plane. Iso-density contours are superimposed ($\times\ 10^8$ gm/cc). The velocities of the shaded regions exceed escape velocity.

Figure 1 displays the velocity vector profile, at the end of the computation, in one quadrant of the RZ-plane. R is the distance from the Z-axis. The Z-axis is the axis of rotation, with the equator being the Z=0 plane. The largest vector has a magnitude of 44,000 km/s and the others are scaled linearly. Iso-density contours are superimposed in units of 10^8 gm/cc. The peaking of the density contours along the Z-axis behind the shock front (Z ~ 1200 km) demonstrates that a wholesale explosion has begun. The portions of the expansion region that are shaded in the figure have radial velocities that exceed escape velocities, which defines the jet. The table inset in Figure 1 gives the mass (in solar units), the radial kinetic energy (KE_r), the rotational kinetic energy (KE_ϕ), the material thermal energy (E_{TH}), the magnetic field energy (E_H), and the total energy (E_{TOT}), both in the expanding regions and in the jet. Figure 2 shows the structure behind the shock front and within the polar jet via density, temperature, and n_n/n_p contours, where n_n and n_p are the neutron and proton number densities, respectively. The material at the base of the explosion is electron poor with a charge per baryon of 0.15.

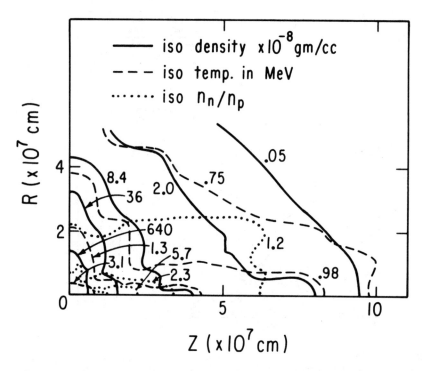

Fig. 2 - Structure behind the shock front within the polar jet.

The final equilibrium core has a radius of 60 km, an average density of 2.5×10^{12} gm/cc (with a corresponding mass of 1.1 $M_\odot$), an average angular velocity of 163 rad/s, and an average field strength of 5×10^{15} gauss. The huge field strength may be unrealistic but is necessary to produce a LW jet. It should be noted that $10^{13} - 10^{15}$ gauss fields were necessary for LW, even though the LW collapse was halted at the much lower density of 10^{11} gm/cc. Extreme field strengths are necessary in both models because the jet is an atmospheric phenomenon, i.e., it starts beyond the core equilibrium radius where the density is 3×10^9 gm/cc. Therefore in the new evolution the magnetic pressure is competing with approximately the same material pressure as in the LW model.

The interplay between rotation and magnetic fields can be examined by tracing the evolution of the rotational energy ratio as a function of radius $\beta_\phi(r)$, the magnetic energy ratio $\beta_H(r)$, and their ratio β_H/β_ϕ. These quantities are defined as

$$\beta_\phi(r) = \frac{1}{GE(r)} \ I(\frac{1}{2}\rho v_\phi^2)$$

and

$$\beta_H(r) = \frac{1}{GE(r)} \ I(\frac{H^2}{8\pi}),$$

where

$$GE(r) = I(\frac{1}{2}\rho F),$$

$$I(x) = \int_o^r \int_\phi \int_\theta xr^2 dr \ sin\theta d\theta \ d\phi,$$

and F is the gravitational potential. Figures 3, 4, and 5 plot time sequences of β_ϕ, β_H, and $\log(\beta_H/\beta_\phi)$, respectively, for the four times 229, 236, 243, and 247 ms. At t = 229 ms the rotational quasi-equilibrium has been established with a central density of 1.9×10^{13} gm/cc. At this time there is no jet, but only a circulation pattern, as in the rotation-only models. This pattern is centered at r ∼ 70 km and an angle (measured from the Z-axis) of 25°. This quasi-equilibrium persists for about 7 ms, until t = 236 ms. By this time, a genuine jet has developed extending to a radius of 400 km, and the core has begun to collapse further. The central density is now 2.8×10^{13} gm/cc. The core rapidly collapses for the next 7 ms, until t = 243 ms. The central density is now 1.1×10^{14} gm/cc and the maximum jet radius is 850 km. The evolution is stopped 4 ms later, when the jet extends to 1000 km (see Fig. 1) and the central density is 1.4×10^{14} gm/cc. This is actually 1.3 times nuclear matter density for the equation of state used here because the charge per baryon is only 0.19 (see Fig. 6).

The calculation is halted at this time for several reasons. Beyond r ∼ 2000 km the zoning becomes coarse and thermonuclear burn should probably be included. Also, the Courant hydrodynamic timestep is now 1 μs, and, even with jet velocities one tenth the speed of light, it would require several thousands of cycles for appreciable movement of the jet, which is costly.

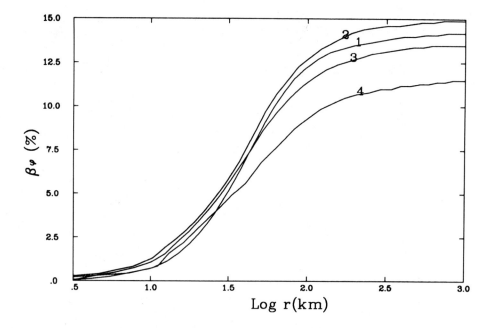

Fig. 3 - Time sequence of β_ϕ vs. r. In figures 3 - 5, the labels 1, 2, 3, and 4 correspond to the times 229, 236, 243, and 247 ms, respectively.

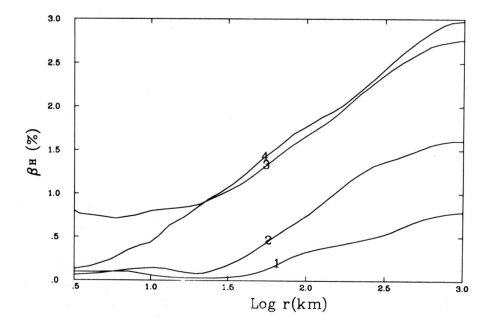

Fig. 4 - Time sequence of β_H vs. r.

The rotational energy ratio peaks at 236 ms, reaching 14.9% at 1000 km, which is only a 0.7% gain from the rotational quasi-equilibrium value (see Fig. 3). After 236 ms, β_ϕ decreases steadily to a value of 11.5% at 247 ms. The circulation pattern has disappeared entirely and has been replaced by a rapidly growing polar jet. In contrast, the rotation model evolved to a final β_ϕ of 16.9%. The magnetic energy ratio $\beta_H(r)$, for r greater than 25 km, steadily increases from its 229 ms value of 0.8% (at 1000 km) to a final value of 3.0% (see Fig. 4). The quantity β_H grows rapidly until nuclear matter density is reached (243 ms) and gradually increases thereafter. The lost rotational energy is clearly the magnetic field's gain. For radii less than 25 km, β_H actually peaks at 243 ms, because of the fact that the strongly twisted fields do not smooth out immediately. The depression of log (β_H/β_ϕ) at r = 32 km (see Fig. 5) at t = 229 ms, which then shifts inward 10 km by t = 236 ms, is thought to be the reason why magnetic pressure not only powers an LW jet, but also forces collapse to nuclear matter density. This depression has disappeared by 243 ms.

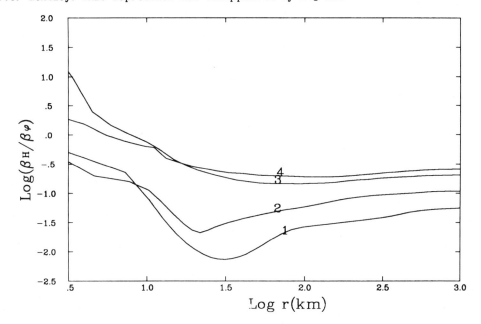

Fig. 5 – Time sequence of log(β_H/β_ϕ) vs. r.

In summary, I have shown that the LW jet survives the improvements in stellar collapse physics since 1970, but the details are quite different. The production of the jet requires even more intense fields than LW and such fields ($10^{15} - 10^{16}$ gauss) have not been observed in nature. In the evolution described here 1.0 $M_\odot$ is expanding outside a 1.1 $M_\odot$ equilibrium core with a total energy of 4.2 x 10^{51} erg.

The escaping mass is 0.007 $M_\odot$ with a total energy of 0.12 x 10^{51} erg. If 10^{15} gauss fields can be realized, then the further evolution of the jet should provide an interesting site for element formation, as is the case for the rotation-only models (Symbalisty et al. 1984).

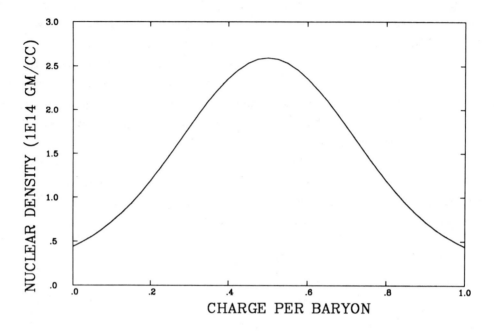

Fig. 6 - The nuclear matter density as a function of the charge per baryon from the equation of state used in this calculation.

This research was supported by the DOE at Lawrence Livermore Laboratory, by NASA NSG 7212 Supp # 6 at the University of Chicago, and by NSF AST 81-19545 at Harvard.

REFERENCES

Bowers, R.L., and Wilson, J.R. 1982, Ap. J., 263, 366.

LeBlanc, J., and Wilson, J.R. 1970, Ap. J., 161, 541 (LW).

Meier, D.L., Epstein, R.I., Arnett, W.D., and Schramm, D.N. 1976, Ap. J., 204, 689.

Schramm, D.N., and Barkat, Z. 1972, Ap. J., 173, 195.

Symbalisty, E.M.D. 1984, Ap. J., in press (Oct. 15: Paper I).

Symbalisty, E.M.D., Schramm, D.N., and Wilson, J.R. 1984, Ap. J. (Letters), in press.

Weaver, T., Zimmerman, G., and Woosley, S. 1978, Ap. J., 225, 1021.

Matter at Subnuclear Densities

C. J. Pethick
NORDITA, Copenhagen, Denmark
University of Illinois at Urbana-Champaign

D. G. Ravenhall
University of Illinois at Urbana-Champaign

ABSTRACT

We give a brief review of the properties of matter at subnuclear densities, and at temperatures less than some tens of MeV, paying particular attention to some of the unusual shapes nuclei may adopt at densities close to the nuclear saturation density.

As we have heard in a number of other contributions at this symposium, the equation of state of matter at densities comparable with that of nuclear matter and at temperatures of the order of tens of MeV is one of the important ingredients in stellar collapse calculations (see, e.g., Baym 1983, Bludman and Lichtenstadt 1983 and Bowers 1983). The densities of interest are at most a few times nuclear matter density, and therefore the hadronic part of matter may be regarded as being made up of nucleons, rather than quarks. In addition to the nucleons, matter contains electrons, which preserve the electrical neutrality, and neutrinos, which by blocking neutrino final states prevent protons from capturing energetic electrons.

The first question we address is: under what conditions does dense matter contain nuclei? The electrons are spatially uniform to a very good approximation, since the electronic screening length is large compared with typical nuclear length scales, and the neutrinos may be treated as a free Fermi gas. Thus the problem is to determine the state of the nucleons. A simple way of describing

nuclei is by means of the compressible liquid drop model, which is a generalization of the Bethe-Weizsäcker semi-empirical mass formula. Nuclei are regarded as drops of nuclear matter whose energy may be expressed as a sum of bulk,
surface, Coulomb and other contributions. In contrast to the usual semi-
empirical mass formula, the density of nuclear matter is not fixed, but is
determined by the condition for pressure equilibrium. (This is an essential
refinement for the astrophysical situations for which the equation of state is
designed.) Such models have been introduced by Myers and Swiatecki (1969), and
by Baym, Bethe, and Pethick (1971). The model may appear excessively crude -- it
is, after all, based on ideas developed about 50 years ago, and nuclear physics
has advanced in that time. It has, however, a number of great virtues for the
problem we are considering. First of all, the model is rich enough that
important new pieces of physics can be incorporated: among them are the effect
of finite temperature on bulk nuclear properties, the presence of evaporated
nucleons outside nuclei and their effect on surface properties of nuclei, and
the reduction of the nuclear Coulomb energy due to interactions between nuclei.
Second, calculations using the model are simple, making it ideal for obtaining
properties of matter over a wide range of conditions. It is true that the model
does not give a detailed description of the properties of individual nuclear
energy levels, but such information is largely superfluous for most applications
to stellar collapse. We note, though, that when calculating nuclear reaction
rates at the low temperatures encountered in stars burning hydrogen, helium,
carbon, oxygen and other relatively light elements, one does need detailed
information about individual energy levels, and therefore the liquid drop model
is not very useful there.

If one neglects all contributions to the energy except the bulk ones, the
problem of determining when nuclei are present reduces to finding the conditions
under which hot nuclear matter can be in equilibrium with a nucleon vapor. At
a low (but finite) temperature, matter forms a vapor at low densities. As the
density is increased, a point is reached when a liquid begins to condense, and
with further increase in density the fraction of space occupied by the liquid
will increase until eventually the liquid occupies all of space. Condensation
will not occur if the temperature exceeds some particular value, which is usually
close to the critical temperature. The condition for coexistence of two phases
is that the chemical potentials of the constituents be equal in the two phases
and the pressures be equal. A review of such calculations is given by Lattimer
(1981). The boundary of the two-phase region calculated by Lattimer and

Ravenhall (1978) using the Skyrme I' interaction for the internuclon potential
is shown in Figure 1, where it is the line marked "Bulk equilibrium". An
important point to notice is that for densities approaching nuclear matter
density, the two-phase region persists to temperatures approaching 20 MeV.

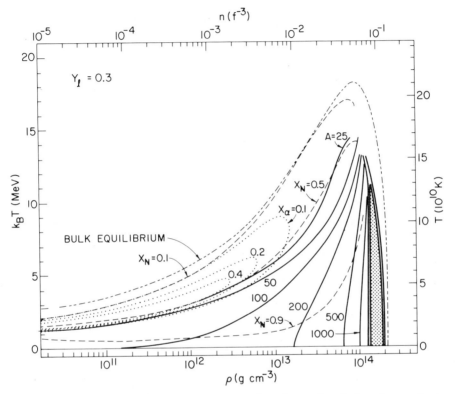

Fig. 1.- Properties of hot dense matter at subnuclear densities for a lepton
fraction $Y_\ell = 0.3$. The line labelled "Bulk equilibrium" denotes the boundary of
the two-phase region when surface and Coulomb effects are ignored. Finite
nucleus effects were calculated using the methods of Lamb, Lattimer, Pethick, and
Ravenhall (1978, 1984). X_α is the fraction of baryons in alpha particles, and X_N
the fraction in heavy nuclei (including alpha particles). Bubbles are present in
the dotted region, and mixtures (nuclei-bubbles, bubbles-uniform matter, or
nuclei-uniform matter) in the surrounding narrow regions.

    Now let us turn to other contributions to the free energy. First consider
the Coulomb energy. In most circumstances nuclear energies are very large
compared with typical "solid-state" energies, and it is therefore often possible
to neglect solid-state effects when determining nuclear properties. Matter at
the densities of interest here provides a striking counterexample to this general
rule: typical spacings between nuclei are comparable to the size of a nucleus,
and therefore the Coulomb lattice energy, a solid-state effect, can be

comparable to the Coulomb energy of an individual nucleus. If nuclei were to fill all of space, the total Coulomb energy would vanish, since the net charge density, proportional to the difference of the electron and proton charge densities, would vanish everywhere. A simple calculation of the size of this effect can be made in the Wigner-Seitz approximation, in which one imagines each nucleus to be at the center of a spherical cell containing just enough electrons to render the cell electrically neutral. If one neglects the interaction between cells one finds that the total Coulomb energy is

$$E_{Coul} = \frac{3}{5} \frac{Z^2 e^2}{r_N} \left(1 - \frac{3}{2} \frac{r_N}{r_c} + \frac{1}{2} \left(\frac{r_N}{r_c}\right)^3\right),$$ (1)

where Z is the atomic number of the nucleus, r_N the nuclear radius and r_c the radius of the Wigner-Seitz cell. The prefactor is the energy of an isolated nucleus and the second term is $-9/10\ Z^2 e^2/r_c$, the well-known result for the lattice energy in this approximation. The final term, proportional to r_N^2/r_c^3, is due to the finite size of the nucleus. Note that when nuclei fill all of space ($r_N = r_c$), the total Coulomb energy vanishes. The lattice effect reduces the Coulomb energy significantly even when nuclei fill only a small fraction of space; for example, when nuclei fill 10^{-3} of space, r_N/r_c is 0.1 and the Coulomb energy is reduced by 15%, and when nuclei fill half of space, the Coulomb energy is less than 6% of its value for an isolated nucleus.

Now let us turn to the nuclear surface. In most applications, the surface property of most interest is the surface tension, which is the thermodynamic potential per unit area. It is important to note that for nuclei with a neutron excess, the thermodynamic potential per unit area is not the same as the free energy per unit area, as has been stressed particularly by Ravenhall, Pethick and Lattimer (1983). The surface tension is reasonably well determined experimentally only for cold nuclei with roughly equal numbers of neutrons and protons, and there is little information available about how it behaves for nuclei with a neutron excess, or at finite temperatures. The surface thermodynamic potential per nucleus may be written as

$$\Omega_{surf} = 4\pi r_N^2\ \sigma(x,T),$$ (2)

where $\sigma(x,T)$ is the surface tension as a function of the proton concentration, x, of matter in the nucleus, and of the temperature T. As T is increased the surface of a nucleus becomes more diffuse and the surface tension decreases, vanishing at the critical temperature, when the matter inside the nucleus and the evaporated matter outside become identical. Calculations of the T and x dependence of the surface tension have been carried out by Ravenhall, Pethick, and Lattimer (1983) using the Skyrme I' interaction.

To obtain a qualitative understanding of the sizes of nuclei in dense matter, consider the case of low temperature. The main contributions to the free energy are from the bulk, Coulomb and surface terms. The most favorable nuclear size is determined by minimizing the free energy with respect to the nuclear size, and one finds the simple condition

$$\Omega_{surf} = 2\ E_{Coul}. \tag{3}$$

If one writes $r_N = r_o A^{1/3}$, where A is the mass number of the nucleus, one finds

$$A = \frac{\sigma}{\frac{3}{5}\frac{e^2}{r_o^3}x^2}\ (1 - \frac{3}{2}u^{1/3} + \frac{1}{2}u)\ , \tag{4}$$

where $u = (r_N/r_c)^3$ is the fraction of space filled by nuclei. This result enables one to understand simply the trends of A as a function of density and temperature exhibited by the results of more detailed calculations shown in Figure 1. As the density increases, the fraction of space filled by nuclei increases, thereby reducing the size of the Coulomb energy coefficient and increasing A. With increasing temperature, σ decreases and therefore A decreases.

We now turn to the question of the <u>shapes</u> that the nuclei adopt. When nuclei begin to fill an appreciable fraction of space, they become aspherical, as a result of the Coulomb interaction with neighboring nuclei. To obtain some idea of the possibilities, consider spherical nuclei at zero temperature made of incompressible matter. The only contributions to the energy we consider are the bulk, Coulomb, and surface energies of the nuclei, together with the energy of electrons and neutrinos, which play no role in determining the nuclear properties. When nuclei fill half of space ($u = 1/2$), both the Coulomb and surface energies are unchanged if the nuclei are turned inside out. Matter then consists of a lattice of holes (bubbles) in otherwise uniform nuclear matter, rather like an ordered variant of Swiss cheese. When $u < 1/2$, the state with nuclei has the lower energy, while when $u > 1/2$ the bubble state is energetically favorable. In Figure 1 the region where bubbles are preferable to nuclei is also shown.

Recently it was found that states even more exotic than Swiss cheese are energetically favorable at certain densities. Two lines of thought led to the discovery: first, a couple of years ago Jim LeBlanc and Jim Wilson calculated properties of cylindrical nuclei in the Thomas-Fermi approximation, and found that they had a lower energy than spherical nuclei for $u \geqslant 0.1$. The other train of thought started from Jog and Smith's (1982) calculations which showed that at lower densities mixed crystals containing two different nuclei could have a lower energy than a mixture of pure crystals. The physical reason for the stability of the mixed crystal state is the interplay of nuclear and solid-state energies. These results led us to ask, in a paper written with Jim Wilson (Ravenhall, Pethick, and Wilson 1983) whether there may be phases of dense matter in which nuclei (or bubbles) are not spherical. The first possibilities considered were rods, or alternatively plates, of nuclear matter, together with the bubble analog of the rod state -- for obvious reasons the first two states are referred to as spaghetti and lasagna, respectively. (Note that the bubble analogue of lasagna is lasagna, and therefore it does not have to be considered separately.) We considered the case of zero temperature, and in the spirit of the semi-empirical mass formula, expressed the nuclear energy as a sum of bulk, surface and Coulomb terms. The surface and Coulomb energies play the most important role in determining the optimal nuclear shape, and the bulk term has little influence. Each of these states, as well as spherical bubble ones, was found to be energetically favorable for some range of densities. With increasing density the sequence of states encountered is nuclei, spaghetti, lasagna, the bubble analog of spaghetti, bubbles, and finally uniform nuclear matter. One of the surprising results of these calculations is that the more exotic phases are energetically favorable even at densities as low as about a tenth of nuclear matter density.

The few rather symmetrical shapes we considered above are clearly an over-simplification of the ones nuclear matter will actually adopt. For example, the cross section of a strand of 'spaghetti' will not be circular, due to the Coulomb interaction with other strands. Also the spaghetti may be subject to necking instabilities, in which the cross sectional area varies with distance along the strand. To attempt to model the more complicated shapes we regard matter as being made up of objects whose shape is specified by a parameter d, which gives the number of spatial dimensions in which the density of nuclear matter varies. Thus d = 1, 2, and 3 correspond to lasagna, spaghetti, and nuclei, respectively. To allow for shapes intermediate between the ones considered above we treat d as

a continuous variable, whose value is to be determined by minimizing the energy
of the state with respect to d. The surface and Coulomb energies of the various
bubble phases are obtained by replacing u by 1-u in the expressions for the corresponding phases with nuclei. The energetically most favorable values of d are
shown in Figure 2. The symbols N (for nuclei) and B (for bubbles) denote objects
in which the surface of the nuclear matter is convex and concave, respectively.

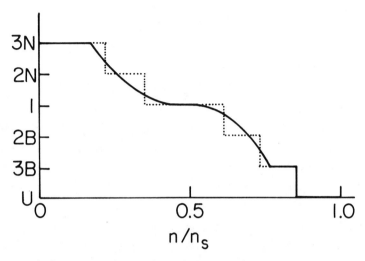

Fig. 2.– Optimal dimensionality of nuclei as a function of density. The
continuous curve is what is obtained if d is treated as a continuous variable.
If d is allowed to take on only the discrete values 1 (plates), 2 (rods) and 3
(spheres) one obtains the dotted line. U denotes uniform matter.

U denotes spatially uniform nuclear matter. If nuclear matter is treated as
incompressible, the curve of d versus n/n_s, the ratio of the density to saturation density, is symmetrical about $n/n_s = 1/2$. The fact that the curves in
Figure 2 do not show this symmetry precisely is due to the fact that in the
calculations we allowed for the finite compressibility of nuclear matter.

The physical reason for aspherical shapes being favorable is that with
increasing density, nuclei become larger and hence less stable to fission. If
one neglects the presence of the electronic background, the condition for a
nucleus to be unstable to small quadrupolar deformation is

$$\Omega_{surf} = 1/2 \; E^o_{Coul}, \tag{5}$$

as was first shown by Bohr and Wheeler (1939). Here $E^o_{Coul} = \frac{3}{5} \frac{z^2 e^2}{r_N}$ is the
Coulomb energy of an isolated nucleus. If we combine this result with equation

(3), which determines the size of the nucleus, one finds that spontaneous fission will occur when

$$1 - \frac{3}{2} u^{1/3} + \frac{1}{2} u = \frac{1}{4} \tag{6}$$

or $u \simeq 0.17$. This value is close to that at which the nuclei-spaghetti transition occurs in detailed calculations.[†]

To obtain a more detailed picture of the shape nuclear matter will have in dense matter requires further calculation. Among the possibilities we can imagine are deformed nuclei located on a lattice which does not have cubic symmetry. Only when the ground state of matter is better understood will it be possible to make a meaningful calculation of finite temperature properties.

The structures we have considered here have a number of similarities with liquid crystals -- in particular we remark that the spaghetti state resembles a so-called discotic liquid crystal, which consists of long molecules which can move relatively freely along their axes, and which are ordered on a two-dimensional lattice in the plane perpendicular to their axes.

To illustrate the effects of the nuclear pressure on the equation of state we show, in Figure 3, results calculated using the compressible liquid drop model (Lamb, Lattimer, Pethick and Ravenhall 1983). Finite temperature effects were included in the calculations, and the plot is for an entropy per nucleon of 1.0 k_B. The results are for a fixed electron fraction $Y_e = 0.3$, with no neutrinos. Roughly speaking, this corresponds over the densities of the phase changes to a lepton fraction $Y_\ell \sim 0.35$. The only possible configurations of the nuclear matter taken into acount were spherical nuclei and spherical bubbles. Over the density range shown, the electrons provide most of the pressure. In the nuclei phase, however, the nuclear pressure is negative at the higher densities, due mainly to the Coulomb lattice effect; the total pressure is reduced by as much as 6%. In the bubbles phase the negative nuclear pressure is even larger, and can amount to almost 17% of the electronic pressure. This is due to the fact that

---

[†]At this stage we should enter a caveat: when the electronic background is taken into account the Bohr-Wheeler condition is modified by terms of order u, which are sufficiently large that the equation corresponding to Eq. (3) has no solution. Thus it appears that the optimal spherical nucleus will not undergo spontaneous fission as the density increases. However, while the nucleus may not be unstable to small distortions, we believe that the basic physical mechanism we have described is correct.

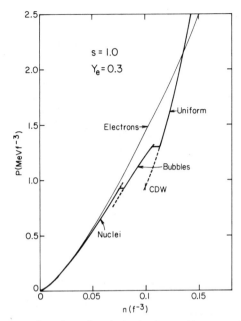

Fig. 3.– Pressure versus density for hot dense matter on the s = 1.0 adiabat for an electron fraction Y_e = 0.3. (Neutrinos are neglected in this calculation.) The dashed portions of the curves correspond to metastable regions, and the vertical line marked "CDW" denotes the point at which the uniform phase becomes unstable to small distortions, leading to a charge density wave (Pethick, Ravenhall, and Lattimer 1983).

both the Coulomb energy, which is lowered by making the charge distribution as uniform as possible, and the surface tension tends to favor shrinking the bubbles. The fact that bubbles can exist only in nuclear matter under tension also accounts for the fact that bubbles disappear at densities somewhat less than the nuclear saturation density. As the density increases further, the pressure rises much more rapidly, due to the large bulk modulus of the uniform nuclear matter.

When the more exotic states described above are taken into account, the first order transitions between nuclei and bubbles will be replaced by a smooth series of transitions through the spaghetti- and lasagna-like states, but the final first order transition between bubbles and uniform matter will remain.

The nuclear pressure in the nuclei and bubble phases may at first sight appear insignificant compared with the electronic contribution. However, one must remember that stellar collapse calculations are very sensitive to the difference between the effective adiabatic index $\Gamma = (\partial \ln P / \partial \ln n)_s$ and 4/3. Since Γ is 4/3 for the electronic contribution, $\Gamma - 4/3$ is determined almost exclusively by the nuclear contribution, and therefore it is important to know that well. In Figure 4 we show Γ as a function of density on the s = 1 adiabat.

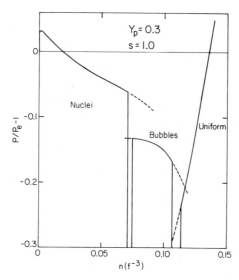

Fig. 4.- Adiabatic index as a function of density for matter on the s = 1.0 adiabat with an electron fraction Y_e = 0.3. (Pethick, Ravenhall, and Lattimer 1983).

When the $d \neq 3$ phases are taken into account the very low value of Γ at the first order nuclei-bubbles transition will be replaced by a general lowering of Γ at densities of the order of $n_s/2$.

The work reported here was performed with support from the U.S. National Science Foundation grants NSF PHY80-25406 and NSF PHY82-01948.

REFERENCES

Baym, G. 1983, these proceedings.

Baym, G., Bethe, H. A., and Pethick, C. J. 1971, Nucl. Phys., A175, 225.

Bludman, S. A., and Lichtenstadt, I. 1983, these proceedings.

Bohr, N., and Wheeler, J. A. 1939, Phys. Rev., 56, 426.

Bowers, R. 1983, these proceedings.

Jog, C. J., and Smith, R. A. 1982, Ap. J., 253, 839.

Lamb, D. Q., Lattimer, J. M., Pethick, C. J., and Ravenhall, D. G.
    1978, Phys. Rev. Lett., 41, 1623;

----. 1984, submitted to Nucl. Phys.

Lattimer, J. M. 1981, Ann. Rev. Nucl. Part. Sci., 31, 337.

Lattimer, J. M., and Ravenhall, D. G. 1978, Ap. J., 223, 314.

Myers, W. D., and Swiatecki, W. J. 1969, Ann. of Phys., 55, 395.

Pethick, C. J., Ravenhall, D. G., and Lattimer, J. M. 1983,
    Nucl. Phys., A414, 513.

Ravenhall, D. G., Pethick, C. J., and Lattimer, J. M. 1983,
    Nucl. Phys., A407, 571.

Ravenhall, D. G., Pethick, C. J., and Wilson, J. R. 1983,
    Phys. Rev. Lett., 50, 2066.

VI. Numerical
Physics

The Early Days of Lagrangian Hydrodynamics at Lawrence Livermore Laboratory*

Bryce S. DeWitt

The University of Texas at Austin

ABSTRACT

Reminiscences about the earliest 2-dimensional hydrodynamic calculations and their impact on later colliding
black hole calculations.

I first arrived at Livermore on September 1, 1952 and was placed
in what they called the "leper colony" for two or three months, waiting for my clearance to come through. I was given two books and told
to read them. One was Chandrasekhar's Radiative Transfer, the other
was Courant and Friedrichs' Supersonic Flow and Shockwaves. I
couldn't understand Chandrasekhar's book, but I did enjoy Courant and
Friedrichs. The day finally arrived when my clearance came through
(this was a little before Jim arrived at the Lab), and I was shown to
my office, right across the hall from Edward Teller. The first thing
that happened was that Teller took me into his office and told me how
bombs were made, with diagrams. I guess he wanted me to lose my vir-
ginity immediately. Then I was asked to study how to calculate problems in neutron diffusion when there are very rapidly changing parameters. So I learned about energy groups and diffusion equations,
about matrices and operators which are not Hermitian and which don't

*This paper was presented at the festschrift banquet in honor of
Jim Wilson.

have complete sets of eigenvectors. I remember seeing some papers of Dirac and Wigner that were still classified, on rather straightforward mathematical problems.

I had an officemate whose name I have forgotten (Jim can't remember it either). Bob Jastrow, who had arranged for me to come to the Lab (the deal was made at the APS Washington meeting, the previous May), was trying to get a two-dimensional hydrodynamic code operating. The reason for this effort had something to do with NATO, which I suppose I mustn't discuss. (But gosh, after 30 years!) At any rate my officemate was involved in it. I, too, began to think about hydrodynamical problems occasionally, particularly after Jim's arrival in the spring of '53. The kind of practical hydrodynamics the Lab had been involved with was spherical, one-dimensional. One used Lagrangian coordinates because they were generally the most accurate. Similar accuracy was needed in the two-dimensional effort, but everyone was afraid of using Lagrangian coordinates because they would inevitably become curvilinear and require the introduction of Jacobians! Being a relativist, I never could understand why people were so worried. I always thought that curvilinear coordinates were as good as any other. Well, you must understand that computers were a little slower in those days than they are now, and it was the Jacobians that really had everyone scared.

I was still working on neutron diffusion, but every once in a while I would talk to my officemate, or he would talk to me, giving me an account of the two-dimensional code. They had decided to try to model the fluid by means of individual mass points and to introduce forces between nearest neighbors. In the end that code just never flew. One evening, breaking the rules of the lab, I decided to work on the problem at home, actually writing things down on paper. I took the hydrodynamic equations in two dimensions and differenced them.

The basic equations are:

$$\dot{U} = -\frac{1}{\rho}\,\partial(P + Q)/\partial X \quad,$$

$$\dot{V} = -\frac{1}{\rho}\, \partial(P + Q)/\partial Y \ ,$$

$$\dot{X} = U \ , \qquad \dot{Y} = V \ ,$$

$$\dot{\rho} = -\rho(\partial U/\partial X + \partial V/\partial Y) \ , \qquad \text{and}$$

$$d(P/\rho^\gamma) = (\gamma - 1)Q\, d\rho/\rho^{\gamma+1} \ .$$

The variables X and Y are the Eulerian coordinates of a fluid element, U and V are its velocity components, P is the pressure, Q (we already called it Q in those days) is the artificial viscosity, and ρ is the density. The first four equations are the hydrodynamic equations, the dots denoting total or Lagrangian time derivatives. I've also written down a γ-law equation of state and introduced a particular form for the artificial viscosity. This form will only give you bulk viscosity and won't be very good if you have slippage or severe shear in the fluid. These defects were removed later.

Now if you want to do Lagrangian hydrodynamics these derivatives with respect to the Eulerian coordinates have to be converted to derivatives with respect to Lagrangian coordinates x and y. It turns out that it's very convenient to introduce something like a Poisson bracket. If A and B are functions of x and y, their Poisson bracket is defined to be $[A,B] \equiv \dfrac{\partial A}{\partial x}\dfrac{\partial B}{\partial y} - \dfrac{\partial B}{\partial x}\dfrac{\partial A}{\partial y}$. Let ρ_0 be the density relative to the Lagrangian coordinates and ρ the Eulerian density. There is a simple relation between ρ and ρ_0 involving the Jacobian J, which is just the Poisson bracket of the Eulerian coordinates with respect to the Lagrangian coordinates:

$$J = \begin{array}{cc} \dfrac{\partial X}{\partial x} & \dfrac{\partial x}{\partial y} \\[2mm] \dfrac{\partial Y}{\partial x} & \dfrac{\partial Y}{\partial y} \end{array} \ , \qquad \text{and}$$

$$\rho_0 = \rho[X,Y] \ .$$

Now the dynamical equations involve partial derivatives with respect to the Eulerian coordinates, but in the Lagrangian system, and hence in the code, you actually compute Lagrangian derivatives. The problem is to convert from Eulerian to Lagrangian, and this involves 1/J and the Poisson bracket with the variable conjugate to whatever you're differentiating with respect to. If you put this into the dynamical equations, you'll notice that on the right hand side of the $\dot{U}$ and $\dot{V}$ equations ρ^{-1} appears together with a gradient. The gradient introduces a 1/J which gets together with the $1/\rho$ to give you a $1/\rho_0$:

$$\dot{U} = -\frac{1}{\rho_0}[P + Q, Y] \quad ,$$

$$\dot{V} = +\frac{1}{\rho_0}[P + Q, X] \quad .$$

The Jacobians simply drop out and you're left with very simple equations. At least they seemed simple to me. So the next morning I went to Teller and said, "I must be missing something. I don't really understand what the difficulty is," and showed him these equations. That afternoon he called a meeting of the whole lab, and I stood up and went through essentially what I've just done for you here and was the overnight expert on two-dimensional hydrodynamics! I was told that I had to have a program coded and run before a certain date in June. There was going to be a test shot and the lab wanted some numbers. Well, it's one thing to have these simple-looking equations and another to apply them. I had to sit down and think about things that had never occurred to me before.

The first problem was the perennial one of what to do at the edge of the mesh. But things were even worse than that, as you can see in the accompanying sketch. Shown is a representation of a small portion of a certain "device". The crosshatched region represents a certain material that surrounds things, the horizontal lines represent some high explosive, and the vertical lines represent something else. The worrisome thing was that there was obviously going to be some strong slippage at the interfaces between different materials. I thought at first that maybe I could just treat it as all one fluid with the density simply changing abruptly at the interfaces and allowing the mesh to stretch. But it was clear that the mesh was going to stretch far too much to be reliable, so I had to figure out how to tell the programmer (we didn't do the actual programming our- selves in those days) to make tests so that the various mesh points at the edge of one material would know which mesh points at the edge of the other material they were near to.

Sketch

I had never done a hydrodynamic calculation before, so I figured I had better do at least one 1-dimensional calculation. Of course I went to Jim for guidance, particularly on the artificial viscosity. I had seen the paper by Richtmeyer and von Neumann on the stability condition. Now it was all very nice to read that paper, which was done in terms of Fourier transforms, but it lacked a certain gut feeling. Jim pointed out the simple explanation of the stability condition: when you difference the differential equations you only hook neighboring mesh points together, and if you make the time step too large the pressure wave simply can't get out as fast as the sound velocity, so the program blows up in your face. It's a little harder to understand the physical basis of the stability criterion for the parabolic heat equation, but even that you can sort of absorb.

After reasonable success with one-dimensional problems I tackled the two-dimensional problem in earnest. What I finally sent to the programmer must have been a sheaf of 20 or 30 pages. Of course, I was worried. When you have to come up with a number by a certain date, well, it focusses the mind! I had tried very carefully to think out every single step, to give correct sequences of commands like $\rho_{k\ell n} = \rho_{k\ell n-1} + \ldots$, or something like that, repeated with k and ℓ ranging over certain values, and with occasional iterations. Then there were all the special commands at the interfaces. Incidentally, there were no textbooks in numerical analysis, but I don't think they would have helped. We had all attended a course in which we learned a little bit of machine language, and I remember there were commands like BOOM... and ZOOM... One had to tell the machine every step. Our instructors were great; full of enthusiasm. They prayed to our computer every night, I believe. For them it was God. They were fascinated by being so close to such a great machine, which, of course, was just a piddling little machine by present standards.

Anyway, to get back to my story, I gave my sheets of paper to the programmer. I don't know what his own personal debugging problems were, but he didn't come back to me before the program actually ran. They got a number out after two or three hundred hours of computer time, before the test shot! Then I was told to prepare another program. Not until then did the programmer come to see me again. He didn't know what the computation was all about. He had previously just taken my instructions and done what I had indicated. He now thought it might be a good idea if he knew a little bit about the problem. So I spent two or three days going step by step and explaining everything. Then he pointed out to me that one could greatly improve the data input scheme and the way the computations were organized. This gave birth to a new program, but I don't know what ever happened to it. I left the lab before the next test shot came up. All I know is that it was a much more efficient code and ran more rapidly.

When I left Livermore, I went to the University of North Carolina and all these hydrodynamical problems were put out of my mind for years. But in 1970 I had begun to think about the gravitational two-body problem. I thought it was a scandal that nobody had ever tackled this problem. The three-body problem had been the great challenge in Newtonian mechanics. The two-body problem was the analogous challenge in general relativity. I discovered that my time at Livermore hadn't been wasted. (Nothing you learn is ever wasted.) All the lore of differencing partial differential equations came back to me, and I guided my student Andrej Cadez on the first colliding-black-hole computation. Then I moved to Texas, and Larry Smarr was induced to continue the work. By that time, textbooks on numerical analysis were available. Students nowadays seem to be afraid to get into big computations before they've checked what the textbooks say. I would tell Larry: "Listen, Jim Wilson doesn't operate that way. Just take the damned equations and difference them" I think my having referred to Jim so often, as a kind of model for how to attack big problems, led Larry to seek Jim out later. Well, to me at any rate, it seemed that you should just use common sense. Don't be afraid to try something. If there are physical constraints that can help you choose how to do the differencing, fine, but don't be afraid to go ahead anyway. Larry proved to me later that, occasionally, it is good to use fancy techniques. He pointed out that in the case of the diffusion equation there was a method that had been developed in the years since 1952 known as overrelaxation. He was all fired up about it, and I said "Yeah, okay, I'm glad."

Just this last summer, I had a student working on a problem in which we needed to compute the world function (which is one-half the square of the geodetic distance between two space-time points) in a Robertson-Walker universe. The world function satisfies a certain partial differential equation, which is basically a Hamilton-Jacobi equation, so I said, "It seems to me that the simplest thing to do would be to use this Hamilton-Jacobi equation." So he put it on the computer and got bad results no matter what he tried. I said, "Gosh, I don't know. Maybe you should give it a stability analysis," that is, look at the Fourier transform. We discovered that this is an equation which is unconditionally unstable no matter how you difference it. So sometimes it does pay to do a little analytical work ahead of time.

Let me end by showing you what the hydrodynamic equations look like in 3-D:

$$\dot{U} = - \frac{1}{\rho_0} \, [P + Q, \, Y, \, Z] \quad ,$$

$$\dot{V} = - \frac{1}{\rho_0} \, [P + Q, \, Z, \, X] \quad ,$$

$$\dot{W} = - \frac{1}{\rho_0} \, [P + Q, \, X, \, Y] \quad ,$$

$$\dot{X} = U \quad , \qquad \dot{Y} = V \quad , \qquad \dot{Z} = W \quad ,$$

$$\rho_0 = \rho[X, \, Y, \, Z] \quad , \quad \text{and}$$

$$[A,B,C] \equiv \frac{\partial A}{\partial x}\frac{\partial B}{\partial y}\frac{\partial C}{\partial z} + \frac{\partial A}{\partial y}\frac{\partial B}{\partial z}\frac{\partial C}{\partial x} + \frac{\partial A}{\partial z}\frac{\partial B}{\partial x}\frac{\partial C}{\partial y}$$

$$- \frac{\partial A}{\partial x}\frac{\partial B}{\partial z}\frac{\partial C}{\partial y} - \frac{\partial A}{\partial z}\frac{\partial B}{\partial y}\frac{\partial C}{\partial x} - \frac{\partial A}{\partial y}\frac{\partial B}{\partial x}\frac{\partial C}{\partial y} \quad .$$

They have the same form as in 2-D, only a triple bracket appears instead of a Poisson bracket. I had shown these equations to Teller that day, too. He once came to me later saying that we must get _them_ on the computer because they are what is needed for the attack on the turbulence problem! As far as I know, that problem still stands.

Warmest birthday greetings, Jim, and thanks for giving me this chance to reminisce.

Development of a Multimaterial Two-Dimensional, Arbitrary Lagrangian-Eulerian Mesh Computer Program

Robert T. Barton

Lawrence Livermore National Laboratory,

ABSTRACT

We* have developed a large, multimaterial, two-dimensional
Arbitrary Lagrangian-Eulerian (ALE) computer program.**
The special feature of an ALE mesh is that it can be either
an embedded Lagrangian mesh, a fixed Eulerian mesh, or a
partially embedded, partially remapped mesh. Remappping is
used to remove Lagrangian mesh distortion. This general
purpose program has been used for astrophysical modeling,
under the guidance of James R. Wilson. The rationale
behind the development of this program will be used to
highlight several important issues in program design.

I. INTRODUCTION

Currently, several astrophysicists have access to powerful
computers. Since costs for computer memory and functional units
seem likely to continue decreasing, we expect that all universities
will enjoy computational facilities that have in the past been
available only at major national laboratories and at research
centers of the transportation industry. Our experience in developing large general-purpose programs may alert you to important issues
and help you avoid some pitfalls that often cause ambitious
programdevelopment projects to fail.

Large programs (the equivalent of hundreds of thousands of
FORTRAN statements) that are to be used by many people have special
requirements that may not be important for small, single-user
programs. Large programs must be understandable to the programmers,
so that they can adapt them to evolving user requirements and

---

*J. Wilson, J. LeBlanc, K. Hainebach, G. Henderson and R. Barton.
**The designation "Arbitrary Lagrangian-Eulerian" was coined at
the Los Alamos National Laboratory. Amsden et al. (1980) describe
one of their recent ALE programs.

machine resources. In addition, large numbers of calculations require careful attention to computational efficiency. Thus, we must often tailor the algorithms to the hardware characteristics. nature of this mesh is very important in determining what types of problems can be solved; it is also a major factor in determining the efficiency of the calculation.

The overall efficiency in carrying a problem from conception to completion depends upon the algorithms, the computer speed, and the time the users must spend interacting with the program. To maximize efficiency, programs must be written to make optimal use of the available computer resources. But it is equally important to provide powerful and convenient service programs and understandable documentation.

I will briefly describe how our ALE program treats discontinuous velocities and how it advects mass, energy, and momentum from zone to zone as the mesh remaps. These features have proved useful in astrophysics modeling. I will mention some of these applications.

Finally, I hope to give you some idea of how Jim guided this and other program development during the 24 years that I have been privileged to work with him.

II. IMPORTANT GOALS OF LARGE PROGRAM DEVELOPMENT

Development of a large program involves many design decisions that strike an appropriate balance between desirable, but competing, characteristics. Some of these characteristics are ease of modification, computer-resource efficiency, user efficiency, and accuracy.

(a) Ease of Modification

<u>A modifiable program is modular, well-documented, and understandable.</u>

A large program is not static. It evolves as new demands are made on it. It must be modified as new computers and peripheral equipment are acquired. Large programs require large investments. A functionally modular, well-understood program can be changed with minimum effort, thus retaining most of the prior investment.

Modularity is achieved on several levels in our ALE program.

On the highest level, a controller, or master program, coordinates the operation of several independent programs by passing
messages and data files between itself and them. These programs
include utility routines for listing, editing, storing, and
retrieving files. In addition, several programs perform independent
ALE program functions. One program generates the initial conditions
and mesh configuration and can also refine, coarsen, or repair an
existing mesh. Another program numerically and graphically edits
the problem at any stage of evolution. The higher the dimensionality, the more important are graphics. The amount of data can be
overwhelming if only numerical edits are provided. The physics-
cycle program advances the physical variables in time. The
differential equations relate time derivatives to space derivatives.
When these are converted to finite-difference equations, a time
interval is introduced. The process of advancing the problem by one
time interval is called a computational cycle. Beginning with the
initial conditions, the solution is advanced in time cycle by cycle.

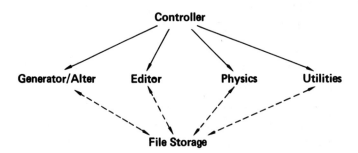

The next level of modularity comprises the subroutines that make
up the programs. Where possible, we use routines from specialized
libraries -- graphical, equation-of-state, mathematical functions,
and input/output drivers. Unfortunately, most of the program must
be coded specifically for this application. Although algorithms may
be adapted from other programs, differences in the data bases
require us to recast those algorithms.

When many people are involved in the development of a large
program, clear definitions of variables and explanations of
algorithms are vital. A powerful programming language greatly aids

_in understandability. We are fortunate to have the LRLTRAN
language, an extension of FORTRAN that can concisely express complex
one-dimensional arrays (vectors). All elements of a vector are
implied when its name is used without an index. We will see next
that vector operations are crucial to obtaining dense data packing
and maximum execution speed on pipeline (CDC Star and Cray)
computers.

b)   Computer-Resource Efficiency

<u>Computer resources are used most efficiently by vectorized programs
and appropriate meshes.</u>

Some astrophysical objects are symmetrical about an axis so that
only two coordinates are needed to define their geometry: (a) the
distance along the axis of symmetry with respect to some reference
point, and (b) the distance out from the axis of symmetry. A two-
dimensional model calculation saves computer time and data storage
compared to a three-dimensional model calculation.

A Lagrangian mesh is usually more efficient than a fixed
rectangular Eulerian mesh. Since zones are imbedded, they can be
put and will remain where they are needed most. On the other hand,
spherical Eulerian meshes can be quite efficient for astrophysical
problems. Our ALE program combines the best features of Eulerian
and Lagrangian meshes by using a mesh that can be Eulerian,
Lagrangian, or a combination where appropriate. We can tailor the
mesh to the problem by following the initial material contours
instead of extending the mesh into uninteresting regions. This
reduces the amount of data that must be stored. Later, we will see
how this tailoring can improve accuracy. Unlike Eulerian meshes
employed in other programs, the Eulerian portion does not need to be
rectangular or even orthogonal.

More efficient use of computer memory is also achieved by
dynamic addressing of memory (pointers to where variables are
stored) when the program is run, rather than by static dimensioning
of arrays during compilation. Vectors have special pointers
(descriptors) to facilitate dynamic addressing. Also, vector
operations allow unused parts of vectors to be removed. An

operation in LRLTRAN called "compress", V1=V2(B), selects only elements of vector V2 to store in V1 where the logical (bit) vector contains "true" bits. B could be an expression like V3>V4. Bit vectors are much more compact (64:1) than word vectors. The inverse operation to compress is decompress, V2(B)=V1, where elements of V1 replace those elements of V2 where B is "true". The same compress and decompress operations can be controlled by a vector of indexes instead of a bit vector. "Gather", V1=V2(N), packs elements of V2 that are at the indexes stored in N consecutively into V1. Similarly, "scatter", V2(N)=V1, replaces only those elements of V2 referenced by elements of N by consecutive elements of V1.

Vector arithmetic operations execute much faster than scalar arithmetic. Much of vector programming involves separating testing from arithmetic. The results of testing are stored as logical vectors. The controlled store operation, V1=B.CTRL.V2, can be used selectively to overwrite elements of V1 with corresponding elements of V2 only where the corresponding element of B is "true". V2 may be a vector expression and B may be a logical vector expression. If all results are used, long vector expressions are more efficient than short ones, since there is a start-up time for filling the vector pipelines. We have increased the average vector length by adding extra mesh elements to facilitate imposition of boundary conditions; this often allows boundary nodes and zones to be calculated along with interior mesh nodes and zones. LRLTRAN allows vectors to have subscript limits that can exclude unneeded parts of a vector. For example, $V(\ell1:\ell2:n)$ would access only element $\ell1$ and every nth element thereafter until $\ell2$ is reached. V(n1;n2) exempts the first n1 and last n2 elements from the vector operation. LRLTRAN allows us to express vector algorithms in a compact, elegant way. It encourages vectorization and promotes understandability.

By removing distortion, our ALE program can often run with larger time steps than a Lagrangian mesh program because the Courant condition for hydrodynamic stability will increase when the shortest distance across the zone with the shortest sound-transit-time increases. With all other factors constant, a larger time step would reduce the calculation time. This is not necessarily the case, though, because the remapping calculations increase the time

needed to calculate a cycle. We will see later that remapping to
remove distortion offers another benefit; namely, that it often
improves the accuracy of the calculation.

c) User Efficiency

<u>User efficiency has been enhanced by automatic mesh correction,
powerful service programs and good manuals.</u>
     One of the main goals in designing our ALE program was to
reduce, substantially, the time needed for the user to repair
Lagrangian meshes. Since a Lagrangian mesh is tied to material
motion, kinking or necking off of the material will distort the mesh
enough to cause large errors in the difference equations, or will
result in a small time step. One of the main advantages of an ALE
mesh program over Lagrangian mesh programs is its ability to detect
and reduce mesh distortion automatically. Two tests are made to
detect unacceptable distortion. One test (Figure 1) checks whether
or not the angles at each grid-line intersection (node) are within
specified limits.

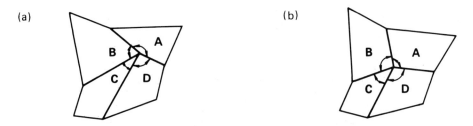

Fig. 1 - A Lagrangian mesh tends to distort when used to model
turbulent material. Our program can detect and reduce mesh
distortion automatically. One test for mesh distortion compares the
angles (A,B,C,D) formed by the intersection of mesh lines with a
user-specified value. (a) If any angles are too large or too small,
as are A and C, the program will remap to approximate more closely a
configuration (b) in which all four angles are closer to 90 degrees.

If any angles are outside the limits, the node is remapped unless it
has been exempted by the user. The other test (Figure 2) compares
the area of the smallest of the four triangles surrounding a node to
the sum of all four areas. If the ratio is below a threshold value
and the node has not been exempted, the node will be remapped. Only
the angle test is made at the boundaries of the problem.

(a)   (b)

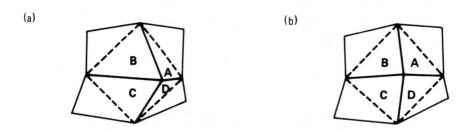

Fig. 2 - (a) A Lagrangian mesh can distort the four triangles
(A,B,C,D) around a node so that their areas become quite different.
Our program tests for this condition by automatically comparing the
areas of the triangles and remapping the node if the area of the
smallest triangle is less than a specified percentage, say 5%, of
the total area of all four. (b) After remapping, the areas of the
triangles are much more similar.

The user can have nodes remapped in many ways. Nodes can be
returned to specific coordinates or to their initial position (which
produces a not necessarily orthogonal Eulerian mesh). Nodes can be
interpolated between other nodes. Most of the remapped nodes are
repositioned according to a weighted average of the coordinates of
their eight neighbors; this tends to produce orthogonal mesh lines.
This is called an "equipotential" method (Winslow 1963, Winslow and
Barton 1982). The mesh can remap in polar or Cartesian coordinates,
and mesh lines can be uniformly or geometrically spaced. Remapping
can be prevented or reduced if it would make the smallest adjacent
triangle smaller. Equipotential remapping can be repeated several
times if the initial remapping leaves the mesh distorted. If
distortion persists, the program maximizes the area of the smallest
triangle around the distorted node. To reduce diffusion of the
physical quantities, the coordinate shift due to remapping can be
limited to a multiple of the shift in position of the fastest
neighbor node. If unconstrained, diffusion can obscure real
gradients, such as those produced by shocks.

Distortion near nodes along the outer boundary must be removed
by special means, since these nodes do not have the eight neighbors
required by the equipotential method. Remapping a curved outer
boundary brings material into or removes material from the problem;
thus it should be allowed only if the outer boundary is not critical
to the problem. In order to remap boundary nodes, the program

initially tries to space them more uniformly. If that fails to reduce interior-angle disortion, the program reduces the curvature of the boundary instead.

Expert knowledge is needed to make the many decisions required to set up a two-dimensional problem. A good Users' Manual provides some of this knowledge. For example: the user must decide how many zones are needed to define each material adequately. Will the region be allowed to remap? Which details will be included and which will be ignored? Is material strength important? Where can tangential velocity components be different (i.e., where can sliding be allowed to occur)? In addition, the user must supply key node coordinates in either Cartesian or polar form. The user can instruct the program to interpolate lines between nodes and to interpolate regions between the lines. The program can smooth lines and can shift them to generate other lines. The user must specify initial zone properties and node velocities. Boundary conditions and velocity constraints must be specified. Material properties must be either specified or obtained from data bases. Boundary conditions must be established when the problem is generated; the code applies these conditions during each calculational cycle. Boundaries may be fixed, reflection, or free. The pressure and temperature outside free boundaries may be specified as tabular functions of time and of the mesh-line indexes. The velocities of the boundary nodes may be specified as functions of time or be constrained to move only in certain directions.

As mentioned before, we provide facilities for generating, editing, plotting and altering. These facilities provide extensive checking to guard against input errors that could invalidate results. Incorrect results are worse than no results!

d) Accuracy

Accuracy is improved by choosing a suitable mesh.

We have found that a Lagrangian mesh can calculate the initial motion with maximum accuracy since there is little distortion. It is usually only after important transient phases have passed that turbulence and shear motions appear and persist, causing mesh distortion and making it necessary to remap.

For a given number of zones, a Lagrangian mesh can give a more accurate representation than an Eulerian mesh as long as grid lines remain regular (usually quasi-orthogonal). However, as the mesh becomes badly distorted, difference formulations become inaccurate. As described before, our ALE code can automatically detect and remove these distortions as they appear.

On the other hand, departure from a Lagrangian mesh in a problem with several materials can result in "mixed" zones containing several components. Treatment of mixed zones usually requires additional approximations. In any case, as the mesh is moved through the materials, some diffusion is introduced. When our ALE program is run initially Lagrangian with only occasional remapping as zones distort, the amount of advection and mixing is kept small. This minimizes typical Eulerian-mesh errors and reduces distortion that could cause a Lagrange-mesh calculation to be in error.

A problem is usually run so that the mesh starts completely Lagrangian, i.e., imbedded in the material. Only after significant distortion is detected does remapping begin. Remapping is confined to the distorted region and typically involves only a small displacement relative to the material in each cycle. Any node can be temporarily or permanently prevented from remapping.

III. SAMPLE MODELING METHODS
We now describe a few modeling features used in astrophysical problems.

a) Velocity Discontinuities
When solids and fluids slide past one another, we need to describe discontinuities in tangential velocities at the interface. If we can ignore the thin, relatively sluggish boundary layer and allow a velocity discontinuity at the interface, we need not use the small zones necessary to discriminate the boundary layer.

In our ALE program, discontinuities in tangential velocities are allowed at certain nodes called slide nodes (see Figure 3).

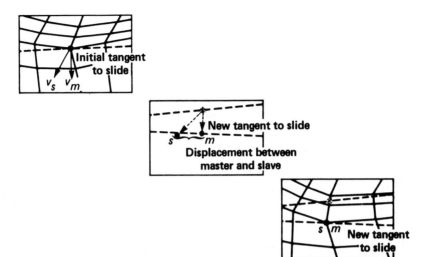

Fig. 3 - The program can model discontinuities in tangential
velocity components at material boundaries and still maintain a
continuous mesh by means of special slide nodes. As shown in (a),
each slide node has a "master" and "slave" component (respectively
denoted m and s), which can temporarily move somewhat independently
according to the velocity of the material with which each is
associated. The displacement between master and slave components
shown in (b) represents the difference in tangential velocity
between the two materials. Before the end of each computational
cycle the slave component remaps back to its master position so that
the mesh remains continuous (c).

Some pure-Lagrangian-mesh programs allow nodes to slide at an

interface, so that the mesh becomes discontinuous.Our ALE program,

however, maintains a continuous mesh at the sliding interface by

treating each slide node there as if it were actually two nodes that

can temporarily move somewhat independently. We call one the master

component and one the slave component. Each half of the master/

slave pair moves at its own velocity and separates from the other

when their velocities differ. However, to preserve the continuity

of the mesh, each separated slave component is remapped to its

master position before the end of the calculational cycle. This

ensures that the mesh lines will be continuous for all of the other

calculations. Mesh continuity eliminates some disadvantages of

discontinuous meshes (such as those produced by Lagrangian codes

that allow sliding at interfaces); additional approximations caused

by averaging and interpolation are avoided; coarse zone patterns
will not be imprinted on fine zones; and narrow zones will not pass
over wide zones, which would cause the narrow zones to rotate
unrealistically about their centers. Mesh continuity also greatly
simplifies advection and diffusion calculations.

On the other hand, the zoning flexibility of a discontinuous
mesh has been lost. To overcome this, the physical properties of
several adjacent zones and velocities of adjacent nodes can be
averaged together where the mesh resolution is not needed (such as
near the center of a polar mesh). This averaging stabilizes the
calculation, so a larger time step can be used. Mesh continuity at
slides also means that on at least one side of the slide the mesh
must remap. This may degrade accuracy because of the approximations
introduced by remapping. Whether this error is less or greater than
the errors that would be introduced by mesh discontinuity depends on
the problem.

b)   Advection

The Lagrangian part of our cycle is almost identical to the
calculations done by other two-dimensional Lagrangian programs
(Maenchen and Sack 1964, Wilkins 1969). However, since the mesh can
be remapped in a very general way (not just back to an orthogonal
grid), the rather straightforward Eulerian advection calculations
are not applicable. In particular, some two-dimensional Eulerian
programs use boundary-centered, single component (x or y) velocities. In our ALE program, velocity vectors at mesh nodes are used.
Thus, the motion of advection boundaries is not usually one-
dimensional.

The program calculates the volume swept from one zone into
another each time a boundary shifts. The energy and mass density in
that volume are determined in one of two ways. If a material
boundary lies in or between the adjacent zones, or if there is a
large density change (e.g., when a shock occurs), the density in the
zone that loses the volume is used. Otherwise, the densities in the
zones near the boundary are interpolated to the center of the
advected volume. This interpolation is crucial to obtaining
acceptable accuracy in an Eulerian or a remapped mesh because, if

the donor zone's density is always used, gradients are not preserved. The method of interpolating densities uses monotonicity
conditions to ensure that the new densities are not less than the
pre-advection minimum density nor larger than the maximum density
near the advection boundary.

Mixed-zone calculations are the most complex in the program.
Advection that involves or produces mixed zones requires that the
transferred volume be apportioned among the constituent materials in
the new zones. Our ALE program infers the information it needs on
the positions of mixed-zone components from volume fractions of
neighboring zones. To simplify these calculations further, they are
done in directional sweeps. Thus, only two zones need to be
considered at each remapped boundary. Details of the calculation
are quite complex, but they are based on the following constraints:
(a) a zone cannot donate more of a material than it contains, (b)
component mass and energy must be conserved, (c) total volume must
be conserved, and (d) the sum of the component volumes must equal
the total zone volume. Extensive use is made of logical vector
operations for selecting which materials are transported. Sharp and
Barton (1981) describe the algorithms used.

Each node has a portion of the surrounding zones' mass associated with it. Consequently, as mass is transferred from zone to
zone by advection, there is a momentum transfer. The velocity
associated with the mass transfer between nodes is usually interpolated from the node velocities. In some exceptional cases, only one
node velocity is used. This process is analogous to the advected
density determination described above. Again, velocity interpolation is critical. It reduces kinetic energy loss due to momentum
diffusion. Once the momentum transfer has been determined, a node's
new velocity is simply its new momentum divided by its new mass.
Slave velocities are calculated in the same way as boundary node
velocities, since only the slave side remaps.

IV. ASTROPHYSICAL APPLICATIONS

We have taken advantage of the ALE mesh's great versatility to
calculate a variety of astrophysical problems. For all of these
problems, Jim Wilson formulated the special, astrophysical calculations that were added to our general purpose program.

Several astrophysical problems run on our ALE program required mixed zone advection. Our calculation (Wilson and Bowers 1980) of lepton-induced convective instability in a hot supernova remnant modeled the displacement of hot, low density, lepton-poor matter by outer cool, high density, lepton-rich matter. "Rayleigh-Taylor Overturn in Supernova Core Collapse" (Smarr et al. 1981) (Figure 4) also involved turbulent mixing. These calculations used spherical Eulerian meshes to simplify the gravitational acceleration calculation greatly.

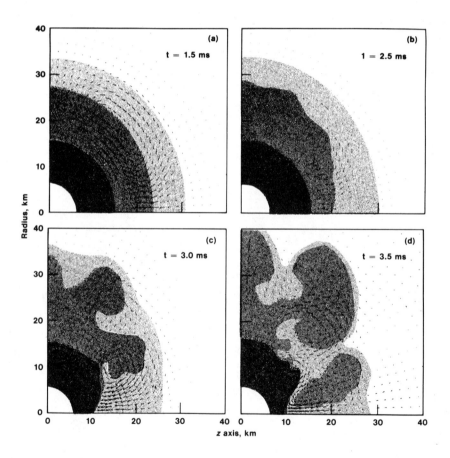

Fig. 4 - Computed Rayleigh-Taylor overturn during the core collapse of a star entering the supernova stage, showing motions of the fluid regions obtained with a 90-degree model for times of (a) 1.5 ms, (b) 2.5 ms, (c) 3.0 ms, and (d) 3.5 ms. Only the inner portion of the collapse is shown. The central region (at a radius less than 6 km) was excluded from the calculation. Boundaries separate the stellar matter according to its initial density distribution.

An astrophysical calculation that employed both a slide and
mixed-zone advection was described in "Radiation from an
Asteroid-Neutron Star Collision" (Howard et al. 1981).   In this
problem, a slide along the surface of the neutron star decoupled the
asteroid-remnant velocity from that of the stationary neutron star.
The slide automatically provided a curved, rigid boundary at the
interface (Figure 5).

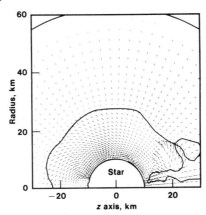

Fig. 5 - Result of the collision of an asteroid with a neutron star,
computed with our program. The asteroid material is flowing around
the surface of the neutron star.

The initial phase of this problem followed an iron meteoroid as it
fell toward the star. The mesh was initially Lagrangian. Shortly
before the collision, small amounts of internal remapping occurred.
This calculation included the iron's strength; as expected, it
proved to have a negligible effect. The distortion of the meteoroid
is shown in Figure 6. The result of this free fall was used to set
up the initial conditions for the collision calculation.

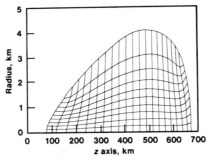

Fig. 6 - Initial gravitational distortion of a spherical asteroid,
computed with out program, just before it collides with a neutron
star. Note that the scales of the r and z axes differ by a
factor of 100. The asteroid is moving to the left toward the star.

A Lagrangian mesh was also used to validate an Eulerian difference scheme used in an Eulerian mesh program to calculate the angular momentum of a rotating protostar undergoing collapse (Norman et al. 1980). A closeup view of the inner mesh is shown in Figure 7.

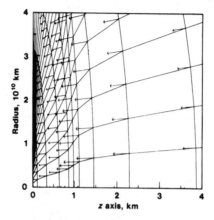

Fig. 7 - Collapse of a rotating protostar computed with our program. A portion of the Lagrangian grid is shown at the termination of the calculation, indicating the flattening induced by the collapse. At this time, the central region is compressed by a factor of 10^4 over its initial density. Arrows show the velocities of the zone corners. The initial radius of the protostar cloud was 7×10^{11} km.

The Lagrangian-mesh solution had no diffusive effects due to advection; thus it could be relied on until mesh distortion was large.

We have used an arbitrary Lagrangian-Eulerian mesh to calculate the growth of Rayleigh-Taylor instabilities between shells of different density. These problems start with a Lagrangian mesh. Near the end of the linear growth phase, distortion becomes large enough to trigger remapping. By the time bubbles and spikes are well formed, the mesh becomes equivalent to a moving-grid Eulerian mesh. Eventually, three-dimensional effects become important and the detailed flow is unrealistic thereafter.

V. PERSONAL COMMENTS

It is a privilege to participate in this tribute to Jim Wilson -- an outstanding individual. Jim is a problem solver. He really listens to problems, quietly analyzes them, and formulates practical solutions. This sounds quite ordinary; however, it certainly is not. Jim is accessible. He is open to solutions proposed by others, sometimes suggesting simplifying modifications or adding essential elements that may have been overlooked.

Jim's closeness to nature in his private and in his professional life may account, in part, for his ability to see the whole problem and to extract the significant aspects and reject unimportant details.

This acknowledgment would not be complete without mentioning the pioneering contributions and continuing guidance of Jim LeBlanc. His extensive experience with large, multidimensional, Eulerian-mesh computer programs has been the basis of much of this ALE program.

REFERENCES

Amsden, A., Ruppel, H., and Hirt, C. 1980, *SALE: A Simplified ALE Computer Program for Fluid Flow at All Speeds* (Los Alamos National Laboratory, Los Alamos, NM, LA-8095).

Howard, W., Wilson, J., and Barton, R. 1981, *Ap. J.*, **249**, 302.

Maenchen, G., and Sack, S.1964, "The TENSOR Code", in *Methods in Computational Physics*, B. Alder, S. Fernbach, and M. Rotenberg, Vol.3, (New York: Academic Press).

Norman, M., Wilson, J., and Barton, R. 1980, *Ap. J.*, 239, 968.

Sharp, R., and Barton, R. 1981, *HEMP Advection Model* (Lawrence Livermore National Laboratory, Livermore, CA, UCID-17809, Rev. 1).

Smarr, L., Wilson, J., Barton, R., and Bowers, R. 1981, *Ap. J.*, **246**,515.

Wilkins, M. L. 1969, *Calculation of Elastic-Plastic Flow* (Lawrence Livermore National Laboratory, Livermore, CA, UCRL-7322, Rev. 1).

Wilson, J., and Bowers, R. 1980, "Supernova: The Explosive Death of a Star", *Energy and Technology Review* (Lawrence Livermore National Laboratory, Livermore, CA, UCRL-52000-80-2).

Winslow, A. 1963, *Equipotential Zoning of Two-Dimensional Meshes* (Lawrence Livermore National Laboratory, Livermore, CA, UCRL-7312).

Winslow, A., and Barton, R. 1982, *Rescaling of Equipotential Smoothing* (Lawrence Livermore National Laboratory, Livermore, CA, UCID-19486).

Work performed under the auspices of the U. S. Department of Energy by the Lawrence Livermore National Laboratory under contract No. W-7405-ENG-48.

Radiation Transport in Numerical Astrophysics

C. M. Lund

Lawrence Livermore National Laboratory

ABSTRACT

We consider some implicit differencing schemes for
solving one-dimensional time-dependent multifrequency
radiation transport problems arising in astrophysical
calculations. These schemes have the property that they
correctly describe both the streaming and diffusion
limits of transport theory, and are stable with time
steps comparable with the changes in physical variables.
Methods are described to solve these equations by
operator-splitting techniques and by an iterative
matrix-inversion technique. A numerical example is used
to illustrate these points.

I. INTRODUCTION

In this article, we discuss some of the numerical techniques
developed by Jim Wilson and co-workers for the calculation of
time-dependent radiation flow. Difference equations for
multifrequency transport are given for both a discrete-angle
representation of radiation transport and a Fick's law-like
representation. These methods have the important property that
they correctly describe both the streaming and diffusion limits of
transport theory in problems where the mean free path divided by
characteristic distances varies from much less than one to much
greater than one. They are also stable for timesteps comparable to
the changes in physical variables, rather than being limited by
stability requirements.

These methods have been derived from a physical rather than
mathematical point of view. Thus while, like all methods, they

have their limitations, these limitations are easily understood from a physical point of view. Since one rarely has as large a computer or as much computer time as one would like, the physical nature of the finite-difference equations allows a realistic evaluation of the accuracy inherent in a given calculation.

These methods have been applied to many astrophysical calculations over the years. Wilson (1971) has used the discrete-angle method to calculate nondegenerate neutrino transport in a collapsing star. Wilson (1978) has also extended the diffusion method to fully-degenerate neutrino transport in a collapsing star. Alme and Wilson (1973, 1974, 1976) have applied the diffusion method to several situations arising in X-ray star systems.

In this article, we consider radiation at point $\underline{r}$ travelling in direction $\underline{\Omega}$ with frequency ν to be described by the prototype transport equation

$$\frac{\partial I}{\partial t} = - c \ \underline{\Omega} \cdot \underline{\nabla} I + \rho \ c \ \kappa \ [\frac{B(T)}{c} - I],$$

and coupled to material via

$$\rho \ C_v \ \frac{dT}{dt} = - \rho \ \int d\nu \ c \ \kappa \ \int d\underline{\Omega} \ [\frac{B(T)}{c} - I],$$

where

$I(\underline{\Omega},\nu,\underline{r})$ = radiation energy density,

$\rho(\underline{r})$ = material density,

$T(\underline{r})$ = material temperature,

$B(T)$ = Planck emission function,

$$= \frac{2 \ h \ \nu^3}{c^2} \ \frac{1}{e^{h\nu/kT} - 1},$$

$\kappa(\nu,\underline{r})$ = material absorption opacity,

$C_V(\underline{r})$ = material heat capacity,

c = speed of light,

h = Planck's constant,

k = Boltzmann's constant.

These equations display the key features that make radiation transport in general such a difficult numerical problem. These features are short radiation transport times (because of the high speed of light), and the wide range of coupling rates to material (since κ varies over orders of magnitude as a function of material and frequency).

We further restrict the problem to one-dimensional (1-D) spherical geometry:

$$\frac{\partial I}{\partial t} = -c \left\{ \frac{\mu}{r^2} \frac{\partial}{\partial r}(r^2 I) + \frac{1}{r}\frac{\partial}{\partial \mu}(1-\mu^2)\ I \right\} + \rho\ c\ \kappa\ [B(T) - I],$$

$$\rho\ C_V\ \frac{dT}{dt} = -\rho \int d\nu\ c\ \kappa \int d\mu\ [B(T) - I],$$

where

$$I(\mu,\nu,r) = 2\pi\ I(\underline{\Omega},\nu,\underline{r})$$

$$B(T) = \frac{2\pi}{c}\ B(T),$$

and

μ = cosine of the angle between $\underline{\Omega}$ and $\underline{r}$,

r = distance from origin.

To illustrate the important characteristics of the numerical algorithms, we consider a simple test problem loosely based on the parameters involved during neutrino cooling of a neutron star. The neutron star is represented by a static exponential density distribution

$$\rho = \rho_0 \, e^{-r/r_0},$$

with

$$\rho_0 = 10^{15} \text{ gm cm}^{-3},$$

$$r_0 = 10^6 \text{ cm}.$$

The initial temperature distribution is then calculated by assuming

$$T = T_0 \, (\rho/\rho_0)^{\gamma-1},$$

with

$$\gamma = 4/3,$$

$$kT_0 = 24.4 \text{ MeV}.$$

An isotropic initial energy density

$$I = B(T)$$

is assumed for the neutrinos.

The material is assumed to have a constant heat capacity

$$\frac{1}{k} C_V = 10^{15} \text{ ergs gm}^{-1} \text{ MeV}^{-1}$$

and an absorption opacity

$$\kappa = \kappa_0 \, (h\nu)^2,$$

with

$$\kappa_0 = 1.24 \times 10^{-20} \; cm^2 \; gm^{-1} \; MeV^{-2}.$$

This problem is to be calculated with minimum resolution, reflecting the fact that for most real problems one is short of computer time and memory. We use 30 equal spatial zones of thickness $r_0/3$ cm; 20 neutrino energy groups with group centers starting at 0.5 MeV and increasing a factor of $2^{1/2}$ between groups to 362 MeV; and 8 equally-spaced μ's to describe the angular distribution.

Figure 1 shows the initial state of the problem. The plot at the lower left is the average mean free path, defined by

$$<\lambda> = \frac{\int d\nu \; \dfrac{I}{\rho \; \kappa}}{\int d\nu \; I}.$$

One notes that $<\lambda>$ varies from under 10^2 cm to over 10^8 cm in a problem whose scale height is 10^6 cm. The material and neutrino energy densities are shown in the lower right of the figure. Initially approximately twice as much energy is in the neutrino field as is in the material.

Figure 2 shows the time evolution of the energies in the problem. One notes the steep initial slopes of the neutrino and energy-out curves, compared to the relatively constant material energy curve. One infers that at early times the neutrinos initially present are flowing out unimpeded from the thin regions of the neutron star. Later, material energy is converted to neutrinos which then flow out. Initially, the characteristic timescale of the problem is

$$\frac{r_0}{c} \sim 10^{-4} \; s.$$

Later it rises to on the order of seconds.

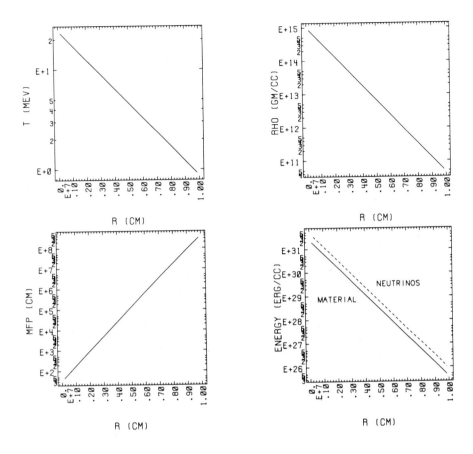

Fig. 1. — Initial conditions for neutron star neutrino-cooling test problem.

Figure 3 shows the spectrum of the neutrino radiation from the star. One notes that this spectrum is roughly characteristic of a 1 MeV source.

Figure 4 shows the temperature distribution in the neutron star at 0.1 s. The curve marked T is the material temperature, while T_C and T_R are "temperatures" that characterize the neutrino field. T_R is given by

$$kT_R = \left\{ \frac{\mathcal{E}}{a} \right\}^{1/4},$$

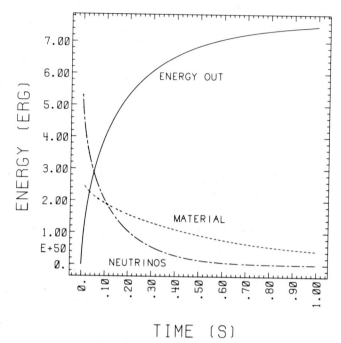

Fig. 2. —Energy balance for cooling neutron star test
problem.

where

$$a = \frac{8 \pi^5}{15 (h c)^3},$$

and

$$\mathscr{E} = \int d\nu \int d\mu \; I.$$

For material in thermal equilibrium at temperature T,

$$\mathscr{E}^{eq} = a (kT)^4,$$

where $\mathscr{E}^{eq}$ is the equilibrium neutrino density. Thus T_R is the

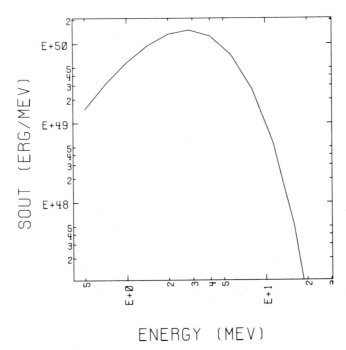

Fig. 3. — Spectrum of radiated neutrinos.

temperature the neutrinos would have if they were in thermal equilibrium for the current value of $\mathcal{E}$.

T_C is defined from

$$kT_C = \frac{1}{\beta} \, \langle h\nu \rangle,$$

where

$$\langle h\nu \rangle = \frac{\int d\nu \int d\mu \; I}{\int d\nu \int d\mu \; \frac{I}{h\nu}},$$

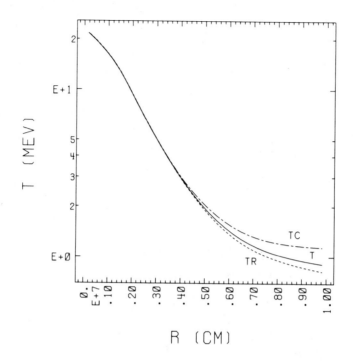

Fig. 4. — Temperature distributions at 0.1 s.

$$\beta = \frac{\displaystyle\int_0^\infty dx\, \frac{x^3}{e^x - 1}}{\displaystyle\int_0^\infty dx\, \frac{x^2}{e^x - 1}} \approx 2.7012.$$

The quantity $\langle h\nu \rangle$ is the average neutrino particle energy, and β is chosen so that material in thermal equilibrium will have

$$T_C = T.$$

T_C gives an indication of the "hardness" of the neutrino spectrum compared to a black-body spectrum.

Regions where T_R and T_C are not equal to T are regions where

the neutrinos are not in thermal equilibrium with the material.   In
this problem they correspond to regions of long mean free paths.

II.   DISCRETE-ANGLE DIFFERENCE SCHEME

In order to set up a finite-difference representation of the
differential equations, we first define a discrete representation
of the independent variables.   Define a computational grid

$\Delta\mu_i$ in μ,

$\Delta\nu_j$ in ν,

Δr_k in r.

Define boundary values

$\mu_{i+1/2}$ so that $\Delta\mu_i = \mu_{i+1/2} - \mu_{i-1/2}$,

$\nu_{j+1/2}$ so that $\Delta\nu_j = \nu_{j+1/2} - \nu_{j-1/2}$,

$r_{k+1/2}$ so that $\Delta r_k = r_{k+1/2} - r_{k-1/2}$.

Define zone-centered quantities

$$\mu_i = \frac{1}{2}(\mu_{i-1/2} + \mu_{i+1/2}),$$

$$\nu_j = \frac{1}{2}(\nu_{j-1/2} + \nu_{j+1/2}),$$

$$r_k = \frac{1}{2}(r_{k-1/2} + r_{k+1/2}).$$

Then

$$I(\mu,\nu,r) \to I(\mu_i,\nu_j,r_k) \equiv I_{i,j,k}.$$

Finite difference equations update variables from time t^n to $t^n+\Delta t$. Define

$I_{i,j,k}$ = value at t^n,

$I'_{i,j,k}$ = value at t^{n+1},

$\underline{I}_{i,j,k}$ = "average" value between t^n, t^{n+1}.

The easiest way to understand how the following finite-difference equations are generated is to apply the operator

$$\frac{1}{\Delta V} \int_{(i,j,k)} dV\ dt$$

to each term in the differential equation. Here

$$\Delta V = \Delta\mu\ \Delta\nu\ r^2\ \Delta r,$$

and "(i,j,k)" means the computational cell centered on (μ_i, ν_j, r_k). For example,

$$\frac{1}{\Delta V} \int_{(i,j,k)} dV\ dt\ \frac{\partial I}{\partial t} \rightarrow I'_{i,j,k} - I_{i,j,k}.$$

This implies we are interpreting $I_{i,j,k}$ as the average value of I in $\Delta V_{i,j,k}$.

a)   Advection Terms

For the spatial advection term we get

$$- c\ \frac{\mu}{r^2}\ \frac{\partial}{\partial r}(r^2 I) \rightarrow - \frac{\mu\ c\ \Delta t}{r^2\ \Delta r}\ \{r^2_{k+1/2}\ \underline{I}_{k+1/2} - r^2_{k-1/2}\ \underline{I}_{k-1/2}\}.$$

(Note: drop all indices equal to i,j or k for simplicity, i.e. μ means μ_i, etc.)   To insure energy conservation, we define

$$r^2 \, \Delta r = \frac{1}{3} \, (r^3_{k+1/2} - r^3_{k-1/2}) = \frac{1}{4\pi} \, (\text{volume of zone } k).$$

Defining $\underline{I}_{k-1/2}$ involves two different averaging techniques:

   1) time-averaging of I, I$'$, and

   2) spatial averaging of I_{k-1}, I_k.

For the time centering of the advection term, we let

   $\underline{I} = I'$,

so that

$$- \frac{\mu \, c}{r^2} \, \frac{\partial}{\partial r} (r^2 I) \;\rightarrow\; - \frac{\mu \, c \, \Delta t}{r^2 \, \Delta r} \, \{r^2_{k+1/2} \, I'_{k+1/2} - r^2_{k-1/2} \, I'_{k-1/2}\}.$$

If large flows dominate in a region, the advective term in the transport equation determines I$'$ through $\underline{I}$.   If the difference scheme has

   $\underline{I} = I'$,

then I$'$ is determined by the condition that, at the end of the timestep, the amount of radiation that is flowing in one boundary of a zone is the same as the amount that is flowing out the other, i.e.,

$$r^2_{k+1/2} \, I'_{k+1/2} = r^2_{k-1/2} \, I'_{k-1/2}.$$

This is a physically reasonable choice.   In general, for stability at large Δt it is best not to have $\underline{I}$ a function of I at the beginning of the timestep.

The spatial form of the advection term is determined by requiring that the finite difference equation recover the diffusion limit, i.e., we want the analog of

$$c \int d\mu \; \mu \; I \; \rightarrow \; - \; \frac{\lambda \; c}{3} \; \frac{\partial E}{\partial x}$$

as

$$\frac{\lambda}{E} \; \frac{\partial E}{\partial x} \; \rightarrow \; 0 \; ,$$

where

$$E = \int d\mu \; I \; ,$$

$$\lambda = \frac{1}{\rho \; \kappa} \; .$$

This is accomplished by defining

$$I_{i,k+1/2} = \frac{I_{i,k}}{1 + \dfrac{\Delta\tau_{k+1/2}}{2 \; |\mu_i|}} \quad \text{for } \mu_i > 0 \; ,$$

$$I_{i,k+1/2} = \frac{I_{i,k+1}}{1 + \dfrac{\Delta\tau_{k+1/2}}{2 \; |\mu_i|}} \quad \text{for } \mu_i < 0 \; ,$$

where

$$\Delta\tau_{k+1/2} = \frac{2 \; \Delta\tau_k \; \Delta\tau_{k+1}}{\Delta\tau_k \; + \; \Delta\tau_{k+1}} \; ,$$

$$\Delta\tau_k = \frac{\Delta r_k}{\lambda_k} = \rho_k \; \kappa_k \; \Delta r_k \; .$$

Thus at $r_{k+1/2}$, we take I from the center of the zone from which the radiation is flowing (upwind differencing) and extrapolate to the boundary with the factor

$$\frac{1}{1 + \frac{\Delta\tau_{k+1/2}}{2\;|\mu_i|}}.$$

One can think of this procedure as using the first term of the expansion

$$I_{i,k+1/2} = I_{i,k}\; e^{-\Delta\tau_{k+1/2}/2\mu_i} \quad (\mu_i > 0).$$

Note that the definition of $\Delta\tau_{k+1/2}$ picks the minimum $\Delta\tau$ across a boundary. Experience has shown this is usually a good choice if neighboring zones differ considerably, since it allows radiation to flow into thick zones from thin regions.

Then the flux across a boundary is determined by

$$\sum_i \Delta\mu_i\; \mu_i\; I_{i,k+1/2} = \sum_{\mu_i<0} \frac{\Delta\mu_i\; \mu_i\; I_{i,k+1}}{1 + \frac{\Delta\tau_{k+1/2}}{2\;|\mu_i|}} + \sum_{\mu_i>0} \frac{\Delta\mu_i\; \mu_i\; I_{i,k}}{1 + \frac{\Delta\tau_{k+1/2}}{2\;|\mu_i|}}.$$

As

$$\Delta\tau \to \infty,$$

one uses

$$I \to \frac{1}{2}\; E,$$

$$\sum_{\pm\mu_i>0} \Delta\mu_i\; \mu_i\; |\mu_i| = \pm\frac{1}{3},$$

to get the diffusion limit

$$c \sum_i \Delta\mu_i \; \mu_i \; I_{i,k+1/2} \rightarrow -\frac{c}{3} \frac{E_{k+1} - E_k}{\Delta\tau_{k+1/2}}.$$

For pure transport,

$$\Delta\tau \rightarrow 0,$$

and

$$c \sum_i \Delta\mu_i \; \mu_i \; I_{i,k+1/2} \rightarrow$$

$$c \sum_{\mu_i < 0} \Delta\mu_i \; \mu_i \; I_{i,k+1} + c \sum_{\mu_i > 0} \Delta\mu_i \; \mu_i \; I_{i,k}.$$

Note that we are still solving the correct equation in the differential limit. Extra information has been put into the finite-difference equations to "enhance" the physics description far from the differential limit.

The angular advection term gives

$$\frac{c}{r} \frac{\partial}{\partial\mu} (1-\mu^2) \; I \rightarrow$$

$$\frac{c \; \Delta t}{r \; \Delta\mu} \left\{ (1-\mu^2)_{i+1/2} \; \underline{I}_{i+1/2} - (1-\mu^2)_{i-1/2} \; \underline{I}_{i-1/2} \right\}.$$

Previous arguments suggest

$$\underline{I}_{i+1/2} = \frac{I_i'}{1 + \dfrac{\Delta\tau}{2 \; |\mu|}}.$$

This is "upstream differencing" in angle, since a free-streaming ray in a 1-D spherical geometry travels so that μ is always increasing. We also have a conservative form of angular derivative, since what leaves one angular group goes into its angular neighbor.

Figure 5 shows the average μ as a function of distance at

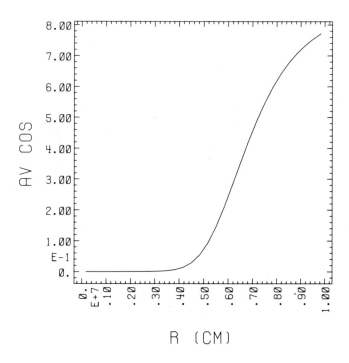

Fig. 5. — Average μ as a function of position at 0.1 s.

0.1 s in the test problem using this form for the advection term. One sees that the problem goes smoothly from a diffusion region at the center of the problem to a transport region on the outside.

b) Coupling Terms

The coupling of the radiation to the material is governed by the term

$$\rho \, c \, \kappa \, [B(T) - I].$$

This generates the finite-difference term

$$\rho \; c \; \Delta t \; \underline{\kappa} \; [B(\underline{T}) - \underline{I}].$$

Many practical problems have radiation and transport strongly coupled. This means that $B(\underline{T})$ and $\underline{I}$ give large and nearly cancelling rates. This implies that we want

$$B(\underline{T}) = B(T'),$$

$$\underline{I} = I'.$$

This choice forces equilibrium for large timesteps, i.e.,

$$\Delta t \to \infty \; \text{implies} \; I' = B(T').$$

We choose

$$\underline{\kappa} = \kappa$$

for simplicity.

The desired temperature dependence of the difference equations is then

$$I'_{i,j} - I_{i,j} = - \; \Delta t \; R_{i,j}(T') + \text{transport},$$

$$T' - T = \Delta t \; \{R_{1,1}(T') + R_{1,2}(T') + \ldots\} = \Delta t \sum_{i,j} R_{i,j}(T'),$$

where

$$R_{i,j} = \frac{\Delta\mu_i \; \Delta\nu_j}{\rho \; C_V} \; R_{i,j}.$$

With transport, this is a very complicated set of coupled equations for $I'_{i,j}$ and T'! We first consider the simpler "operator-split" difference equations

$$I'_m - I_m = - \; \Delta t \; R_m(T'_m) + \text{transport},$$

$$T_m' - T_m = \Delta t \, R_m(T_m'),$$

where

$$m = (i,j),$$

$$T_m = T_{m-1}',$$

and

$$T_1 = T,$$

$$T_{mmax}' = T'.$$

The intermediate (or "partial") temperatures T_m are introduced to decouple the equations for the final neutrino densities at different energies and angles, which would otherwise be coupled through their mutual dependence on T'. However, this procedure still gives the correct differential limit, since adding material equations gives

$$(T_1' - T) + (T_2' - T_1') + \ldots + (T' - T_{mmax}) = T' - T$$

$$= \Delta t \sum_m R_m(T_m').$$

We note that strong coupling forces equilibrium at the appropriate partial temperature, rather than the final temperature.

To solve the operator-split algorithm,

$$I_m' - I_m = \rho \, c \, \Delta t \, \kappa \, [B(T_m') - I_m'] + \text{transport},$$

$$\rho \, C_V \, (T_m' - T_m) = - \rho \, c \, \Delta t \, \kappa \, \Delta\mu_i \, \Delta\nu_j \, [B(T_m') - I_m'],$$

linearize the temperature dependence about T_m,

$$B(T_m') \equiv B_m' \approx B_m + \frac{\partial B_m}{\partial T} (T_m' - T_m).$$

Solving the material energy equation for T_m' as a function of I_m' gives

$$T_m' - T_m = - \frac{1}{\rho \ C_V} \frac{\rho \ c \ \Delta t \ \kappa \ \Delta \mu_i \ \Delta \nu_j}{R_m} [B_m - I_m'],$$

where

$$R_m = 1 + \frac{\rho \ c \ \Delta t \ \kappa \ \Delta \mu_i \ \Delta \nu_j}{\rho \ C_V} \frac{\partial B_m}{\partial T}.$$

Substituting in the transport equation for I_m' leads to

$$I_m' - I_m = \frac{\rho \ c \ \Delta t \ \kappa}{R_m} [B_m - I_m'] + transport.$$

This equation depends only on T_m, not T_m'. It can be solved if we can solve the transport part alone.

One notes an important property of this procedure. The energy radiated by material is

$$\frac{\rho \ c \ \Delta t \ \kappa \ \Delta \mu_i \ \Delta \nu_j}{R_m} B_m = \frac{\rho \ c \ \Delta t \ \Delta \mu_i \ \Delta \nu_j \ B_m}{1 + \frac{\rho \ c \ \Delta t \ \kappa \ \Delta \mu_i \ \Delta \nu_j}{\rho \ C_V} \frac{\partial B_m}{\partial T}}.$$

But

$$\frac{\partial B}{\partial T} > \frac{B}{T}.$$

Thus

$$\frac{\rho \ c \ \Delta t \ \kappa \ \Delta \mu_i \ \Delta \nu_j}{R_m} B_m < \frac{(\rho \ C_V \ T_m)(\rho \ c \ \Delta t \ \kappa \ \Delta \mu_i \ \Delta \nu_j \ B_m)}{(\rho \ C_V \ T_m) + (\rho \ c \ \Delta t \ \kappa \ \Delta \mu_i \ \Delta \nu_j \ B_m)}.$$

Thus the energy radiated by material over Δt is the minimum of what would be radiated at the initial zone temperature, or (approximately) what is available as material energy. This keeps the T_m positive. This is why T_m is updated for each angle-frequency group.

We should note one special feature of an operator-split algorithm. In a numerical calculation, the timestep Δt is usually chosen so that the relative change in the variables over the timestep is less than a small number, typically something like 5 percent. This is done so that the rates involved can be considered relatively constant over the timestep. In an operator-split code, the variables vary over a range during the cycle as each subprocess is calculated. Thus instead of requiring

$$\frac{|T'_k - T_k|}{T'_k} < \varepsilon,$$

for a given order ε of accuracy, we should require

$$\frac{|T'_k - T'_{k,m}|}{T'_k} < \varepsilon.$$

If the $T'_{k,m}$ all lie between T'_m and T_k, then the operator-split algorithm should be able to run with the same timestep as one in which the coupling is done simultaneously. If the changes in the $T_{k,m}$ are in opposite directions, the operator-split code should be run with a small timestep. This factor is problem dependent. Figure 6 shows the partial-temperature swings in the test problem at the zone that is limiting the timestep at 0.1 s. (The number of angles at each frequency is imx.)

c) Finite-Difference Equations

Collecting pieces, the finite-difference equations reduce to

$$A^{\pm} \ I' = B \ I'_{i-1} + C^{\pm} \ I'_{k \mp 1} + D,$$

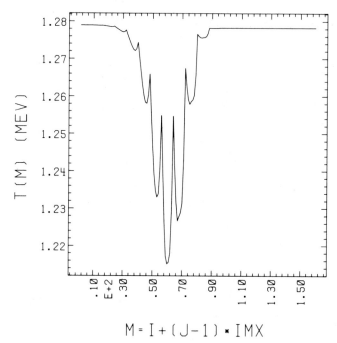

Fig. 6. — Partial temperatures in timestep-limiting zone at 0.1 s.

$$Q\ T' = R\ I' + S,$$

where

$$A^{\pm} = 1 + \frac{\rho\ c\ \Delta t\ \kappa}{R} + \frac{c\ \Delta t\ |\mu|\ r^2_{k\pm 1/2}}{r^2\ \Delta r\ \left[1 + \frac{\Delta\tau_{k\pm 1/2}}{2\ |\mu|}\right]} + \frac{c\ \Delta t\ (1-\mu^2)_{i+1/2}}{r\ \Delta\mu\ \left[1 + \frac{\Delta\tau}{2\ |\mu|}\right]},$$

$$B = \frac{c\ \Delta t\ (1-\mu^2)_{i-1/2}}{r\ \Delta\mu\ \left[1 + \frac{\Delta\tau}{2\ |\mu_{i-1}|}\right]},$$

$$C^{\pm} = \frac{c\ \Delta t\ |\mu|\ r^2_{k\mp 1/2}}{r^2\ \Delta r\ \left[1 + \frac{\Delta\tau_{k\mp 1/2}}{2\ |\mu|}\right]},$$

$$D = I + \frac{\rho \ c \ \Delta t \ \kappa}{R} \ B,$$

and

$$Q = \rho \ C_V,$$

$$R = \frac{\rho \ c \ \Delta t \ \kappa \ \Delta\mu \ \Delta\nu}{R},$$

$$S = \frac{1}{R} \{\rho \ C_V \ T + \rho \ c \ \Delta t \ \kappa \ \Delta\mu \ \Delta\nu \ (T \ \frac{\partial B}{\partial T} - B)\}.$$

Note that all the coefficients are positive. This guarantees well-behaved solutions even if the coefficients of $\Delta\mu$, $\Delta\nu$, Δr and Δt are not small!

These equations are solved by starting at i = 1 ($\mu_1 = -1$), k = kmax (r_{kmax} = outside boundary) and stepping through the mesh with fixed (μ_i, ν_j). Then i is incremented, and one loops over k again. For values of i that correspond to outward angles ($\mu_i > 0$), the k index starts at kmin (r_{kmin} = inside boundary). This sequence is repeated until all (i,k) values have been calculated for a given ν_j, then j is incremented.

III. DIFFUSION DIFFERENCE SCHEME

In many calculations, the angular distribution of the radiation is not of interest. One is tempted to try generating moment equations and getting by with just a few. This leads to

$$\frac{\partial E}{\partial t} = - \nabla \cdot F + \rho \ c \ \kappa \ [\mathscr{B}(T) - E],$$

$$\frac{1}{c} \ \frac{\partial F}{\partial t} = - c \int d\Omega \ \Omega \ \Omega \cdot \nabla I - \rho \ \kappa \ F,$$

etc.,

where

$$\mathcal{B}(t) = \frac{4\pi}{c} B(T),$$

$$E = \int d\underline{\Omega} \; I,$$

$$\underline{F} = c \int d\underline{\Omega} \; \underline{\Omega} \; I.$$

In the diffusion limit, one assumes that the rate of change of $\underline{F}$ is slow compared to the rate of absorption and emission. One also assumes that the high rate of absorption and emission results in nearly isotropic radiation. Then

$$\int d\underline{\Omega} \; \underline{\Omega} \; \underline{\Omega} \cdot \underline{\nabla} I \approx \frac{1}{3} \underline{\nabla} E,$$

$$\underline{F} = -\frac{c \; \lambda}{3} \underline{\nabla} E,$$

where

$$\lambda = \frac{1}{\rho \; \kappa}.$$

Now

$$\underline{F} = -\frac{c \; \lambda}{3} \underline{\nabla} E$$

cannot hold in general, since for large λ it would predict

$$|\underline{F}| > c \; E.$$

This raises the following question: can one write a

phenomenological relation of the form

$$\underset{\sim}{F} = - D \underset{\sim}{\nabla}E$$

that is generally useful?

In many cases one can use

$$D = \frac{c}{\frac{3}{\lambda} \min\left[1, \frac{\mathscr{B}}{E}\right] + \frac{|\underset{\sim}{\nabla}E|}{E}} .$$

This expression gives the diffusion limit when

$$\frac{\lambda}{E} |\underset{\sim}{\nabla}E| \to 0.$$

When

$$\frac{\lambda}{E} |\underset{\sim}{\nabla}E| \to \infty,$$

or

$$\mathscr{B} < E,$$

$$\frac{\lambda}{\mathscr{B}} |\underset{\sim}{\nabla}E| \to \infty,$$

it predicts

$$|\underset{\sim}{F}| \to c\, E \qquad \text{(streaming limit)}.$$

There are many situations where these relationships between the flux and the energy density hold. Thus it has been found experimentally that often a useful radiation transport scheme in one-dimensional spherical geometry is

$$\frac{\partial E}{\partial t} = -\frac{1}{r^2} \frac{\partial}{\partial r} (r^2 F) + \rho c \kappa [\mathcal{B}(T) - E],$$

where

$$E = \int d\underline{\Omega} \; I,$$

$$F = -D \frac{\partial E}{\partial r},$$

$$D = \frac{c}{\frac{3}{\lambda} \min[1,\frac{\mathcal{B}}{E}] + \left| \frac{1}{E} \frac{\partial E}{\partial r} \right|}.$$

Clearly this scheme is not as general as the full transport scheme, but it has proven adequate for many practical calculations, and it is much less expensive.

a) Finite-Difference Equations

The discrete form of the transport term follows from

$$\frac{1}{r^2} \frac{\partial}{\partial r} (r^2 F) \rightarrow \frac{1}{r^2 \Delta r} \{(r^2 \underline{F})_{k+1/2} - (r^2 \underline{F})_{k-1/2}\},$$

$$(r^2 \underline{F})_{k+1/2} = -\mathcal{D}_{k+1/2} (E'_{k+1} - E'_k),$$

$$\mathcal{D}_{k+1/2} = \frac{c \; r_{k+1/2}^2}{3 \, (\Delta\tau \, \min[1,\frac{\mathcal{B}}{E}])_{k+1/2} + \left| \frac{E_{k+1} - E_k}{\max(E_k, E_{k+1})} \right|},$$

$$(\Delta\tau \, \min[1,\frac{\mathcal{B}}{E}])_{k+1/2} = \frac{1}{2} \{(\Delta\tau \, \min[1,\frac{\mathcal{B}}{E}])_k + (\Delta\tau \, \min[1,\frac{\mathcal{B}}{E}])_{k+1}\}.$$

Note that E′ is used to calculate the flux. This gives the steady-state fluxes in the $\Delta t \rightarrow \infty$ limit.

The diffusion finite-difference equations reduce to

$$- A\ E'_{k+1} + B\ E' - C\ E'_{k-1} = D,$$

$$Q\ T' = R\ E' + S,$$

where

$$A = \frac{\Delta t}{r^2\ \Delta r}\ \mathcal{D}_{k+1/2},$$

$$B = 1 + \frac{\rho\ c\ \Delta t\ \kappa}{\mathcal{R}} + \frac{\Delta t}{r^2\ \Delta r}\ \{\mathcal{D}_{k-1/2} + \mathcal{D}_{k+1/2}\},$$

$$C = \frac{\Delta t}{r^2\ \Delta r}\ \mathcal{D}_{k-1/2},$$

$$D = E + \frac{\rho\ c\ \Delta t\ \kappa}{\mathcal{R}}\ \mathcal{B},$$

$$\mathcal{R} = 1 + \frac{\rho\ c\ \Delta t\ \kappa\ \Delta\nu}{\rho\ C_V}\ \frac{\partial\mathcal{B}}{\partial T},$$

and

$$Q = \rho\ C_V,$$

$$R = \frac{\rho\ c\ \Delta t\ \kappa\ \Delta\nu}{\mathcal{R}},$$

$$S = \frac{1}{\mathcal{R}}\ \{\rho\ C_V\ T + \rho\ c\ \Delta t\ \kappa\ \Delta\nu\ (T\ \frac{\partial\mathcal{B}}{\partial T} - \mathcal{B})\}.$$

Again note that the recursion coefficients are all positive. With

$$B > A + C,$$

this guarantees a well-behaved solution. This set of equations can be solved using standard techniques for linear tridiagonal systems as, for example, in Richtmyer and Morton (1967).

Figure 7 shows a comparison of the time dependence of the

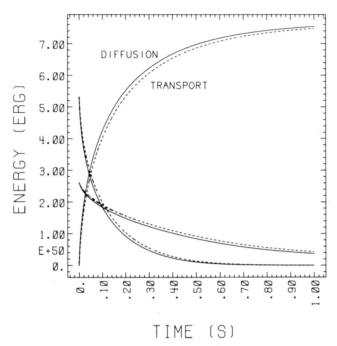

Fig. 7. — Energy balance, transport/diffusion comparison (refer also to Fig. 2).

energies in the test problem for the transport and diffusion calculations. The differences come from the less complete handling of the streaming transport in the diffusion scheme, but the agreement is quite satisfactory when one considers that the diffusion calculation takes approximately $1/20^{th}$ the computer time.

Figure 8 compares the calculated radiated neutrino spectra from the two calculations. Figure 9 compares the various "temperatures" in the test problem at 0.1 s.

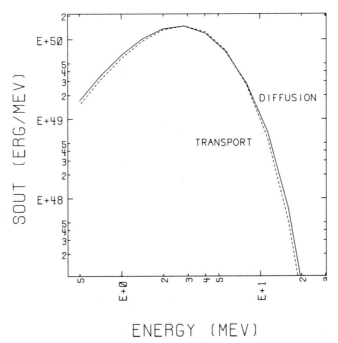

Fig. 8.—Radiated neutrino spectrum, transport/diffusion comparison.

IV.   FULLY-IMPLICIT RADIATION-MATERIAL COUPLING SCHEME

For some applications, it is desirable to replace the operator-split algorithm with one using a fixed temperature for all radiation groups. Since we still want an implicit calculation, we need a simple method to predict the final temperature.

Consider the finite-difference equation for the total radiation energy density obtained by integrating over ν the diffusion equation of the previous section, but assuming that the same temperature is used for all frequency groups:

$$\mathcal{E}' - \mathcal{E} = \rho \; c \; \Delta t \; \left[\int d\nu \; \kappa \; \mathcal{B}' - <\kappa>' \; \mathcal{E}' \right] + \frac{\Delta t}{r^2} \; \frac{\partial}{\partial r} (r^2 \; <D>'_{\hat{\partial}} \; \frac{\partial \mathcal{E}'}{\partial r}),$$

$$\rho \; C_V \; (T' \; - \; T) \; = \; - \; \rho \; c \; \Delta t \; \left[\int d\nu \; \kappa \; \mathcal{B}' \; - \; \langle \kappa \rangle' \; \mathcal{E}' \right],$$

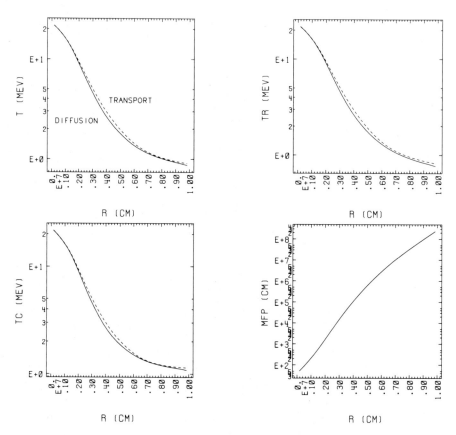

Fig. 9. ── Temperatures and average mean free path, transport/diffusion comparison at 0.1 s.

where

$$\mathcal{E} \; = \; \int d\nu \; E$$

and

$$\langle \kappa \rangle' \; = \; \frac{1}{\mathcal{E}'} \; \int d\nu \; E' \; \kappa,$$

$$<D>'_{\partial} = \frac{1}{\frac{\partial \mathcal{E}'}{\partial r}} \int d\nu \; \frac{\partial E'}{\partial r} \; D.$$

Note that if $<\kappa>'$ and $<D>'_{\partial}$ were known, one could easily solve for T' and $\mathcal{E}'$.

We would expect that a good guess for $<\kappa>'$ and $<D>'_{\partial}$ would be κ and D averaged over the last known spectrum. This suggests the following iterative scheme:

(1)   Define

$$<\kappa>^{m-1} = \frac{1}{\mathcal{E}^{m-1}} \int d\nu \; E^{m-1} \; \kappa,$$

$$<D>^{m-1}_{\partial} = \frac{1}{\frac{\partial \mathcal{E}^{m-1}}{\partial r}} \int d\nu \; \frac{\partial E^{m-1}}{\partial r} \; D.$$

(2)   Linearize the equations for $\mathcal{E}'$ and T'. Use $<\kappa>^{m-1}$ and $<D>^{m-1}_{\partial}$ in place of $<\kappa>'$ and $<D>'_{\partial}$. Let $\mathcal{E}^m$ and T^m be solutions of the linearized equations. This gives

$$\mathcal{E}^m - \mathcal{E} = \frac{\rho \; c \; \Delta t}{\mathcal{R}^{m-1}} \left\{ \int d\nu \; \kappa \; \mathcal{B}^{m-1} + (T - T^{m-1}) \int d\nu \; \kappa \; \frac{\partial \mathcal{B}^{m-1}}{\partial T} \right.$$

$$\left. - <\kappa>^{m-1} \; \mathcal{E}^m \right\}$$

$$+ \frac{\Delta t}{r^2} \frac{\partial}{\partial r} \left(r^2 \; <D>^{m-1}_{\partial} \; \frac{\partial \mathcal{E}^m}{\partial r} \right),$$

$$\rho \; C_V \; (T^m - T^{m-1}) =$$

$$- \frac{1}{\mathcal{R}^{m-1}} \left\{ \rho \; c \; \Delta t \left[\int d\nu \; \kappa \; \mathcal{B}^{m-1} - <\kappa>^{m-1} \; \mathcal{E}^m \right] \right.$$

$$\left. + \rho \; C_V \; (T^{m-1} - T) \right\},$$

where

$$\mathscr{R}^{m-1} = 1 + \frac{\rho \ c \ \Delta t}{\rho \ C_V} \int d\nu \ \kappa \ \frac{\partial \mathscr{B}^{m-1}}{\partial T} \ .$$

(3)   Solve for the new E^m,

$$E^m - E = \rho \ c \ \Delta t \ [\mathscr{B}^m - E^m] + \frac{\Delta t}{r^2} \frac{\partial}{\partial r} (r^2 \ D \ \frac{\partial E^m}{\partial r}) \ .$$

To test for convergence, define an "energy conservation" temperature T^m_{ec} such that

$$\rho \ C_V \ (T^m_{ec} - T) \equiv - \rho \ c \ \Delta t \int d\nu \ \kappa \ [B(T^m) - E^m],$$

and let convergence be defined by

$$\left| \frac{T^m_{ec} - T^m}{T} \right| < \varepsilon \ .$$

Note that this is not the same thing as

$$\left| \frac{T^m - T^{m-1}}{T} \right| < \varepsilon \ .$$

Use of the former insures that we are solving the complete set of finite difference equations to the desired order, while the latter is really only an indication of the rate of convergence — not convergence itself.

Note that if we did not iterate, we would essentially be using the multifrequency grey (MFG) method of H. Wilson (1969).

There can be technical trouble (Hendrickson 1977) with

$$<D>_{\partial} = \frac{1}{\frac{\partial \mathscr{E}}{\partial r}} \int d\nu \ \frac{\partial E}{\partial r} \ D,$$

if

$$\frac{\partial \mathcal{E}}{\partial r} = 0.$$

To circumvent this, let

$$<D>_{\partial} \frac{\partial \mathcal{E}}{\partial r} \rightarrow \frac{\partial}{\partial r}(<D> \ \mathcal{E}) - \mathcal{E} <\frac{\partial D}{\partial r}>,$$

where

$$<D> = \frac{1}{\mathcal{E}} \int d\nu \ E \ D,$$

$$<\frac{\partial D}{\partial r}> = \frac{1}{\mathcal{E}} \int d\nu \ E \ \frac{\partial D}{\partial r}.$$

Since the same temperature is used for all frequencies, the iterative scheme produces slightly different (and better) answers than the operator-split algorithm for corresponding limits on the partial and final temperatures. Figure 10 shows the difference this makes in the radiated neutrino spectrum of the test problem when all the temperatures are kept within 5 percent of their final values. These differences can be made as small as desired by running each calculation with smaller timesteps, but for this example the errors are commensurate with the overall accuracy of the problem.

Figure 11 shows the number of iterations needed to make T_{ec} and T' to agree to one part in 10^3. Figure 12 shows the rate of convergence at 0.1 s. The solid curve labeled "T(EC)-T" is the maximum of $(T^m_{ec,k}-T^m_k)/T_k$ over the whole grid, while the dotted curve labeled "T(M)-T(M-1)" is the maximum $(T^m_k-T^{m-1}_k)/T_k$ in the problem. Note that a convergence criterion based on T^m_{ec} is much more stringent.

Figure 13 plots the number of cycles used by the iterative algorithm (simple dashed line) compared with the non-iterative

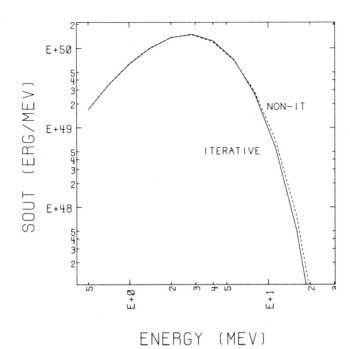

Fig. 10. — Radiated neutrino spectrum, iterative/non-iterative comparison.

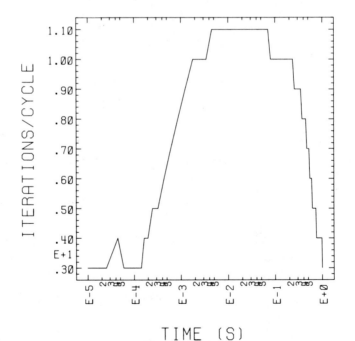

Fig. 11. — Iterations/cycle for iterative calculation.

partial-temperature scheme (solid line). Also plotted is the
number of "cycles" used by the iterative scheme counting iterations
as cycles (patterned broken line). One sees that in this problem,
the total number of iterations in the iterative scheme is
comparable to the number of cycles used in the partial-temperature
scheme. In effect, one has traded partial-temperature cycles for
iterations. In some problems, there may be more pronounced
differences. In problems near steady-state flow, the iterative
scheme would be expected to be cheaper, while in problems with
rapid change, the iterative scheme becomes more nearly equivalent
to the partial-temperature scheme.

V.   SUMMARY

In this article, we have described how the radiation transport
algorithms developed in Jim Wilson's computer programs directly
address the physical factors that affect the usefulness of
numerical algorithms. Since one often does not have enough
computer time or computer memory to resolve physical details as
well as one would like, it is important that the computer
algorithms reflect those details that are resolvable in a
physically reasonable manner. The neutrino transport problem
considered here illustrates the compromises common in practical
calculations. This problem exhibits neutrino mean free paths
ranging from much smaller than material scale lengths to much
larger, and involves time scales that range from neutrino transit
times to much longer than transit times. This is typical of most
realistic calculations, as one can see by considering the
references mentioned in the introduction.

Much of the original programming for the testing of the
operator-split algorithms was done by M. Alme and D. Post.
J. LeBlanc has provided valuable advice and criticism over the
years that these methods were developed.

This work was performed under the auspices of the U.S.
Department of Energy by Lawrence Livermore National Laboratory
under contract No. W-7405-Eng-48.

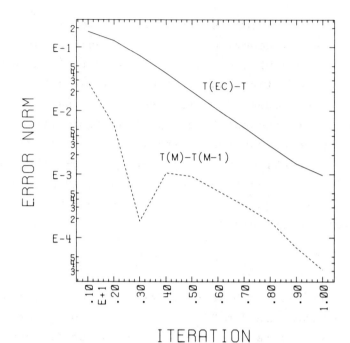

Fig. 12.—Convergence of iterative temperatures.

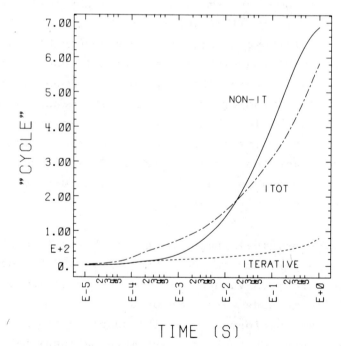

Fig. 13.—Relative costs of iterative and non-iterative
schemes.

REFERENCES

Alme, M. L., and Wilson, J. R. 1973, *Ap. J.*, 186, 1015.

———— . 1974, *Ap. J.*, 194, 147.

———— . 1976, *Ap. J.*, 210, 233.

Hendrickson, C. 1977, private communication.

Richtmyer, R. D., and Morton, K. W. 1967, *Difference Methods for Initial-Value Problems*, 2nd ed. (New York: Interscience).

Wilson, H. L. 1969, in *Progress in High Temperature Physics and Chemistry*, Vol. 5, ed. C. Rouse (New York: Pergamon).

Wilson, J. R. 1971, *Ap. J.*, 163, 209.

Wilson, J. R. 1978, in *Proc. of the International School of Physics "Enrico Fermi", Physics and Astrophysics of Neutron Stars and Black Holes*, ed. R. Giacconi and R. Ruffini (Amsterdam: North-Holland).

The Future of Numerical Astrophysics*

James M. LeBlanc
Lawrence Livermore National Laboratory

ABSTRACT

The future of numerical astrophysics is projected by reviewing trends of the past, describing the present state of the field, and extrapolating in the apparent directions of change. Although the present discussion is primarily concerned with numerical astrophysics, an attempt is also made to describe the role of this discipline in the field of astrophysics as a whole. Predictions are made about computers and code writing tools, and some of the hazards of numerical work are discussed.

I. INTRODUCTION

When I was asked to give this talk on the future of numerical astrophysics, my first reaction was that it was an easy topic on which to speak. It did not take much thought on the subject to make me see my error. Anyone who attempts to predict the future in such a rapidly evolving field has to be a little crazy. So, having established my credentials, I will describe my view of the future.

For the purpose of this discussion I will define the future as the next ten years. Anything beyond that is much too uncertain. And I will restrict my statements to numerical considerations. Many of the attendees at this meeting are much more qualified than I to predict the future of astrophysics, but, considering the rate at which the field has changed in the past ten years, I doubt that any of them would attempt to predict the next ten. I don't know what problems astrophysicists will then be calculating; however, many of them will still be pushing the capacity of their computers.

* Work performed under the auspices of the U. S. Department of Energy by the Lawrence Livermore National Laboratory under contract No. W-7405-ENG-48.

II. THE PRESENT STATUS OF NUMERICAL ASTROPHYSICS

Before starting on the future, I would like to comment briefly on the past ten years. This time has been an exciting one for numerical astrophysics: the field has rapidly expanded, and many important calculations have been published. In my opinion, however, the most important contribution to the field has not been any of these calculations. I believe the most important accomplishment is that numerical astrophysics has started to be recognized as a discipline that can make valuable contributions to the understanding of astrophysical phenomena. If at this stage we feel inclined to take such recognition for granted, we should remember that acceptance by others of the value of our work was not something to which we were entitled, but something we had to earn.

In science it is commonly assumed that results presented in any paper can be reproduced by the reader. But how many readers have the computational capacity we need in numerical astrophysics? We are in a position somewhat like that of the workers in experimental particle physics who use the very large accelerators, but with this significant difference: the accelerator groups are large, so it is reasonable to assume that much cross-checking of procedures and results is done within the groups, while our groups tend to be small. Since everyone knows that large computer programs have bugs, the reader of our papers must place his confidence in us before he can believe the details of our results. I think that the acceptance of our results at this time is a reflection of the quality of the work that has been done in the past.

III. COMPUTER TRENDS

a) Single Instruction Processors

Between 1950 and 1970 the designers of digital computers made great advances. During this time the speed of the fastest computers increased by a factor of two every year and a half. This speed increase was achieved primarily by increases in the speed of the electronic components. Although there were improvements in the architecture of the computers, they were all of the type we now call scalar, or single instruction single data (SISD), processors. Computers of this type are all enough alike that their relative speeds can be determined simply by comparing the speeds at which they transfer data from their memories to their central processing units. In addition, when codes written in FORTRAN are moved from one SISD computer to another, only minimal coding changes are needed to make them run efficiently.

By 1970, computer speeds had reached the point where the speed of light began to become important in determining the memory transfer time. As a result it became necessary to consider computer component sizes as well as their speeds. At this time there was much pessimism about the rate at which computer speed would continue to increase.

The computer designers are an ingenious group, however. They introduced a new concept into computer architecture, the single instruction multiple data (SIMD) processor, in which a single instruction is performed on an array of data. The ILLIAC IV, in which the University of Illinois had a major design role, was such a computer. It consisted of 64 computers which executed exactly the same instruction simultaneously. At about the same time, Control Data introduced the CDC STAR 100, a vector machine, whose mode of operation can be illustrated by a description of vector addition. ("Vector", here, means an array of data.) The addition of vectors A and B to produce a sum vector C starts by beginning to transfer the first elements of A and B from the memory. On the next machine cycle the second elements start their transfer. After some number of cycles the first C result has been stored in memory. At each cycle after this a new element of C is stored. At this time the computer has many values of A, B, and C flowing through the vector addition unit and the wires to and from memory units. So long as the start-up time (the time needed to produce the first element of C) is short compared to the time required to calculate the entire C vector, vector processing will give a significant increase in speed over scalar processing. (Vector computers also contain scalar processors in order to execute those operations that cannot be done efficiently in a vector processor.)

All SIMD computers, such as the CRAY 1S and the CYBER 205, require special care in the writing of codes in order to make efficient use of the computers. Since various operations are performed at different speeds, the maximum speed of the computer is seldom a measure of the speed at which the computer will perform on a given code. Since one must sum up the times spent in each operation of the code and then take the inverse to get an overall effective speed for the computer, the relation between the effective speed and the fraction of the operations done in the faster mode is not a straight line but a hyperbola (Fig. 1).

Our experience at Lawrence Livermore National Laboratory (LLNL) has shown that it is usually easy to construct codes that are 75% vector, and difficult to construct codes that are more than 95% vector. Even if the vector speed were infinite, a code that is 95% vector would execute only 20 times faster than it would if it were entirely scalar. The same argument applies to all SIMD

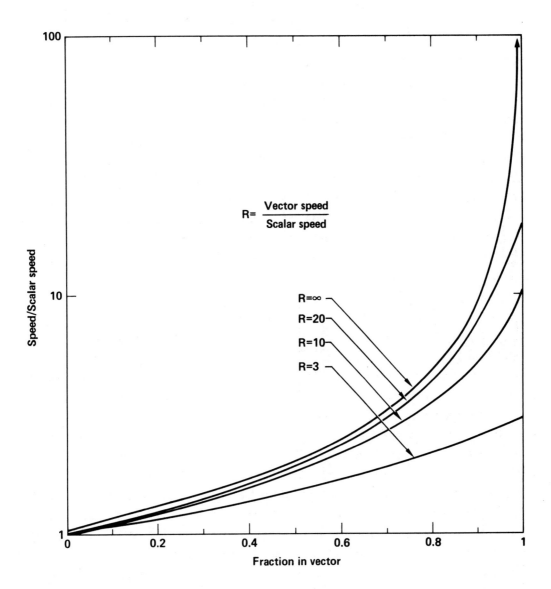

Fig. 1. - The speed of a vector computer is plotted as a function of the fraction of a code's operations it executes in its vector processor. This relationship is shown for four computers having different values of the ratio of vector speed to scalar speed. The upper curve is the limit for infinite vector speed. The curves with R=3 and R=10 represent the CDC 7600 and the CRAY 1S respectively.

computers. Thus there is a practical limit to the speed gains that can be expected from the SIMD architecture. (The gains in scalar speed are, of course, still of great importance; however, the speed-up of scalar processors in the last ten years has only been by a factor of about 2.5, as we expected in 1970.)

What about the future? There are still some gains to be made in both scalar and vector processors. In the next few years most of the gain in improved vector design will have been achieved. However, there are still important gains to be made in semiconductor speed. Significant advances are being made in both silicon and gallium arsenide technology (Long et al. 1982). The higher electron mobility in gallium arsenide compared to silicon suggests that in a few years the basic circuits will have at least four times the speed of present ones. Since this advance applies to scalar as well as vector components, it implies a real computer speed-up of the same factor as that for the components. By the end of the decade, component speeds will probably have increased by a factor of ten relative to CRAY 1S components.

b) Multiple Instruction Processors

The design of new computer architectures is proceeding at a very rapid pace. Most of the new computer designs are of the multiple instructions multiple data (MIMD) type. These designs all make use of some form of parallel processing, which makes possible large increases in maximum speed over a single scalar or vector processor. They consist of a number of processors which can, in principle, all perform different operations at the same time. Such computers are fundamentally different from the ILLIAC IV, which required that each processor execute the same instruction at the same time. It would appear that the parallel processor computers would allow a speed that is directly proportional to the number of processors. It seems the MIMD computers may come close to achieving this ideal performance, when executing codes that can be put into suitable form. However, for many codes the speed saturates at some number of processors and, for some codes, may then actually decrease as more processors are used. At least a portion of the difficulty is due to the need to transfer data between processors. Another cause of trouble may be processors interfering with one another's access to the memory. These difficulties, and their effects on code writing, are just starting to be recognized. Each computer will have its own coding requirements for efficient use.

Other difficulties are surely waiting to be found. For example, how does one construct an interactive time sharing system for such machines? At present we are in the position of not understanding enough about MIMD machines to be able to make a good evaluation of their overall capabilities. Much of the next ten years will be spent in developing compiler extensions, time sharing systems, and new numerical algorithms for multiple processors.

But MIMD supercomputers will be built, and we will find ways to use them in numerical astrophysics. How much can we expect from them? People talk about large numbers (1024 or even 100,000) of processors in future computers. I doubt that we will see more than 128 CRAY 1S-speed processors in a single computer in the next ten years.

c) Other Computer Developments

Speed is not the only requirement of a scientific computer; a large memory is also needed. In fact, there is a trade-off between speed and memory size for most codes. The status of memory size is in even better shape than computer speed. The computers planned for the late 1980s will have memories with 256 million 64-bit words. In my view, memory size will no longer be a limitation on our codes.

Before leaving computer design I need to discuss intermediate size computers and chip technology. Consider minicomputers like the VAX. This class of machines has undergone a revolution in the last decade. Their speed has increased and their cost has dropped, mostly as a result of advances in chip technology. The density of circuits on a chip is still growing and at the present time is up to 500,000 gates per chip (Aviation Week & Space Technology 1981). In contrast, the CRAY 1S has 16 gates per chip. The width of the conducting lines on the chips is down to one micron (Long et al. 1982). As the size of the components has been reduced, so have the power requirements, as is necessary if the computer is to be kept at a reasonable temperature. But as the power level decreases one finally approaches the point where natural radioactivity could produce signals which interfere with the computer signals. Clearly there is a practical limit on the minimum size of semiconductor components that can be manufactured reliably; however, present technology is far enough from any known limit so that over the next ten years the size and cost per circuit should continue to decrease.

One consequence of developments in chips is that a computer with the capability of a CDC 7600 is likely to become a desk top computer and will cost less than $50,000. Such computers will not be scarce items; in fact, most universities will have several of them. The computational capacity of such machines is adequate for calculating many interesting problems in astrophysics (the supernova calculations that Jim Wilson presents in this volume take about one hour to complete on the CDC 7600). Such a computer could produce sufficient output to saturate the capacity of all but the fastest high speed printers. Printer speeds have increased more slowly than computer speeds, and I expect that this will continue in the future. The cost of an adequate printer could be several times that of the computer.

Printed output is one way to store the results of a calculation. This kind of record is bulky but permanently available. The same information can be filed in a data storage system using magnetic tapes, magnetic discs, laser discs, or a mass store device. In this form the data can be read and manipulated by a microcomputer and portions of interest displayed on a CRT terminal. Printed output will still be wanted, but the volume needed is greatly reduced. The equipment and codes needed to store, read, and process output files already exist, and their capabilities will be expanded. Thus even the output problem has a solution.

The role of minicomputers in numerical astrophysics will continue to grow in the future; but numerical astrophysics will also continue to be done on supercomputers, for the simple reason that the simulation of many important astrophysical phenomena requires them.

IV. NETWORKS

There is a need to facilitate the transfer of data between computer and user and also between different computers. Data transfer is probably best accomplished by means of interactive time sharing systems and computer networks, of which the Magnetic Fusion Energy computer system and network is a good example. With this system someone at Princeton can use the CRAY 1S at Livermore in the same interactive mode as can a user in Livermore. If a problem fails to execute properly on the computer, the user does not need to transfer an entire memory dump to his office. He can use an interactive debug routine (called DDT) to examine the file that remains in Livermore, find the difficulty, fix his code, and rerun the problem. The amount of data transferred across the network in this procedure is kept to a minimum, and the clock time involved in debugging the code is also minimized.

Another use of networks is the transfer of codes and data between users of the network. For example, a user at Livermore can give to another user at

Princeton a code and the input and output data from several problems by executing a one-line instruction on his computer. Such facility in information transfer has obvious advantages, but there is also a less obvious potential disadvantage. The people with access to a network form a group with special characteristics, in that they can communicate much more easily and comprehensively with one another than with workers who lack access to the network. Sharing via a network should not be allowed to replace normal publication, lest advances in the field be slowed by a net restriction of information.

The need for large and efficient networks is well recognized at this time. Existing networks will be extended, and new ones will be constructed.

V. CODING METHODS
a) Coding Language

The question of what coding language will be used in the future is one that usually generates an emotional response. I will make a prediction; however, one should consider that such a prediction can only be very uncertain. I believe that FORTRAN will be the major language used in numerical astrophysics for the next ten years. This is not to say that the language will be identical to the FORTRAN of today; the use of any language implies continuing development. Extensions to FORTRAN are already being developed for use on MIMD machines. Improvements in and extensions to the compilers that produce vector coding will continue to be made.

Toward the end of the next ten years I expect to see very high level languages start to become important. Just what form these will take is uncertain, but their purpose will be to make possible a significant reduction in both the routine work of writing codes, and bugs in the resulting codes. The input to a code might be:

1) a list of the differential equations to be solved,

2) definitions of the difference form of the operators in the equations,

3) definitions of parameters including logical choices,

4) a specification of boundary conditions including logical choices,

5) definition of data structure,

6) centering of variables, and

7) averaging methods.

The output from the code would be a FORTRAN source code ready to compile on a given computer. Some might consider the prediction of such a language to be simply wishful thinking; however, I believe that such a language is practical and will be constructed in the near future.

b) Numerical Approximations and Algorithms

As computers grow in capability, we will be able to improve the approximations used in our physical models. What is of equal importance is that we can also improve our numerical approximations. There are efforts at many places to continue to improve old numerical algorithms and to develop new ones that are faster or more accurate than those in present use. There is no end in sight for developments in this area; our problem is, and will be, to keep up to date.

VI. EXPANSION OF THE FIELD

We have seen a large increase in the number of workers in numerical astrophysics in the last ten years. This growth has occurred in spite of constraints on workers in the field, the most obvious of which is the need to acquire sufficient computer capability to develop a code and carry out the calculations. Other difficulties have included the necessity of traveling to a distant place to work on the computer, the commitment of the large time needed to develop and test a code before one can reasonably expect publishable results, and the scarcity of knowledgeable people from whom to learn the necessary numerical methods.

The point I wish to make is that the developments in computer equipment and codes that I have discussed previously operate in the direction of reducing the constraints on our use of computers. Their effects will not be felt overnight, but by the end of the next decade our working environment will be much improved. As it improves there will be more people who want to work in the field. The fact that young people find both computers and astrophysics to be fields that excite their interest will insure a good supply of graduate students.

VII. FUTURE DIFFICULTIES

a) Conditions for Orderly Development

Numerical astrophysics will continue to grow; the only question is, how will it grow ? Ten years from now it may have developed into an orderly, well understood field of science, or it may have become a morass full of pitfalls for the unwary. I will first present what I believe numerical astrophysics should be; then I will address some of the difficulties that may lead the field into a morass.

By my definition, numerical astrophysics is the field which attempts to improve our understanding of astrophysical phenomena by simulating them through calculations performed on a digital computer. The simulation process consists of several discrete steps:

1) A theoretical model is constructed.

2) The model is simplified by a set of approximations, such as representing the transport equation by a diffusion equation, ignoring relativistic effects, etc.

3) The resulting equations are approximated by a set of either finite difference or finite element equations.

4) Methods are chosen for solving these equations.

5) Boundary conditions are defined and represented numerically.

6) The computer code is written and debugged, and its accuracy is verified.

7) Initial conditions are chosen.

8) A simulation is calculated.

9) The results are analyzed. This step may involve extensions of the code and more calculations. It certainly requires many hand calculations using the state variables that were calculated by the code.

10) A paper describing the simulation and results is written and published.

Numerical simulation is sometimes called a computer experiment. The results of a computer experiment are the values of all the state variables of the problem. In contrast, a laboratory experiment measures only a subset of these data, and often indirectly. On the other hand, the laboratory experiment gives information from the real world, while the computer experiment can give, at best, information relative to the simplified theoretical model. If one can somehow establish that the code produces an accurate representation of the theory, then one can use the comparison of calculated results and real experiments to evaluate the theory. Similarly, if one can demonstrate that the theory is an adequate representation of the phenomena that are measured, then one can use the computer experiment either to aid in the interpretation of the laboratory experiment or to evaluate the accuracy of the code.

The connections between these aspects of the field are illustrated in Figure 2. The dotted line joining theory to the real world represents thought experiments. The connection from theory, via experiments, to the real world is the fundamental basis of the physical sciences. Numerical physics does not have any direct connection to the real world. The path from theory through numerical physics is one that we take only when it is not possible to obtain analytic solutions to the equations that represent either the theory or the simplified theoretical model.

If we use numerical physics to connect the theoretical model and experiments, then at least one of the connections in the path must be firmly established before we can draw reliable conclusions. In practice, the establishment of the connections between theory, numerical work, and experiments is a vitally important part of numerical physics. This is why workers in numerical physics consider it

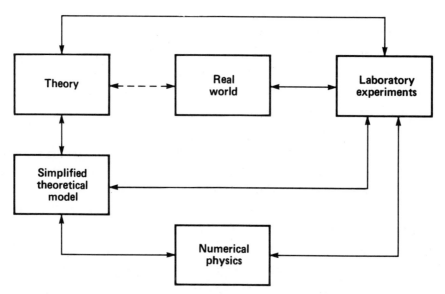

Fig. 2. - This diagram illustrates the transfer of information between various fields of physics.

important to have a companion experimental program. In addition, their codes are extensively tested by calculating problems with known analytic solutions.

In most fields of physics one can choose and vary the objects of one's experiments. In astrophysics this is seldom possible; one must take what is there. In consequence, the connection between theory and numerical work is of prime importance.

The high quality numerical work that has established the field of numerical astrophysics has been done by people who, I believe, take care in performing all of the ten steps outlined above. Many examples are presented in this volume.

b) Possible Pitfalls

Thus far I have described a set of necessary conditions for well-ordered work in numerical astrophysics. If enough care is taken in their implementation, they may even be a sufficient set. Unfortunately, if one does not take care, the morass may start to become apparent. Errors can be introduced at each step. At present there are many pitfalls for the unwary. Let us consider a few of the sources of error that may cause problems in steps (3) through (9).

In steps (3) and (4) one chooses the numerical methods to be used. It is possible to construct an infinite number of difference equations all of which approach the same differential equation in the differential limit. But, for a given computer capability and class of problems to be solved, only a subset of these difference equations will be stable and give sufficient accuracy. One can find in the literature descriptions of several numerical algorithms for almost any problem we might want to solve. Usually the method is described in some detail; an error analysis may be presented; comparisons are made with other methods; and numerical results obtained using the algorithm are presented. One might think that such a description of the method would be complete enough so that someone else could safely apply it in his own work. Unfortunately, this conclusion may be unwarranted for a number of reasons. First, the description of the method, though extensive, may still be incomplete. Sometimes the little coding tricks that make a method useful over a wide range of problem types are not included in the description of the code. Second, the method presented in the paper may be accurate over only a limited class of problems. Third, the stability analysis may be incomplete, and the method may actually be unstable for the type of problem that is of interest to the reader. Fourth, extensions of the method to more complicated equations that the reader may need to solve may introduce problems not addressed in the paper. These types of difficulties may be summarized by the cliche, "A code is known to be accurate and reliable only in the parameter space over which it has been tested." Newly developed algorithms are particularly subject to these difficulties, since they are usually published before they have had extensive use.

Step (5) has to do with boundary conditions and may at first seem to offer little possibility for errors. However, in principle, the boundary conditions must be represented to at least as high an order as that used in the interior of the problem. Unfortunately, it is sometimes difficult to accomplish this, and failure to do so may result in artificial signals generated at the boundaries of the problem.

Next consider step (6), the writing and testing of the code. The present state of the art of code writing effectively guarantees that all but the simplest codes have bugs. We find and fix <u>almost</u> all of our bugs during the development and testing of the code. However, we can never be sure that all of the bugs have been eliminated.

The greatest scope for the introduction of errors is afforded by step (7), the selection of initial conditions. Once again I quote an LLNL cliche: "One can run <u>any</u> code in such a way that it will give the wrong answer." The most obvious difficulty is that the initial conditions actually used in a given problem may not be those we thought we generated. Computers are nasty; they do what we tell them to do, not what we tried to tell them to do. Errors of this type are surprisingly hard to find. Error also results from insufficient accuracy of the initial data in representing the phenomena we wish to calculate. Such inaccuracy may be due to the numerical representation used, or it may be an error in the physics. The latter is usually easier for a physicist to find than the former.

There is a third type of initial condition error that results from poor choices of the parameters that define the numerical algorithm. One source of such errors is the finite spatial mesh on which the problem is defined. Clearly the mesh must be fine enough for adequate definition of the spatial gradients in all important state variables, and this definition must stay adequate over the full range of time used in the calculation. It may be necessary to execute several problems in order to find the proper mesh to use in a final, accurate calculation. Unfortunately, the criteria for choosing the mesh needed for accurate answers to a given problem are not always obvious. Given complete knowledge of the error characteristics of the algorithms used in the code, one can make intelligent trade-offs between the often conflicting requirements. The best solution to the difficulty is to tailor the algorithms to the specific problem so as to minimize errors.

Step (8) should be relatively free of errors. The principal error source here is the computer, and modern computers are remarkably reliable machines.

Step (9), the analysis of the results, is of vital importance in the process of error detection and elimination. It is at this step that the connections of our numerical work with theory and experiments are evaluated, and here, too, that the results of the calculations are used to aid in understanding the astrophysical phenomena. It is difficult, though hardly necessary, to overemphasize the importance of this step. Unfortunately, the readers of our papers do not always find here the detail and completeness they would like to see.

The final step is publication. A complete description of our numerical work is so difficult that it is almost never done. The complete code listing cannot usually be published, nor even complete computer results for just a single problem. What is published is the small subset of data and analyzed results that the astrophysicist believes contains the most significant information about his code and the information he obtained from the analysis of his calculations. In the best of all worlds, one would ask for a lot more.

The reader should not suppose that the preceding list of possible errors is complete; it is given only to illustrate the types of pitfalls that are waiting for the unwary. Workers in numerical physics become aware of most of these difficulties early in their work. The learning process is not painless; it is in part accomplished by trial and error. What is needed is a good textbook on the subject. I believe that numerical astrophysics will become a well-ordered field of science; however, as yet there is still an element of art in our work.

VIII. SUMMARY

In order to evaluate predictions of the future, it is important to determine whether the person making them is an optimist or a pessimist. I think Jim Wilson would say that I am a pessimist, and he is probably correct. Even so, I think the prospects for numerical astrophysics are extremely bright. The tools we need in our work are being improved and made available at an extraordinary rate. The education of graduate students in the field is, at the present time, in its early stage of growth. Recognition of the value of numerical simulation will, I think, grow rapidly, and the field will take its proper place in scientific research. The attendees at this conference have played a major role in the development of the field and will continue to help guide our future. Finally, we can expect Jim Wilson to continue to set an example for us to follow.

I have spent about 25 years working with Jim in numerical simulation. During this time Jim has led me into a very wide range of topics in physics and astrophysics. Jim's breadth of knowledge and his quickness in learning a new field are impressive, to say the least. Working with him insures that one works at the forefront of knowledge. For me it has meant 25 years full of exciting, productive, and satisfying work.

REFERENCES

Aviation Week and Space Technology, April 13, 1981, p. 71.

Long, Steven I., et al. 1982, Proc. IEEE, 70, 35.